# SAXIFRAGES

## OF EUROPE

OTHER BOTANICAL BOOKS
PUBLISHED BY CHRISTOPHER HELM

**Conifers**
Keith D. Rushforth

**The Genus Cyclamen**
Christopher Grey-Wilson

**The Genus Cymbidium**
David Du Puy and Philip Cribb

**Hardy Geraniums**
Peter F. Yeo

# SAXIFRAGES

## OF EUROPE

With notes on African, American and
some Asiatic Species

# D.A.Webb and R.J.Gornall

CHRISTOPHER HELM
London

© 1989 D.A. Webb and R.J. Gornall
Christopher Helm (Publishers) Ltd, Imperial House,
21–25 North Street, Bromley, Kent BR1 1SD

ISBN 0-7470-3407-9

A CIP catalogue record for this book
is available from the British Library

First published in North America in 1989 by
Timber Press
9999 S.W. Wilshire
Portland, Oregon 97225, USA

Library of Congress Cataloging-in-Publication Data

Webb, D.A. (David Allardice), 1912–
    A manual of saxifrages and their cultivation/D.A.
  Webb and R.J. Gornall.
        p.    cm.

    Bibliography: p.
    Includes index.
    ISBN 0-88192-130-0
    1. Saxifraga—Handbooks, manuals, etc.  I. Gornall,
      R.J.
  II. Title
SB413.S28W43 1988                          88–20060
635.9′3338—dc19                              CIP

Typeset by Florencetype Ltd, Kewstoke, Avon BS22 9YR
Printed and bound in Great Britain by Butler and Tanner, Frome, Somerset

# CONTENTS

# Preface and Acknowledgements

Several books on saxifrages have been published recently, after a period of long neglect, but they are all intended primarily for gardeners. Harding (1970), which is a reprint of articles first published in the *Quarterly Bulletin of the Alpine Garden Society*, forms a useful introduction to the genus, and is unusual in that, although it mentions a fair number of hybrids, it concentrates mainly on species. It makes brief mention of all the European species, much of the information being derived from the first edition of *Flora Europaea*, volume 1 (Webb 1964b), and even briefer mention of a fair number from outside Europe, but within its slender compass it is unable to give much detail, and in some of its taxonomy and nomenclature it is now out of date. Köhlein (1984, in English translation from the original German edition of 1980) writes mainly for gardeners, with much useful advice on cultivation. He deals with numerous species, often in a few lines, dismissing some of them, unfairly we think, as of no garden value, and has good coloured photographs of about two dozen species as well as of numerous cultivars. Horný *et al.* (1986) deal in detail with the numerous species, primary hybrids and cultivars of section *Porphyrion* (= their section *Porophyllum*). They provide an authoritative guide, with keys to all the species, and many coloured pictures, but are concerned mainly with the plants in the garden rather than in the wild.

In our book we are addressing a wider public. We hope it will be of interest to gardeners, but we are catering mainly for gardeners of the 'plantsman' type, who value plants for their rarity or oddity, as well as for their conventional beauty, and who are keen to find out more about them, what their relatives are, and where they come from. But we address ourselves also to professional botanists and to botanical tourists—travellers who like to see new plants, whether to collect them, to photograph them or simply to tick them off in their Floras. In addressing such a varied readership we have had to make some compromises in our style. We provide, we believe, all the essential information that the taxonomist might reasonably expect, but we have tried to present it in a form less off-putting to the amateur than is customary, by limiting our technical vocabulary to the essentials, by eliminating certain conventional Latin phrases, and by spelling out in full, in place of the often baffling abbreviations, the names of persons, books, journals and herbaria.

Finally, a word ought to be said about the title of the book. Although the bulk of the text deals in detail with European species, we nevertheless describe species in neighbouring areas which might either be visited by the traveller, or from which species might reasonably be expected to turn up in cultivation. Thus we provide brief, summary accounts of the saxifrages to be found in Madeira, Africa, the Near East and the Caucasus, as well as of a small sample from the Himalaya and the Far East. There is also a final chapter which, it must be said, does not really fit into this category. It describes the North American species on a continent-wide scale for the first time since 1905, and in much more detail than is given in the other subsidiary chapters. In doing this we hope to bring the saxifrage flora of the New World to the attention of the Old, and *vice versa*, and thereby provide botanists and gardeners with a much more balanced view of the genus. Ideally we would also have liked to have dealt with all the Asiatic species, but the time is not yet ripe for this as most are still very poorly known, and the book had to be kept within reasonable bounds. Perhaps it should be subtitled 'Not the Himalayan saxifrages'.

*Acknowledgements*: D.A.W. would like to offer his warm thanks to the staffs of the Royal Botanic Gardens, Kew and the British Museum (Natural History) for all their help over the past 40 years, and to acknowledge a grant from the Percy Sladen Trust towards the expenses of an extensive collecting trip in 1959. R.J.G. would like to thank Dr P.E. Elvander for his comments on a draft account of the North American species, and Mr B. Arnold for helpful discussions about Himalayan species in cultivation.

The following people kindly contributed photographic illustrations: I.K. Ferguson, Plate 26; S.L. Jury, Plates 6, 20, 22, 55; G. Lonergan, Plate 19; W.H. Palmer, Plate 39, Figures 9, 10, 12–20, 23, 24, 26–31, 33, 34, 40–42, 44, 46, 48–50, 52–55, 57–59; O. Polunin, Plates 1, 3, 8, 9, 15, 25, 60; M. Rix, Plate 34; W. Schacht, Figures 8, 22; D. Simpson, Plate 4; M. Wyse Jackson, Plate 13.

# I

# The Genus
## *Saxifraga*

The genus *Saxifraga* includes some 440 species, and is by far the largest genus in the Saxifragaceae, the family to which it gives its name. Most of its species are to be found in the Arctic or North Temperate zone, and the areas in which the genus shows the greatest diversity are the mountains of Europe, the Himalayan-Tibetan region, and on both sides of the northern Pacific, in western North America and in eastern Asia. Northwards it extends to the northern coast of Greenland; southwards in the Old World it reaches Ethiopia and northern Thailand; but in America it stretches down the Andes to Tierra del Fuego. This geographical pattern bears a striking resemblance to that of *Ribes* (comprising the currants and gooseberries), to which *Saxifraga* is, perhaps, relatively closely related.

## Origin and relationships

The limits of the Saxifragaceae have been very variously interpreted by different authors. The most recent detailed treatment on a world-wide scale is that of Engler (1930), who gave the family a very wide circumscription, but recognised within it no fewer than 15 subfamilies. But most botanists today regard Engler's family as an unnatural assemblage, and believe, partly on morphological, partly on chemical and partly on geographical grounds, that many of his subfamilies (including those represented by such genera as *Escallonia* and *Hydrangea*) are only remotely —some of them very remotely indeed— related to *Saxifraga*.

Within the subfamily Saxifragoideae there are 28 genera close enough to *Saxifraga* to be included with it in the tribe Saxifrageae. This tribe, however, falls fairly clearly into two main groups: one with parietal placentation and a racemose inflorescence (of which *Heuchera* provides a familiar example), and the other (to which *Saxifraga* belongs) with axile placentation and a cymose inflorescence. Only one genus, *Chrysosplenium*, the golden saxifrage, falls between the two groups, as it combines parietal placentation with a cymose inflorescence. In the *Saxifraga* group there are 19 genera and, of these, *Bergenia*, *Darmera*, *Leptarrhena* and *Peltoboykinia* are among those which appear to be closest to *Saxifraga*. They all, however, seem to be more specialised than *Saxifraga*, and it is more likely that they are derived from a *Saxifraga*-like ancestor than *vice versa*. Outside the tribe, a hunt for possible relatives does not disclose any genus of which it can be said with confidence that it shares a recent common ancestor with *Saxifraga*, but a systematic analysis of characters suggests that within the subfamily the herbaceous genera *Francoa* and *Tetilla* and the shrubby genus *Ribes* may be not too distantly related, and the same is true of representatives of three other subfamilies—*Parnassia* and *Penthorum* (herbaceous) and *Itea* (shrubby).

As far as we can tell, then, the closest living

relatives of *Saxifraga* are a rather diverse group of shrubs and herbs, and all have already evolved a considerable distance in morphological terms from any hypothetical common ancestor.

## Morphological variation and classification

In its morphology and chromosome complement, *Saxifraga* shows considerable variation, as might be expected in such a large genus, but it is held together by its remarkably constant floral structure, in which the only important variable is the position of the ovary (Figure 1). The flowers are usually characterised by five sepals and five petals, ten stamens in two whorls of five (an outer whorl opposite the sepals and an inner whorl opposite the petals), and two carpels, which are united to a variable extent, or occasionally free. There are a few species in the Himalayan region which have four sepals and petals and eight stamens, and there are two species which have three carpels. The general architecture of the flower, however, makes them immediately recognisable as saxifrages.

An important feature of the flower is the absence, or near absence, of a free hypanthium (such as is seen, for example, in *Prunus*); the stamens are inserted where the perianth-segments meet the ovary wall. (A very few species have free hypanthia of negligible length—less than 0.5mm.) The pollen, although there is variation in the ornamentation of the surface, is of the same fundamental type throughout the genus; it is the type known as 3-colpate, i.e. the grain has three longitudinal furrows. In vegetative characters, however, the variation is wide and often complex, and it is these characters that are mainly used to divide the genus into sections, subsections and series. A synopsis of the classification that we have adopted is presented in Table 1. In order to avoid the account of the European species in Chapter 4 becoming top-heavy with descriptions of subsections and series, we have refrained there from subdividing groups

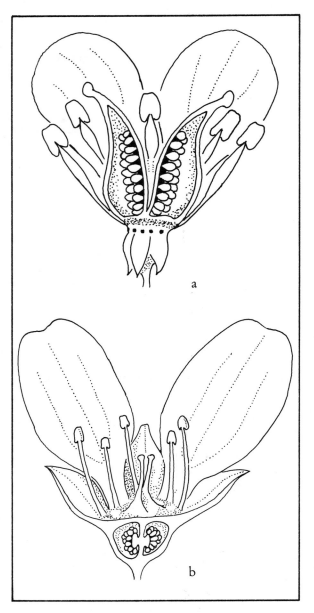

Figure 1. Longitudinal sections through flowers showing variation in the position of the ovary:
(a) superior ovary (*S.nelsoniana*);
(b) inferior ovary (*S.fragilis*)

which have only a limited representation in Europe.

It is convenient to divide the taxonomically useful features into macro-characters, which can be apprehended by looking at the plant with the naked eye or a simple hand-lens, and

## Table 1. A synopsis of the Genus *Saxifraga* (after Gornall 1987b)

1. Section **CILIATAE** Haworth
   Subsection *HIRCULOIDEAE* Engler & Irmscher
     Series *Hirculoideae* (Engler & Irmscher) Gornall
     Series *Lychnitidae* (Engler & Irmscher) Gornall
     Series *Nutantes* (Engler & Irmscher) Gornall
     Series *Cinctae* (H. Smith) Gornall

   Subsection *GEMMIPARAE* Engler & Irmscher
     Series *Gemmiparae* (Engler & Irmscher) Gornall
     Series *Spinulosae* (C.B. Clarke) Gornall
   Subsection *CINERASCENTES* Engler & Irmscher

   Subsection *ROSULARES* Gornall

   Subsection *SERPYLLIFOLIAE* Gornall

   Subsection *FLAGELLARES* (C.B. Clarke) Engler & Irmscher

   Subsection *HEMISPHAERICAE* (Engler & Irmscher) Gornall

2. Section **CYMBALARIA** Grisebach

3. Section **MERKIANAE** (Engler & Irmscher) Gornall

4. Section **MICRANTHES** (Haworth) D. Don
   Subsection *STELLARES* (Engler & Irmscher) Gornall

   Subsection *CUNEIFOLIATAE A.M. Johnson*
     Series *Birostres* Gornall
     Series *Melanocentrae* (Engler & Irmscher) Gornall
     Series *Astasianthes* (Sternberg) Gornall

   Subsection *MICRANTHES* (Haworth) Gornall
     Series *Aulaxis* (Haworth) Gornall
     Series *Dermasea* (Haworth) Gornall
     Series *Micranthes* (Haworth) Gornall

   Subsection *ROTUNDIFOLIATAE* A.M. Johnson

5. Section **IRREGULARES** Haworth

6. Section **HETERISIA** (Rafinesque ex Small) A.M. Johnson

7. Section **PORPHYRION** Tausch
   Subsection *KABSCHIA* (Engler) Rouy & Camus
     Series *Aretioideae* (Engler & Irmscher) Gornall

     Series *Juniperifoliae* (Engler & Irmscher) Gornall
     Series *Lilacinae* Gornall
     Series *Marginatae* (Engler & Irmscher) Gornall
     Series *Squarrosae* (Engler & Irmscher) Gornall
     Series *Rigidae* (Engler & Irmscher) Gornall
     Series *Subsessiliflorae* Gornall

   Subsection *ENGLERIA* (Sündermann) Gornall

   Subsection *OPPOSITIFOLIAE* Hayek
     Series *Oppositifoliae* (Hayek) Gornall
     Series *Tetrameridium* (Engler) Gornall

8. Section **LIGULATAE** Haworth
   Subsection *MUTATAE* (Engler & Irmscher) Gornall
   Subsection *FLORULENTAE* (Engler & Irmscher) Gornall
   Subsection *AIZOONIA* (Tausch) Schott

9. Section **XANTHIZOON** Grisebach

10. Section **TRACHYPHYLLUM** (Gaudin) W.D.J. Koch

11. Section **GYMNOPERA** D. Don

12. Section **COTYLEA** Tausch

13. Section **ODONTOPHYLLAE** Gornall

14. Section **MESOGYNE** Sternberg

15. Section **SAXIFRAGA**
    Subsection *SAXIFRAGA*
      Series *Saxifraga*
      Series *Biternatae* (Engler & Irmscher) Gornall

    Subsection *TRIPLINERVIUM* (Gaudin) Gornall
      Series *Aquaticae* (Engler & Irmscher) Pawłowska
      Series *Arachnoideae* (Engler & Irmscher) Gornall
      Series *Axilliflorae* (Willkomm) Pawłowska
      Series *Ceratophyllae* (Haworth) Pawłowska
      Series *Cespitosae* (H.G.L Reichenbach) Pawłowska
      Series *Gemmiferae* (Willkomm) Pawłowska

    Subsection *HOLOPHYLLAE* (Engler) Engler & Irmscher
    Subsection *TRIDACTYLITES* (Haworth) Gornall

micro-characters, which call for the use of a dissecting microscope, a compound microscope or even an electron microscope.

## Macro-characters

### Habit

Most species are perennial (less than a dozen are annual or biennial) and most of them are evergreen, even if covered by snow in winter. There are, however, a number which perennate by bulbils at or below ground-level, and these may lose all their leaves either in summer (section *Saxifraga* subsection *Saxifraga*) or in winter (section *Mesogyne*). In some species belonging to section *Saxifraga* subsection *Triplinervium*, the leaves wither and turn brown in summer, except for those which comprise the characteristic summer-buds. In members of sections *Ligulatae* and some *Ciliatae* seed-production is followed by the death not only of the flowering stem but also of the leaf-rosette from which it arose. Usually by this time new rosettes have been produced as offsets from the base, but in a few species such offsets are seldom or never produced, so that the plant is monocarpic.

The general habit varies from that of a tall, leafy-stemmed plant to a wide-spreading mat or a compact cushion, and very often the habit is constant throughout a section or subsection. It is, of course, an adaptation to the habitat. Cushion-plants are especially characteristic of situations in the Arctic or of high mountains which are exposed to frequent violent winds; mat-formers are especially characteristic of more sheltered habitats, where the snow lies late; taller, single-stemmed species are mostly found in meadows or woodland-margins.

### Leaves

The leaves vary from small, entire, leathery, almost scale-like structures to those with broad laminae, often deeply lobed, and with long, slender petioles. Here again there is some correlation with habitat, though it is by no means perfect; plants in the most exposed situations tend to have small leaves, entire or nearly so, while larger, deeply lobed leaves are found mainly in sheltered habitats. Leaves are usually arranged in an alternate fashion on the stem, but in most species of section *Porphyrion* subsection *Oppositifoliae* and some of section *Cymbalaria* they are opposite.

### Flowers

All conditions from a completely superior to a completely inferior ovary can be found in the genus and, although in some groups the position is constant, in others it is variable. In some cases, as the ovary matures, there is differential growth in the ovary wall such that its position becomes increasingly superior. There is also some variation in the extent to which the carpels are united. If the ovary is more or less superior, the most usual condition is for the carpels to be united to at least half-way, leaving only the styles and the uppermost (usually sterile) part of the ovary free; but in some species, particularly those belonging to section *Micranthes*, the free portion is much larger. If the ovary is more or less inferior, the carpels are usually united over most of their length (except for the styles, which are always free), but there are a few species in which the outer faces of the carpels are united to the hypanthium but the inner faces remain free. The extent of the union of the carpels affects the manner of dehiscence of the capsule: if they are nearly free the split extends nearly to the base of the pericarp, but if they are largely united there is only a relatively small hole between the styles.

In many species, nectar is secreted from a disc or band of tissue (often conspicuous by virtue of its yellow colour) which surrounds the base of the ovary or, if the ovary is inferior or semi-inferior, the base of the styles.

The pollen-sacs usually remain parallel on dehiscence; a longitudinal slit appears in the outer edge of each sac and the pollen is released. In sections *Cotylea*, *Odontophyllae*, *Trachyphyllum*, *Gymnopera*, *Mesogyne* and some species of *Ciliatae* and *Cymbalaria*, however, the dehiscing pollen-sacs pivot upwards on the filament, thus presenting the pollen upwards rather than to the sides

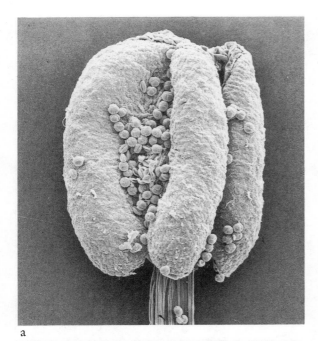

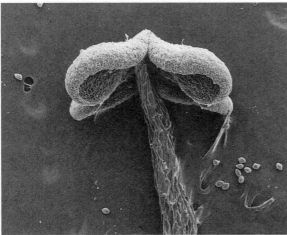

Figure 2. Two kinds of anther dehiscence:
(a) pollen-sacs remaining parallel (*S.exarata*);
(b) pollen-sacs pivoting upwards (*S.cuneifolia*)

(Figure 2). The adaptive significance of this is presumably related in some way to pollination ecology.

The colour of the petals varies from pure white through cream to pink, yellow, orange, red or purple; white petals may be spotted with yellow or purplish-red or both. In some sections the colour is constant with few exceptions (yellow in section *Ciliatae*, white in section *Saxifraga*), whereas in others, such as section *Porphyrion*, it varies widely.

## Micro-characters

### Hairs

Nearly all species possess hairs of one kind or another (Figure 3). They are usually most abundant on the pedicels and hypanthia, but they are often to be found also on the sepals, stems and leaves, and, in a few species of section *Saxifraga*, on the upper surface of the petals as well. Most of the hairs terminate in a spherical or ovoid gland, which produces a usually sticky secretion; the stalk on which the gland is borne may consist of a single row of cells, or may be several cells thick, at least at the base. The two types of hair are known respectively as uniseriate and multiseriate. They can often be distinguished, at least on the petioles, under a hand-lens, the multiseriate hair having an obviously broadened base, but in a few species multiseriate hairs can be fairly narrow-based, so that confirmation under a microscope is always desirable. Some species have uniseriate hairs on certain organs and multiseriate elsewhere. Generally speaking, uniseriate hairs predominate in the European species (though multiseriate predominate in some of the smaller sections), but in the genus as a whole multiseriate hairs are at least as common.

A few species in section *Saxifraga* from south-western Europe and Madeira have no hairs (except in seedlings and occasionally in the inflorescence), but are covered with glands lying flush with the surface of the leaf or stem.

Non-glandular hairs occur occasionally throughout the genus. In some cases they seem to be derived from glandular hairs, and sometimes a small vestige of a gland can be seen. Others, however, seem to have arisen independently as distinct structures; these are short and are especially characteristic of the pedicels in sections *Porphyrion* and *Xanthizoon*, and less consistently in sections *Ligulatae* and *Ciliatae*. Many species in the last

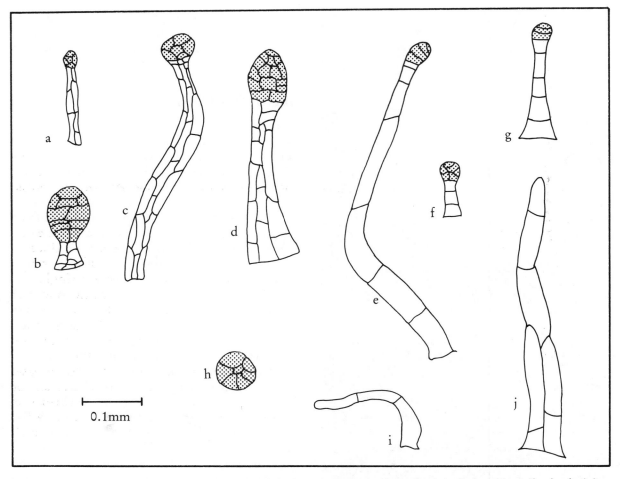

Figure 3. Hair anatomy: (a–d) multiseriate, glandular hairs; (e–g) uniseriate, glandular hairs; (h) sessile gland; (i–j) non-glandular hairs. (a) *S.michauxii*, (b) *S.turfosa*, (c) *S.tsangschanensis*, (d) *S.signata*, (e) *S.manschuriensis*, (f) *S.moschata*, (g) *S.aphylla*, (h) *S.canaliculata*, (i) *S.biflora*, (j) *S.stribrnyi*

section also have characteristic, brown, 'crisped', non-glandular hairs. Functionally, the hairs may help to protect the plants against feeding or egg-laying by herbivorous insects (Levin 1973). For detailed information on hairs see Gornall (1986).

## Stomata

The stomata of 38 species of *Saxifraga* have been studied by Moreau (1984). Although all lacked subsidiary cells (anomocytic stomata), taxonomically interesting variation was reported in their mode of formation. Thus, species in which the stomata arise irregularly over the lower leaf surface belong to sections *Micranthes, Irregulares, Gymnopera, Mesogyne, Cotylea* and *Cymbalaria*. Regular development of the stomata (sequentially from the base of the leaf upwards) occurs in sections *Trachyphyllum, Xanthizoon, Ligulatae* and *Porphyrion*. Both patterns occur in sections *Ciliatae* and *Saxifraga*. It would be premature to say anything about the former because only two species were examined; but in section *Saxifraga* the data indicate that regular development occurs in subsection *Holophyllae*, whereas irregular development is found in subsections *Tridactylites* and *Saxifraga*; subsection *Triplinervium* is variable.

## Leaf Crystals

In nearly all species of the sections *Micranthes* and *Irregulares*, crystals of calcium oxalate occur in the cells of the leaves, and sometimes of other parts. They usually take the form of star-like clusters, but in two species from section *Irregulares* separate needle-like crystals are found (Gornall 1987a).

## Hydathodes

Hydathodes are specialised glands associated with epidermal pores through which water and solutes pass by a process known as gutta-tion. They are found at or near the tips of the leaves, and sometimes along the margins as well. Lobed leaves usually have a hydathode on each major lobe or segment, on the upper surface near the tip. Undivided leaves normal-ly have only one, except in sections *Ligulatae* and *Porphyrion*, where there are usually several, arranged in a row along each side.

Hydathodes vary in their position, their structure and the nature of their secretion (Figure 4). In most species they open on the upper surface of the leaf, but in sections *Micranthes* and *Mesogyne* and in some species of section *Ligulatae* they are truly marginal, the opening being equidistant from the upper and lower surfaces. Two types of structure can be distinguished. One has its opening flush with the surface of the leaf, or even slightly raised; the other is sunk in a pit, and is further distinguished by the fact that the surface of the gland which opens into the pit is usually perforated by small holes, as in a pepper-pot. Generally speaking, there is a good correlation between the structure of the hydathode and the nature of the liquid sec-reted. The hydathodes which open directly on to the leaf surface secrete almost pure water, which leaves no deposit on evaporation; those sunk in pits secrete water containing in solu-tion salts of calcium (largely, we presume, calcium bicarbonate), which leaves on eva-poration a white crust of calcium carbonate on the surface of the leaf.

There are, however, a few exceptions. *S.aizoides* has hydathodes which open on the leaf surface, but its leaves often bear a trace of

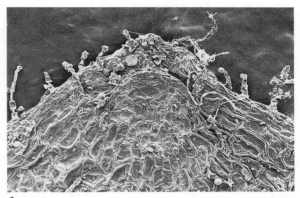

a

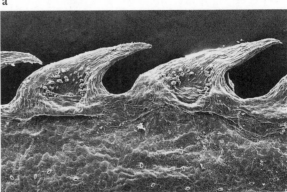

b

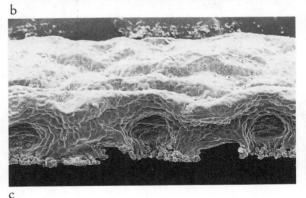

c

Figure 4. Hydathode morphology: (a) flush with the surface, not lime-secreting (*S.rotundifolia*);
(b) on the surface but sunk in a pit, lime-secreting (*S.cotyledon*);
(c) set in the margin and sunk in a pit, lime-secreting (*S.longifolia*)

limy incrustation; on the other hand, in several species such as *S.florulenta*, *S.biflora*, *S.tombeanensis* and *S.juniperifolia*, which have sunken hydathodes, the calcareous incrustation is very scanty or completely absent, at least in the majority of plants. In some such cases, a drop of hydrochloric acid on the surface of the leaf will produce a few bubbles of carbon dioxide from a hydathode, showing the presence of minute traces of calcium carbonate, but this is not always true, and some species with sunken hydathodes show no evidence whatsoever of the secretion of calcium salts.

The functional importance of the hydathodes is rather obscure. In species such as *S.hirsuta* which favour damp, shady and sheltered habitats, the loss of water by guttation may be of some benefit to the plant, as to the plants of other genera which grow in this kind of habitat. The presence of simple (non-calcareous) hydathodes in species growing in drier and exposed sites may indicate merely that there has been no evolutionary pressure following the presumed change of habitat to bring about the loss of hydathodes. The lime-secreting hydathodes suggest a mechanism for eliminating excess calcium. It is not clear, however, why *S.paniculata* should require such a mechanism, while *S.exarata* subsp. *moschata*, often seen beside it on the same rock, does not. Kurt (1929) has claimed that the amount of calcium secreted is determined by soil chemistry, but although most of the heavily encrusted species grow on limestone or dolomite, this is not always the case. *S.cotyledon*, for example, is strictly calcifuge, and is usually seen on quartzite or other rocks that are very poor in base, yet the calcareous incrustation on its leaves, though not very abundant, is constant. *S.paniculata* can be seen either on limestone or on siliceous rocks, but there is no obvious difference in the amount of calcareous incrustation. Finally, there are species such as *S.tombeanensis* which grow on limestone and possess hydathodes sunk in pits, but which show, at any rate on most plants, no trace of calcium secretion. The negative correlation between the presence of calcium oxalate crystals and calcium-secreting hydathodes is interesting but of obscure significance. Schmidt (1930) observed that guttation from hydathodes occurs only before the onset of flowering, and that the amount of secretion is related to a combination of light, temperature and humidity.

## Pollen Grains

The details of the sculpturing of the pollen grain are of considerable help in defining the sections of the genus. Four main types can be recognised (Figure 5): (a) reticulate, found in sections *Micranthes* and *Merkianae*; (b) granular, found in sections *Saxifraga*, *Irregulares* and *Heterisia*; (c) finely striate, found only in section *Ciliatae*; and (d) coarsely striate, which is widespread in the rest of the genus, although with small modifications in various subsections. Developmentally, the reticulate type is basic and on it the various kinds of striate or granular surface are superimposed. For further details, reference may be made to Ferguson & Webb (1970), Kaplan (1981) and Hideux & Abadie (1986). Little is known of the functional significance of the sculpturing.

Some confirmation of the recognition of section *Ciliatae* as a natural group is provided by the fact that in it alone the pollen has three nuclei when shed; in other sections it only has two.

## Ovules and Seeds

Most species of *Saxifraga* have two integuments to the ovule, but in section *Micranthes* there is only one (Kaplan 1981). This probably represents the outer of the two integuments found elsewhere, for in *S.mertensiana*, in the related section *Heterisia*, the inner

a

b

c

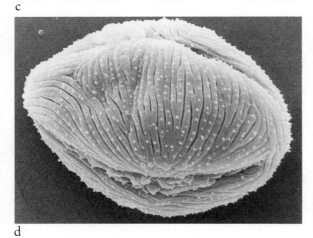

d

Figure 5. Variation in the surface of the pollen grains:
(a) reticulate type (*S.clusii*); (b) granular type (*S.exarata*);
(c) finely striate type (*S.hirculus*);
(d) coarsely striate type (*S.cuneifolia*)

integument is of half the usual length, suggesting that it is on its way to disappearance.

As the ovule ripens into the seed and the integument is transformed into the testa or seed-coat, its cells may develop various kinds of surface ornamentation, or the integument as a whole may be thrown into folds. The ornamentation consists of raised projections of two kinds: relatively broad *papillae*, which may be low and rounded or long and cylindrical, and much finer *tubercles*, which are rounded. Very often both are present, each papilla being surrounded by a ring of tubercles. The raphe, the ridge on one side of the seed, which is developed from the stalk by which the ovule was attached to the placenta, varies considerably in size and conspicuousness; it may be smooth or tuberculate, but does not bear papillae. The essential features of this ornamentation can be seen under an ordinary microscope, but for detailed study an electron microscope is needed. Excellent photographs of the seeds of a large number of species are provided by Kaplan (1981).

When the seeds germinate, hairs are visible on the endosperm in most species except for those in sections *Micranthes* and *Irregulares* (Favarger 1957; Kaplan 1981).

## Chromosome numbers

For each species for which data are available, we give in the text the diploid chromosome number, or several numbers if variation seems to be reliably reported. These are mostly derived from Federov (1969) and the volumes in the *Index to plant chromosome numbers* series (Moore 1973, 1974, 1977; Goldblatt 1981, 1984, 1985), and in most cases we have consulted the original article in which the count was published. We have given preference to counts from plants of known wild origin, as a fair proportion of plants grown in botanic gardens—even those of the highest repute—are wrongly named. We have also, as a general rule, cited only exact counts and then only those which were made in 1950 or later, since many of the earlier records (summarised by Hamel (1953)) are under suspicion of errors arising from defective technique or misidentification. If, however, an earlier count or one from cultivated material is all that is available and seems plausible, we have cited it. The numbers range from $2n = 10$ (*S.tempestiva*) to $2n = 198$ and c.220 (*S.androsacea*).

## Ancestral base number

Table 2 shows the distribution of haploid chromosome numbers among the sections of the genus, but we would emphasise that much further work is needed before such a table can be regarded as reliable or complete. It will be seen from Figure 6 that the numbers range from 5 to 99, and that within this range 8, 10, 13 and 14 (and to a lesser extent 11) are the commonest. Peaks at higher numbers can be interpreted as multiples of these and are presumably of polyploid origin. It seems to us that x = 8 is the most likely as the original base number. Three pieces of evidence can be cited in support of this view. First, it is the lowest haploid number that is at all widely represented and of which multiples occur. Secondly, it is characteristic of section *Ciliatae*, which possesses a large number of primitive characters. Finally, 8 is a basic number in

some genera (*Ribes*, *Parnassia*, *Penthorum*) which, as we have mentioned earlier, are probably fairly closely related to *Saxifraga*. It is true that x = 7 is very widespread among members of the tribe Saxifrageae, but these genera are more derived in their features than is *Saxifraga*, and if 7 had been the original basic number in *Saxifraga* also, it is unlikely that it should now be so conspicuous by its absence.

## Chromosomal evolution

Various possible explanations can be suggested for the origin of the basic numbers 10, 11, 13 and 14; they might have arisen by aneuploid increase from 8, or by aneuploid decrease from 16. Several examples of straightforward polyploidy are known. *S.foliolosa* ($2n = 56$), for example, is probably an autotetraploid derived from *S.stellaris* ($2n = 28$), and this is consistent with its very small (and perhaps non-existent) seed-production. Sometimes, as in *S.hypnoides* ($2n = 26, 52$) diploid and tetraploid show so little morphological difference that they must be included in the same species. Examples of probable allopolyploids are provided by *S.nathorstii* ($2n = 52$), derived from hybridisation between *S.aizoides* and *S.oppositifolia* (both $2n = 26$) (Böcher 1983;

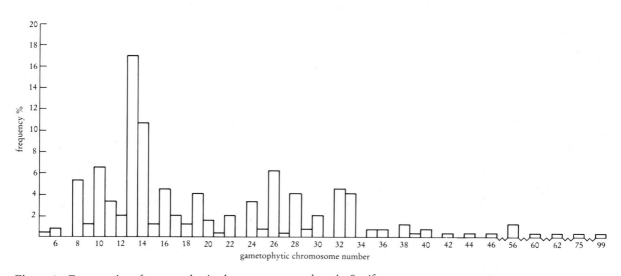

Figure 6. Frequencies of gametophytic chromosome numbers in *Saxifraga*

**Table 2. Frequencies of gametophytic chromosome numbers in sections of *Saxifraga***

| Gametophytic chromosome number | *Ciliatae* | *Cymbalaria* | *Merkianae* | *Micranthes* | *Irregulares* | *Heterisia* | *Porphyrion* | *Ligulatae* | *Xanthizoon* | *Trachyphyllum* | *Gymnopera* | *Cotylea* | *Odontophyllae* | *Mesogyne* | *Saxifraga* |
|---|---|---|---|---|---|---|---|---|---|---|---|---|---|---|---|
| 5 |  |  |  | 1 |  |  |  |  |  |  |  |  |  |  |  |
| 6 | 1 |  |  |  |  |  | 1 |  |  |  |  |  |  |  |  |
| 7 |  |  |  |  |  |  |  |  |  |  |  |  |  |  |  |
| 8 | 9 |  |  |  |  |  |  |  |  |  |  |  |  | 1 | 3 |
| 9 |  | 2 |  | 1 |  |  |  |  |  |  |  |  |  |  |  |
| 10 | 1 |  |  | 9 | 3 |  |  |  |  |  |  |  |  |  | 3 |
| 11 |  |  |  | 1 | 2 |  |  |  |  |  |  | 2 |  |  | 3 |
| 12 |  |  |  | 2 |  |  | 1 |  |  |  |  |  |  | 1 | 1 |
| 13 |  |  | 1 |  |  |  | 20 | 1 | 1 | 6 |  |  |  | 5 | 7 |
| 14 |  |  |  | 3 |  |  | 1 | 10 |  | 2 | 4 |  |  |  | 6 |
| 15 |  |  | 1 | 1 |  |  |  |  |  |  |  |  |  |  | 1 |
| 16 | 2 |  |  | 1 | 1 |  |  |  |  |  |  |  |  |  | 7 |
| 17 |  |  |  |  |  |  |  |  |  |  |  |  |  |  | 5 |
| 18 |  |  |  |  | 1 | 1 |  |  |  |  |  |  |  |  | 1 |
| 19 |  |  |  | 8 |  |  |  |  |  | 1 |  |  |  |  | 1 |
| 20 |  |  |  | 4 |  |  |  |  |  |  |  |  |  |  |  |
| 21 |  |  |  |  |  |  |  |  |  |  |  |  |  |  | 1 |
| 22 |  |  |  |  |  |  |  |  |  |  |  |  |  |  | 5 |
| 23 |  |  |  |  |  |  |  |  |  |  |  |  |  |  |  |
| 24 | 1 |  |  | 1 |  |  |  |  |  | 1 |  |  |  | 3 | 2 |
| 25 |  |  |  |  |  |  |  |  |  |  |  |  |  | 1 | 1 |
| 26 |  |  |  | 1 |  |  | 2 |  |  | 1 |  |  |  | 4 | 7 |
| 27 |  |  |  |  | 1 |  |  |  |  |  |  |  |  |  |  |
| 28 |  |  |  | 6 |  |  | 1 |  |  |  |  |  |  | 1 | 2 |
| 29 |  |  |  | 1 |  |  |  |  |  |  |  |  |  |  | 1 |
| 30 |  |  |  | 2 |  |  |  |  |  |  |  |  |  | 1 | 2 |
| 31 |  |  |  |  |  |  |  |  |  |  |  |  |  |  |  |
| 32 |  |  |  |  |  |  |  |  |  |  |  |  |  | 1 | 10 |
| 33 |  |  |  |  |  |  |  |  |  | 1 |  |  |  |  | 9 |
| 34 |  |  |  |  |  |  |  |  |  |  |  |  |  |  |  |
| 35 |  |  |  | 1 |  |  |  |  |  |  |  |  |  | 1 |  |
| 36 |  |  |  | 1 |  |  |  |  |  |  |  |  |  | 1 |  |
| 37 |  |  |  |  |  |  |  |  |  |  |  |  |  |  |  |
| 38 |  |  |  | 3 |  |  |  |  |  |  |  |  |  |  |  |
| 39 |  |  |  |  |  |  |  |  |  |  |  |  |  |  | 1 |
| 40 |  |  |  | 1 |  |  |  |  |  |  |  |  |  |  | 1 |
| 41 |  |  |  |  |  |  |  |  |  |  |  |  |  |  |  |
| 42 |  |  |  | 1 |  |  |  |  |  |  |  |  |  |  |  |
| 43 |  |  |  |  |  |  |  |  |  |  |  |  |  |  |  |
| 44 |  |  |  |  |  |  |  |  |  |  |  |  |  |  | 1 |
| 45 |  |  |  |  |  |  |  |  |  |  |  |  |  |  |  |
| 46 |  |  |  |  |  |  |  |  |  | 1 |  |  |  |  |  |
| 56 |  |  |  | 2 |  |  |  |  |  | 1 |  |  |  |  |  |
| 60 |  |  |  | 1 |  |  |  |  |  |  |  |  |  |  |  |
| 62 |  |  |  |  |  |  |  |  |  |  |  |  |  |  | 1 |
| 75 |  |  |  |  |  |  |  |  |  |  |  |  |  |  | 1 |
| 99 |  |  |  |  |  |  |  |  |  |  |  |  |  |  | 1 |

see also p. 136, and *S.osloensis* ($2n = 44$), derived from *S.adscendens* and *S.tridactylites* (both $2n = 22$) (Knaben 1954).

It seems that sometimes the appearance of a polyploid is soon followed by an aneuploid decrease. In *S.rhomboidea*, counts of $2n = 20$, 38 and 40 have been recorded, and this set of numbers is found in several other species of section *Micranthes*, with $2n = 40$ the least frequent of the three.

There are two difficulties in the way of reaching as complete an understanding of the chromosome picture in *Saxifraga* as might be wished. One is that in many species the chromosomes are small and rather numerous, so that even experienced cytologists have been reduced to publishing approximate counts. The second lies in the fact that in a few species there are supernumerary chromosomes in addition to the usual complement. Sometimes these can be distinguished only at prophase (Soltis 1983), so that it appears probable that at least a few of the apparent aneuploid counts arise from a mistaken inclusion of these supernumeraries.

# Reproductive biology

The flowers of saxifrages are pollinated mainly by insects, but they are unspecialised and not clearly adapted to any one particular kind of insect. The visitors most often recorded are flies and beetles; also, less frequently, bees. The insects are attracted by the nectar which, as has been explained earlier, is secreted by a band or disc surrounding the ovary or styles. In a few North American species, a sickly-sweet odour is produced at the same time as the nectar, but European species are scentless, except for *S.geranioides*, which has a faint but pleasant scent like that of the primrose. Most species have conspicuous, white or brightly colored petals, but in species such as *S.aphylla*, *S.presolanensis* and *S.paradoxa* the drab flowers are so inconspicuous that we suspect that they must rely largely on self-pollination.

In most species, the flowers are protandrous—that is to say the anthers release their pollen about a week before the stigmas are ready to receive it. This arrangements improves the chances of cross-pollination, but only in plants bearing relatively few flowers which open more or less simultaneously. In plants with large panicles and a flowering period lasting over several weeks there is a strong chance that insects will pollinate a stigma with pollen from a different flower on the same inflorescence—which is, of course, genetically equivalent to the self-pollination of a single flower.

There is a good deal of evidence to suggest that temperature, and perhaps other environmental factors, influence the relative rate at which stamens and carpels mature. This means that a species may be protandrous in one part of its range and protogynous (with stigmas mature before pollen is shed) in another. Arctic species such as *S.cespitosa* cultivated under glass in temperate regions, and thus given a much higher temperature in spring than that to which they are normally accustomed, can sometimes develop flowers showing extreme protogyny; mature stigmas protrude from the flower while the petals and stamens are still no more than rudiments. In some protogynous species, e.g. *S.androsacea* and *S.muscoides*, the diameter of the flowers in the female stage is smaller than it is in the male stage.

In many species the stamens, which at the time of opening of the flower are directed outwards so as to lie against the petals, pivot inwards as they mature (outer whorl first, followed by the inner), so that when the pollen is shed the anthers stand over the still immature stigmas. This clearly facilitates cross-pollination, as that same part of an insect's body which brushes pollen from the dehiscing anthers will, if it then visits a flower in a later stage of development, come in contact with the mature stigmas. After the pollen has been discharged, the stamens move outwards again, and usually shed their pollen-sacs.

We have little precise information as to self-incompatibility in *Saxifraga*. Indirect and circumstantial evidence suggests that most species are wholly or partly self-compatible, and that a few are regularly self-fertilising. There are certainly many species of which a single plant isolated in a glasshouse will set a good crop of seed if self-pollinated with a paint-brush. Two American species from section *Micranthes* (*S.pensylvanica* and *S.californica*) are, however, reported to be self-incompatible (Elvander 1984), and the same is probably true of *S.cernua*. This species, which reproduces mainly by bulbils, was believed until quite recently never to set seed, but Godfree (1979), by crossing a Scottish plant with a Norwegian one, obtained a good crop of seed. It seems probable that all the small, isolated populations of *S.cernua* outside the Arctic are single clones, and that even in the Arctic this is true of large populations. Natural cross-pollination between two plants of different genetic constitution is, therefore, a rare event. This is a field in which systematic experimental work is badly needed, and might yield very interesting results.

Separation of the sexes is also known in *Saxifraga*. In some species, the terminal flower is often female but the others are hermaphrodite, as in *S.aizoides* (Knuth 1908). Male-sterile plants have been reported in otherwise hermaphrodite populations of *S.oppositifolia*, *S.hirculus*, *S.tricuspidata*, *S.cernua*, *S.cespitosa* (Knuth 1908), *S.integrifolia* (Elvander 1982) and *S.granulata* (Stevens & Richards 1985), although none of these species is consistently gynodioecious. Judging from herbarium specimens, dioecy is quite frequent in section *Ciliatae*, although it has seldom been reported in the literature, the case of *S.eschscholtzii* being one of the few exceptions (Chambers 1964).

There is no specialised mechanism for the dispersal of seeds from the dehiscent capsules. In the taller species with stiff stems, the seeds are jerked out as the stem sways in the wind; this does not carry them far, but it ensures that they are not released in a single mass. In species that grow in crevices of vertical rock-faces, dispersal can only be by wind. In many others, water probably plays an important part, especially the trickles from melting snow.

Although almost all species reproduce by seed, there are several in which vegetative reproduction by bulbils (underground or aerial), runners or offsets is at least as important. In some populations of species like the bulbiliferous *S.cernua*, vegetative reproduction can sometimes completely replace sexual reproduction. Seed-set without fertilisation (agamospermy) is unknown in the genus. The saxifrages, however, differ from many other genera in that there is no marked correlation between polyploidy and vegetative reproduction. For further information on floral biology the reader is referred to Knuth (1908), Kevan (1972a,b), Savile (1975) and Elvander (1984).

## Hybridisation

Interspecific hybrids, both natural and man-made, are common in *Saxifraga*. Most of the latter are well-documented, and there is little doubt about the parentage, but there are a few, including unfortunately some of the most popular among gardeners, of which the origin is uncertain. Natural hybrids are certainly more numerous in the literature than in the field, as a few authors have become obsessed with the subject and have tended to explain away in terms of hybridity every deviation from the typical appearance of the species. But even when these have been discounted, the number of well-authenticated natural hybrids is considerable. Many of them have only been found once or twice, but a dozen or more have been reported from a wide enough scatter of localities to show that they must arise fairly frequently.

There is a category intermediate between natural and man-made: hybrids which are supposed to have arisen spontaneously in private or botanic gardens, sometimes between two species which would have no opportunity to meet in nature. Several of these do not stand up to critical examination, but there are a few for which the suggested parentage is quite plausible.

Most of the recorded crosses are, as one might expect, between species of the same section. There are, however, a few undoubted instances of intersectional crosses (Figure 7). *S.aizoides* (section *Xanthizoon*) is particularly noteworthy in this respect. It hybridises in the wild both with members of section *Porphyrion* and of section *Ligulatae*; and the cultivar 'Primulaize' is suspected by some of being a hybrid between it and a species from section *Gymnopera*. The enigmatic *S.andrewsii* is almost certainly a hybrid between members of sections *Gymnopera* and *Ligulatae*; it is discussed in detail on p. 72. Hybrids reported between sections *Ligulatae* and *Porphyrion*, between *Cotylea* and *Gymnopera* and between *Trachyphyllum* and *Saxifraga* are all subject to some doubt and require experimental confirmation.

The frequency of interspecific hybrids varies widely from section to section. In sections *Saxifraga*, *Gymnopera*, *Ligulatae* and *Porphyrion* hybrids are quite common, although in *Porphyrion* they are mostly man-made; natural hybrids are curiously rare. In North America, hybrids in section *Micranthes* can be found in the Columbia River Gorge and the northern ranges of the Rocky mountains. In the remaining sections, hybrids are unknown or rare.

The species with most hybrids to their name are, as one might expect, those which are fairly common and widespread, such as *S.paniculata* and *S.exarata* subsp. *moschata*. There are, however, a few species of restricted range, such as *S.geranioides*, which seem to hybridise promiscuously with most of their neighbours. Hybridisation between potentially interfertile species growing in the same region is in some cases prevented by differences in the flowering season; in others by differences in soil preferences or in altitudinal range.

Information on the fertility or sterility of hybrids is regrettably scarce. As far as the evidence goes, however, it suggests that the majority are wholly or partly sterile. This has

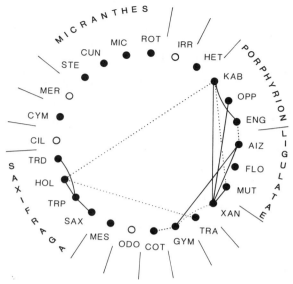

Figure 7. Network to illustrate hybridisation within and between sections and subsections of *Saxifraga*. ● intra-sectional or intra-subsectional hybrids reliably reported; ○ no hybrids reported. — inter-sectional or inter-subsectional hybrids reliably reported; ...... inter-sectional or inter-subsectional hybrids reported but of doubtful authenticity. Sections and subsections are abbreviated to their first three letters, except for TRP = *Triplinervium*, TRD = *Tridactylites*

been demonstrated in a few cases involving artificially produced hybrids in section *Saxifraga* (Marsden-Jones & Turrill 1956) and section *Micranthes* (Perkins 1978), but it can also be inferred in many cases from the frequency of inviable pollen in herbarium specimens and from the absence even from detailed descriptions of hybrids of any mention of the seeds. There are, however, a few natural hybrids which are undoubtedly fertile, not only among themselves but also in backcrosses with the parent species; this gives rise to the formation of hybrid swarms. *S.hirsuta* × *umbrosa*, *S.hirsuta* × *spathularis* and *S.exarata* subsp. *moschata* × *pubescens* may be cited as examples. There are also examples of man-made hybrids having been crossed with other related species or backcrossed to one of their parents. *S.* × *apiculata* (*S.sancta* × *marginata*) has been crossed with *S.burseriana* to give *S.* × *bursiculata*, and *S.* × *boydii* (*S.aretioides* × *burseriana*) has been backcrossed to *S.burseriana* to give a variety of *S.* × *boydii* originally described as *S.* × *luteola*.

However, much more experimental work is needed, as well as many more reliable chromosome counts, before we can fairly assess the role that hybridisation has played in the evolution of the genus. Whether the high chromosome numbers indicated for several species have arisen from hybridisation is in most cases uncertain. Stebbins (1984) has suggested that most arctic-alpine polyploids have arisen by hybridisation between distinct populations of the same species, which have been separated long enough to become genetically distinct but have later expanded their territories so as to come into contact with each other. In this case they belong to a category which he elsewhere called 'segmental allopolyploids'. As we have seen, however, there are at least two examples in *Saxifraga* (*S.nathorstii* and *S.osloensis*) when the hybridisation prior to chromosome-doubling was probably between two distinct species.

# Chemistry

Detailed lists of certain phenolic compounds known as flavonoids have been provided for twelve species in six sections of *Saxifraga* by Miller & Bohm (1980) and Bohm *et al.* (1984). The compounds consist mainly of glycosides of myricetin, quercetin and kaempferol; structures with 6-oxygenation or 3-O-methylation are less common. No clear taxonomic correlations above the species level have yet emerged.

Andersen & Øvstedal (1989) have investigated the occurrence of anthocyanin flavonoids in 22 species of *Saxifraga* from six sections. Mono- and diglucosides of cyanidin, delphinidin, petunidin, peonidin and malvidin were recorded in combinations and quantities which show some correlation with sectional or sub-sectional boundaries.

# Pests and pathogens

Griffiths (1972) has recorded various leaf-miners of the genus *Phytomyza* (Agromyzidae, Diptera) as attacking saxifrages, and three species appear to be constant to the genus. One of them has been recorded on seven species from section *Micranthes*, another is found on *S.rotundifolia* (section *Cotylea*), and a third on *S.paniculata* (section *Ligulatae*). The data, so far as they go, indicate that these leaf-miners discriminate between the different sections of *Saxifraga*. Other insect parasites include larvae of the family Incurvariidae (Lepidoptera) and some Coleoptera, but these insects do not seem to show the same taxonomic discrimination.

Saxifrages, along with other members of the tribe Saxifrageae, are attacked by a number of short-cycled heteroecious rust fungi (*Puccinia* spp.) and these have been investigated by Savile (1973, 1975). Eight species of rust have been found, parasitic on 48 different species of *Saxifraga*. The one section that seems to be completely free from rusts is section *Ciliatae*, but most of its species grow in the Himalaya, a mycological *terra incognita*. The parasites show in some cases a taxonomic correlation with their hosts; within section *Ligulatae*, for example, the species belonging to subsection *Mutatae* is attacked by *Puccinia pazchkei* var. *huteri*, but members of subsection *Ligulatae* by its var. *pazchkei*. In other cases, the parasite shows a wider range of hosts: *P.saxifragae* is found mostly on members of section *Micranthes*, but is recorded also from members of sections *Cotylea* and *Saxifraga*. Moreover, the fact that the same rust is often found on a saxifrage and on another member of the tribe Saxifrageae suggests that the correlation between host and parasite is seldom very precise. In general, it would appear that the rusts have evolved *pari passu* with their hosts, the most primitive rusts being found on the more primitive species of *Saxifraga*. Only occasionally does one see in the field a saxifrage suffering severely from the attacks of either insects or fungi.

# Evolution

Careful examination of the characters in different sections of the genus, and also in related genera, enables one to draw up a list of characters which can reasonably be presumed to be primitive, and a contrasting list of characters which are regarded as derived. The characters in the first list may be combined to build up a tentative model of the hypothetical ancestor of the genus. It may be pictured as a rhizomatous, perennial herb, perhaps woody at the base, with a basal rosette of leaves and a leafy, terminal stem bearing few flowers in a lax cyme or panicle. The glandular hairs were multiseriate, and the leaves had neither lime-secreting hydathodes nor calcium oxalate crystals in the cells. The flowers had a superior ovary, with carpels free or united only at the base; they contained ovules with two integuments, which matured into a smooth testa. The binucleate pollen had a reticulate surface. The plant was diploid, probably with $2n = 16$.

Whether a plant answering exactly to this description ever existed is of course a matter of speculation; certainly no living species does so. There are, however, some groups of species which come fairly close. Engler was of the opinion that section *Micranthes* was the nearest to the ancestral archetype of the genus. In many aspects of its morphology and in its pollen it is certainly primitive, but derived features such as leafless flowering stems, calcium oxalate crystals and ovules with a single integument also characterise its species. Engler's circumscription of the section was, however, in our opinion unduly wide; and certain species which he included in it but which we exclude have a larger number of primitive features. These species include *S.tolmiei*, from western North America, and *S.merkii* from Japan (section *Merkianae*). They possess all the presumed primitive characters, including bitegmic ovules and leaves without crystals, but differ in the fairly complete union of their carpels, their mat-forming habit and their high chromosome numbers. Three other species from the Hima-laya and north-eastern Asia, which we have detached from Engler's section *Micranthes* to constitute the section *Odontophyllae*, are also primitive in most of their characters. Worth mentioning in connection with this group is section *Cotylea*, a group of two species from central and southern Europe which bears a remarkable resemblance to section *Odonto-phyllae*. The relationship between these two sections needs to be investigated more fully. We also consider section *Ciliatae* to be in the main primitive (as did Engler), notably in the possession by many of its species of the diploid chromosome number $2n = 16$.

It would seem then that there are several sections which can claim to be regarded as fairly primitive, but none that can be linked directly to the hypothetical ancestor of the genus. This suggests that the genus showed some degree of evolutionary radiation early in its life. We must next ask ourselves where this took place.

## Geographical origin

Three very different ideas have been proposed as to the place of origin of the genus. The first, originally proposed by Symkiewicz (1937) and endorsed by Cain (1944), suggests that it was in Europe, on the grounds that although the number of *species* known from the Himalayan-Tibetan region greatly exceeds that from Europe, the number of *sections* represented in Europe is much greater than in any other region. This conclusion is open to criticism on two grounds. First, it seems equally likely that Europe could be a centre of secondary diversi-fication rather than of origin; even if the later stages of evolution have been more active here than elsewhere this does not necessarily apply to the earlier stages. Nor is Europe the centre of those genera which seem to be most closely related to the presumed ancestor of *Saxifraga*. Secondly, the sections recognised by these authors were, naturally enough, those of Engler. But it seems probable that Engler, like most taxonomists, was most easily impressed by differences in the parts of the genus familiar to him in Europe and by resemblances in those parts which he knew only from the literature and dried specimens. This led him to set up too many sections in Europe and too few elsewhere. If the sectional classification presented here is to be adopted, and if western North America and Asia east of the Himalaya are regarded as a single region ('Beringia'), then it appears that Beringia and Europe score a draw, each with eleven sections to its credit.

The second hypothesis makes Beringia the original home of the genus (Kaplan 1981). The main support for this theory is that, as we have already seen, the more primitive sections are mainly clustered around the northern shores of the Pacific Ocean. Support for this theory is given by the data on parasitic rust fungi reviewed by Savile (1975); he found that the more primitive rust taxa occur on species whose distribution is centred around Japan. It should of course be borne in mind that this area could equally well be a refuge for primitive saxifrages (and their rusts), rather than their place of origin.

The third hypothesis is that of Stebbins (1984). He suggested that the origin of the genus should be sought in the arctic and subarctic zones, without specifying a particular region of them. His suggestion is based largely on an analysis of chromosome numbers, the lower numbers being supposedly concentrated mainly in the higher latitudes. We regard such an analysis as premature; many more reliable chromosome counts are needed before a statistically significant contrast between arctic-subarctic and temperate-alpine species can be established. Nor should we forget that a few species-pairs such as *S.stellaris* and *S.foliolosa* point in exactly the opposite direction.

We believe that an alternative viewpoint regarding the origin and evolution of the genus can be constructed by taking into account geological events (McKenna 1983) and linking them to what we know about the morphological relationships of the different sections. It is believed nowadays that the striking disjunction between eastern Asia and eastern North America that is shown in the distribution-patterns of a number of genera (*Magnolia* and

*Liriodendron* are the most frequently cited) resulted from the disruption of an Eocene boreotropical flora or of its succeeding Miocene, temperate, mixed evergreen and deciduous, mesophytic forest, which was continuous across the land-masses of the northern hemisphere (Tiffney 1985a,b). In the latter part of the Miocene, the forest flora was fragmented by climatic change, vulcanism and mountain-building. Several genera of the tribe Saxifrageae (e.g. *Boykinia*, *Mitella* and *Tiarella*) show a rather similar disjunction to that described above, and it therefore appears probable that they had evolved at least by the late Miocene. Fossil evidence based on fruits and seeds indicates an origin of the *family* by mid-Miocene (Tiffney 1985a). We suggest that the 'proto-*Saxifraga*' grew in disturbed areas of, or on the margins of, this mixed, temperate forest, along with the other members of its tribe mentioned above; the model we sketched earlier for this plant is entirely consistent with such a habitat, and furthermore, two of the subsections of section *Micranthes* show a similar disjunct distribution, in eastern North America and also in eastern Asia. We do not believe it is possible at the moment to be more precise about the centre of origin, but even if the hypothesis of a Beringian origin is accepted, the genus may soon have spread westwards to central Asia and Europe, and eastwards to eastern North America with relatively little evolutionary change, so that its later evolution and differentiation into sections may have been scattered over three continents. At all events, we know that the forest began to degenerate in the late Miocene and became further fragmented and pushed southwards during the steady fall of temperature in the Pliocene, a cooling which culminated in the glaciations of the Pleistocene. Meanwhile, there had been major movements which resulted in mountain-building, and the Alps and Himalayas had arisen. The evolving saxifrages were accordingly presented with two new evolutionary opportunities which they could exploit—the newly formed tundra in the north, or the new mountain chains in the south. The most recent migration has been the invasion, during and after the Pleistocene, of regions formerly covered by ice.

## Relationships of the sections

Many of the sections are highly distinctive in one way or another, and our understanding of their relationships is rather sketchy; it is for this reason that we have refrained from recognising subgenera. Nevertheless, some comment on relationships would seem worthwhile. As explained, we envisage an early differentiation of the proto-saxifrage into present-day sections in different parts of its range. Remnants of this ancestral, forest stock, all of which retain its morphological imprint to varying degrees, are now found around the northern Pacific rim (sections *Micranthes*, *Irregulares*, *Merkianae* and *Heterisia*); in the Himalaya (sections *Odontophyllae*, *Mesogyne* and parts of section *Ciliatae*); in south-eastern Europe (sections *Cotylea* and *Cymbalaria*); and in western Europe (section *Gymnopera*). The relationships of these sections are often rather loose, although sections *Micranthes* and *Irregulares* may be regarded as sister groups because they alone share the presence of calcium oxalate crystals. Section *Heterisia* probably stands fairly close to these. Section *Cymbalaria* is interesting in that it may provide a link with section *Ciliatae*: both groups have yellow petals with small swellings at the base, a combination of characters unknown elsewhere; the chromosome numbers are also close (x = 8 in section *Ciliatae*, x = 9 in section *Cymbalaria*). The striking similarities between sections *Odontophyllae* and *Cotylea* have already been pointed out. The affinities of section *Gymnopera* are problematic; possible relatives include section *Ligulatae* (with which it shares the chromosome base number of x = 14, and forms one putative hybrid), and section *Micranthes* (which has similar floral and vegetative morphologies, as well as x = 14 as one of its chromosome base numbers). The latter seems to us to be the more likely.

The European stock eventually produced section *Saxifraga*, which diversified in the various mountain ranges, although several subsections or series have circumpolar representatives, probably of fairly recent (Pleistocene) origin. Section *Trachyphyllum* is a circumpolar group whose affinities are unclear, although they may lie with section *Ciliatae* on the basis of certain similarities and parallelisms in morphology.

The sections with lime-secreting hydathodes probably have a common ancestor which originated in Asia. Although none now resembles the forest progenitors, those which possess ovaries that are superior, or nearly so, occur today in the Sino-Himalayan region (section *Porphyrion*). Section *Porphyrion* evidently became dispersed along a broad front in the mountain ranges of Asia and Europe. Section *Xanthizoon*, represented now only by *S.aizoides*, could be considered as an early circumpolar tundra derivative, evolving from the same stock as *Porphyrion*, its long evolutionary separation being reflected in its rather different morphology. Circumpolar species of section *Porphyrion* are possibly of a more recent, Pleistocene origin. The European section *Ligulatae* is probably a derivative of *Porphyrion* ancestry, and in many ways its species are simply elaborate versions, with larger, monocarpic rosettes and highly branched inflorescences, of their *Porphyrion* cousins.

# 2

# History of our knowledge of the genus

The name *Saxifraga* (breaker of rocks or stones) dates back to Dioscorides, the writer on medical botany of the first century AD. As he wrote in Greek he spelt the word Σαξιφρα-γιον, and it is rather remarkable that he should have chosen a word derived from Latin roots (*saxum*, a rock; *frangere*, to break), but as he had travelled widely as an army doctor he was presumably familiar with Latin. The word is then lost sight of until it crops up again in the herbals of the later Middle Ages. It is usually explained as a slightly fanciful allusion to the fact that many species grow in rock-crevices, and can be supposed to split the rocks by the expansion of their roots. But there are several reasons for rejecting this interpretation. For one thing, such saxifrages as were known to the ancients, and the sole species to which the name was attached in the sixteenth century (*S.granulata*), normally grow in grassland, not in rock-crevices. And the illustration which accompanies Dioscorides' account in the Vienna codex, though its identify is inscrutable, is certainly not a rock-plant.

The true interpretation is that the stones referred to are urinary calculi; Dioscorides himself emphasises this point and makes no allusion to habitat. The small bulbils to be found at the base of the stem of *S.granulata* and of *S.carpetana* have a superficial resemblance to such calculi, and the doctrine of signatures taught that a plant of medicinal value bears in its external form some indication of the sphere of its efficacy. The belief may well have derived support from the fact that some of the leaves of

*S.granulata* are kidney-shaped. It is doubtful whether any species of the genus actually possesses any medicinal properties, but the name was widely applied by the herbalists and early botanists of the Renaissance to a variety of plants as diverse as species of *Sisymbrium*, *Melilotus*, *Scleranthus*, *Filipendula* and *Oenanthe*, presumably in the belief that these plants had the same medicinal virtue; and this indiscriminate use of the word is preserved in names such as *Pimpinella saxifraga* and *Kohlrauschia saxifraga* which are current today.

## Discovery of the species

The earliest illustration, whether manuscript or printed, which is recognisable as a saxifrage is in the *Herbarum vivae icones* of Brunfels (1530), where his *Saxifragia* or 'hoher Steynbrech' on p. 185 is quite unmistakably *S. granulata*, and it is the only representative of the genus. Rather surprisingly, the next plants to be included in it were the two common species of *Chrysosplenium*, by l'Obel in 1576, for although we believe them to be closely related to saxifrages, their lack of petals obscures the resemblance to all but a very critical eye. Gradually, as the exploration of the Alps gathered impetus during the late sixteenth and early seventeenth centuries, the number of known species increased, but with the exception of *S.bulbifera*, whose resemblance to *S.granulata* is obvious, they were not referred to *Saxifraga* but to other genera such as

*Cotyledon, Sanicula, Geum* and above all, *Sedum*. It is true that the leaves of some saxifrages are more or less succulent, but *S.aizoides* is the only species in which they bear any close resemblance to those of a *Sedum*. Bauhin, however, in his influential *Pinax* (1623) followed the practice of his predecessors, so that as late as 1688, Ray, in his *Historia Plantarum*, found it necessary to classify *Saxifraga hypnoides* under *Sedum* and *S.stellaris* under *Cotyledon*.

The *Élémens de Botanique* of Tournefort (1694) marked, however, an important step forward in our understanding of the genus. He made a clear distinction between those plants hitherto called *Sedum* which have an inferior or semi-inferior ovary of two carpels, and those which have a superior ovary of five or more free carpels, and he transferred the former to *Saxifraga*. It is curious that in spite of this percipience he left in the genus *Geum* those saxifrages known to him which have a superior ovary, such as *S.umbrosa* and *S.stellaris*.

It was Linnaeus who finally put this right, and as early as 1737 in his *Flora Lapponica* he gave the genus the same circumscription as we do today (except that *Bergenia* was later excluded), although he only knew of 37 species. These, however, included representatives of eleven out of the 15 sections which we recognise today, so that future progress lay rather in the discovery of new species than in modification of our idea of the generic character.

Already in the lifetime of Linnaeus the exploration of the Alps by Haller and Allioni, and of the Pyrenees by Gouan, was bringing in a trickle of new species, a trickle which was soon to swell to a flood, thanks to the work of Lapeyrouse and Sternberg in particular, and was later to be powerfully reinforced by the discoveries of Boissier in Spain and Greece, who added eleven new species between 1839 and 1856. Soon after this latter date it could be said that the exploration of Europe was nearly complete, and only work for gleaners remained. Nevertheless, the last hundred years have seen, apart from much re-arrangement and re-naming, the discovery of nine new species in Europe, and the fact that one of these was found beside a main road in Spain as lately as 1980 suggests that the list may not yet be completely closed.

So far we have spoken only of Europe and the adjacent parts of Asia. A brief word must be said in conclusion of discoveries in the Himalayan-Tibetan region (including western China), the Far East and the Americas. The second supplement that completed Sternberg's revision of the genus in 1831 contained descriptions of six Himalayan species collected by Wallich. Not much more was done in this region until J.D. Hooker visited Sikkim in 1848–9; this led to the description of 14 more species in 1857. Towards the end of the century, the explorers became more numerous and extended the range of their travels, so that new species of saxifrage came pouring in, and by 1919 something like 100 new species endemic to this region had been described. Delavay, David, Wilson and Forrest were among the most productive of the collectors; their species were described largely by Franchet in Paris, and Engler & Irmscher in Berlin.

In the next 20 years attention was focused more on western China than on the Himalayan region, but plenty of new species were to be found there. After 1935 the stream dried up for a while, but resumed with renewed vigour in 1958, when Harry Smith of Uppsala, working mainly on the collections of recent British expeditions to the Himalaya, described 32 new species in section *Porphyrion* alone (Smith 1958), followed two years later by 24 new members of section *Ciliatae* (Smith 1960). As Smith himself pointed out, a large number of these Himalayan species are known only from the type-locality, and the discovery of intermediates elsewhere may be expected to reduce their number, but the number is even more likely to be increased by new discoveries in this very thinly explored terrain. The Indian species are at present undergoing revision by K. Whadwa, but it will be many years before an accurate estimate can be made of the number in China and Upper Burma, although work is in progress (Pan 1978).

The eastern fringe of Asia (including Japan) probably contains barely a tenth of the number of species in the Himalayan region, but it is of interest as being possibly the area in which the genus originated, and in being the home of the remarkable section *Irregulares*, in which the unequal development of the petals, hinted at in two other sections, is carried to an extreme. The most familiar member of the section, *S.stolonifera*, was described as long ago as 1778; since then, discovery has proceeded with a fairly even pace.

In North America, the genus is concentrated mainly in the mountain ranges of the west, although many species also found in Europe or Asia extend to the arctic regions. Of the eight species found in the temperate parts of eastern North America, one was recognised by Linnaeus, six more were described by Michaux, Asa Gray and others before 1862, and only one has been distinguished in this century. Many of the non-European arctic species were described between 1820 and 1840 from collections made in Alaska and eastern Siberia by explorers such as Richardson, Menzies, Nelson and Chamisso.

Most of those species found in the Rocky mountains and associated ranges running parallel to the Pacific coast had to wait for the opening up of the west before they could be described. Exploration of this huge area was largely achieved following the gold rushes to California (1849) and to the Yukon (1896); and between 1860 and 1905 more than 50 new species were discovered. Small described 33 of these, 31 from the west, one from the Arctic and one from the east. Only four, however, are accepted today (and two of these were actually replacement names, superseding earlier names that were illegitimate under the *International Code of Botanical Nomenclature*). Towards the end of the same period, Greene described eleven new species, all from the west, seven of which are currently recognised. This success rate of 64 per cent is a little surprising, because Greene shared Small's reputation for being a somewhat eccentric 'splitter' of species.

The final, but ineffective, taxonomic fling of any magnitude was that of A.M. Johnson in 1923, who set out to revise the species of section *Micranthes* in North America. In his account, he described ten new ones, all of which now languish in synonymy.

Only two new species have been discovered and accepted since 1923, but one wonders how many others may lurk undetected in botanically under-explored areas.

# Schemes of classifications

The first botanist to attempt to divide *Saxifraga* into smaller groups of related species was Adrian Haworth, an English gardener. In 1803 he published his *Miscellanea naturalia*, in which he distributed the 49 then known species among six sections, three of which are still in use today, while a fourth does duty as a subsection. His division of the genus soon became more far-reaching, initially in his *Synopsis plantarum succulentarum* (1812), in which three segregate genera were split from *Saxifraga*, and later in the *Saxifragarum enumeratio* (1821), where a total of 16 genera (plus *Megasea* [= *Bergenia*]) were made out of Linnaeus' old one. As a horticulturalist, Haworth had the great advantage of being able to observe his plants in the living condition. Without going into too much detail here, we may note that the circumscriptions of nearly all of his genera correspond quite closely to the sections, subsections or series that we recognise today.

Most subsequent botanists, however, reverted to the broad, Linnean interpretation of the genus, and proceeded to re-define and merge Haworth's genera into new sections, often with new names. The chief architects of this re-structuring were David Don (1822) in London and, in Prague, Tausch (1823) and Sternberg, whose *Revisio Saxifragarum* of 1810 was followed by two supplements in 1822 and 1831. It is the second supplement of 1831 which is the most important and in which a detailed sub-division of the genus into 14 sections is presented. The systems produced by the three authors show little agreement and, although some of the names are familiar, the collections of species that many of them encompass are today considered unnatural assemblages. Seringe's account of *Saxifraga* in De Candolle's *Prodromus* (1830) was important partly because it largely followed Tausch's system, partly because it appeared in what was to become an influential, standard work of reference, and partly because it is the source of one error and four changes of spelling of sectional names which were subsequently perpetuated.

There matters rested for about 30 years, until a series of publications by Engler (1867, 1869, 1872), culminating in a full monograph, completely overhauled the confusing and unworkable classifications of his immediate predecessors. Engler was probably the first botanist since Haworth to understand the pattern of variation in the genus. The monograph of 1872 divided *Saxifraga* into 15 sections, two of which we now recognise as constituting separate genera. The circumscriptions of the remaining 13 sections correspond rather well with Haworth's genera, although the names are mostly different. Engler's treatment of the genus in the first edition of the *Pflanzenfamilien* (Engler 1891) introduced a few improvements, and gave elaborate keys for the determination of species in the larger sections. Finally, the monumental monograph in the *Pflanzenreich*, written in collaboration with Irmscher (Engler & Irmscher 1916, 1919; usually bound together) elaborated his earlier work in great detail, and included many species from Asia and North America which had been described since 1891. Stunning in its treatment of the minutest details of variation, with an overwhelming profusion of subspecies, varieties, subvarieties, forms and subforms in those variable species to which he gave the description of *typus polymorphus*, it remains an indispensable work of reference, for which our respect must be increased when we remember that it was produced in wartime.

Nevertheless, it has its imperfections. These stem largely from the fact that it was completed almost entirely from herbarium material, supplemented only to a small extent by records from the literature. Engler's days of field-work were over, and the Botanic Garden at Berlin contained little material of known wild origin. In consequence some of the drawings are unsatisfactory; no attempt is made to distinguish between environmentally and genetically determined variation; and there are many errors in transcription of place-names from herbarium labels.

We have, therefore, deviated from the *Pflanzenreich* at various taxonomic levels, from variety to section, but our account is to a very large extent based on it, and we are happy to pay tribute to it as one of the last examples of the noble tradition of thorough, detailed and well-ordered work, which was the hallmark of German scholarship in the nineteenth century—all the more so as modern studies of embryology and the fine structure of seeds and pollen grains have confirmed Engler's system far more often than they have suggested modifications.

Although most botanists have adopted the broad, Linnean concept of the genus, Haworth's phoenix rose briefly in 1905 when Small resurrected his genera in an account of North American saxifrages published in the *North American Flora*. Seventy-eight years later, Á. Löve attempted something similar in his *Flora of Iceland* (1983), but we doubt if this approach will ever prove popular.

# 3
# Ecological and horticultural notes

Neither of the authors can claim to be an expert alpine gardener, so that the remarks under this head are of a very general nature. For more detailed advice we refer the reader to specialised horticultural works such as Köhlein (1984) and Horný *et al.* (1986), or to relevant articles in the *Quarterly Bulletin of the Alpine Garden Society*. For each species we give in the main text a brief note, based mainly on experience in the botanic gardens of Cambridge and Trinity College, Dublin, on the ease or difficulty of cultivation and on any special requirements. However, it seems appropriate here to make some general comments about the interrelated topics of ecology and cultivation because, as with any other plant, in order to understand the cultural conditions required by saxifrages in the garden, it is first necessary to know something of their ecological behaviour in the wild.

## Natural habitats

Gardeners usually picture saxifrages as growing tightly wedged in rock-crevices; and for several species this is true enough. *S.valdensis* and *S.diapensioides* are usually so firmly wedged that nothing short of a skilfully placed charge of dynamite would extract their root system intact, and many others, such as *S. tombeanensis*, *S.spruneri* and *S.squarrosa*, are also primarily crevice-plants.

But although most species in sections *Ligulatae* and *Porphyrion*, and quite a large number in section *Saxifraga*, are rock-dwellers, they often grow in wider crevices or in crumbling rock, and from here the habitat passes gradually into scree, moraine or other rock-debris. Other species are characteristic of grassland; a few are found on shady banks or in open woodland; and two or three are sufficiently dependent on mountain streams to be classed as aquatic or semi-aquatic.

Nearly all the species are commoner in shade than in full sun, and there are a few in which this preference is so strong that they are confined to the entrances to caves or to hollows under overhanging rocks. Exceptions to this rule can be found in northern latitudes and on the highest mountains, but generally speaking the climber can expect the best ground for saxifrages (as for many alpines) to lie on rocks and screes facing north or north-east.

A list of the principal habitats follows, with the names of a few European species characteristic of each. The eight categories inevitably are rather arbitrary, although they serve as a useful general guide.

1. Vertical rock-faces
   (a) in the high mountains: *S.florulenta*, *S.tombeanensis*, *S.spruneri*.
   (b) at lower levels: *S.fragilis*, *S.globulifera*, *S.cochlearis*.
2. Boulders and broken rock-surfaces: *S.paniculata*, *S.corymbosa*, *S.bryoides*, *S.caesia*.
3. Screes and moraines, often in late snow-lies: *S.sedoides*, *S.biflora*, *S.seguieri*.

4. Lowland and montane grassland: *S.granulata*, *S.carpetana*.
5. Woodland-margin and shady banks: *S.umbrosa*, *S.cuneifolia*, *S.rotundifolia*.
6. Under rocks, or at the mouth of caves: *S.arachnoidea*, *S.petraea*, *S.paradoxa*, *S.hederacea*.
7. In or beside mountain streams: *S.aquatica*, *S.stellaris*, *S.aizoides*.
8. Tundra: *S.foliolosa*, *S.flagellaris*.

About half the European species are strictly calcicole, and are seldom, if ever, seen on any substratum other than limestone or dolomite. A considerable number, though not so rigorous in their requirements, show a calcicole tendency; they are more abundant on limestone than on other rocks, though they can be found on a variety of rocks or soils provided that the base-status is not too low. It is not surprising to find that the most widespread species, such as *S.paniculata*, *S.granulata* and *S.exarata* subsp. *moschata*, belong to this category. Finally, there are some eight to ten species which are faithful to siliceous rocks or humus-rich soils, and can be classed as constantly calcifuge; these include *S.clusii*, *S.spathularis*, *S.bryoides* and *S.cotyledon*.

## Where to find them

For botanical tourists and those gardeners who like to see at first hand how their plants grow in the wild, we offer the following notes on the best places to go.

### Europe

Saxifrages here are for the most part mountain plants, and although a few species such as *S.hirculus*, *S.granulata* and *S.tridactylites* are common in the lowlands, there is none that cannot be found in the mountains as well. There are also some species characteristic of moderate altitudes (around 1000–1200m), which are nevertheless much commoner around the skirts of high mountains than in hill-country at the same altitude.

It is to the major mountain ranges of Europe,

therefore, that the saxifrage-hunter must go, and it is between 1800 and 2500m that most of the species are to be found. One thinks first, of course, of the Alps, and they are indeed rich in species, but they are equalled by the Pyrenees and mountains of northern Spain. Each of these two regions can boast of about 40 species, and they are to a large extent complementary, for there are only 14 species common to both regions.

In the Alps the greatest concentration of species is to be found in the south-east; between Lake Como and the Yugoslav frontier one can see over 30 species without leaving Italy. If it is impossible to cover the whole of this region, it is best to concentrate on the Dolomites and the Giudicarian Alps (west of the northern end of Lake Garda). In Switzerland, the upper Engadin and the country around Zermatt provide good hunting-ground, but on the whole the central part of the Alps is relatively poor. From the Mont Cenis pass southwards, however, the variety increases, and in the Maritime Alps near Tende one can see 14 species in the course of a single 3-hour climb.

In the Pyrenees the whole of the central part of the chain is species-rich, although there are a few species to be found only near the eastern or the western end. Mont-Louis, Luchon, Barèges and Luz on the French side, and Viella and Panticosa on the Spanish side all form good bases for a preliminary survey. Further west, in the Cantabrian chain, interest is focused chiefly on the Picos de Europa and the adjacent peaks and passes; these are best explored from Covadonga, Fuente Dé and Reinosa.

After these two giants the regions next in interest are the southern part of the Balkan peninsula, and the sierras of eastern and southern Spain. Between the southern tip of Greece and the mountains of Yugoslav and Bulgarian Macedonia there are 24 species of saxifrage, and eleven of these are not to be found in the Alps or Pyrenees. Mount Taïyetos and Mount Olympus in Greece and the Pirin range in southwestern Bulgaria are among the best places of relatively easy access; much of the good ground lies, unfortunately, in the remoter parts of the Pindus or on the northern frontier of Greece.

In the Spanish sierras there are only 21 species, but 13 of these cannot be seen elsewhere in Europe, though a few are found also in North Africa. They are extended over a wide range of country, from southern Aragon to near Cádiz. One cannot, therefore, speak of a centre for seeking them; Albarracin, Játiva, Cazorla, Granada, Antequera and Ronda may, however, be mentioned as convenient staging-posts. With the sole exception of *S.nevadensis*, these plants grow at moderate elevations and, almost without exception, on limestone rocks.

Finally a word on the arctic and subarctic regions of Europe. There are 17 species native to Iceland or to Scandinavia north of 65°N, and all but two or three are fairly common. Six of these are essentially arctic plants, not to be seen further south except, in some cases, as rarities in Scotland. Most of them can be found without special directions not far from the main road leading northwards from Trondheim; for those who prefer to operate from a single centre, Abisko, in Swedish Lapland, is as good as any.

## North America

It is to the west of the Rocky mountain chain that the traveller must go in order to see most of the North American saxifrages. There are four main areas which together contain most of the species.

Denali National Park, located between Anchorage and Fairbanks in Alaska, is probably the best and most convenient centre from which to see up to 20 of those species native to the arctic or the extreme north-west (beware of Grizzly Bears, however!).

Further south, the most accessible places are in the USA rather than in Canada, and mention may be made first of the area which includes the Bitterroot and Anaconda mountain ranges in eastern Idaho and western Montana. The best bases from which to find 16 species are Missoula and Butte.

The Cascade Range from southern British Columbia to southern Oregon is another rich hunting-ground. This is a large area and is best explored by travelling through it rather than by basing oneself at a centre. Many places of interest may be found by taking any of the roads which lead eastwards from interstate highway 5; Mounts Baker, Rainier and Hood in particular are worth visiting. Also in this area is the Columbia River Gorge, which separates Washington from Oregon, and whose steep cliffs provide suitable habitats for many species.

Finally, probably the best centre from which to see most of the more southerly species is Yosemite National Park, in the Sierra Nevada east of San Francisco, California.

In eastern North America, there are two areas which deserve a mention; one of these, with five species, is in the southern part of the Appalachians, where the best place to go is probably the Unaka mountains and Cherokee National Forest, which straddle the Tennessee/North Carolina state line. The second area, with three species, lies west of the Mississippi River in the general area of the Ozark mountains, roughly where the states of Missouri, Oklahoma and Arkansas meet.

# How to grow them

By far and away the horticulturally most important plants in the genus are those belonging to sections *Porphyrion*, *Ligulatae* and *Saxifraga*—that is the 'Kabschia' and 'Engleria' saxifrages, the 'Silver' saxifrages and the 'Mossy' saxifrages—and thousands are sold by nurseries every year. They make wonderful subjects for the rock-garden but, to grow them successfully, the right conditions must be created at the outset. Essential requirements are shade from the midday sun, good drainage, and a high atmospheric humidity in summer. As far as soil is concerned, all species which are found on rocks or screes in the high mountains respond best to standard 'alpine' treatment— that is to say culture in a well-drained, gritty soil, neither very rich nor very poor, with a liberal supply of water in spring and early summer and more moderate at other seasons. This regime is designed to mimic the natural habitat, which is subject to a flush of moisture, caused by the melting snow in spring and early summer, followed by drier conditions thereafter. Species whose natural habitat comprises woodland clearings and shady banks, including many members of sections *Gymnopera*, *Cotylea*, *Micranthes*, *Irregulares* and *Ciliatae*, usually do best in a sandy loam with a good mulch of organic matter, and a more even supply of water. The pH or acidity of the soil can be an important factor determining success or otherwise at cultivation, and the notes provided under the heading of 'Habitat' for each of the European species should be consulted for guidance.

Many pages have been written in the debate over how much sun is needed by saxifrages in cultivation. For species occurring naturally in shady places, whether it be open woodland, shady banks or shady ledges or rocks, there is plainly no question that they should be given similar conditions in the garden. For the mountain-dwellers, however, which live in the open, the solution is not quite so clear-cut, for it can depend on how much moisture is available. The ideal situation is, of course, a slope facing north or north-east, such as they prefer in the wild. The important thing is to provide an open aspect which avoids hot sun. In the rock garden, the choice of a sunny or shady site depends much on the local climate. If the rainfall is low, a sunny site risks death from desiccation in spring or summer; if the hours of sunshine are low, a shady site may lead to poor flowering or 'legginess'. For most species, a site which gives 3–4 hours of sunshine a day is an acceptable compromise. Nevertheless, species from very high elevations, such as some of the more recent introductions from the Himalaya, will need longer periods of bright light than this, and in such cases a sunnier spot is warranted, but care should be taken to provide an adequate supply of water.

Generally speaking, the sunnier the position the higher the atmospheric humidity should be. In the wild this is provided by the mountain microclimate of clouds or snow-beds, and in many gardens a morning or evening treatment with a mist-spray can be highly beneficial, especially in dry spells. In winter, in contrast, the weather in the British Isles is often too wet for some species, which in the wild would normally be nestling beneath a blanket of snow, quite dry. Protection from winter damp can be afforded simply by covering susceptible plants with a small sheet of glass, but leaving them exposed at the sides.

Very few European species are tender in the ordinary sense of the word — that is to say they can withstand a few degrees of frost if not too prolonged, but those from moderate altitudes in southern Europe tend to look pinched and starved when grown out of doors, except in the more favoured parts of the British Isles, and do themselves justice only in a cool greenhouse. For the true alpines it is best to have a pot indoors as well as a clump outside; the former is usually rather more luxuriant, but the latter more free from pests.

The most dangerous pests in our experience are vine-weevil and mealy bug. The former has a larva which chews away at the roots and rhizomes, often just below soil level, and its presence is first realised only when the plant acquires a dull, dried-up look and comes away in the hand. Mealy bug usually shows itself among the leaves, but sometimes operates entirely underground, with the same results. Both pests can be controlled by systemic insecticides or fumigation, but constant vigilance is necessary to prevent a recurrence. Vine-weevil, however, can prove to be annoyingly resistant to chemical attack, in which case successful control may be achieved by picking out the larvae by hand and repotting the plant in sterilised soil. *Botrytis* and similar fungi can occasionally be troublesome in a damp, warm November, so that a light dusting of fungicide on species with crowded leafy shoots is advisable. Although not a pest in the technical sense of the word, blackbirds have a reputation in some areas for causing the destruction of cushion saxifrages when foraging for grubs.

Most species are easily propagated by division, though it is sometimes surprising to find a large cushion which possesses only a single tap-root. In such cases, however, cuttings of non-flowering side-shoots, taken in spring or autumn, are usually easy to strike. Annuals and biennials must be propagated by seed, and this usually germinates well after a dormant period of about a month. Most species set a fair crop of seed, even under glass, and although there is some risk of hybridisation it is usually not very great, especially if self-pollination has been carried out by hand. We must record with regret our experience that many seeds, even from famous botanic gardens, do not come up true to name.

# 4

# European species

## Key to the species

14. Leaves linear to oblong-lanceolate ................................................................ 15
    Leaves kidney-shaped or almost circular ...................................................... 18
15. Plant with long, slender, leafless runners ............................................ **2.*flagellaris***
    Plant without runners; prostrate shoots leafy ............................................. 16
16. Axillary buds on leafy shoots not conspicuous at flowering time .............. **54.*bronchialis***
    Axillary buds on leafy shoots conspicuous at flowering time ............................... 17
17. Leaves of non-flowering shoots straight, much longer than their axillary buds;
       leaves of flowering stem c.10mm, spreading .................................... **52.*aspera***
    Leaves of non-flowering shoots incurved, scarcely longer than their axillary buds;
       leaves of flowering stem not more than 5mm, nearly erect ............... **53.*bryoides***
18. Flowers solitary, in the axils of foliage-leaves on diffuse stems ........................ 19
    Flowers in terminal cymes or panicles, or solitary at the tip of an erect stem ............... 20
19. Petals 2–3mm, white or pale yellow .................................................... **5.*hederacea***
    Petals 4.5–6mm, bright yellow ........................................................ **3.*cymbalaria***
20. Flower solitary, with bulbils below it .................................................. **59.*cernua***
    Flowers in a cyme or panicle; inflorescence without bulbils .............................. 21
21. Petals with red spots ....................................................................... 22
    Petals without red spots .................................................................... 23
22. Largest leaves not more than 25mm wide, with 5–11 crenations or teeth .......... **14.*taygetea***
    Largest leaves at least 25mm wide, with at least 15 crenations or teeth ........ **13.*rotundifolia***
23. Petals 5–7mm ........................................................................... **56.*carpatica***
    Petals 8–14mm ........................................................................... 24
24. Cauline leaves entire or shortly 3-lobed ................................................ **55.*sibirica***
    Cauline leaves toothed ................................................................. **13.*rotundifolia***
25. Petals bright yellow or orange ............................................................ 26
    Petals white, pink, purple, red or pale yellow .............................................. 31
26. Larger leaves at least 7mm wide .................................................... **49.*mutata***
    Larger leaves not more than 6mm wide .................................................. 27
27. Leaves fleshy and fairly soft, usually with a single hydathode ................... **51.*aizoides***
    Leaves stiff and hard, with 3–7 hydathodes ............................................ 28
28. Stamens at least as long as the petals; leaves with a long, sharp point ................... 29
    Stamens shorter than the petals; leaves obtuse or with a very short point ................... 30
29. Flowering stem, pedicels and hypanthium glandular-hairy ................... **28.*juniperifolia***
    Flowering stem, pedicels and hypanthium hairless ............................... **29.*sancta***
30. Inflorescence usually with not more than 6 flowers; most of the leaves with a
       short, erect point ................................................... **31.*aretioides***
    Inflorescence usually with more than 6 flowers; leaves obtuse, or with a short,
       incurved point ................................................... **30.*ferdinandi-coburgi***
31. Bulbils present, at or below ground level, in the axils of the basal leaves ................... 32
    Basal leaves without bulbils in their axils ................................................ 43
32. Petals glandular-hairy on upper surface, at least towards the base ........................... 33
    Petals hairless ........................................................................... 37
33. Bulbils present in the axils of cauline leaves and bracts ............................ **66.*bulbifera***
    Bulbils confined to the axils of the lower leaves .......................................... 34
34. Inflorescence diffuse; flowering stems usually branched from the middle or below it ..... 35
    Inflorescence compact; flowering stems usually branched only in the uppermost
       quarter ................................................................................ 36
35. Petals 5–6mm; lower leaves obovate, deeply lobed ............................... **62.*haenseleri***
    Petals 8–11mm; lower leaves rhombic to nearly circular, crenate ............... **65.*cintrana***

36. Basal leaves deeply divided into linear-oblong or oblanceolate lobes .......... **63.***dichotoma*
    Basal leaves crenate or somewhat pinnately lobed, but not deeply so .......... **64.***carpetana*
37. Basal leaves deeply dissected with 3 primary lobes, which are stalked or at least narrowed at the base ................................................................................. 38
    Basal leaves divided for not more than ⅔ of the distance to the base; lobes broad-based ................................................................................................. 39
38. Stems erect, forming a compact tuft; nearly all the leaves basal ................. **67.***gemmulosa*
    Stems diffuse, ascending, leafy ................................................................ **68.***bourgaeana*
39. Petals 7–16mm ........................................................................................ 40
    Petals 2–6mm .......................................................................................... 41
40. Leaves distinctly 3-lobed; flowering stem usually branched from near the base .. **61.***corsica*
    Leaves crenate but not lobed; flowering stem usually branched only in the upper half ............................................................................................. **60.***granulata*
41. Leaves obovate ..................................................................................... **62.***haenseleri*
    Leaves kidney-shaped or semicircular ..................................................... 42
42. Plant not more than 4cm tall; leaves somewhat tapered to the petiole, mostly 3-lobed; petals red ......................................................................... **58.***hyperborea*
    Plant up to 15cm tall; leaves with truncate or cordate base, mostly 5-lobed; petals white or pink, rarely red ............................................................... **57.***rivularis*
43. Leaves sessile, not lobed, leathery, often lime-encrusted .............................. 44
    Leaves often stalked or lobed; if sessile and undivided, then soft or fleshy, not leathery; very seldom lime-encrusted ....................................................... 77
44. Leaves opposite .................................................................................... 45
    Leaves alternate or basal ........................................................................ 47
45. Sepals without marginal hairs ................................................................ **39.***retusa*
    Sepals with marginal hairs ..................................................................... 46
46. Leaves hard and rigid, usually lime-encrusted, keeled beneath; petals usually contiguous ............................................................................................. **38.***oppositifolia*
    Leaves soft and rather fleshy, rarely lime-encrusted, not keeled beneath; petals narrow, widely separated ....................................................................... **40.***biflora*
47. Calyx bell-shaped or urn-shaped, enclosing and largely concealing the petals ............. 48
    Calyx cup- or saucer-shaped, not concealing the petals ......................................... 51
48. Petals yellow ........................................................................................ **37.***corymbosa*
    Petals pink or purple ............................................................................. 49
49. Most of the flowers sessile; inflorescence not branched ............. **32–34.***porophylla* group
    Most of the flowers distinctly stalked; inflorescence often branched ......................... 50
50. Inflorescence sparingly branched, with 1–2 flowers on each primary branch ...... **35.***media*
    Inflorescence freely branched, with 3–4 flowers on each primary branch ........ **36.***stribrnyi*
51. Larger leaves at least 15mm long ............................................................ 52
    All leaves less than 15mm long ............................................................... 60
52. Rosette solitary, without offsets; plant dying after flowering ............................ 53
    Flowering rosettes producing offsets which persist after the flowering rosette has died ................................................................................................ 54
53. Leaves glaucous, lime-encrusted, subacute; flowers white ...................... **41.***longifolia*
    Leaves dull green, not lime-encrusted, apiculate; flowers dull pink .............. **50.***florulenta*
54. Flowering stem not more than 10cm tall; flowers 1–8 ............................. **21.***marginata*
    Flowering stem more than 10cm tall; flowers numerous ................................ 55
55. Leaves spathulate, obtuse ...................................................................... **43.***cochlearis*
    Leaves linear to oblong; if somewhat expanded near the tip, then subacute ................ 56

56. Leaves more or less entire; translucent margin very narrow or absent; lime-secreting hydathodes opening on the margin, not on the upper surface ................... 57

  Leaves with a distinct translucent margin, which is toothed or crenate; lime-secreting hydathodes opening near the margin but clearly on the upper surface ........ 58

57. Lower branches of panicle bearing 5 or more flowers ................................. **42.*callosa***

  Lower branches of panicle bearing 1–4 flowers ................................. **44.*crustata***

58. Flowering stem branched from below the middle, and usually from near the base; primary branches in lower part of the inflorescence bearing more than 12 flowers, which are not crowded together at the tip of the branch ........................ **47.*cotyledon***

  Flowering stem branched from the middle or above it; primary branches of inflorescence bearing not more than 12 flowers, which are crowded together near the tip of the branch ................................................................. 59

59. Basal leaves tending to curve downwards near the tip, to give a flat or slightly convex rosette; primary branches of the inflorescence with 4–12 (rarely 3) flowers ................................................................. **45.*hostii***

  Basal leaves tending to curve upwards, giving a concave, sometimes almost hemispherical rosette; primary branches of the inflorescence with 1–3 (rarely 4) flowers ................................................................. **46.*paniculata***

60. Petals purple or deep pink ................................................................. 61

  Petals white, sometimes with red spots ................................................ 62

61. Flowers solitary; leaves with 1–5 lime-secreting hydathodes ................. **38.*oppositifolia***

  Flowers 5–14; leaves with 9–13 lime-secreting hydathodes ........................ **24.*scardica***

62. Leaves mucronate or apiculate ................................................. 63

  Leaves obtuse or subacute ................................................. 70

63. Leaves not more than 5mm long ................................................. 64

  Leaves at least 6mm long ................................................. 67

64. Mucro of leaves sharply incurved ................................... **23.*tombeanensis***

  Mucro of leaves straight ................................................. 65

65. Middle part of leaf-margin finely toothed ................................. **24.*scardica***

  Middle part of leaf-margin entire ................................................. 66

66. Leaves distinctly keeled beneath, curved outwards at the tip ................... **21.*marginata***

  Leaves convex beneath but scarcely keeled, not curved outwards at the tip **22.*diapensioides***

67. Flowers solitary, rarely 2 on a stem ................................... **26.*burseriana***

  Flowers in cymes of 3–14 ................................................. 68

68. Leaves deep green, not lime-encrusted, triangular-lanceolate, tapered to a long fine point ................................................. **27.*vandellii***

  Leaves glaucous, usually lime-encrusted, oblong to obovate-elliptic, rather suddenly narrowed to a short point ................................................. 69

69. Middle part of leaf-margin finely toothed ................................. **24.*scardica***

  Middle part of leaf-margin entire ................................................. **21.*marginata***

70. Petals 7–12mm ................................................. 71

  Petals 3–6mm ................................................. 73

71. Pedicels hairless, sometimes with a few very shortly stalked glands ............. **43.*cochlearis***

  Pedicels densely glandular-hairy ................................................. 72

72. Leaves usually more than 1.5mm wide, broadest above the middle ............. **21.*marginata***

  Leaves usually less than 1.5mm wide, broadest at or below the middle ................................................. **22.*diapensioides***

73. Leaves finely toothed in upper half ................................. **46.*paniculata***

  Leaves entire in upper half ................................................. 74

74. Leaves glandular-hairy beneath .................................................... **25.*spruneri***
    Leaves hairless except for a few marginal hairs near the base ...................... 75
75. Upper surface of leaf irregularly pitted ................................... **48.*valdensis***
    Upper surface of leaf smooth, except for the lime-secreting hydathodes near
        the margin ........................................................................ 76
76. Leaves curved outwards from near the base; upper part of flowering stem more
        hairy than lower part ................................................ **19.*caesia***
    Leaves curved outwards only from near the tip; lower part of flowering stem
        more hairy than upper part .................................... **20.*squarrosa***
77. Leaves opposite ................................................................ **40.*biflora***
    Leaves alternate or basal ............................................................ 78
78. Leaves linear-oblong, fleshy; flowers dark red ...................... **51.*aizoides***
    Leaves not fleshy .................................................................... 79
79. Leaves all entire .................................................................... 80
    Some of the leaves toothed, crenate or lobed ...................................... 94
80. Petals conspicuous, larger than the sepals and usually pure white ............... 81
    Petals inconspicuous, dull in colour and scarcely longer than the sepals ........ 89
81. Dormant axillary buds on leafy shoots conspicuous at flowering time ............. 82
    Leafy shoots without conspicuous, summer-dormant, axillary buds ................. 83
82. Leaves obovate, obtuse; petals turning pink after pollination ........ **72.*erioblasta***
    Leaves linear-oblong, apiculate; petals remaining white after pollination ........ **74.*conifera***
83. Leaves hairless except for a few on the margin ..................................... 84
    Leaves more or less hairy on the surface ........................................... 86
84. Leaves 3–6mm wide; flowering stems with 1–2 cauline leaves
        and 1–3 flowers .................................................... **105.*androsacea***
    Leaves 1–2mm wide; flowering stems with 4–7 cauline leaves
        and 3–9 flowers .................................................................. 85
85. Leaves and sepals apiculate ...................................... **115.*tenella***
    Leaves and sepals obtuse .......................................... **114.*glabella***
86. Annual; petals 2–3mm .......................................... **116.*tridactylites***
    Perennial; petals 4–7mm ............................................................ 87
87. Leaves firm, usually lime-encrusted, with translucent margin; inflorescence
        with 5–12 flowers ................................................ **25.*spruneri***
    Leaves soft, not lime-encrusted, without translucent margin; inflorescence
        with 1–4 flowers ................................................................ 88
88. Leafy shoots up to 10cm, numerous, crowded, forming a compact cushion;
        leaves mostly less than 2.5mm wide; petals contiguous ........ **109.*muscoides***
    Leafy shoots shorter, relatively few, forming a dense but low mat; leaves mostly
        more than 2.5mm wide; petals not contiguous ............... **105–108.*androsacea* group**
89. Leaves 10–30mm wide; flowering stem leafless .................... **6.*hieracifolia***
    Leaves not more than 5mm wide; flowering stem leafy .............................. 90
90. Some of the leaves apiculate .................................... **112.*sedoides***
    All leaves obtuse or subacute ...................................................... 91
91. Flowering stems not more than 2.5cm tall, scarcely exceeding the leafy
        shoots ............................................................ **110.*fachinii***
    Flowering stems at least 4cm tall; flowers standing well above the level
        of the leafy shoots .............................................................. 92
92. Petals gradually tapered to a narrow base and notched at the tip ........... **111.*presolanensis***
    Petals not tapered to a narrow base, rounded at the tip .......................... 93

93      Leafy shoots very short, forming a thick mat rather than a cushion, with all leaves appearing more or less basal ..................................................................... 108.*seguieri*
     Leafy shoots fairly long, forming a rounded cushion; living leaves obviously not basal .................................................................................................... 82.*exarata*

94.      Petals greenish, cream-coloured, dull yellow or dark red ...................................... 95
     Petals white, pink or bright red ......................................................................... 102

95.      All leaves in a basal rosette ..................................................................... 6.*hieracifolia*
     Plant with leafy stems and without a basal rosette ................................................ 96

96.      Larger leaves more than 6mm wide, usually wider than long .................................. 97
     Leaves not more than 6mm wide, longer than wide ............................................... 98

97.      Leaves hairless or very nearly so ............................................................. 104.*paradoxa*
     Leaves covered in long, cobweb-like hairs ................................................ 103.*arachnoidea*

98.      Leaf-segments furrowed on the upper surface .................................................... 99
     Leaf-segments flat on the upper surface ........................................................... 100

99.      Leaf-segments strongly mucronate, more or less hairless ......................... 83.*hariotii*
     Leaf-segments obtuse or subacute, glandular-hairy .................................... 82.*exarata*

100.      Petals linear, much narrower than the sepals ........................................... 113.*aphylla*
     Petals ovate or oblong, as wide as the sepals or only slightly narrower ..................... 101

101.      Leafy shoots more or less prostrate; some of the leaf-segments mucronate; petals mucronate or notched .............................................................. 112.*sedoides*
     Leafy shoots more or less erect; leaf-segments obtuse; petals obtuse .............. 82.*exarata*

102.      Mature leaves hairless, though often with sessile glands ............................... 103
     Mature leaves hairy, at least on margin or on petiole (hairs sometimes very short and visible only under a lens) ................................................................... 108

103.      Leaf-segments broadly triangular, 4–8mm wide at the base ......................... 97.*cuneata*
     Leaf-segments linear-oblong to lanceolate, 1–3mm wide at the base ......................... 104

104.      All leaf-segments obtuse or subacute .............................................................. 105
     Some of the leaf-segments apiculate or conspicuously mucronate ........................... 106

105.      Leaf-segments usually not more than 2mm wide wide, parallel-sided, furrowed on upper surface; petals 3.5–5.0mm ............................... 92.*pentadactylis*
     Leaf-segments usually more than 2mm wide, often with curved sides, flat on upper surface; petals 7–14mm ................................................... 93.*fragilis*

106.      Larger leaves with 15–25 segments; segments often curved, crowded and overlapping ........................................................................... 95.*trifurcata*
     Leaves with not more than 11 segments, which are not curved, crowded or overlapping ......................................................................................... 107

107.      Leaf-segments oblong to elliptical, 1.5–2.5 times as long as wide ................. 94.*camposii*
     Leaf-segments linear, 3–6 times as long as wide .................................. 96.*canaliculata*

108.      Leafy shoots bearing conspicuous, more or less dormant axillary buds at flowering time ................................................................................... 109
     Leafy shoots without conspicuous, dormant axillary buds at flowering time ............. 117

109.      Petals 11–20mm ............................................................................. 110
     Petals 4–10mm .............................................................................. 112

110.      Leaves much divided, with 3 primary lobes which are narrowed to stalk-like bases ........................................................................ 69.*biternata*
     Leaves palmately lobed, the lobes not narrowed at the base ................................... 111

111.      Outer leaves of axillary buds entire, more or less papery and translucent, fringed with cobweb-like hairs ............................................................. 73.*rigoi*

Outer leaves of axillary buds lobed, green and leaf-like in texture, without cobweb-like hairs ................................................................ **86.**_pedemontana_

112. Leaf-segments mucronate or apiculate ........................................................ 113
Leaf-segments obtuse to acute ................................................................ 114

113. Dormant axillary buds stalked, their outer leaves entirely papery and translucent ...................................................................... **75.**_continentalis_
Dormant axillary buds sessile, their outer leaves partly green ................... **76.**_hypnoides_

114. Leaves much divided, with 3 primary lobes which are stalked or narrowed at the base ........................................................................ **68.**_bourgaeana_
Leaves palmately lobed, the lobes not narrowed at the base ............................... 115

115. Dormant axillary buds shrouded in white, woolly hairs; petals turning pink after pollination ...................................................................... **72.**_erioblasta_
Dormant axillary buds hairy, but not shrouded in white, woolly hairs; petals remaining white .............................................................................. 116

116. Sepals 4 × 3mm; margins of petals turned downwards; inflorescence with 1–3 flowers .......................................................... **71.**_reuteriana_
Sepals 2.0 × 1.5mm; petals flat; inflorescence usually with at least 4 flowers ...................................................................... **70.**_globulifera_

117. Petals conspicuously notched, often unequal ............................................... 118
Petals not or only slightly notched, equal ................................................. 119

118. Biennial; basal leaves divided almost to the base; petals 8–10mm, contiguous .......................................................................... **101.**_petraea_
Perennial; basal leaves divided not more than half-way to the base; petals 4–8mm, not contiguous .......................................................................... **102.**_berica_

119. Annual or biennial ......................................................................... 120
Perennial ................................................................................... 121

120. Basal leaves kidney-shaped, with a long, clearly defined petiole ............. **100.**_latepetiolata_
Basal leaves oblanceolate with a short, scarcely distinct petiole ...................................................... **116–119.**_tridactylites_ **group**

121. Petals at least 7mm ........................................................................ 122
Petals not more than 7mm ................................................................... 128

122. Leaves with more than 11 ultimate segments ................................................ 123
Leaves with not more than 11 ultimate segments ............................................ 125

123. Aquatic; flowering stems 2–5mm in diameter ........................................ **98.**_aquatica_
Not aquatic; flowering stems less than 2mm in diameter ................................... 124

124. Stems woody at the base, spreading, forming a lax cushion .................... **88.**_geranioides_
Stems not woody at the base, forming a compact tuft ................................ **99.**_irrigua_

125. Plant with prostrate, non-flowering shoots, on which some of the leaves are entire ...................................................................... **76.**_hypnoides_
Plant without prostrate, non-flowering shoots ............................................. 126

126. Petals more than 10mm .............................................................. **86.**_pedemontana_
Petals not more than 10mm ................................................................. 127

127. Leaves with numerous glandular hairs, at least on the petiole; segments apiculate .......................................................................... **87.**_babiana_
Leaves either without glandular hairs, or with obtuse to subacute segments ........................................................................ **77.**_rosacea_

128. Leaves crenate to shortly toothed on the margins, with 5 or more teeth or crenations, but not lobed ................................................................ 129
Leaves distinctly lobed, or shortly 3-toothed at the tip ................................. 130

129. Flowering stem not more than 1mm in diameter, the lower part with
     short glandular hairs or almost hairless ............................................. **8.*tenuis***
     Flowering stem up to 2mm in diameter, the lower part with fairly long
     shaggy hairs ..................................................................................... **7.*nivalis***
130. Leaf-segments furrowed on the upper surface ....................................... 131
     Leaf-segments not furrowed on the upper surface .............................. 136
131. Hairs on leaves and calyx not more than 0.15mm, the stalk being scarcely
     longer than the diameter of the gland, giving a finely warty rather than a
     downy appearance ............................................................................. 132
     Hairs on leaves and calyx mostly at least 0.3mm, with the stalk
     considerably longer than the gland, giving a downy appearance .......................... 134
132. Plant forming cushions up to 30cm in diameter; larger leaves 20–30mm
     long ............................................................................... **89.*moncayensis***
     Plant forming cushions seldom more than 10cm in diameter; leaves not
     more than 15mm long ........................................................................ 133
133. Stems woody at the base; leaves dark green; leafy stems tending to diverge,
     forming lax cushions ............................................................ **91.*intricata***
     Stems scarcely woody at the base; leaves fresh green; leafy stems tightly packed,
     forming compact cushions .................................................. **82.*exarata***
134. Leaves with rather short, sometimes few, glandular hairs; petals about twice as
     long as wide, not contiguous ............................................. **82.*exarata***
     Leaves densely covered with rather long glandular hairs; petals about 1.5
     times as long as wide, usually contiguous .......................................... 135
135. Leaves darkish green; rosettes often 20–25mm in diameter; cauline
     leaves usually lobed ............................................................ **79.*pubescens***
     Leaves fresh green; rosettes not more than 15mm in diameter; cauline
     leaves usually entire ........................................................ **81.*cebennensis***
136. Leaves shortly 3-lobed at tip, with broadly triangular or ovate lobes; leafy shoots
     short, forming a tuft or mat rather than a cushion .............. **105–108.*androsacea* group**
     Leaves sometimes with more than 3 lobes, which are lanceolate, oblong or
     elliptical; leafy shoots fairly long, forming a cushion ......................... 137
137. Petals more than 5mm ........................................................................ 138
     Petals not more than 5mm .................................................................. 144
138. Leaf-hairs not more than 0.2mm; foliage with a strong spicy scent .............. **90.*vayredana***
     Leaf-hairs mostly at least 0.5mm; foliage scarcely scented .................... 139
139. Leaf-segments apiculate ..................................................................... 140
     Leaf-segments obtuse to shortly mucronate ....................................... 141
140  Leaves with numerous glandular hairs, at least on the petiole ............ **87.*babiana***
     Leaves with few hairs, mostly or entirely non-glandular ................... **77.*rosacea***
141. Leaves without glandular hairs ........................................... **77.*rosacea***
     Leaves with numerous glandular hairs .............................................. 142
142. Flowers not more than 10mm in diameter; sepals and hypanthium
     crimson; petals often red-veined .......................................... **80.*nevadensis***
     Flowers at least 10mm in diameter; sepals and hypanthium mainly
     green; petals not red-veined ............................................................ 143
143. Petals 5.5–6.5mm, usually with a slight greenish or yellowish
     tinge; most of the leaves 3-lobed ......................................... **78.*cespitosa***
     Petals usually more than 6.5mm, pure white; some of the leaves
     usually with 5 or more lobes .............................................. **77.*rosacea***

# Notes on the text

The information relating to each species is given under a number of standardised headings as follows:

*SYNONYMS*: The list does not aim at completeness, but it includes all those which are used in works which the reader is likely to come across.

*HISTORY & NOMENCLATURE*: This paragraph explains the Latin epithet of the species, and gives, as far as it can be ascertained, the history of its discovery and recognition, and in some cases the reason for a recent change in its name. It is not always possible to name with any confidence the botanist who first found it, as the descriptions in books of the sixteenth and early seventeenth centuries are very brief and hard to interpret, and in many cases much more space is devoted to the supposed medicinal qualities of the plant than to its appearance and structure. The illustrations in some of these works are good enough to allow instant recognition, but in others they are very poor. One has also to beware of many errors made by some writers in citing as synonyms names which really refer to a different plant.

*TYPE*: For each species and subspecies the type specimen, which fixes the application of the name, is cited along with the herbarium in which it may be found. In many cases the precise specimen is not indicated in the original description and, for these, we have selected one from among those mentioned (a lectotype), following the rules and guidelines set out in the *International Code of Botanical Nomenclature*. Sometimes we have been unable to trace a type specimen, either because all the original collections have been lost or destroyed, or because they have yet to be located. In the former case we have designated an entirely new specimen as a type (a neotype); in the latter case we simply say 'type not traced', although we have made enquiries to likely herbaria.

*DESCRIPTION*: This concentrates on giving an idea of the general appearance of the plant, and in describing those details in which it differs from other related species. In consequence, some organs, such as stamens, are rarely mentioned, as they vary little from one species to another.

The descriptions must be interpreted as referring to 'normal' plants, ignoring those that are very stunted by exposure or drought or drawn up by excessive shade. Some very rare or local variants are also excluded. We have tried to avoid technical terms wherever possible, and the descriptions should be readily understandable by the reader lacking an extensive botanical vocabulary. There are, however, four terms which require explanation:

'leafy shoots'—this term is usually used in the context of a mat- or cushion-forming plant, and refers to the leafy, vegetative shoots emanating from a surface-creeping stem, or underground rhizome.

'flowering stem'—this term refers to the axis which bears the flowers; the base of the flowering stem is taken as the point at which it emerges from the terminal rosette on the leafy shoot (or occasionally from the axil of a leaf lower down the shoot).

'cauline leaf'—this is a leaf located on a flowering stem.

'summer-dormant bud'—this term refers to the buds produced in the axils of the leaves on leafy shoots in some species; they are formed in the spring and remain dormant through the summer; in early autumn they recommence growth and develop into leafy shoots the following year.

*ILLUSTRATIONS*: These have all been checked by the authors to ensure that they are reliable and helpful. It is surprising how many illustrations in well-known books are very unhelpful or positively misleading. We have tried to include those which give a life-like representation of the general appearance of the plant, with others which give detailed drawings of its various parts. Those which are in colour are distinguished by an asterisk. In a few of the older books, some copies have the plates hand-coloured, but others do not; in such cases we have followed the copy in the library at Kew.

*RECOGNITION*: This section gives hints on how to distinguish the species from others with which it might be confused.

*VARIATION*: Part of this is often covered in the description, but in this paragraph the characters in which variation is most conspicuous are detailed, and an attempt is made to distinguish between those produced by differences in the habitat and those which have a genetic basis. In the latter case any subspecies or varieties worth recognising are briefly described.

*HYBRIDS*: All the described natural hybrids which seem at all plausibly diagnosed are listed, and a few others are mentioned only to be dismissed. It should be realised that a few authors who have specialised in the recognition of hybrids have become obsessed by the notion, and have tended to describe as a hybrid any plant which departs at all from the norm. The number of supposed natural hybrids that have been confirmed by controlled cross-pollination is, unfortunately, very small.

*CHROMOSOME NUMBER*: Many of the older published counts are clearly erroneous, because the techniques at that time were defective. We have, as a general rule, ignored approximate counts, those which were published before 1950, and those made on cultivated material (unless of known wild origin). Even so, the number of contradictory results is disconcerting. Some of them are due, no doubt, to variation in the chromosome number within the limits of a morphological species, but others must be due to error. In many species the chromosomes are very small, and an accurate count of a large number requires great skill.

*DISTRIBUTION*: The data here are derived mainly from the literature, supplemented occasionally by personal observations on living or dried material. The maps set out to give the same information in a form which can be more readily apprehended, but they should be regarded as approximate, giving mainly the limits of a species' area, without detailing the gaps within this area from which it is absent, unless they are very large.

*HABITAT*: This requires no explanation.

*ACCESS*: Here we attempt to indicate to the reader one or more places where the species can be looked for with some confidence, if possible not too far from a road; the information is in most cases based on the personal experience of one of us (D.A.W.). We realise that we may be censured for giving this information by the more extreme type of conservationist, but in the case of the species that are really vulnerable in Europe, we accompany it by a warning against collection. Generally speaking, saxifrages are under much less severe threat from collectors than are such genera as *Primula*, *Cyclamen* and *Narcissus*; even very local species are often safeguarded by their abundance within their limited area and the inaccessibility of a large proportion of the plants. Generally speaking, our counsel is to collect seeds rather than plants (they are far more likely to succeed than a plant which has had to survive for a week or so in a plastic bag); not to collect species such as *S.cochlearis*, which can be obtained from nurseries in a form virtually identical with the wild plant; and if you do collect plants, not to take more than 1 per cent of what you can see from a given spot.

Many readers, of course, will not wish to collect at all; they are content merely to look or to photograph. It is for them rather than collectors that the information under this head is given.

*CULTIVATION*: We aim here chiefly to indicate whether a species is worth trying or not, and whether it has special requirements different from the standard 'alpine' treatment which most saxifrages require. For details of the latter, we must refer the reader to specialised books for the horticulturalist.

# The species

## Section *Ciliatae* Haworth (section *Hirculus* (Haworth) Tausch)

Usually evergreen perennials. Leaves herbaceous, occasionally stiff or leathery, usually entire, alternate. Lime-secreting hydathodes absent. Hairs multiseriate. Flowering stems terminal, leafy, sometimes with a prominent basal leaf-rosette. Flowers usually solitary or few, sometimes in panicles. Petals yellow, usually with swellings near the base. Ovary superior or nearly so. Bulbils absent.

A very large section of about 150 species, almost entirely confined to the Himalayan-Tibetan region; two circumpolar species extend into Europe.

## 1. *Saxifraga hirculus* Linnaeus, *Species Plantarum* 402 (1753)

SYNONYMS: *S.autumnalis* Linnaeus
*S.nutans* Adams
*S.propinqua* (Haworth) R. Brown
*Leptasea hirculus* (Linnaeus) Small

*HISTORY & NOMENCLATURE*: The epithet *hirculus* was taken by Linnaeus from Clusius, who used it as a generic name; it means a small goat, and is said to refer to the smell of the plant, but this is something which escapes most observers. The species was first described by Clusius (1611) as *Hirculus frisicus Dortmanni qui Chamaecisti genus*. European plants belong to subsp. **hirculus**, a variant with a circumpolar distribution. Other populations from North America and eastern Asia have been named subsp. *propinqua* (R. Brown) Löve & Löve (see p. 271).

*TYPE*: Sheet 575.38 in the Linnean herbarium, London (**LINN**) has been designated as lectotype (Webb 1987a). The type-localities are Sweden, Switzerland, Lapland and Siberia; the type-specimen is almost certainly from Sweden.

*DESCRIPTION*: Stems loosely tufted, ascending, connected above or below ground by short, slender rhizomes. Leaves 10–30 × 3–6mm, linear-lanceolate, obtuse, entire, narrowed to a base which clasps the stem and bears long, slender, reddish-brown hairs; in the lowest leaves this base is separated from the lamina by a distinct, slender petiole. Flowering stems up to 35cm, but only 4–12cm in exposed situations, furnished, especially in the upper part, with reddish-brown hairs like those on the leaf-bases, and bearing a single flower or a lax corymb of 2–4. Cauline leaves numerous, similar to the basal but smaller. Sepals 3–5mm, oblong, obtuse, reflexed in fruit. Petals 9–16 × 4–6mm, elliptical to obovate-oblong, bright yellow, sometimes with red spots towards the base, which bears 2 prominent swellings. Ovary superior; styles short, stout, curving outwards; capsule 8–10mm long. Seeds 1 × 0.6mm, ellipsoid, smooth; raphe conspicuous. Flowering season: August to October.

*ILLUSTRATIONS*:
* Sowerby (1865, Plate 550)
  Warming (1909, Figures 18–19)
  Ross-Craig (1957, Plate 3)
  Mądalski (1962, Plate 1312)

*RECOGNITION*: The tall stems, narrow, entire leaves, yellow flowers and superior ovary make *S.hirculus* quite distinct among European species. A number of species from the Himalayan region resemble it rather closely, and the difficulty of separating them is increased by the variability of *S.hirculus* in that region.

*VARIATION*: In Europe this is not great. Icelandic plants have been distinguished as subsp. *alpina* (Engler) Löve, *Taxon* 19:300 (1970), but the fact that the type of this taxon comes from Sikkim does not inspire confidence, and in any case the distinctive characters are only of varietal value.

*HYBRIDS*: None is known.

*CHROMOSOME NUMBER*: $2n = 32$ (for subsp. *hirculus*). Diploid populations ($2n = 16$) have been reported from arctic North America and north-eastern Siberia (as subsp. *propinqua*, see p. 271).

*DISTRIBUTION* (Map 1): In general the range is arctic–subarctic, but in Europe this species extends (or formerly extended) discontinuously southwards, not as an alpine but mainly in lowland or montane stations, as far as 45°N in north-western Italy and 46°30′N in central Romania. Over the past 150 years, however, the plant has shown a serious decline throughout western Europe, and in France, Italy, Switzerland and Austria it is either extinct or confined to one or two stations where its future is very precarious. In Holland it has been extinct for over a century. In Ireland, Britain, Norway and Romania it is, though rare, still extant. In Germany, though greatly diminished, it persists in fair quantity, and in eastern Europe, as also in Iceland, Denmark and Sweden, it is holding its own fairly well.

Outside Europe it has a fairly continuous range in the Arctic, apart from Greenland

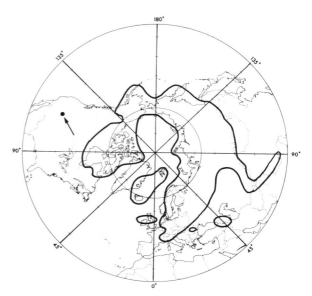

Map 1. Distribution of *S.hirculus*

where it is very local. In North America it extends southwards fairly continuously as far as the Aleutian Islands and to 53°N on the shores of Hudson Bay; there is also a very remote outlier in the high Rockies of Colarado (see p. 271). In Asia it is thinly scattered over much of Siberia; it is plentiful in the Altai, and has some mostly rather isolated stations in all the major mountain ranges from the Caucasus to the Himalaya and western China.

*HABITAT*: Everywhere it demands a habitat which is saturated, or at least well irrigated with water. In the Arctic it grows mainly on moss-tundra. In western Europe it favours those regions of peat-bogs where there is some water movement and therefore some small supply of basic ions; in this type of flush it is often associated with species of similar requirements such as *Ranunculus flammula*, *Pedicularis palustris*, *Cardamine pratensis* and *Menyanthes trifoliata*. In Europe it is mainly lowland; altitudinal data are curiously scanty both in the literature and on herbarium labels, but it appears to ascend to 1000m in the French Jura and to 1500m in central Romania.

*ACCESS*: For someone living in western Europe, the most convenient places to look for this species in fair abundance would seem to be eastern Jutland, central Finland or Iceland. There are a few places in the northern Pennines where it is said to grow in some quantity, but it is usually eaten down by sheep before it comes into flower. There is one not too inaccessible site in Ireland where it is locally plentiful; this is in a flush, made conspicuous by the coarse, marshy vegetation which it supports, in the middle of the vast blanket-bog of West Mayo. The flush lies some 15km north-west of Crossmolina, near a tributary of the Oweninny river, about 400m south of a conspicuous hillock marked on the Ordnance Survey maps as 127m (417ft.). Even when the flush has been located there is some difficulty in finding the saxifrage because of its close superficial resemblance, at least at a distance, to the *Ranunculus flammula* which accompanies it.

CULTIVATION: This is difficult, but not impossible. It grew for seven years in the Botanic Garden of Trinity College, Dublin, in a moss-filled pan standing in a saucer of water, but it did not flower. The National Botanic Garden at Glasnevin was more successful, and has induced it to flower in several years. The best site would probably be a moss-filled backwater of a slow stream; in such a position a good flowering clump would be worth some trouble, especially in view of its late flowering season.

## 2. *Saxifraga flagellaris* Willdenow, in Sternberg, *Revisio Saxifragarum* 25 (1810)

SYNONYMS: *S.platysepala* (Trautvetter) Tolmatchev
*Leptasea flagellaris* (Willdenow) Small

HISTORY & NOMENCLATURE: The species was first described by Willdenow from plants received from Adams; these came from Mount Kazbek, a peak near the centre of the main range of the Caucasus. It had been collected earlier from western Alaska by David Nelson on Cook's last voyage in 1778, but this escaped notice until 1814, when Pursh described Nelson's plant as *S.setigera*. It was subsequently found to be widespread in the Arctic, the higher mountains of Asia and the Rocky mountains in North America. To the plants of these regions various names have been attached, some of them at specific level, but Hultén (1964) has convincingly shown that many of the distinctions are based on fluctuating characters, and that all plants of the complex are best treated as a single species with eight or ten subspecies. In accordance with this treatment the European plant is named subsp. *platysepala* (Trautvetter) Porsild, *Botanisk Tidskrift* 51:295 (1954).

The epithet *flagellaris* refers to the long, slender runners; the epithet *platysepala* was coined by Trautvetter to indicate the broad, flat sepals of the arctic plant in contrast to the narrower sepals of the plant from Alaska and the Rocky mountains, which he called var. *stenosepala*; this latter is now included in subsp. *setigera* (Pursh) Tolmatchev (see p. 271).

TYPE: *S.flagellaris*. Mount Kazbek, Caucasus. (Holotype: No. 8422 in the Willdenow herbarium, Berlin (**B**) ).

*Subsp. platysepala*. Specimens numbered 1–5 on the sheet labelled: Saxifraga flagellaris. E. coast of Greenland, Sabine. Lindley 1830. (Lectotype: Kew (**K**), designated here.)

DESCRIPTION: Leafy shoots short, erect, with many of the leaves aggregated into a basal rosette; from these shoots arise the flowering stems, and the whole shoot dies after flowering, the runners being the only means of perennation. Rosette-leaves 7–16 × 2–5mm, oblong-oblanceolate to elliptic-obovate, acute to sub-obtuse, hairless except for the margins, which are fringed by multiseriate hairs. From the axils of several of these leaves arise thread-like, sparsely glandular-hairy, leafless runners up to 15cm long, terminating in a leafy bud which roots and forms a rosette in the following year. Flowering stem up to 6cm (rarely 10cm), hairy, with most of the hairs bearing dark red glands; cauline leaves numerous, similar to the basal but narrower and usually glandular-hairy at least beneath. Flower often solitary, but sometimes 2–4 in a lax cyme. Sepals ovate-triangular, often dark red, glandular-pubescent. Petals 6–10mm, obovate, bright yellow. Ovary mainly superior, but united at the base for about ⅕ of its height to the shallow, bowl-shaped hypanthium; styles very short and stout; capsule about 9mm. Seeds 0.9mm long, oblong, pale brown, smooth; raphe fairly conspicuous. Flowering season: August.

The above description is valid only for subsp. *platysepala*. Other subspecies differ in the frequency and distribution of hairs, number of flowers, size and shape of petals and shape of hypanthium.

*ILLUSTRATIONS*: Plate 1
✳ *Botanical Magazine* 77: Plate 4261 (1851)
  Warming (1909, pp.185, 186)
  Tolmatchev (1959, p.173)

*RECOGNITION*: No other European species has long, thread-like runners. A few other species from the Himalayan region possess these, but only one (*S.brunonis* Wallich ex Seringe) is in cultivation. It differs from *S.flagellaris* in its shining leaves, almost hairless stem and calyx, bright red runners and much more numerous flowers (see p. 270).

*VARIATION*: Within the subspecies *platysepala* there is little, apart from height.

*HYBRIDS*: None has been recorded.

*CHROMOSOME NUMBER*: $2n = 32$ has been reported from Spitsbergen, Siberia and Greenland, and seems to be constant for subsp. *platysepala*. $2n = 16$, however, has been recorded for numerous plants from North America, Siberia and the Caucasus, in most cases referable to other subspecies.

*DISTRIBUTION* (Map 2): The subspecies *platysepala* is circumpolar-arctic, ranging from the northern coast of Greenland southwards to about 68°N in Alaska. In Europe it occurs only in Spitsbergen. Other subspecies are found in Alaska and the Rocky mountains southwards to Colorado; in the Caucasus; in the subarctic zone of eastern Siberia and in Kamchatka; and in a broad arc running

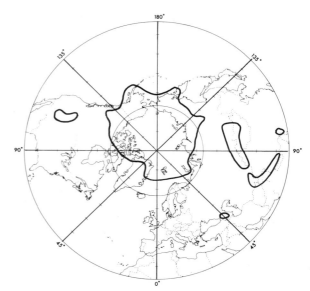

Map 2. Distribution of *S.flagellaris*

through the mountains of Asia from near Lake Baikal through Mongolia, the Altai, the Tien-Shan, the Pamirs and the Himalaya to Yunnan.

*HABITAT*: Over much of its range information is lacking, but it would seem that *S.flagellaris* always favours open habitats, such as stony slopes in the mountains and sandy or gravelly tundra in the Arctic.

*ACCESS*: Only the most adventurous readers of this book are likely to see subsp. *platysepala* in its native terrain, but for other subspecies, Kashmir (down to about 3,600m) and the Rockies of British Columbia or Colorado seem to be the most accessible places in which to look.

*CULTIVATION*: Like all arctic plants, *S.flagellaris* has difficulty in accommodating itself to mild winters, but it has been successfully cultivated in various parts of Britain, at least for a few years. Given plenty of water in summer and as low a temperature as possible in winter it is not too difficult in a frame or alpine house, but care must be taken to see that a sufficient number of rosettes from the runners are rooted each year.

# Section *Cymbalaria* Grisebach

Delicate annuals or biennials (perhaps sometimes short-lived perennials) with ascending, diffuse or nearly prostrate stems. Leaves alternate (occasionally some opposite), slightly fleshy, soft, with long petioles, hairless or with sparse to frequent, slender, uniseriate, glandular hairs; lamina usually at least as broad as long, palmately lobed, toothed or almost entire. Lime-secreting hydathodes absent. Flowering stems leafy; flowers few on each stem, on long pedicels arising from the axils of usually leaf-like bracts. Petals white, yellow or orange. Ovary superior, or nearly so. Bulbils absent.

A small section of four species, centred on the eastern Mediterranean region, but with one outlying species in the mountains of northern Ethiopia (see p. 259).

## 3. *Saxifraga cymbalaria* Linnaeus, *Species Plantarum* 405 (1753)

SYNONYMS: *S.orientalis* Jacquin
*S.hederacea* of several authors, not of Linnaeus
*S.reticulata* Willdenow
*S.huetiana* Boissier
*S.baborensis* Battandier

HISTORY & NOMENCLATURE: The epithet was taken by Linnaeus from Buxbaum, who compared the leaves to those of the genus *Cymbalaria*. It is worth noting, however, as an example of the unexpected transfer of plant-names in early days, that the name *Cymbalaria* seems to have been first used for a species of *Umbilicus*, of which the leaves were, aptly enough, compared to cymbals.

*S.cymbalaria* was first noted by Buxbaum "in the Orient", and was described by him in 1728. It has been much confused both with *S.hederacea* and with *S.sibthorpii*.

TYPE: Plate 45, Figure 2 in *Plantarum minus cognitarum Centuria II* (Buxbaum 1728) has been designated as lectotype (Webb 1987a).

DESCRIPTION: Annual, perhaps sometimes biennial, hairless, or more usually with a few glandular hairs, mainly on the stems and leaf-margins. Stems ascending, branched, usually 10–25cm long. Leaves mostly alternate but sometimes opposite, especially on the upper part of the stems, bright, shining green; lamina up to 22 × 22mm, but often not more than 10 × 13mm, kidney-shaped, semicircular, circular or broadly triangular-ovate, cordate or truncate at the base, more or less 5- to 9-lobed, the lobes varying from triangular-ovate and acute to very low and rounded, and sometimes scarcely developed; petiole up to 35mm. Flowers in lax, terminal cymes of 2–6; upper bracts small, elliptical, entire. Sepals 2mm, triangular, acute, spreading horizontally both in flower and fruit. Petals 4.5–6mm, elliptic-oblong, narrowed at the base to a very short claw, above which are 2 small swellings, bright shining yellow towards the tip, duller orange-yellow towards the base. Ovary superior or nearly so; styles short, straight, erect. Seeds 0.5 × 0.35mm, broadly ovoid-oblong with obtuse ends, dark brown, evenly covered with low, rounded or conical papillae, each surrounded by a circle of about 10 tubercles; raphe smooth, very narrow. Flowering season: April to September.

ILLUSTRATIONS: Plate 2
  Săvulescu (1956, Plate 12)
  Harding (1970, p.98)
* Köhlein (1984, Plate [11])

RECOGNITION: The diffuse stems, broad leaves, bright yellow flowers and superior ovary distinguish this species from all others except *S.sibthorpii*; this differs most conspicuously in the sepals, which are reflexed soon after the flower opens.

VARIATION: There is considerable variation in the depth of lobing of the leaf and the shape of its base; also in the size of the petals and some other characters. This variation shows some correlation, but the three varieties set out below must be regarded as themselves variable and not very well defined.

(i) Var. **cymbalaria**. Leaves nearly all alternate, boldly lobed with acute lobes, truncate or slightly cordate at the base. Petals 4.5–5mm. Ovary completely superior.

(ii) Var. *huetiana* (Boissier) Engler & Irmscher, *Pflanzenreich* 67 (IV.117): 203 (1916). Some of the leaves opposite, all with 5–7, low, rounded lobes, or almost entire, truncate or cuneate at the base. Petals and ovary as in var. *cymbalaria*.

(iii) Var. *atlantica* Battandier, *Bulletin de la Société botanique de France* 39:xxii (1892) (including *S.baborensis* Battandier). Leaves mostly alternate, shaped as in var. *huetiana*. Sepals enlarging in fruit. Petals 5–6mm, narrow. Ovary nearly superior.

*HYBRIDS*: *S.* × *vetteriana* Beauverd was described in 1908 from a plant in the Geneva Botanical Garden, which seemed to be a chance hybrid between *S.cymbalaria* and *S.hederacea*. Plants intermediate between the two species have been recorded from various parts of Anatolia (Matthews 1972, p.259), and are probably natural hybrids of the same parentage.

*CHROMOSOME NUMBER*: $2n = 18$.

*DISTRIBUTION* (Map 3): Mainly in the Caucasus, northern and eastern Turkey and north-western Iran. There are scattered records for other parts of Turkey, and some outlying stations in Lebanon, Algeria and Romania. The last, which represents the only native station of the species in Europe, is near Slănic, which lies on the southern slopes of the Carpathians above Ploesti. Var. *cymbalaria* occurs throughout the range of the species except Algeria; var. *huetiana* is scattered through most of the Asiatic range of the species; and var. *atlantica* is known only from the Djebel Babor, a range of hills near the coast in eastern Algeria.

*HABITAT*: Damp and usually shady places, including river-banks, rock-crevices and subalpine grassland. It ranges from near sea-level to at least 2300m.

*ACCESS*: To see this species in Romania, local guidance will be needed. It is, of course, strictly protected. In Asia it would seem to be commonest in Georgia, especially in the south and west.

*CULTIVATION*: No information seems to be available about the cultivation of var. *cymbalaria*. Var. *huetiana* is very easily grown in a damp and shady corner, and it has become a weed in the rock-gardens of some botanical gardens of western Europe. It is rather underestimated as a decorative plant, but if given a moist and not too poor soil in semi-shade in an unheated greenhouse it will provide from early April onwards a very attractive display, the shining, bright green foliage providing an effective background for the starry, golden flowers.

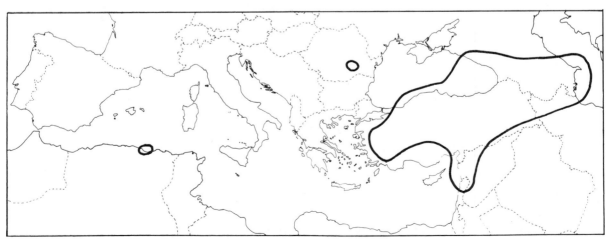

Map 3. Distribution of *S.cymbalaria*

## 4. *Saxifraga sibthorpii* Boissier,
*Diagnoses Plantarum orientalium novarum* 1(3):22 (1843)

SYNONYM: *S.cymbalaria* of Sibthorp & Smith, but not of Linnaeus

HISTORY & NOMENCLATURE: Sibthorp seems to have been the first to have found this species, on Mount Parnassus in 1787, but he and Smith confused it both with *S.cymbalaria* and with *S.hederacea*, and the description of *S.cymbalaria* in their *Florae Graecae Prodromus* is based partly on that species and partly on *S.sibthorpii*. But there is no doubt that Plate 378 of their *Flora Graeca* (1823) and the accompanying description, though presented under the name of *S.cymbalaria*, in fact represent *S.sibthorpii*. It was only in 1843 that Boissier clearly distinguished the two species, and called the new one after its discoverer, based on material sent to him by Spruner.

TYPE: In umbrosis humidis montis Parnassi. 1842, *Spruner* [labelled *S.orientalis* Jacq.]. (Holotype: Flora Orientalis herbarium, Geneva (**G**).)

DESCRIPTION: Biennial, or perhaps sometimes annual or perennial, hairless or with very few short, glandular hairs, without the straggling, diffuse habit of *S.cymbalaria*, but with a fairly compact tuft of basal leaves and of very short leafy shoots, from many of which arise ascending to nearly erect, slender, sparsely leafy flowering stems up to 8cm long. Lamina 7–15 × 10–15mm, with a truncate to cordate base and 3–7 crenations or short, obtuse lobes; petiole usually much longer than the lamina; most of the leaves are semicircular or kidney-shaped, with 3–5 rounded lobes, and are reminiscent of the leaves of *Ranunculus hederaceus*, but in some plants they are circular, with a deep, narrow sinus and 5–7 flat-topped crenations, recalling (appropriately enough) the leaves of *Sibthorpia europaea*. Flowers solitary, on long, slender pedicels. Sepals 2–2.5mm, obtuse, reflexed soon after the flower opens and remaining reflexed in fruit. Petals 5–7mm, golden-yellow to orange, narrowly ovate, acute, with a very short claw at the base, above which are 2 small swellings. Ovary superior; styles very short. Seeds 0.6 × 0.3mm, blackish-brown, covered evenly with broad, low papillae, each with about 8 tubercles on its upper surface; raphe inconspicuous. Flowering season: June to August.

ILLUSTRATIONS: Plate 3
\* Sibthorp & Smith (1823, Plate 378), as *S.cymbalaria*

RECOGNITION: It is likely to be confused only with *S.cymbalaria*, from which it may be readily distinguished by the reflexed sepals and solitary flowers on leafless stalks.

VARIATION: There is a good deal of variation in leaf-shape and a small amount in other characters, but it is not clear whether this is constant within a population or even within a single plant.

HYBRIDS: None is known.

CHROMOSOME NUMBER: $2n = 18$.

DISTRIBUTION (Map 4): Apart from a single station in south-western Anatolia, this species is endemic to southern Greece; within this region it is found on most of the higher mountains. Its range extends from Vardhousia

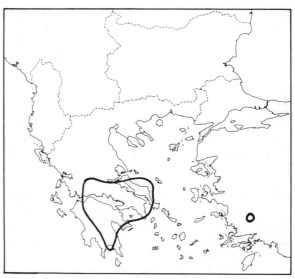

Map 4. Distribution of *S.sibthorpii*

and Euboea in the north to Taïyetos in the south.

*HABITAT*: In the shade of overhanging rocks, in crevices in damp rocks, among stones beside streams, or rarely in damp grassland. It is found mainly between 1700 and 2400m.

*ACCESS*: It is fairly frequent on the upper part of Mount Parnassus, above Delphi.

*CULTIVATION*: No information is available, and it is doubtful whether it is in cultivation. Seeds labelled *S.sibthorpii* received at Dublin from three reputable botanic gardens have all yielded plants of *S.cymbalaria* var. *huetiana*.

It should not be very difficult to cultivate, and it is very desirable that authentic material should be brought into cultivation, to resolve the many gaps in our knowledge of its lifespan and its pattern of variation.

## 5. *Saxifraga hederacea* Linnaeus, *Species Plantarum* 405 (1753)

*SYNONYM*: *S.scotophila* Boissier

*HISTORY & NOMENCLATURE*: The first mention of this plant was by Tournefort, who discovered it in Crete around 1700 and published it in his *Corollarium* (1703) as *Saxifraga cretica annua minima, hederaceo folio*. From this phrase Linnaeus derived his epithet *hederacea* (meaning ivy-leaved). There was much confusion among earlier authors between this species and *S.cymbalaria*, but the distinction was made clear by Smith (1806).

*TYPE*: Saxifraga cretica annua minima, hederaceo folio, *Tournefort 2129*. (Neotype: Tournefort herbarium, Paris (**P**); see Webb (1987a).)

*DESCRIPTION*: A winter annual, almost hairless or with variable amounts of slender, glandular hairs. Habit very variable, the plant sometimes consisting of a fairly compact rosette of basal leaves and ascending flowering stems 5–8cm long, but sometimes without a basal rosette, and with a few straggling, leafy stems up to 25cm long. Leaves very variable in size and shape, even on the same plant; the lamina occasionally up to 20 × 30mm, but more usually 6–13mm long and wide, broadly ovate to semicircular or kidney-shaped, entire or with 3–7 short, broad-based, acute or mucronate lobes; base cuneate to slightly cordate; petiole slender, usually longer than lamina. Flowers solitary, or 2–4 in a diffuse, leafy cyme; pedicels 5–12mm in flower, increasing to 20–45mm in fruit, much longer than in related species. Sepals 2mm, triangular, arising from the rim of a saucer-shaped hypanthium, nearly erect both in flower and fruit. Petals 2–3mm, obovate-elliptical, only slightly exceeding the sepals, sometimes with 2 small swellings at the base, white or pale sulphur-yellow. Ovary nearly superior, with only a small part of its base immersed in the hypanthium; styles short, straight, divergent. Capsule often reflexed. Seeds 0.4 × 0.3mm, truncate at one end, somewhat tapered at the other; pattern on the testa as in *S.cymbalaria* except that the papillae are cylindrical and longer. Flowering season: April to June.

*ILLUSTRATIONS*:
* \* Sibthorp & Smith (1823, Plate 379)
* \* Sternberg (1831, Plate 15)
  Fiori & Paoletti (1895, Figure 1647)

*RECOGNITION*: From *S.cymbalaria* it is distinguished by its much smaller and paler petals; from *S.sibthorpii* by these characters and also by the sepals, which are never reflexed. It has some similarity in habit to *S.arachnoidea* and *S.paradoxa*, but is distinguished from both by its largely superior ovary, and also from the former by its much shorter and less abundant hairs, and from the latter by its smaller leaves.

*VARIATION*: As the description makes plain, there is much variation in leaf-shape, but a considerable part of this range can often be seen on a single plant. Variants from Turkey, Syria and Lebanon with small, pale yellow petals, numerous glandular hairs and nearly entire leaves have been distinguished as var. *libanotica* (Bornmüller) Matthews in

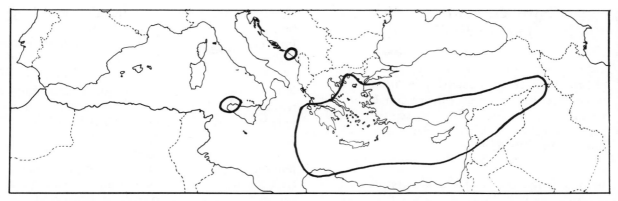

Map 5.  Distribution of *S.hederacea*

Davis, *Flora of Turkey* 4:259 (1972). The typical plant is, however, found alongside them and intermediates are frequent.

*HYBRIDS*: See under *S.cymbalaria*.

*CHROMOSOME NUMBER*: Not known.

*DISTRIBUTION* (Map 5): Confined to the Mediterranean region, from Sicily eastwards, except for a few outlying stations in eastern Turkey and northern Iraq. It is found in the hill-country of north-western Sicily, in Greece and the Aegean islands, and has been recorded from one station in southern Dalmatia (near Dubrovnik). In Greece it is mainly in the southern third of the country, but it is known also from Mount Athos and from the northern islands of Thasos and Samothraki. Outside Europe it extends through western and southern Turkey, Cyprus, Syria and Lebanon to Israel; it is also found in Libya, in the hills east of Benghazi.

*HABITAT*: Damp, shady rocks, shady walls, under bridges and at the mouths of caves. It ranges from near sea-level to 1600m in Sicily, and to over 2000m in Turkey.

*ACCESS*: Much the most convenient place in which to see this species is in the small hill-town of Erici, near Trapani in western Sicily. Here, at the extreme western end of its range, it is frequent on old walls which are north-facing or shaded by another wall.

*CULTIVATION*: This is seldom attempted, but presents no great difficulty in a well-drained but well-watered pan kept in the shade. It is certainly not a showy plant, but it has a delicate charm of its own.

# Section *Micranthes* (Haworth) D. Don (section *Boraphila* Engler, in part)

Evergreen perennials. Leaves herbaceous, or somewhat fleshy or leathery, entire, toothed or lobed, alternate, usually all basal. Lime-secreting hydathodes absent. Hairs uni- or multiseriate. Flowering stems terminal, usually without leaves, though sometimes with large, leaf-like bracts. Inflorescence a panicle. Petals white, tinged or spotted with red and sometimes with yellow; more rarely greenish, tinged with reddish-purple. Flowers regular or somewhat irregular, sometimes replaced wholly or in part by bulbils or leafy buds. Ovary superior to more than half inferior. Capsule dehiscing for at least half its length.

This large section contains about 68 species which are mainly to be found in northern and eastern Asia and in temperate and subarctic North America. Only seven species are found in Europe.

## Subsection *Micranthes* (Haworth) Gornall

Leaves with or without a distinct petiole, entire, crenate or obscurely toothed. Hairs uniseriate. Bracts small. Inflorescence without bulbils or leafy buds. Flowers regular. Sepals erect or reflexed. Ovary nearly superior to more than half-inferior.

### 6. *Saxifraga hieracifolia* Waldstein & Kitaibel ex Willdenow, *Species Plantarum*, 4th edn, 2:641 (1799)

*SYNONYMS*: *Micranthes hieracifolia* (Willdenow) Haworth
*Saxifraga nivalis* var. *racemosa* Townson, *Travels in Hungary* 488 (1797)
*S.racemosa* (Townson) Simonkai

*HISTORY & NOMENCLATURE*: First discovered by Robert Townson (often mistakenly cited as Townsend), an English traveller with a strong interest in natural history. He gave a good description (Townson 1797), and in Plate 15 an excellent drawing which leaves no doubt as to the plant's identity, though he mistook it, pardonably enough, for a variety of *S.nivalis*. He gave no locality, but from his narrative it must have been discovered in the southern part of the High Tatra (now in Slovakia), somewhere to the west of Kežmarok.

The epithet indicates, of course, the resemblance of the leaves to those of some species of *Hieracium*.

*TYPE*: The holotype is No. 8391 in the Willdenow herbarium, Berlin (**B**). It is annotated simply 'Carpath.', and was almost certainly sent to Willdenow by Kitaibel from the High Tatra.

*DESCRIPTION*: Rhizome short, producing each year a single rather lax rosette of upwardly inclined or somewhat drooping basal leaves. These have an ovate-elliptical lamina, 2–6 × 1–3cm, tapered gradually to a short but distinct, winged petiole; margin entire to bluntly toothed, usually fringed with short glandular hairs; on the margin of the petiole are longer, non-glandular hairs. Flowering stem stout, hollow, unbranched except at the top, up to 50cm tall, but usually 10–25cm, densely glandular-hairy above, and with longer, mainly non-glandular hairs towards the base. Flowers numerous, in a narrow, spike-like panicle, consisting of dense clusters of flowers in the axils of oblong bracts, which vary from 3mm to 3cm in length. Sepals 1.5–3mm, triangular-ovate, reflexed in fruit. Petals as long as the sepals but rather narrower, purplish-crimson at the tip and sides, green elsewhere. Ovary about ½ inferior, less so in fruit; styles short, stout, divergent; capsule broad, dark vinous red. Seeds 1.5 × 0.7mm, flattened on one face; testa very loose-fitting, with many of the cells inflated so as to form low, rounded, soft, bladder-like papillae; raphe inconspicuous. Flowering season: July and August.

*ILLUSTRATIONS*: Plate 4
Townson (1797, Plate 15)
* Waldstein & Kitaibel (1800, Plate 18)
Mądalski (1962, Plate 1315)
* Rasetti (1980, Figure 243)

*RECOGNITION*: The single rosette of fairly large, ovate-elliptical leaves, and a spike-like inflorescence on a leafless stem are together quite distinctive among European species. Related North American species have white petals, except for *S.subapetala* (see p. 280). Stunted specimens can be confused with *S.nivalis*, but this has longer, whitish petals and sepals more or less erect, even in fruit.

*VARIATION*: In Europe it varies only in stature, hairiness, toothing of leaves and size of bracts; there are no very distinct varieties. In Alaska it is much more variable, and some plants there have much longer, narowly oblong leaves.

*HYBRIDS*: Possibly with *S.nivalis*; see under that species.

*CHROMOSOME NUMBER*: Counts of $2n = 112$ have been recorded from Norway and North America; of $2n = 120$ from France,

Czechoslovakia and Siberia. The significance of the difference is not clear.

*DISTRIBUTION* (Map 6): In Europe it is fairly common in the islands of the high Arctic and in parts of the Carpathians; elsewhere it is rare and disjunct. It occurs in three distinct areas of the Carpathians: the Tatra and Fatra ranges, mainly in Czechoslovakia but extending into Poland; the Rodnei mountains in north-eastern Romania; and the Făgăraşului mountains (Transylvanian Alps) further south. In Norway it is found in several stations in and near the Jotunheim, and more sparsely in the extreme north (near Skibotn and Talvik); it is recorded also from the Kola peninsula in north-western Russia. It was known from the mountains of Cantal (central France), but here it has been almost, if not completely, exterminated by collectors. It occurs also in a few places in the Austrian Alps, mainly in the province of Steiermark, but here also it is rare and decreasing.

Outside Europe it ranges throughout arctic Asia and North America, extending southwards to the central Urals and to Kamchatka, and more sparingly in the eastern part of the Canadian Arctic and in a restricted area of eastern Greenland. It re-appears in Asia much further south, in the Altai and the region of Lake Baikal, and many authors consider *S.rydbergii* Small, described from the Rocky mountains at 45°N, to be merely a dwarf variant of *S.hieracifolia*, although it may be treated better as a synonym of the closely related *S.subapetala* (see p. 280).

*HABITAT*: It favours damp conditions, and is found mainly in mossy tundra, by streams, and on damp rock-faces. In central Europe it ranges from 1200 to 2500m.

*ACCESS*: The best places to see this species in Europe are probably the higher valleys on the northern side of the Transylvanian Alps or, in Norway, on the north-eastern slopes of the Jotunheim or the south-western side of the Gudbrandsdal, near Dovre. For details of Norwegian localities see Nordhagen (1930, p.15).

*CULTIVATION*: *S.hieracifolia* can be grown without much difficulty in a frame or cold house if it is kept shaded and given plenty of water in the growing season. It cannot be described as an attractive plant, and has little garden value.

### 7. *Saxifraga nivalis* Linnaeus, *Species Plantarum* 401 (1753)

*SYNONYM*: *Micranthes nivalis* (Linnaeus) Small

*HISTORY & NOMENCLATURE*: The specific epithet (of the snows) was devised by Linnaeus. He included *S.tenuis* under the name, and it was probably this species, which is characteristic of late snow-lies, that he mainly had in mind when he chose the epithet.

The first mention of the species in print was by Johnson (1641), who found it on Snowdon, in Wales, and gave it the name *Sedum serratum*. This is not exactly diagnostic, but the identification has been generally accepted, and it is difficult to see what other plant could have been intended.

*TYPE*: The left-hand specimen on sheet 575.18 in the Linnean herbarium, London (**LINN**) has been designated as lectotype

Map 6. Distribution of *S.hieracifolia*

(Webb 1987a). The localities given by Linnaeus are Spitsbergen, Lapland, North Wales, Virginia and Canada, but the last two are referable to *S.virginiensis* Michaux, which Linnaeus did not distinguish from *S.nivalis*.

*DESCRIPTION*: Rhizome short, usually bearing several leaf-rosettes. Leaves 1–4cm long, in compact rosettes, spreading or semi-erect, ovate or diamond-shaped to nearly round, dark green above, usually deep purple-red beneath, rather thick and firm, tapered to a broad petiole, usually with some tawny hairs on the margin and lower side; margin crenate or bluntly toothed. Stem 5–20cm tall, 1–2mm thick, simple or branched near the top, densely clothed with rather long, mainly glandular hairs. Flowers in an irregular cyme, usually congested, with very short branches and pedicels, but sometimes relatively lax; bracts narrow, up to 10mm long. Sepals ovate, obtuse, more or less erect, even in fruit. Petals 2–3mm, slightly exceeding the sepals, oblong to obovate, white, usually tipped with pink. Ovary half-inferior; styles short, divergent, straight or slightly curved. Seeds 0.7–0.85 × 0.35–0.4mm, ellipsoid, but flattened on one face and tapered at one or both ends to a short beak; testa rather loose-fitting, smooth or with low, soft, bladder-like papillae in rows; raphe inconspicuous. Flowering season: July and August.

*ILLUSTRATIONS*:
* Sowerby (1865, Plate 541)
  Ross-Craig (1957, Plate 1)
  Mądalski (1962, Plate 1314)
* Huber (1963, Plate 143)

*RECOGNITION*: Very close to *S.tenuis*; for distinctions see under that species. The only other European species which has a half-inferior ovary, erect sepals, petals not more than 3mm and leaves all basal is *S.hieracifolia*, which has purplish-green petals and much larger seeds.

*VARIATION*: There is little variation in Europe, apart from the degree of compactness of the inflorescence. A curious variant, very robust and with a freely-branched inflorescence, occurs in Greenland; it has been distinguished as var. ***ramosa*** Engler, *Monographie der Gattung Saxifraga L.* 147 (1872). Some plants from Sweden show an approach to this condition.

*HYBRIDS*: Hybrids with *S.hieracifolia* have been reported from Spitsbergen, Novaja Zemlya and arctic Norway, but it seems probable that they are only aberrant forms of *S.hieracifolia*. Hybrids with *S.tenuis* might be expected, but they would be very difficult to recognise.

*CHROMOSOME NUMBER*: $2n = 60$.

*DISTRIBUTION* (Map 7): Widespread in the arctic and subarctic regions of Europe (including Iceland), and extending southwards fairly continuously to the Faeroes, southern Norway, central Sweden, Lake Ladoga and the central Urals; it is found also in the mountains of Scotland (mainly the central and southern Highlands) and very sparingly in isolated stations in the mountains of northern England, North Wales and north-western Ireland. It re-appears in Central Europe in one very isolated station on the borders of Poland and Czechoslovakia.

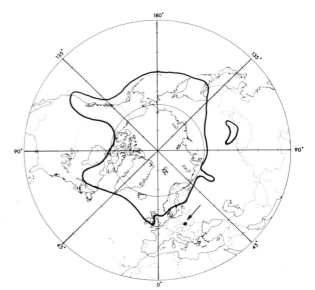

Map 7. Distribution of *S.nivalis* and *S.tenuis*; there are too many ambiguous records to permit separate mapping of the two species

Outside Europe it ranges throughout the Arctic without any wide gaps, extending southwards to Kamchatka and Labrador; also here and there in the Canadian Rockies and in isolated stations in Central Asia (in the Altai and near Irkutsk).

HABITAT: In the Arctic it grows in a wide variety of open situations, such as mossy or gravelly tundra or rocky ridges. Further south it is restricted to damp or shady mountain rocks or ledges, usually on basalt, schist or other base-rich but not calcareous rock. In spite of its name, it is usually found in situations that are relatively free of snow.

ACCESS: It is easy to find in most of the mountainous regions of Norway, and can be seen in several stations near Abisko. In Scotland it is nowhere common and seems to be declining; it should not be collected in the British Isles.

CULTIVATION: Provided that it can be kept cool in summer and moist in the growing season it is not too difficult to cultivate; it is probably best kept in a cool house in winter and spring and plunged in a shady place out of doors in summer and autumn. It is not a showy plant, but the neat foliage, often crimson beneath, is quite attractive.

## 8. *Saxifraga tenuis* (Wahlenberg) H. Smith ex Lindman, *Svensk Fanerogamflora* 300 (1918)

SYNONYM: *S.nivalis* var. *tenuis* Wahlenberg, *Flora lapponica* 114 (1812)

HISTORY & NOMENCLATURE: Linnaeus included this species under *S.nivalis*, which he admitted to be variable; and in his *Flora lapponica* he described several varieties without naming them (Linnaeus 1737); none of them, however, is clearly referable to *S.tenuis*. Wahlenberg was the first to distinguish it clearly.

The epithet *tenuis* (slender) draws attention to its most immediately obvious difference from *S.nivalis*. It has been somewhat indiscriminately applied, however, to minor variants of the latter. Some authors still prefer to treat it as a variety of *S.nivalis*.

TYPE: Not traced.

DESCRIPTION & RECOGNITION: The species is best described by enumerating the differences from *S.nivalis*:
(1) Habit. *S.tenuis* is smaller in nearly all its parts, and of more delicate habit. The lamina of the leaf usually measures 10–15 × 6–9mm; the stem is seldom more than 12cm tall, and is not more than 1mm in diameter.
(2) Hairs. The leaves in *S.tenuis* are almost hairless, and the stem, though glandular-hairy above, lacks the long, tawny, shaggy hairs in the lower part that are found in *S.nivalis*. This is probably the most reliable of the differences.
(3) Capsule. The styles in *S.tenuis* are more widely divergent, and more strongly curved outwards and downwards.
(4) Inflorescence. This tends to be more open and diffuse in *S.tenuis*, with longer pedicels, but although this is the character on which most stress is laid in the Floras, it is in our experience not very reliable.

It would be foolish to pretend that it is easy in all cases to distinguish the two species, and it is mainly the apparently constant difference in chromosome number that justifies the recognition of *S.tenuis* as a distinct species.

ILLUSTRATION: Rønning (1964, Figure 28)

VARIATION: There is very little except in the degree of compactness of the inflorescence.

HYBRIDS: None is known.

CHROMOSOME NUMBER: $2n = 20$.

DISTRIBUTION (Map 7): Most of the older records do not distinguish this species from *S.nivalis*; it is impossible, therefore, to give a very accurate summary of its distribution. In general it follows that of *S.nivalis*, but is more strictly arctic. In Europe it extends southwards to southern Norway, but in Asia it seems to be strictly arctic, with some doubtful exceptions in eastern Siberia, and in North America it finds its southern limit near 60°N in eastern Canada.

*HABITAT*: Damp tundra, flushes and late snow-lies, generally in wetter and less exposed situations than *S.nivalis*.

*ACCESS*: It is fairly widespread in arctic Norway, and is to be found in several places near Abisko, from 900 to 1400m.

*CULTIVATION*: No information is available. It is not likely to be easy, and would hardly be worth the trouble except for taxonomic research.

## Subsection *Rotundifoliatae*
### A.M. Johnson

Leaves circular to kidney-shaped, with a slender, distinct petiole. Hairs uniseriate. Bracts small. Inflorescence without bulbils or leafy buds. Flowers regular. Sepals reflexed. Ovary superior.

### 9. *Saxifraga nelsoniana* D. Don,
*Transactions of the Linnean Society of London* 13:355 (1822)

*SYNONYMS*: *Micranthes nelsoniana* (D. Don) Small
*S.punctata* of Sternberg and many other authors, not of Linnaeus
*S.aestivalis* Fischer & Meyer
*Micranthes aestivalis* (Fischer & Meyer) Small

*HISTORY & NOMENCLATURE*: The intrinsic difficulties of the group to which this species belongs have been greatly aggravated by nomenclatural confusion. By almost all authors, until quite recently, this plant has been equated with *S.punctata* Linnaeus; the warning given by Fischer & Meyer (1835) that this was mistaken was ignored, and it was not until Pugsley (1936) elaborated the argument further and reproduced a photograph of the type-specimen of *S.punctata* Linnaeus (showing it to be identical with the plant usually known as *S.davurica* Willdenow) that the situation was finally clarified. Pugsley's work was, however, ignored by Soviet and American authors, and it is only to be hoped that the

later re-iteration of his arguments (Webb 1964a) and the use of the name *S.nelsoniana* in *Flora Europaea* (Webb 1964b) will put an end to the misuse of the name *S.punctata* at last. It only remains to add as a warning that Rottboell (1772) used the name for *S.tenuis*, Gunnerus (1772) for *S.nivalis*, Pallas (1776) for *S.sibirica*, and Hooker (1847, p. 231) for *S.mertensiana*, while *Robertsonia punctata* Haworth is a variant of *S.spathularis*.

*S.nelsoniana* belongs to a complex of species distributed through northern Asia and western North America in which the specific limits are by no means clear. It seems best to follow Hultén (1945) in taking a wide view of *S.nelsoniana* (which was originally described from Alaska) and subordinating *S.aestivalis* Fischer & Meyer (the only representative of the complex in Europe) to it as a subspecies — *S.nelsoniana* subsp. *aestivalis* (Fischer & Meyer) D.A. Webb, *Feddes Repertorium* 69:154 (1964).

The species was named after David Nelson, a botanist on Cook's last voyage, who collected it in Alaska. No obvious explanation is apparent for the epithet *aestivalis* used by Fischer & Meyer; the plant flowers in summer, but so do most Siberian species. Gmelin (1769, p. 161) was probably the first to publish a description of the plant, as *Saxifraga foliis reniformibus, obtuse crenatis, caule plerumque simplici, nudo*.

*TYPE*: *S.nelsoniana*. NW coast of America. Cape Newnham. *Nelson*. (Holotype: Banks herbarium, British Museum (**BM**).)
Subsp. *aestivalis*. Not traced.

*DESCRIPTION*: Rhizome rather stout, usually branched. Leaves suberect, in loose rosettes, all basal. Lamina 2–8 × 3–9cm, kidney-shaped to nearly circular, usually broader than long; margin regularly and rather boldly crenate with 15–21 broadly ovate, shortly mucronate crenations; base usually cordate; surface usually almost hairless, but sometimes with fairly numerous glandular hairs; petiole narrow, chanelled, hairless to densely glandular-hairy, always longer than the lamina and sometimes 4 times as long. Flowering stem 10–35cm, glandular-hairy at least above, branched in the upper half to give a narrow, sometimes rather dense panicle. Sepals obtuse, reflexed, hairless, often dark red. Petals 2.5–4.5mm, longer than the sepals, ovate to oblong, narrowed at the base to a short, broad claw, white or pale pink, occasionally with orange spots. Filaments club-shaped; anthers sometimes abortive. Ovary superior; styles very short, straight, divergent in fruit. Seeds 0.9 × 0.3mm, narrowly ellipsoid, pale brown, with several rows of soft, bladder-like papillae; raphe inconspicuous. Flowering season: June and July.

*ILLUSTRATIONS*:

Sternberg (1822, Plate 4), as *S.punctata*
Hitchcock & Cronquist (1961, p.57), as *S. punctata*

It should be noted that the Plate labelled *S. nelsoniana* in Hooker & Arnott (1832) in fact represents *Boykinia richardsonii* (Hooker) Rothrock.

*RECOGNITION*: The kidney-shaped leaves with long petioles, together with the reflexed sepals and the leafless flowering stem, separate this from all other European species except *S.hirsuta*. From this it differs in three inconspicuous but constant characters. *S.hirsuta* has a narrow translucent margin to its leaf; *S.nelsoniana* does not. In *S.hirsuta* most of the hairs on the leaves are multiseriate and broad-based; in *S.nelsoniana* they are all of the uniseriate, slender type. Finally, the seed of *S.hirsuta* is covered in hard, opaque papillae, whereas those on the seed of *S.nelsoniana* are soft and translucent.

*VARIATION*: The species as a whole is variable, permitting its subdivision into several subspecies (see p. 281), but in the European subsp. *aestivalis*, which is distinguished chiefly by its soft and thin, not fleshy leaves, and its glandular-hairy inflorescence, there is little variation except in the size of the leaves and their hairiness.

*HYBRIDS*: None is known in Europe.

*CHROMOSOME NUMBER*: Plants from the Altai, probably belonging to subsp. *aesti-*

*valis*, are reported as having $2n = 28$. Counts for other subspecies include $2n = 30, 32, 60, 70, 72, 80$ and $84$.

*DISTRIBUTION* (Map 8): In Europe this species is known only from a small area in north-eastern Russia. In the Ural mountains it extends from the Arctic southwards to about 59°N, and it is found for some distance on the European side along the River Pechora and its tributaries, finding its western limit at 52°30′E on the River Vishera, further south.

Outside Europe the species as a whole ranges throughout Siberia, southwards to the Altai and adjoining ranges; thence to Korea and northern Japan and across the Bering Sea to Alaska and the Rocky mountains as far south as Oregon and Montana. The limits of subsp. *aestivalis* are subject to some uncertainty, but it seems probable that it is confined to the USSR.

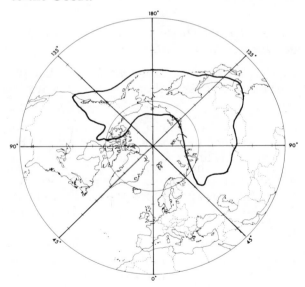

Map 8. Distribution of *S.nelsoniana*

*HABITAT*: In Europe it grows on tundra, on calcareous rocks, or rarely in moist forest-clearings (Govoruhin 1937). In North America it is found mostly by mountain streams.

*ACCESS*: Readers of this book are unlikely to go hunting for this species in the Urals; the most convenient region of access is probably the Cascade mountains in Washington State.

*CULTIVATION*: No information is available. The species is obviously hardy and moisture loving. Brown (1907) describes it in the Canadian Rockies as 'a rather rare though very beautiful alpine flower', so it should be worth a trial.

## Subsection *Stellares* (Engler & Irmscher) Gornall

Leaves elliptical to oblanceolate, coarsely toothed; petiole broad, scarcely distinct. Hairs multiseriate. Bracts usually fairly large. Flowers sometimes replaced wholly or partly by bulbils or leafy buds; sometimes irregular. Sepals reflexed. Ovary superior.

**10. *Saxifraga clusii* Gouan,** *Illustrationes et Observationes botanicae* 28 (1773)

*SYNONYM*: *S.leucanthemifolia* of Lapeyrouse and other authors, not of Michaux

*HISTORY & NOMENCLATURE*: First recorded by Clusius (1576) as *Saniculae montanae alterius, secunda species*, and named by Gouan in his honour.

*TYPE*: *S.clusii*. S.clusii Gouan [in Gouan's hand, fide Jussieu]. (Lectotype: No. 3414 in the Jussieu herbarium, Paris (**P**), designated here.)
  Subsp. *lepismigena*. Procedente de los peñascos húmedos immediatos a los molinos del Noguedo in Sanfrinajo. *Pérez Méndez*. (Holotype: Planellas herbarium, Barcelona (**BCC**).)

*DESCRIPTION*: Rhizome short, underground, bearing one or more leaf-rosettes. Basal leaves often up to 12 × 4.5cm, but sometimes as small as 4 × 1.2cm, soft and rather thin. Lamina oblanceolate to elliptic-oblong, coarsely and rather irregularly toothed, with 4–10 teeth on each side, tapered to a rather ill-defined petiole about 8mm wide. The leaves bear numerous hairs, mainly on the upper surface and the margins. Flowering stems up to 40cm, bearing long, slender but broad-based, multiseriate hairs, which mostly terminate in a very small gland; freely branched so as to form a broad, diffuse, rather brittle panicle, of which the lower branches diverge from the main axis almost at right angles. Lower bracts large and leaf-like. Flowers on long, slender pedicels (sometimes replaced in part by leafy buds). Sepals tipped with red, reflexed soon after the flowers open. Petals 4–7 × 2.5mm, narrowed at the base to a well-defined claw, lanceolate, acute, white. Terminal flower of the panicle regular; the others somewhat irregular, with the 3 upper petals symmetrical and bearing 2 mustard-yellow spots near the base, and the 2 lower petals somewhat smaller, unspotted, with one margin straight and the other strongly curved. Ovary superior; styles erect; stigmas very small. Seeds ellipsoid, flattened on one side, bearing tubercles in 7–9 longitudinal rows, those furthest from the fairly conspicuous raphe being the largest. Flowering season: June and July.

*ILLUSTRATIONS*: Plate 5
\* Lapeyrouse (1801, Plate 25)
  Coste (1902, p. 132)
\* Bonnier (1921, Plate 203)

*RECOGNITION*: *S.stellaris* is the only species (in Europe) with which *S.clusii* is likely to be confused. Generally speaking the latter can be distinguished by its larger bracts, more diffuse and fragile panicle and constantly irregular flowers, but both species are sufficiently variable for these distinctions to be sometimes somewhat blurred. In *S.clusii*, however, the leaves have 4–10 teeth on each side, directed outwards, and extending almost to the base of the lamina; in *S.stellaris* there are only 3–5 teeth on each side, usually confined to the apical half of the lamina, and they are directed somewhat towards the tip. Moreover, in *S.stellaris* all the petals bear yellow spots.

Plate 1.　*S.flagellaris*

Plate 2.　*S.cymbalaria* var. *huetiana*

Plate 3.  *S.sibthorpii*

Plate 4.  *S.hieracifolia*

Plate 5.  *S.clusii* subsp. *lepismigena*

Plate 6.  *S.spathularis*

Plate 7. *S.rotundifolia*

Plate 8. *S.scardica*

Plate 9. *S.spruneri*

Plate 10.   *S. tombeanensis* (Monte Tofino, Giudicarian Alps)

*VARIATION*: There are two well-defined subspecies:

(a) Subsp. *clusii*. Hairs on flowering stem short and relatively sparse. Leafy buds absent from inflorescence.

(b) Subsp. *lepismigena* (Planellas) D.A. Webb, *Feddes Repertorium* 68:199 (1963) (*S.lepismigena* Planellas, *S.clusii* var. *propaginea* Pourret ex Lange, *Pugillus* 265 (1865) ). Often more robust than subsp. *clusii*, and with larger bracts. Hairs on flowering stem numerous and long. Many of the flowers replaced by leafy buds which gradually expand into small rosettes, and may be as much as 17mm in diameter before the inflorescence collapses and allows them to take root. The ratio of leafy buds to flowers varies greatly; in the more extreme cases the buds outnumber the flowers, but plants can be found (mainly in the Asturias) transitional to subsp. *clusii*, with the leafy buds few and inconstant.

*HYBRIDS*: Possibly with *S.stellaris*, but confirmation is needed.

*CHROMOSOME NUMBER*: Not known.

*DISTRIBUTION* (Map 9): Endemic to south-western Europe. The two subspecies have separate ranges, without overlap. Subsp. *clusii* is almost confined to south-western France; it extends from the southern slopes of Mont Lozère through the south-western Cévennes to the eastern Pyrenees, and thence westwards (mainly on the French side, though with several stations in Spain) as far as 0°10′W, near Cauterets. There is then a gap of some five degrees of longitude before subsp. *lepismigena* appears in the eastern Asturias, and thence extends through much of north-western Spain and northern Portugal as far as the neighbourhood of Coimbra.

*HABITAT*: On shady, usually damp rock-faces, or occasionally by mountain streams. Although it has been recorded as high as 2600m in the Pyrenees, it is primarily a plant of mountain valleys, foothills and lowland river-gorges. It seems to be confined to siliceous rocks.

*ACCESS*: Subsp. *clusii* is a rather local plant, not very easy to find, but it can be seen in some quantity on a vertical rock-face and the talus below it beside the path which leads to the Lac d'Oô from Astau in the central Pyrenees; also on a shaded rock-face near les Vanels, some 15km south of Florac (dept. Lozère). Subsp. *lepismigena* is fairly frequent in the western Asturias and eastern Galicia; it may be seen by the road 4km south of Tineo, on the road to Cangas.

*CULTIVATION*: As with many species of damp habitats this is not very easy; if not given considerable care plants tend to succumb either to drought or to waterlogged soil. But with care it can be grown in a pan in the cool house; it is best renewed by seed or floral buds each year. If a stream of soft water were available in one of the milder parts of the British Isles, *S.clusii* might be tried in stony ground on its banks.

## 11. *Saxifraga stellaris* Linnaeus, *Species Plantarum* 400 (1753)

*SYNONYMS*: *S.subalpina* Dalla Torre & Sarntheim
*S.gredensis* Rivas Mateos

*HISTORY & NOMENCLATURE*: Linnaeus seems to have chosen the epithet *stellaris* himself, in reference to the star-like

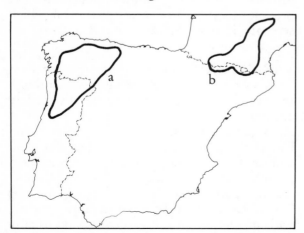

Map 9. Distribution of *S.clusii*: (a) subsp. *lepismigena*; (b) subsp. *clusii*

appearance of the flowers; it fits this species as well as any. The earliest synonym which he cited is by Morison (1680), but the species is common enough at fairly low altitudes in the Alps for it to have attracted the attention of botanists much earlier than this, and it seems very probable that the *Sanicula montana minor* of Clusius (1583), described from the Austrian Alps, is *Saxifraga stellaris*.

*TYPE*: *S.stellaris*. Sheet 575.12 in the Linnean herbarium, London (**LINN**) has been designated as lectotype (Webb 1987a). The type localities given by Linnaeus are Spitsbergen, Lapland, Switzerland, Styria and Westmorland; the lectotype is probably from Lapland. The inclusion of Spitsbergen is due to the fact that Linnaeus did not regard *S.foliolosa* as distinct.

Subsp. *alpigena*. Steiermark . . . im Seewigtale bei Aich, Schladminger Tauern. 1.6.1925, *Vetter*. (Holotype: Natural History Museum, Vienna (**W**).)

*DESCRIPTION*: The habit is rather varied. Stock more or less branched, mainly above ground, sometimes short and compact, but sometimes giving rise to prostrate stems of considerable length, so that the plant may consist of small, more or less isolated tufts of a few crowded rosettes, or of a continuous carpet covering a square metre or more. Leaves all at or near ground-level, and in this sense basal, but although most of them are aggregated into loose rosettes, the internodes are longer than in most rosette-plants, and if stolon-like stems are present they bear small, well-spaced, alternate leaves. Rosette-leaves 12–70 × 8–20mm, oblanceolate, obovate or broadly elliptical, with 3–4 (rarely 5) rather blunt teeth on each side; these are somewhat forwardly directed and are confined to the upper half of the leaf. Lamina narrowed at the base, usually sessile, but sometimes with a short but fairly distinct petiole. The leaves are of a fresh green, crisp and slightly fleshy, but not leathery; they bear, at least on the margins near the base and sometimes on the upper surface, rather coarse, multiseriate, broad-based, whitish hairs. Flowering stems 5–20cm, rather slender, hairless or glandular-hairy, leafless except for small bracts at the points of branching. Inflorescence a lax but fairly narrow panicle of 5–15 flowers. Sepals hairless, obtuse, reflexed. Petals 3–8 × 2–3mm, lanceolate, narrowed at the base to a distinct claw, white with 2 mustard-yellow spots (sometimes confluent) near the base. Flowers usually regular, but sometimes slightly irregular from the shape and orientation of the 2 lower petals. Anthers coral-pink. Ovary superior, white; styles short, straight, erect at first, diverging in fruit. Seeds 0.75 × 0.4mm, similar to those of *S.clusii*, but with a more conspicuous raphe and less regular ornament, the ribs being more numerous (up to 13) and less regular, and the tubercles often flattened and broad-based. Flowering season: June to August.

*ILLUSTRATIONS*:
\* Curtis (1821, Plate 69)
  Ross-Craig (1957, Plate 2)
  Mądalski (1962, Plate 1313)
  Huber (1963, Figures 113, 114)

*RECOGNITION*: The combination of superior ovary with reflexed sepals and toothed basal leaves with a short petiole or none separates this species from all others in Europe except *S.spathularis*, *S.cuneifolia*, *S.foliolosa* and *S.clusii*. The first two have somewhat leathery leaves with a narrow but distinct translucent border which is not present in *S.stellaris*. For the characters which separate it from *S.foliolosa* and *S.clusii*, see under those species.

*VARIATION*: This is a variable species. Two subspecies may be recognised, although their distinguishing characters are not entirely constant:
(a) Subsp. *stellaris*. This is the coarser and hairier of the two, and is seen mostly in small clumps of fairly large rosettes; it has short pedicels, and petals measuring 4–8 × 2–3mm.
(b) Subsp. *alpigena* Temesy, *Phyton (Austria)* 7:85 (1957). This subspecies is more delicate, with smaller, often hairless leaves, and usually forms a continuous mat of small rosettes; its petals measure only 3–6 × 1.5–2mm. The

most extreme variants of subsp. *alpigena* are to be seen in central and southern Spain; in north-central Europe, on the other hand, it shows an approach to subsp. *stellaris*.

A variant of subsp. *alpigena* with some of the flowers replaced by leafy buds was described from the Austrian Alps as var. **prolifera** Sternberg, *Revisio Saxifragarum, Supplementum* II, 13 (1831). A parallel variant of subsp. *stellaris* was recorded from western Ireland by Colgan (1900) and has been named var. **gemmifera** D.A. Webb, *Botanical Journal of the Linnean Society* 95:231 (1987).

*HYBRIDS*: See under *S.clusii*.

*CHROMOSOME NUMBER*: 2n = 28 has been established for both subspecies and for var. *prolifera*. There exists an additional record of 2n = 56 for subsp. *alpigena* from Bulgaria.

*DISTRIBUTION* (Map 10): In Europe *S.stellaris* shows a typical arctic-alpine distribution. It is absent from the high Arctic, but it is found in Iceland, Lapland and the Kola peninsula and is common in the mountains of Norway and western Sweden. In Britain and

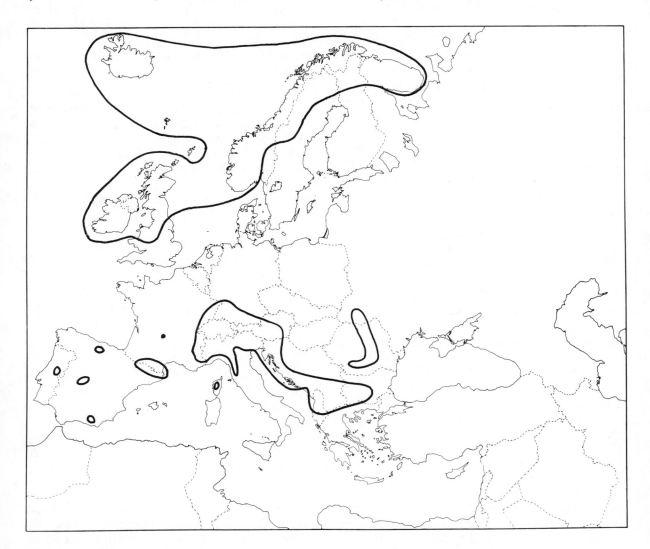

Map 10.  Distribution of *S.stellaris* (also found in southern Greenland and north-eastern Canada)

Ireland it is found in all major mountain-groups as far south as Kerry, Wicklow and mid-Wales. It reappears at about 48°N in the Vosges and Schwarzwald and in the Ukrainian Carpathians above Rakhovo. It is widespread throughout the Alps, and frequent in the Pyrenees, Romanian Carpathians and the mountains of Bulgaria; it is more local in the mountains of Spain and Portugal, Corsica, Auvergne and the Cévennes, the northern Apennines and Yugoslavia. It finds its southern limit in the Sierra Nevada of Spain and in northern Greece. Subsp. *stellaris* is found in the Arctic and northern Europe whereas subsp. *alpigena* occurs in central and southern Europe. Many plants from the Vosges and Schwarzwald are, however, intermediate between the two subspecies.

Outside Europe the distribution is rather uncertain from confusion with *S.foliolosa* and (in North America) *S.ferruginea* (see p. 273). On the whole it seems best to follow Hultén (1958, p. 110) in restricting its range outside Europe to southern Greenland and a few stations in Labrador and Baffin Island.

*HABITAT*: This species demands wet conditions, but with some movement of the water; it also needs a fairly open habitat in which seedlings can become established. It is mostly found, therefore, on mossy tundra or by mountain streams; less often in flushes or soaks, and occasionally on shady rock-faces where there is some seepage of water. It is somewhat calcifuge, but its absence from limestone may be due more to lack of surface water than to chemical factors.

*S.stellaris* descends to low altitudes in the Arctic. In Central Europe it is found mostly between 1800 and 2700m, but has been recorded as high as 3300m in the Sierra Nevada.

*ACCESS*: Both in the Alps and in the mountains of the British Isles *S.stellaris* is common enough in suitable habitats that no special directions are needed for finding it. This is true at least of the mountains of Cumbria and most of the western Highlands of Scotland; in Ireland it is commonest in Co. Donegal, Co. Wicklow and Co. Kerry. Var. *prolifera* has a fairly continuous range in Austria from near Tweng in the Niedere Tauern (13°37'E) eastwards to the Koralpe and Gleinalpe (15°E). It has also been reported from the Julian Alps and elsewhere in Slovenia. It is most conveniently seen at about 1500m in drains beside the very steep road which ascends the western side of the Saualpe from Guttaring to Klippistörl and continues on to St Leonhard; or on wet roadside debris at 1430m on the way up to the Eisenhut from Turrach. Var. *gemmifera* is frequent at 225–250m by the Gleninagh river, which flows from the Twelve Pins into the northern end of Lough Inagh, Co. Galway. Similar plants have been reported from Co. Kerry, Northumberland and Scotland, but there are no voucher specimens and no precise documentation.

*CULTIVATION*: The information given for *S.clusii* applies also to *S.stellaris*. There is some evidence that plants from relatively dry situations, such as mountain ledges, may be easier to cultivate than those from stream-sides.

## 12. *Saxifraga foliolosa* R. Brown, *Chloris Melvilliana* 17 (1823)

*SYNONYMS*: *S. stellaris* var. *comosa* Retzius, *Florae Scandinaviae Prodromus* 79 (1779)

*S.stellaris* subsp. *comosa* (Retzius) Braun-Blanquet in Hegi, *Illustrierte Flora von Mitteleuropa* 4(2):624 (1922), in part

*S.comosa* (Retzius) Fellman

*Spatularia foliolosa* (R. Brown) Small

*HISTORY & NOMENCLATURE*: The epithet *foliolosa* (furnished with small leaves) was coined by Robert Brown, and alludes to the bulbils in the inflorescence. The plant was first described by Linnaeus as a variety of *S.stellaris*, and figured in a crude but unmistakable illustration (Linnaeus 1737: Plate 2, Figure 3).

*TYPE*: R. Brown: Parry's first voyage, 1819–20. Cap. Nels., Melville Island, *Mr James Ross*. (Holotype: British Museum, London (**BM**).)

DESCRIPTION: Stock underground, short, usually unbranched. Leaves all basal in a rosette, 6–15 × 3–7mm, oblanceolate, tapered at the base but without a distinct petiole, with 1–3 (rarely 4) short, sometimes indistinct teeth on each side, with a few multiseriate, broad-based hairs on the margins and sometimes a very few on the upper surface. Flowering stem 5–15cm, erect, hairless or with a few glandular hairs, sparingly branched near the top. Flowers largely or wholly replaced by bulbil-like buds, which are more or less globular and composed of very small, fleshy, usually reddish leaves; these buds are more or less sessile on the main axis or clustered towards the tips of straight, often horizontal branches. The condition without flowers seems to be the commonest, but quite often there is a single terminal flower, or, more rarely, a flower at the end of each primary branch of the inflorescence. The flowers resemble those of S.stellaris, but the petals are narrower and with a longer claw. It seems probable that seed is rarely, if ever, set. Flowering season: August.

ILLUSTRATIONS:
  Warming (1909, Figure 33)
  Stefánsson (1948, Figure 147)
  Lid (1963, Figure 208c)

RECOGNITION: S.foliolosa can be distinguished from those variants of S.stellaris which have leafy buds in the inflorescence by its usually solitary rosettes, its much smaller bracts and usually smaller leaves, its very few flowers and its more bulbil-like buds.

VARIATION: Apart from variation in the number of flowers there is none that cannot be ascribed to environmental differences.

HYBRIDS: None has been reported.

CHROMOSOME NUMBER: $2n = 56$. This species provides a classic instance of a tetraploid with a more northerly range than the corresponding diploid (S.stellaris), and its low fertility is consistent with its being an autotetraploid.

DISTRIBUTION (Map 11): S.foliolosa is essentially an arctic plant. In Europe it is frequent in Spitsbergen and arctic Scandinavia, and occasional in arctic Russia; southwards it extends to northern Iceland and in Norway to the Dovrefjeld. Outside Europe its range is rather uncertain, as it has often been recorded as S.stellaris, but it would seem to be well distributed in the Arctic, northwards to northern Greenland, and extending southwards to Alaska and Labrador. A few outlying stations have been reported as far south as Colorado in North America and northern Mongolia in Asia.

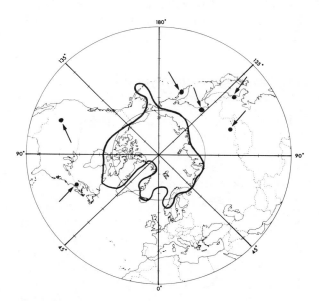

Map 11.  Distribution of S.foliolosa

HABITAT: It is always found in damp situations, by streams, in snow-patches, or in waterlogged moss-tundra. It seems to be commonest on base-rich soil

ACCESS: It is fairly frequent in the mountains of arctic Norway, and is found on wet, level ground between 750m and 1200m near Abisko.

CULTIVATION: No information is available. It is likely to be difficult.

## Section *Cotylea* Tausch (section *Miscopetalum* (Haworth) Sternberg)

Evergreen perennials with underground rhizome. Leaves herbaceous or rather fleshy, mostly basal, the remainder alternate, round or kidney-shaped, with crenate, dentate or slightly lobed margins and long petioles. Lime-secreting hydathodes absent. Hairs slender, uniseriate. Flowering stem terminal, leafy, with several flowers. Sepals erect or spreading. Petals white, usually with red and yellow spots. Ovary superior. Bulbils absent.

A small section of two species confined to Europe and south-western Asia.

### 13. *Saxifraga rotundifolia* Linnaeus, *Species Plantarum* 403 (1753)

*SYNONYMS*: *S.repanda* Willldenow
*S.heucherifolia* Grisebach & Schenk
*S.chrysosplenifolia* Boissier
*S.olympica* Boissier
*S.rhodopea* Velenovský

*HISTORY & NOMENCLATURE*: Being a relatively lowland plant, this species was well known to the botanists of central Europe in the sixteenth century; the earliest description seems to be that of Gesner (1541) as *Sanicula alpina alia*. The epithet *rotundifolia* (round-leaved) was taken by Linnaeus from Bauhin (1623).

The species is treated here in a wide sense; some authors, e.g. Halácsy (1901), make four species from what is here treated as one.

*TYPE*: *S.rotundifolia*. Sheet 575.42 in the Linnean herbarium, London (**LINN**) has been designated as lectotype (Webb 1987a).

Subsp. *chrysosplenifolia*. Ad rupes faucium Taygeti ad Mistra, *Sieber*. (Lectotype: Geneva (**G**), designated by Aldén & Strid (1986).)

*DESCRIPTION*: Rhizome rather stout, giving rise to one or more leafy shoots aggregated into loose clumps. Leaves mostly, but not entirely basal, forming a lax rosette.

Lamina 17–45 × 30–85mm, kidney-shaped to circular, deeply cordate at the base, sometimes with a narrow translucent border, varying from hairless to densely furnished on both sides with slender, uniseriate hairs; margin varying from regularly crenate, with low, broad, obtuse crenations, through irregularly dentate, with broad, triangular, subacute or mucronate teeth, to slightly palmately lobed, with each shallow lobe bearing 3 subacute teeth; the number of teeth or crenations on the larger leaves is at least 13 and is usually 17–23; petiole 4–18cm, slender, hairless to densely hairy. Flowering stem 15–70cm (rarely to 100cm), usually stout, somewhat hairy even in plants with hairless leaves. Cauline leaves usually 1 or 2, sometimes up to 5, rarely absent. Lower bracts leaf-like, the upper progressively smaller, shorter-stalked, and with fewer, larger and more acute teeth. Flowers in a lax panicle with long, erect or slightly spreading branches, of which each bears near its tip 5–13 flowers in a fairly compact cyme. Sepals 2–3mm, sparsely glandular-hairy, erect or somewhat spreading. Petals 6–11 × 2.5–5mm, narrowly oblong to broadly elliptical, contracted at the base to a very short claw, white, usually with numerous crimson-purple spots in the middle part, shading off through orange to yellow at the

Figure 8. *S.rotundifolia*

base. Capsule 4.5–6 × 3–4mm; styles 1–2mm, straight, usually diverging. Seeds 0.5–0.75 × 0.35–0.5mm, oblong with truncate ends, the whole surface covered with low tubercles; raphe rather inconspicuous. Flowering season: May to August.

*ILLUSTRATIONS*: Plate 7; Figure 8
\* *Botanical Magazine* 12: Plate 424 (1798)
\* Lapeyrouse (1801, Plate 26)
   Mądalski (1962, Plate 1316)
   Huber (1963, Figure 139)

*RECOGNITION*: The combination of superior ovary, sepals spreading even in fruit, fairly large white petals and kidney-shaped leaves with long petioles separates this from all other European species except *S.taygetea*; for the differences from this latter see under *S.taygetea*.

*VARIATION*: Very variable in several characters; the variation has received very different treatments from different authors. The scheme adopted here is mainly based on that in Kuzmanov (1970); for further discussion and justification see Webb (1987b). Although the distinction between the two subspecies recognised here is fairly clear, some plants from Bulgaria are intermediate between the two, and some from Switzerland, though agreeing with subsp. *rotundifolia* in most respects, have a translucent border to the leaf which is so narrow as to be scarcely visible.

(a) Subsp. *rotundifolia*. Petiole narrow right up to the junction with the lamina. Lamina with a narrow but distinct translucent border and usually without fringing hairs. Seeds 0.6–0.75mm.
(i) Var. *rotundifolia*. Flowers star-like, with narrow, spreading petals not more than 9mm long and usually lightly spotted.
(ii) Var. *heucherifolia* (Grisebach & Schenk) Engler, *Monographie der Gattung Saxifraga L.* 116 (1872). Flowers cup-shaped, with broad, semi-erect petals up to 11mm long and heavily spotted.
(iii) Var. *apennina* D.A. Webb, *Botanical Journal of the Linnean Society* 95:232 (1987). Plant robust, with basal leaves at least 70mm wide and somewhat fleshy. Petals 10.5–11.5mm, spreading, narrow, heavily spotted.
(b) Subsp. *chrysosplenifolia* (Boissier) D.A. Webb in Jordanov, *Flora Reipublicae popularis Bulgaricae* 4:658 (1970). Petiole expanded in its uppermost 5–7mm so as to pass gradually into the lamina (which is, nevertheless, fairly deeply cordate). Lamina without a translucent border, usually fringed with hairs. Shape, size and orientation of petals much as in var. *heucherifolia*. Seeds 0.5–0.65mm.
(iv) Var. *chrysosplenifolia*. Leaves usually crenate; petals without red spots.
(v) Var. *rhodopea* (Velenovský) D.A. Webb in Jordanov, *Flora Reipublicae popularis Bulgaricae* 4:661 (1970). Leaves usually finely toothed; petals with red spots.

*HYBRIDS*: The only natural hybrid is with *S.taygetea*; see under that species. A plant of obscure garden origin described as *S.cochlearifolia* Schrader ex Kunze has been considered to be a hybrid of *S.rotundifolia* with a member (perhaps itself a hybrid) of section *Gymnopera*. It was sterile, but was propagated vegetatively for many years.

*CHROMOSOME NUMBER*: $2n = 22$ (both subspecies).

*DISTRIBUTION* (Map 12): In Europe this species, though not primarily a mountain plant, is confined to the immediate neighbourhood of the major mountain ranges. Its northern limit is at about 49°N on the southern side of the Tatra mountains in Czechoslovakia. It is widespread in the Romanian Carpathians and in the mountains of the Balkan peninsula, and is found in Crete and a few other islands of the Aegean. It extends throughout the Alps and Jura, and southwards along the Apennines to Sicily; it is in Corsica and Sardinia, in a few places in the Cévennes and Auvergne, and thence through the Corbières to the eastern Pyrenees, where it finds its western limit in Andorra. It has long been naturalised in Belgium, and more recently in northern England.

Outside Europe it is found in Anatolia, on

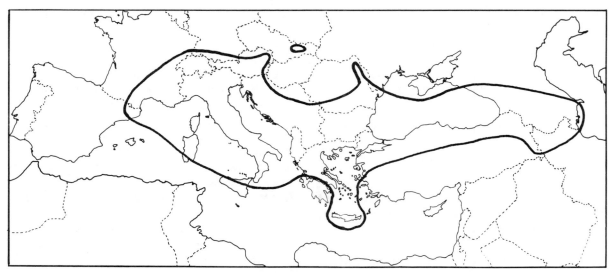

Map 12. Distribution of *S.rotundifolia*

the southern slopes of the Caucasus, and in north-western Iran.

Of the subspecies and varieties here recognised, var. *rotundifolia* is found almost throughout the range of the species except the Aegean region and southern Greece, but in the Balkan peninsula it occurs only at fairly low altitudes. Var. *heucherifolia* is found in the southern Carpathians and the mountains of Greece, Bulgaria and southern Yugoslavia. Var. *apennina* is found in the southern and south-central Apennines. Subsp. *chrysosplenifolia* is confined to the Aegean region and the southern half of the Balkan peninsula (up to 43°30'N in Hercegovina). Of its two varieties, var. *chrysosplenifolia* is mainly in the southern part of this territory, var. *rhodopea* mainly in the northern part.

*HABITAT*: *S.rotundifolia* is mainly a plant of mountain woods and shady banks, but in southern Europe and parts of the Alps it may be seen by mountain streams above the present tree-line. Its altitudinal range runs from 400m to 2300m, but it is rather rare above 1800m.

*ACCESS*: This species is so widespread in the Alps, Apennines and the mountains of western Bulgaria that no directions are needed for its discovery.

*CULTIVATION*: This is easy enough in a shady and fairly damp soil with plenty of humus. It does not thrive in pot-culture in a cool house. Var. *apennina* or var. *heucherifolia* would make the best show.

## 14. *Saxifraga taygetea* Boissier & Heldreich, in Boissier, *Diagnoses plantarum orientalium novarum* 1(10):19 (1849)

*SYNONYMS*: *S.rotundifolia* var. *taygetea* (Boissier & Heldreich) Engler, *Monographie der Gattung Saxifraga L.* 117 (1872)
*S.rotundifolia* subsp. *taygetea* (Boissier & Heldreich) Maire & Petitmengin, *Bulletin de la Société des Sciences de Nancy* 4:91 (1907)

*HISTORY & NOMENCLATURE*: Discovered by Heldreich on damp, shady, moss-covered rocks on Mount Taïyetos in southern Greece, and named after the mountain. It is true that there are occasional plants in north-western Greece intermediate between *S.taygetea* and *S.rotundifolia*, so that its interpretation as a subspecies of the latter is possible, but its very distinct appearance and the fact that the intermediates are found only in a fairly small 'zone of contact' argue for its recognition as a distinct species, with occasional hybrids in the zone where it meets with *S.rotundifolia*.

*TYPE*: Taygetos, 25.7.1844, *Heldreich 382*. (Lectotype: Flora Orientalis herbarium, Geneva (**G**), designated here.)

*DESCRIPTION*: Rhizome short, from which arise small leaf-rosettes. Leaves nearly all basal; lamina usually 5–13 × 8–23mm, kidney-shaped to almost round, truncate or slightly cordate at the base; margins crenate (occasionally shortly toothed) with 5–9 crenations, which are usually broad, low and rounded; surface shining and often hairless but sometimes sparsely hairy on both sides, often red beneath; petiole 15–70mm, slender, usually hairy. Flowering stem not more than 25cm and often much less, glandular-hairy, usually with a few small cauline leaves, branched in the upper half to form a small, lax panicle. Sepals 2.5mm, ovate-oblong, spreading. Petals 7–9 × 2.5–3mm, oblong, with a short but distinct claw, white with rather numerous purplish-red spots. Ovary usually bright red; styles 1–1.5mm, diverging. Capsule and seeds as in *S.rotundifolia*. Flowering season: June to August.

*ILLUSTRATIONS*:
Engler & Irmscher (1916, Figure 47)

*RECOGNITION*: The superior ovary, spreading sepals, white, spotted petals and mainly basal leaves with long petioles, distinguish this species from all others except *S.rotundifolia*. From most plants of the latter it differs in its small size and few and small cauline leaves, and even from dwarfed specimens *S.taygetea* differs in having not more than 9 (as against at least 13) crenations on its largest leaves.

*VARIATION*: There is none of any consequence.

*HYBRIDS*: As mentioned earlier, it probably forms occasional hybrids with *S.rotundifolia* in the northern part of its range. A

supposed garden hybrid with *S.cuneifolia*, known to gardeners as *S.tazetta*, is not convincing; it is probably a variant of *S.cuneifolia*.

*CHROMOSOME NUMBER*: $2n = 22$.

*DISTRIBUTION* (Map 13): *S.taygetea* is fairly widespread in the mountains of southern and western Greece, and extends sparingly through Albania and Yugoslav Macedonia to Montenegro, where Rohlena (1942) finds it quite distinct from *S.rotundifolia*.

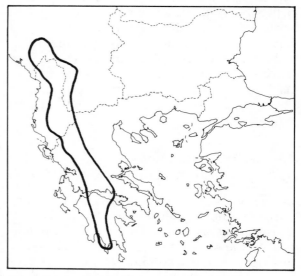

Map 13. Distribution of *S.taygetea*

*HABITAT*: Mountain rocks, usually damp or shady, but at higher altitudes (1800–2400m) and in more exposed positions than is usual for *S.rotundifolia*.

*ACCESS*: The upper slopes of Mount Parnassus, near Delphi, are probably the easiest place to look for it.

*CULTIVATION*: It is not difficult to cultivate in a pan in the alpine house, and would probably survive in a shady pocket of humus-rich soil in the rock-garden, but is not robust enough for naturalisation in woodland. It is a neat, attractive plant.

## Section *Gymnopera* D. Don (sections *Robertsonia* (Haworth) Sternberg and *Hydatica* Tausch, in part)

Evergreen perennials. Leaves usually somewhat succulent and leathery, stalked, toothed or crenate, alternate, in basal rosettes connected by usually short rhizomes or runners. Lime-secreting hydathodes absent. Hairs usually multiseriate. Flowering stems leafless, terminal; flowers fairly numerous, in panicles. Sepals reflexed. Petals white, usually spotted with yellow at the base and reddish-pink higher up. Ovary superior. Bulbils absent.

A small section of four species, endemic to Europe. Its members are similar in general habit to those of section *Cotylea*, but differ in their leafless flowering stems and reflexed sepals.

### 15. *Saxifraga cuneifolia* Linnaeus, *Systema Naturae*, 10th edn, 2:1026 (1759)

*HISTORY & NOMENCLATURE*: Being fairly common at low altitudes in Central Europe, this species was known to the botanists of the sixteenth century, but the early descriptions which seem to refer to it are very vague. Linnaeus was probably correct in citing in his synonymy Gesner (1541), who described it with the non-committal phrase *Cotyledon aut Sedi species quaedam* but accompanied this with a convincing drawing.

The epithet *cuneifolia* (with wedge-shaped leaves) was coined by Linnaeus, and is reasonably apposite for most specimens.

*TYPE*: *S.cuneifolia*. Sheet 575.28 in the Linnean herbarium, London (**LINN**) has been designated as lectotype (Webb 1987a).

Subsp. *robusta*. Kärnten, in fauce fluvii Gail infra Gentschach, c. 800 m, substr. schist. 14.vii.1931. *K.H. Rechinger*. (Holotype: Rechinger herbarium, Geneva (**G**).)

*DESCRIPTION*: Stems slender, somewhat woody, more or less prostrate, bearing at intervals of 2–7cm compact leaf-rosettes, separated by runner-like regions of the stem, which bear only 1 or 2 scale-leaves. Under good conditions many of the rosettes produce a flowering stem in the year following their formation, and in most of them, whether flowering or not, there arise from the axils of the upper leaves one or more shoots which terminate in new leaf-rosettes. The leaves persist green for 2–3 years, and sometimes for longer in a dead state; rooting from the stem takes place only in regions where the leaves have died. The plant so built up consists of a densely to rather loosely tufted, thick carpet of compact rosettes. Lamina 8–25 × 7–22mm, very variable in size and shape, usually broadly ovate or nearly circular, more rarely oblong, often markedly truncate at the tip; usually with a very few marginal, multiseriate broad-based hairs at the extreme base of the petiole; fleshy but also rather leathery, with a narrow but distinct translucent margin, often purplish-red beneath; margin varying from rather boldly toothed or crenate, with 3–7 teeth or crenations on each side, to

Figure 9. *S.cuneifolia* subsp. *cuneifolia*

almost entire. Petiole flat but fairly narrow, from 0.4 to 1.3 times as long as the lamina, into which it is expanded rather gradually. Flowering stems 10–25cm, erect, more or less glandular-hairy, branched above to form a lax panicle of up to 30 (but more usually about 12 and sometimes only 3) flowers on long, slender pedicels. Sepals 1.5mm, ovate-lanceolate, glandular-hairy. Petals 3–5.5mm, oblong, without a claw; white, often with a yellow patch at the base and rarely with a few reddish spots near the middle. Anthers pale pink. Ovary green, sometimes tinged with pink; styles short, erect in flower, slightly divergent in fruit. Seeds 0.75 × 0.4mm, bearing low tubercles over the whole surface; raphe fairly prominent. Flowering season: May to August.

*ILLUSTRATIONS*: Figures 9, 10, 11
    Coste (1902, p. 133)
    Engler & Irmscher (1916, Figure 45)
* Bonnier (1921, Plate 204)
* Köhlein (1984, Plate [9])

*RECOGNITION*: The combination of superior ovary, reflexed sepals, absence of cauline leaves and distinct, almost hairless, petioles separates *S.cuneifolia* from all European saxifrages except *S.spathularis* and its hybrids. Although the difference from *S.spathularis* is usually clear enough, it is not easy to find key-characters which provide an infallible distinction. Normally *S.spathularis* is a more robust and coarser plant with larger leaves and stouter flowering stem; its petioles usually have a few hairs in the upper part; its leaves are more boldly toothed; and there is more red pigment in the anthers, petals and ovary. In poorly grown specimens some of these distinctions can become blurred, but an absolute and invariable difference exists in the seeds, for in *S.spathularis* these bear at least a few, and often many, long, spike-like papillae as well as low tubercles like those on the seed of *S.cuneifolia*. The hybrids *S. × polita* and *S. × urbium* differ from *S.cuneifolia* in their distinctly hairy petioles and the truncate (not cuneate) base of the lamina (Figure 11).

*VARIATION*: This species varies considerably in robustness and in size and shape of leaves throughout its range. Most of this variation is continuous, but in one region (the Maritime Alps and the northern Apennines) most of the plants have such a distinct appearance that they call for taxonomic recognition. We can, therefore, recognise two subspecies, although unfortunately the Linnean type belongs to the subspecies with the restricted distribution.

(a) Subsp. *cuneifolia* (var. *capillipes* Reichenbach, *Flora Germanica excursoria* 560 (1832) ). Plant diffuse, clearly stoloniferous, with intervals between the rosettes usually 3–6cm; largest leaves not more than 20mm long (rarely 25mm), including the petiole; lamina nearly entire; flowering stem slender, nearly hairless, with a panicle of not more than 10 flowers.

(b) Subsp. *robusta* D.A. Webb, *Botanical Journal of the Linnean Society* 97:355 (1988). Compact, with intervals between the rosettes usually less than 2cm; largest leaves at least 25mm long, including petiole; lamina usually distinctly crenate-serrate; flowering stem

Figure 10. *S.cuneifolia* subsp. *robusta*

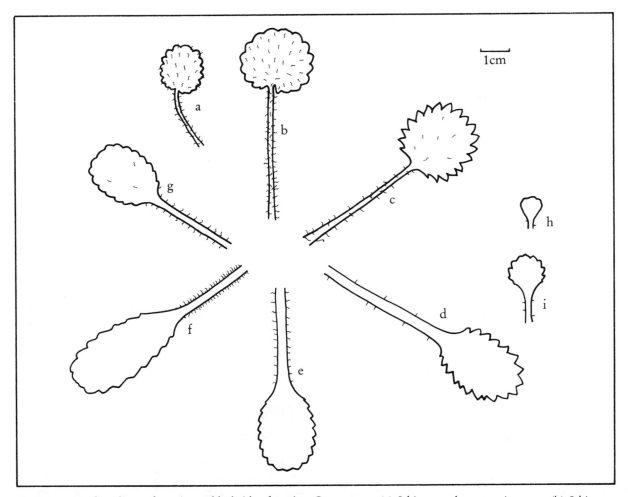

Figure 11. Leaf-outlines of species and hybrids of section *Gymnopera*: (a) *S.hirsuta* subsp. *paucicrenata*; (b) *S.hirsuta* subsp. *hirsuta*; (c) *S.* × *polita* (b × d); (d) *S.spathularis*; (e) *S.* × *urbium* (c × e); (f) *S.umbrosa*; (g) *S.* × *geum* (b × f); (h) *S.cuneifolia* subsp. *cuneifolia*; (i) *S.cuneifolia* subsp. *robusta*

fairly stout, distinctly glandular-hairy, with a panicle of usually more than 10 flowers.

*HYBRIDS*: A hybrid with *S.paniculata* (*S.* × *zimmeteri* Kerner) was described from Austria in 1870 and was in cultivation for some years, but has not been seen since. Supposed hybrids with *S.crustata*, *S.cotyledon*, *S.rotundifolia*, *S.taygetea* and *S.umbrosa* are all subject to considerable doubt, and should not be recognised without experimental confirmation.

Attempts made at Dublin over several years to cross *S.cuneifolia* with other species of the same section have been unsuccessful. This is rather surprising in view of the close morphological similarity and the identity of chromosome number.

*CHROMOSOME NUMBER*: $2n = 28$ (both subspecies).

*DISTRIBUTION* (Map 14): *S.cuneifolia* is widely distributed in and around the principal mountain-ranges of southern and south-central Europe. Its northern limit lies at about 47°30′N in the eastern Carpathians, and its southern limit at 42°20′N in the Spanish

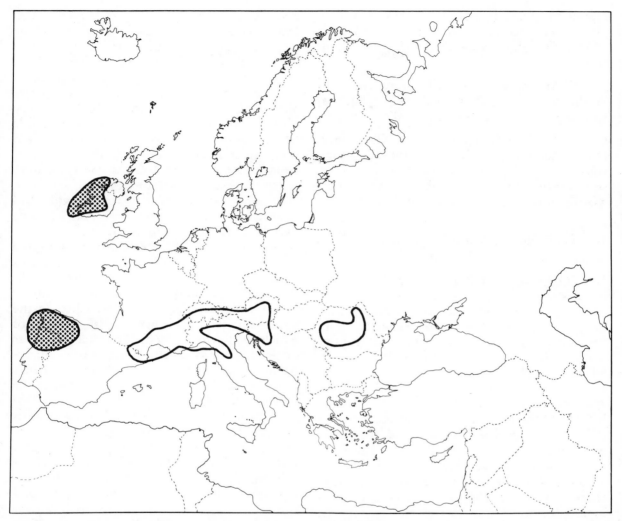

Map 14. Distribution of *S.spathularis* (shaded) and *S.cuneifolia* (unshaded)

Pyrenees. Within this narrow latitudinal belt it ranges through 26 degrees of longitude, from the central Pyrenees through the Corbières, with one station in the Cévennes, to the Alps (where it is frequent almost everywhere except in the north-east), the northern Apennines, the mountains of north-western Yugoslavia and of central Transylvania to the southern and eastern Carpathians.

Subsp. *cuneifolia* is to be found throughout the Maritime Alps (mainly in France, but also in Italy), and here and there in the northern Apennines. Subsp. *robusta* extends through-

out the entire range, but is rare within the territory of subsp. *cuneifolia*. Plants intermediate between the two subspecies can be found in the Cottian Alps and in parts of north-western Italy.

*HABITAT*: This species is essentially a plant of mountain woods, though it can survive deforestation if the situation is shady or damp. It is slightly calcifuge, but can be found on limestone if there is plenty of humus in the overlying soil, as it is a shallow-rooting plant. Although it is almost confined to the major mountain-ranges it is by no means an alpine plant, being commonest between 750 and 1700m, though it can extend as high as 2200m and as low as 200m.

ACCESS: S.cuneifolia is sufficiently common in the western and southern Alps that no special guidance is needed for its discovery.

CULTIVATION: This is easy. The only requirements are a fairly moist, not too calcareous soil with plenty of leaf-mould, and a situation in semi-shade. Subsp. cuneifolia is worth cultivating in a pan in the alpine house.

## 16. *Saxifraga umbrosa* Linnaeus, *Species Plantarum*, 2nd edn, 574 (1762)

HISTORY & NOMENCLATURE: The name is used here in a restricted sense, excluding vars. *smithii*, *serrata* and *cordata* Sternberg, vars. *punctata* and *serratifolia* D. Don, var. *crenatoserrata* Babington and subsp. *spathularis* (Brotero) Rothmaler & Pinto da Silva.

The epithet *umbrosa* was coined by Linnaeus to indicate its preference for shady habitats. It seems clear that Linnaeus, in describing this species, had in mind the plant which we call *S.spathularis* Brotero, as well as *S.umbrosa* in the restricted sense; this partly accounts for the reluctance of nineteenth-century authors to follow Brotero in recognising the former as a distinct species.

The first description of *S.umbrosa* is usually ascribed to Tournefort (1694), but the drawing illustrating the *Sedum montanum serratum, guttato flore* in Parkinson (1640) certainly represents *S.umbrosa*, suggesting that it was already in cultivation in Britain at that time. Parkinson called it 'Prince's Feather'.

TYPE: The plate in *Hortus regius monspeliensis* (Magnol 1697) which illustrates his *Geum folio subrotundo minori pistillo floris rubro* (p. 88) has been designated as lectotype (Pugsley 1936).

DESCRIPTION: Stems short, branched, prostrate, fleshy or somewhat woody, freely rooting and bearing usually closely crowded leaf-rosettes, which build up into a low cushion. Leaves spreading horizontally, forming dense, very flat rosettes. Lamina 15–30 × 10–20mm, oblong-elliptical, sometimes tending towards obovate, regularly crenate almost to the base, with 5–10 low, very obtuse and rounded crenations on each side (the terminal one broader than the others and often much lower), slightly fleshy and somewhat leathery, usually hairless, but sometimes with scattered multiseriate hairs on the margin and upper surface; with a fairly wide and conspicuous translucent margin. Petiole usually ⅓ to ½ as long as the lamina (rarely equalling it), flat, 2–3mm broad, with the margin densely clothed with long, flexuous hairs. Flowering stems up to 35cm, reddish, furnished sparingly below but plentifully above with glandular hairs, branched in the upper part to form a narrow, lax panicle, of which each primary branch bears 2–7 flowers on fairly long pedicels. Bracts small, linear-oblanceolate. Sepals 1.5–2mm, obtuse. Petals about 4mm, broadly elliptical, tapered at the base to a very short claw; white, with 2 yellow spots near the base and several crimson spots near the middle. Anthers bright pink. Ovary bright pink; styles straight, slightly divergent. Capsule 6.5 × 3mm, reddish, cylindrical or subconical. Seeds 0.95 × 0.45mm, ellipsoid, tapered at the ends and sometimes twisted slightly towards an S-shape, covered all over with crowded, prominent, obtuse papillae; raphe fairly large, but papillose like the rest of the testa and therefore rather inconspicuous. Flowering season: June to August.

ILLUSTRATIONS: Figures 11, 12
* Lapeyrouse (1801, Plate 22)
  Coste (1902, p. 132)

RECOGNITION: The combination of superior ovary with reflexed sepals and a short, flat petiole with numerous marginal hairs is distinctive.

VARIATION: If the effects of hybridisation with *S.hirsuta* are excluded, variation is slight. Some plants are, however, both in height and

Figure 12.  *S.umbrosa*

leaf-size, a good deal smaller than the average, and this tends to be associated with the presence of some hairs on the margin and upper surface of the lamina. Such plants have been distinguished as var. **hirta** D.A. Webb, *Proceedings of the Royal Irish Academy* 53B:95 (1950). They are fairly common in and around the Cirque de Gavarnie, and may also be seen at the Col d'Aubisque. The plant known to gardeners as var. *primuloides* is very similar, but the name has never been formally validated. A cultivar of one of these dwarf plants in which the pink colour is better developed than usual is deservedly popular with gardeners under the name of 'Clarence Elliott'.

*HYBRIDS*: The only natural hybrid is that with *S.hirsuta*; it is now known as *S. × geum*

Linnaeus, but the name was long misapplied to *S.hirsuta*, while *S.hirsuta* was known as *S.geum* (for clarification see Pugsley 1936). *S. × geum* is fairly common in the western Pyrenees, and as it is perfectly fertile, populations approximating to hybrid swarms can occasionally be found. Two hybrids of garden origin are also known. One is *S. × urbium* D.A. Webb, the familiar 'London Pride' of gardens, long confused with *S.umbrosa* but differing in its longer and less densely hairy petiole and its fairly boldly crenate-toothed leaf-margin (Figure 11). For some unexplained reason it hardly ever sets seed, although its pollen can serve to fertilise either of the parent species. Its origin is mysterious, though it seems to have been already known in the seventeenth century. It must have originated in a garden, as the ranges of the parent species are separated by more than four degrees of longitude. It is fairly widely naturalised in Britain and Ireland, more rarely in France and perhaps Austria. On the continent it tends to be replaced by *S. × geum* in gardens. The other hybrid is that known to gardeners as 'Primulaize', which is said to be a hybrid between *S.aizoides* and *S.umbrosa* 'Primuloides', but we have been unable to find a full description; nor has it received a Latin binomial.

*CHROMOSOME NUMBER*: 2n = 28.

*DISTRIBUTION* (Map 15): *S.umbrosa* is endemic to the Pyrenees; records from elsewhere are of naturalised plants or of other species or hybrids of the section. Its western limit lies at 0°30′W, just to the west of the Pic du Midi d'Ossau; eastwards it extends certainly to Andorra (Losa & Montserrat 1950), and possibly as far east as 2°E, but it is certainly rare east of the meridian of 1°E. It is naturalised in northern England, and perhaps in Austria.

*HABITAT*: *S.umbrosa* grows in a variety of habitats so long as they are shady or (at higher altitudes) damp. It is perhaps commonest by mountain streams, but can also be seen on rocks, screes and shady banks. It is able to compete better than many other species of the genus with closed vegetation. There are few precise records of altitude in the literature or on herbarium sheets; it certainly ranges from 750 to 2050m, and occasional plants are probably to be found outside these limits.

*ACCESS*: It is fairly abundant in the west-central Pyrenees, especially on the French side. It is especially common, perhaps, in the woods above Eaux-Chaudes, and by the ascent from Luchon to the Port de Vénasque.

*CULTIVATION*: *S.umbrosa*, though not quite so tolerant of hard usage as its hybrid *S. × urbium*, is easy to cultivate; all it requires is shade or semi-shade and a dampish soil, preferably with plenty of leaf-mould. 'Clarence Elliott' is worth growing in a pan in the alpine house.

### 17. *Saxifraga spathularis* Brotero, *Flora Lusitanica* 2:172 (1805)

*SYNONYMS*: *S.umbrosa* subsp. *spathularis* (Brotero) Rothmaler & Pinto da Silva, *Agronomia Lusitana* 2:89 (1940)
*S.serrata* Sternberg
*S.hibernica* of Sternberg, not of Haworth

*HISTORY & NOMENCLATURE*: The first notice of this species in the literature is that of Molyneux (1697), who saw it on Mangerton, Co. Kerry, in Ireland. It was described by Threlkeld (1727) as *Sedum montanum serratum guttato flore*. Linnaeus evidently received material of it, but he did not distinguish it from *S.umbrosa*, and apart from Brotero no author considered it distinct (except at the varietal level) before Pugsley (1936).

The epithet (spoon-shaped) was coined by Brotero to denote the most usual leaf-shape.

*TYPE*: Not traced.

*DESCRIPTION*: Stems prostrate, fleshy or woody, similar to those of *S.umbrosa*, but usually longer and more runner-like, so that the plant is loosely tufted and seldom builds a compact cushion. Leaves semi-erect (except in exposed or dry situations), all basal (except for a few very reduced ones on the longer runners), forming loose rosettes. Lamina

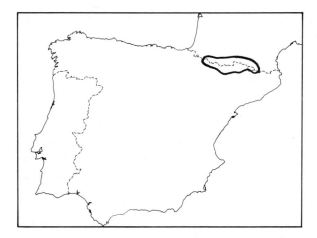

Map 15.  Distribution of *S.umbrosa*

15–50 × 12–30mm, circular to elliptic-oblong, bearing on each side 5–11 (in dwarfed plants 3–4) teeth, which vary from jaggedly and acutely triangular to low and somewhat obtuse; terminal tooth sometimes depressed, but often as long as the others; translucent margin distinct, but narrower and less conspicuous than in *S.umbrosa*; fleshy and somewhat leathery, hairless except for a very few marginal hairs on the petiole. Petiole usually 25–55mm, longer than the lamina in at least some of the leaves. Flowering stems up to 50cm, fairly stout, branched from near the middle to form a lax panicle of 10–50 flowers. Bracts lanceolate, 7–10mm. Sepals 2mm. Petals about 5mm, elliptical; white, with 2 yellow spots at the base and several crimson spots near the middle. Anthers bright pink. Ovary pink, 6 × 4.5mm; styles short, suberect at first but later strongly divergent. Seeds 0.8 × 0.45mm, ellipsoid with fairly blunt ends, ornamented with prominent papillae, usually over most of the surface but sometimes only on the dorsal half, and never extending to the raphe, which is smooth and therefore conspicuous; between the papillae, the testa is marked with numerous small tubercles. Flowering season: May to July.

*ILLUSTRATIONS*: Plate 6, Figures 11, 13
\* Sowerby (1865, Plate 548), as *S.umbrosa* var. *serratifolia*
Ross-Craig (1957, Plate 5)

*RECOGNITION*: Among the species with entirely basal leaves and superior ovary, *S.spathularis* is distinguished by its broad, flat, fairly long petioles, which differ from those of *S.umbrosa* and *S. × urbium* in being almost hairless (Figure 11). For the distinction from *S.cuneifolia* see under that species.

Figure 13. *S.spathularis*

*VARIATION*: Much of the variation to be seen in this species is attributable to environmental conditions; one can see very depauperate plants on a dry rock and others with leaves 4 times as large by a stream nearby. The only other variable (apart from those attributable to hybridisation with *S.hirsuta*) is in the size and sharpness of the teeth on the leaf-margin. In Spain it would seem that there is a rather irregular cline in this character, the more acute teeth being seen in the southern and western parts of the range, but within a small district of Co. Kerry in Ireland it is possible to find both extremes and every possible intermediate.

*HYBRIDS*: The only natural hybrid is with *S.hirsuta*. This is common in south-western Ireland, and hybrid swarms are frequent, with introgression in both directions. The hybrid is best called *S. × polita* (Haworth) Link, of which the original description fits the $F_1$ hybrid quite well (Figure 11c). In Spain it has been found, but is relatively rare since the parent species are better ecologically isolated than in Ireland. The hybrid *S.spathularis × umbrosa* (*S. × urbium* D.A. Webb) is discussed under *S.umbrosa*. Another mysterious hybrid which probably involves *S.spathularis* is *S. × andrewsii* Harvey. This was supposedly found in a remote glen in Co. Kerry by Andrews, but the description was from a plant in his garden, and it is generally assumed that a cross-pollination took place there and that there was a confusion of labels—an assumption justified by the unreliability of several other records by Andrews. It is clearly a cross between members of sections *Ligulatae* and *Gymnopera*. *S.paniculata* seems the most likely species for the former and *S.spathularis* for the latter, but the leaves are longer and narrower than would be expected from such a parentage, and until the hybrid has been re-synthesised its origin must remain doubtful.

*CHROMOSOME NUMBER*: $2n = 28$.

*DISTRIBUTION* (Map 14, p. 67): This species grows in two widely separated regions: north-western Spain and northern Portugal, and Ireland. It thus provides a classical example of the type of distribution known as Hiberno-Cantabrian. Its easterly limit in Spain is at 4°40′W, by the headwaters of the river Carrión in the north-westerly corner of the province of Palencia. Westwards from here it extends through much of the provinces of Oviedo and Lugo and the western corner of Santander; it also occurs more locally in the provinces of León, La Coruña, Orense and Zamora. In Portugal it is widespread in the mountainous country north of the Douro, and extends southwards in the mountains east of Coimbra almost to 40°N. In Ireland it is common in the south-west (Co. Kerry and W Cork) and locally frequent in W Galway and W Mayo; other stations are few and widely scattered. It is rarely cultivated and has not been reported as naturalised.

*HABITAT*: This is rather difficult to define. Although the plant may fairly be called a succulent, and may be found on walls, cairns and boulders, it cannot endure long periods of drought, and as a rule it requires either shade or (as on mountain-tops) frequent mist or cloud-cover. It is more or less confined to regions of high rainfall or high atmospheric humidity (over most of its range the rainfall exceeds a metre a year). Its most characteristic habitats are rocky woods and shady mountain cliffs. In Spain it ascends to 2100m, and in Ireland to the highest summits (1050m), but it descends to sea-level in Ireland and to 150m in Spain. It appears to be consistently calcifuge.

*ACCESS*: In Ireland *S.spathularis* is easy to find in the oakwoods of the Killarney region or, further west, to the south of Caragh Lake; in Co. Galway it is frequent around Kylemore and Leenane. In Spain it can be seen in some quantity on both sides of the Puerto de Ponton (north of Riaño); it also grows in several places by the road which leads from Tineo through Cangas de Narcea to the Puerto de Leitariegos.

*CULTIVATION*: This is very easy, even on somewhat calcareous soil, provided that adequate watering is given in times of drought.

## 18. *Saxifraga hirsuta* Linnaeus, *Systema Naturae*, 10th edn, 2:1026 (1759)

*SYNONYMS*: *S.geum* of Linnaeus (1762) and many authors, but not of Linnaeus (1753)
*Robertsonia geum* Haworth, in part
*Robertsonia crenata* Haworth
*Robertsonia dentata* Haworth
*Saxifraga elegans* Mackay
*S.geoides* Lacaita
*S.lactiflora* Pugsley

*HISTORY & NOMENCLATURE*: The species was described by Tournefort (1694) as *Geum folio circinato acute crenato, pistillo floris rubro*, but it seems probable that the *Sedum montanum rotundifolium minus album non guttatum* of Morison (1680) also represents this species.

The epithet *hirsuta* (hairy) was coined by Linnaeus, and as a distinction from related species it is apt anough. A sad history of confusion, however, surrounds the name; it is discussed at length by Pugsley (1936) and only a brief summary can be given here. On p.401 of the first edition of *Species Plantarum*, Linnaeus set out to describe this species, but by a slip on his part or that of his printer the epithet printed in the margin was *rotundifolia*, and as *S.rotundifolia* is adequately described two pages further on the description on p.401 has no nomenclatural status. Linnaeus soon realised his slip and corrected it in *Systema Naturae* in 1759. But in the second edition of *Species Plantarum* (1762) for some unknown reason he transposed the diagnoses of *S.hirsuta* and *S.geum*, stating quite clearly that the leaves of the former were ovate and the latter kidney-shaped. As most authors of the nineteenth and early part of the twentieth centuries used the second edition of *Species Plantarum* and ignored the first, the name *S.geum* came to be widely used for the plant correctly described in 1759 as *S.hirsuta*, and the name *S.hirsuta* for the plant correctly described in 1753 as *S.geum* (now known to be the hybrid *S.hirsuta × umbrosa*). It might have been better if Pugsley, who was the first to unravel this confusion, had rejected both names on the then legitimate ground that they 'had become

a long-persistent source of error'. But his strict typification has been accepted without challenge for 50 years, and it is best to follow it.

*TYPE: S.hirsuta*. The plate in *Hortus regius monspeliensis* (Magnol 1697, p.87) illustrating his *Geum folio circinato acute crenato pistillo floris rubro* has been designated as lectotype (Pugsley 1936).

Subsp. *paucicrenata*. Voyage en Espagne, 1862. Saxifraga hirsuta var. paucicrenata mihi. Rochers de l'extremité supérieure de la vallée de l'Ebre au nord-ouest de Reynosa. Alt. c. 7000 p.s.m. 29 juillet 1862. *Leresche*. (Holotype: Lausanne (**LAU**).)

*DESCRIPTION*: Stems prostrate, rhizome-like, usually above ground but sometimes buried in leaf-debris, bearing at their tips leaves aggregated into rather loose rosettes. The habit of the plant is more sprawling than that of *S.spathularis* and much more so than that of *S.umbrosa*; it approximates to that of *S.cuneifolia*. Leaves semi-erect to nearly horizontal. Lamina 15–40 × 10–50mm, kidney-shaped, circular or very broadly elliptical, soft and scarcely fleshy, often deep purple-red beneath, usually with rather stiff, multiseriate hairs on both surfaces, but sometimes almost hairless beneath; margin with inconspicuous but constant translucent border, crenate or toothed, with 6–13 (rarely up to 16 or down to 3) crenations or teeth on each side. These vary in shape and size, and may be rounded, truncate, mucronate or acute, but they are always more pronounced and less depressed than the crenations in *S.umbrosa*, and seldom as large or acute as the teeth in *S.spathularis*. Petiole slender, nearly cylindrical, at least as long as the lamina and usually 2–3 times as long, hairy all over. Flowering stems 12–40cm, rather slender, sparsely glandular-hairy, usually green, branched from the middle to form a lax but fairly narrow panicle of 10–60 flowers. Sepals 2mm. Petals 3.5–4mm, oblong, white, usually with a yellow patch at the base and some faint pink spots near the middle, but sometimes quite unspotted. Anthers pale pink. Ovary green or pale pink; styles short, straight, slightly divergent. Seeds

0.5–0.7 × 0.3–0.4mm, ellipsoid to broadly oblong, densely covered with papillae considerably shorter than those in *S.umbrosa* or *S.spathularis*; between them there can be seen with difficulty a minutely tuberculate surface to the testa; raphe small, smooth. Flowering season: May to July.

*ILLUSTRATIONS*: Figures 11, 14
\* Lapeyrouse (1801, Plate 24), as *S.geum*
\* Sowerby (1865, Plate 544), as *S.geum* var. *serrata*
\* Bonnier (1921, Plate 203), as *S.geum*
  Ross-Craig (1957, Plate 4)

*RECOGNITION*: The superior ovary with reflexed sepals, and the entirely basal leaves with slender, hairy petioles, separate this species from all others in Europe except *S.nelsoniana*. For the differences between the two see under the latter species.

*VARIATION*: There is considerable variation in size (which may, in part, have a genetic basis), in hairiness, and in the nature of the leaf-margin. The most acutely toothed vari-

Figure 14. *S.hirsuta* subsp. *paucicrenata*

ants are rare, and are mostly from Ireland. At the other extreme is a variant with very large leaves bearing very broad, flat-topped crenations (recalling on a greatly enlarged scale those on the leaf of *Sibthorpia europaea*); this is occasionally cultivated and has become locally naturalised in Scotland, Ireland and northern England, but has never been reported from a native situation. It perhaps deserves naming as a cultivar. There is also a good deal of variation in the amount of red pigment in leaves and inflorescence. Pugsley (1936) argued that the 'pure species', which he called *S.lactiflora*, had no red pigment at all, and that all pigmented plants, which constitute the bulk of *S.hirsuta* as generally understood, owe their pigment to introgressive hybridisation from *S.umbrosa* or *S.spathularis*. This interpretation has found few supporters and has been challenged by Webb (1950b).

There is one striking variant of *S.hirsuta* of limited geographical range and characteristic habitat which plainly owes nothing to hybridisation and may be recognised as a subspecies. We may accordingly distinguish:

(a) Subsp. **hirsuta**. Lamina seldom less than 15mm wide, 0.8–1.2 times as long as wide, kidney-shaped to circular, with at least 6 crenations or teeth on each side, variably hairy or nearly hairless; base more or less cordate. Petiole usually at least twice as long as lamina.

(b) Subsp. **paucicrenata** (Leresche ex Gillot) D.A. Webb, *Feddes Repertorium* 68:201 (1963) (*S.hirsuta* var. *paucicrenata* Leresche ex Gillot; *S.geoides* Lacaita). Lamina 12–25 × 7–20mm, 1.1–1.8 times as long as wide, ovate or elliptic-oblong to nearly circular, with 2–6 crenations (never teeth) on each side, rather densely hairy; base truncate. Petiole equal to lamina or up to 1.5 times as long. Plant usually small, more compact than subsp. *hirsuta*.

*HYBRIDS*: Natural hybrids are found with *S.umbrosa* in the Pyrenees (see p. 69), and with *S.spathularis*, frequently in Ireland, rather rarely in Spain (see p. 72). They are known respectively as *S.* × *geum* Linnaeus and *S.* × *polita* (Haworth) Link (Figure 11g, c). A possible hybrid with *S.rotundifolia* is discussed under the latter species.

*CHROMOSOME NUMBER*: 2n = 28 (both subspecies).

*DISTRIBUTION* (Map 16): This species, like *S.spathularis*, occupies two distinct regions, one in Ireland, the other in south-western Europe. In Ireland it is much less widespread than *S.spathularis*, being confined to Co. Kerry and a small part of Co. Cork. Evidence of a wider range in the past can, however, be seen in the presence of hybrids (*S. × polita*) in several places in Co. Galway and Co. Mayo. On the continent it has a wider range than either *S.umbrosa* or *S.spathularis*, and bridges the gap between them, as it ranges from about 1°15′E in the east-central Pyrenees, through the central and western Pyrenees, the French and Spanish Basque country and the Cantabrian range to about 6°05′W in the valley of the Narcea. Here its continuous range ends, but there are a few outlying stations in Galicia. Its southern limit in Spain is in the Sierra de Demanda (east-south-east of Burgos), and in France it does not extend beyond the Pyrenean foothills. Subsp. *hirsuta* is found throughout the range of the species. Subsp. *paucicrenata* is recorded only from the Picos de Europa and the Peña Labra (50km to the south-east), and from the western Pyrenees. Here it ranges from near St Jean Pied-de-Port eastwards to near the Pic du Midi d'Ossau.

*HABITAT*: Subsp. *hirsuta* grows only in damp or shady habitats; it is a good deal less tolerant of exposure than *S.umbrosa* or *S.spathularis*. It is usually to be found in woods, on north-facing banks, by stream-sides or waterfalls, or on shady rocks in the mountains. In Ireland it grows only on siliceous rocks, but in Spain it is often to be seen on calcareous tufa, and it is naturalised on limestone in Yorkshire.

Subsp. *paucicrenata* is, on the other hand, known only from fairly exposed situations on limestone mountains. It occurs both on scree and on solid rock-faces. Where the two subspecies grow close together intermediate plants can always be found in habitats of intermediate character.

*S.hirsuta* ranges in Ireland from near sea-level to 900m. On the continent it is found mainly between 800 and 2000m. Subsp. *paucicrenata* is found only in the upper part of this range.

*ACCESS*: *S.hirsuta* can be found in Ireland without much difficulty by the streams which flow through the woods at Glengarriff, Co. Cork, by the lower course of the River Blackwater (west of Kenmare, Co. Kerry) or in the neighbourhood of Torc Waterfall, Killarney. On the continent it may be seen in woods near Covadonga, 70km east of Oviedo, or in the valley of the Nive below St Jean Pied-de-Port (dept. Pyrenées-Atlantiques). Subsp. *paucicrenata* grows by Lake Enol, above Covadonga, and in some quantity at about 1500m on the Pic d'Anie and the Pic d'Orrhy in the western Pyrenees, but is more conveniently seen on shady cliffs to the east of the road on the Spanish side of the Col du Somport.

*CULTIVATION*: This is easy in any shady and fairly damp situation; if planted in quantity it makes effective ground-cover in open woodland. Subsp. *paucicrenata* is worth growing in a pan in a cool house, where its neat velvety foliage shows up to better effect than out of doors.

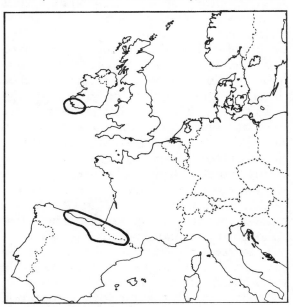

Map 16. Distribution of *S.hirsuta*

## Section *Porphyrion* Tausch (including sections *Kabschia* Engler, *Engleria* Sündermann, *Porophyllum* (Gaudin) Engler and *Tetrameridium* Engler)

Evergreen perennials. Stems somewhat woody, freely branched, bearing usually numerous leafy shoots; these may have the form of rosettes with more or less horizontal leaves, or of longer shoots bearing semi-erect leaves and crowded together so as to form a compact cushion, more rarely of prostrate stems forming loose mats. Leaves usually alternate, but sometimes partly or entirely opposite, usually hard or leathery, often glaucous, usually small, needle-like to almost circular, usually without a distinct petiole, entire or finely toothed, hairless or with marginal hairs, very rarely hairy on the surface. Glandular hairs multiseriate. Lime-secreting hydathodes present in pits, either restricted to a single one at or near the tip, or distributed in regular lines parallel to but not always very close to the margins; calcareous incrustation usually fairly conspicuous. Flowering stems short to medium-sized, terminal; flowers sometimes solitary, but more often in fairly small cymes, which sometimes resemble spikes. Petals white, pink, purple or yellow. Ovary sub-superior to almost inferior.

After flowering few leaves (if any) at the base of the flowering stem die; they mostly persist for another year. (This provides the only absolute distinction from section *Ligulatae*.) New leafy shoots arise either from the upper or from the lower axils of the leafy shoot which has borne the flowering stem, often from both.

A few species (series *Tetrameridium*) have the parts of the flower in 4s instead of 5s (4 sepals and petals and 8 stamens), but they are known only from the Himalaya.

This is a large section of about 100 species, ranging from Spain, through the mountains of central and southern Europe, Turkey and the Caucasus to the Himalaya and south-western China; one species is also circumpolar. About a quarter of the known species occur in Europe.

Plants of this section have long been favourites among gardeners, and although natural hybrids are rare a large number of attractive hybrids have been raised artificially, and have tended to displace the species from gardens.

## Subsection *Kabschia* (Engler) Rouy & Camus

Leafy shoots crowded, forming dense cushions. Leaves alternate, usually stiff and hard. Petals and sepals 5. Sepals spreading or semi-erect, shorter than the petals and not concealing them. Petals white, pink, purple or yellow.

The subsection contains about 70 species distributed through the mountains of central and southern Europe, and also in the Caucasus and Himalayan region.

### 19. *Saxifraga caesia* Linnaeus, *Species Plantarum* 399 (1753)

SYNONYM: *S.recurvifolia* Lapeyrouse

HISTORY & NOMENCLATURE: This was one of the first of the truly alpine species to attract the attention of the early botanists, and many of their Floras have a convincing picture of it. The first description seems to be as *Sedum alpinum tertium sive primum albo flore* in Clusius (1583). The epithet *caesia* (bluish) is apt enough for the leaves.

This species bears a superficial resemblance to some small-leaved members of section *Ligulatae*, and it has been suggested that it (together with *S.squarrosa*, to which it is clearly closely allied) really belongs to that section, or at least should be excluded from section *Porphyrion* (Horný et al. 1986). One piece of evidence offered for this view is that although interspecific hybrids are very common in section *Porphyrion*, neither of these species is claimed to participate in them. On the strength of this, Köhlein (1984, p. 10) states dogmatically that they belong to section *Ligulatae*, but against this it can be maintained first that both species have a chromosome number of $2n = 26$, which is characteristic of section *Porphyrion*, while all members of section *Ligulatae*, save one, have $2n = 28$; secondly that *S.caesia* is said to hybridise with another member of section *Porphyrion* (*S.aretioides*, see under *Hybrids*); thirdly that *S.caesia* and *S.squarrosa* do not form hybrids with members of section *Ligulatae*, with one doubtful exception; and fourthly that their habit of growth, without monocarpic rosettes, is entirely characteristic of section *Porphyrion*.

TYPE: Sheet XVI (1), 70 in the Burser herbarium, Uppsala (**UPS**) has been designated as lectotype (Webb 1987a).

DESCRIPTION: Leafy shoots numerous, moderately crowded, forming a low and moderately dense cushion. Leaves $4 \times 1$–1.5mm, oblong-spathulate, the basal half narrow, pale, nearly erect, edged with long white hairs, the upper part broader, curved rather sharply outwards so as to be nearly horizontal, glaucous, hairless, with a very narrow and some-

times scarcely perceptible translucent margin, entire, obtuse, rounded above, bluntly keeled beneath. Lime-secreting hydathodes usually 7, arranged parallel to the margin but at some distance from it; calcareous incrustation usually conspicuous. Flowering stems 4–12cm, very slender, bearing 3–5 narrow cauline leaves; variably furnished with glandular hairs which are, however, nearly always more abundant in the upper than in the lower part; branched near the top to give a small panicle of 2–8 flowers. Sepals 1.5mm, obtuse. Petals 4–6mm, obovate, contiguous, pure white. Ovary inferior; styles very short. Seeds $0.65 \times 0.35$mm, oblong-ellipsoid, with obtuse ends, dark brown, bearing fairly long papillae, mainly on the dorsal side, and small tubercles; raphe inconspicuous. Flowering season: June to August.

ILLUSTRATIONS: Figure 15
  Huber (1963, Figure 174)
  Mądalski (1962, Plate 1330)
  * Rasetti (1980, Figure 237)

RECOGNITION: The smooth, rosette-like shoots with glaucous, obtuse, outwardly-turned leaves are characteristic. The only plants with which confusion is likely are *S. squarrosa*, *S.valdensis*, and the smallest-leaved variants of *S.paniculata*. For the distinctions from the first see under *S.squarrosa*; *S.valdensis* differs in the higher, very stony cushions of foliage, the irregular disposition of the lime-secreting hydathodes, the stouter flowering stem with larger cauline leaves, and the more numerous flowers; and all varieties of *S.paniculata* differ in the tendency of the leaves to be curved inwards rather than outwards, and by their toothed margin.

VARIATION: There is very little, except in the abundance of glandular hairs on the inflorescence and flowering stem, and the number of flowers in the inflorescence.

*HYBRIDS*: Three natural hybrids are known, two of which are fairly frequent. *S. caesia × squarrosa* (*S. × tiroliensis* Kerner) is occasionally to be seen in the Dolomites and the Julian Alps, with the parents. *S.aizoides ×*

Figure 15. *S.caesia*

caesia (S. × patens Gaudin) is widespread in the Alps and is very variable, perhaps as a result of backcrossing. The third hybrid, and most interesting of all in terms of supporting the position of the species in section *Porphyrion*, is *S.aretioides × caesia* (*S. × saleixiana* Gaussen & Le Brun); it was described from the Pyrenees where it occurs with both parents.† One further hybrid has been claimed, *S. × forsteri* Stein, which is said to be *S.caesia × mutata*, but the characters of *S.mutata* are so feebly developed that it can hardly be accepted until firm evidence has been given by artificial synthesis.

*CHROMOSOME NUMBER*: 2n = 26.

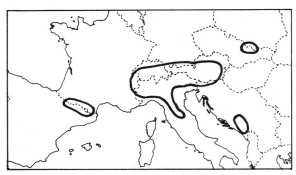

Map 17. Distribution of *S.caesia*

*DISTRIBUTION* (Map 17): *S.caesia* is primarily a plant of the Alps, though it occurs in smaller quantity also in other ranges of central and southern Europe. It is found throughout the Alps, except for a few small, marginal regions, and although its restriction to calcareous rocks means that it is rather local in the main central chain, it extends from near Briançon in the west to Slovenia and the Alps of Lower Austria in the east, and from the Bavarian Alps in the north to Monte Baldo in the south.

Outside the Alps it is found in the eastern and central Pyrenees; in the Apuan Alps and (very locally) in the northern and central Apennines; in the Tatra and a few adjacent ranges in the western Carpathians; and in some rather isolated sites in the mountains of western Yugoslavia (Bosnia, Hercegovina and Montenegro).

*HABITAT*: *S.caesia* is found only on limestone or dolomite; exceptions to this rule are very rare and probably refer to some other calcareous rock. It is often found on the solid rock, but also commonly on fine, gravelly calcareous debris, where it behaves as a pioneer plant, but is often accompanied by sedges and grasses. It is commonest between 1500 and 2200m, but ascends as high as 2600m, and it descends some river-valleys on the northern side of the Alps to below 1000m. On the whole it favours exposed, snow-free situations.

*ACCESS*: One cannot go far at the right altitude in the calcareous Alps without coming across *S.caesia*; it is perhaps especially abundant in the Giudicarian Alps (as on the Passo di Tremalzo, south-west of Riva) and in the Dolomites (especially around the Sella pass and the slopes of the Sassolungo).

*CULTIVATION*: This is not as easy as one might expect; plants that appear well-established are apt, for no obvious reason, to die off in patches. Winter damp is probably the chief enemy. Although it is often seen on fine debris in nature, it is probably best cultivated in a deep crevice in a block of limestone or tufa.

## 20. *Saxifraga squarrosa* Sieber, *Flora (Regensburg)* 4:99 (1821)

*SYNONYMS*: *S.caesia* var. *squarrosa* (Sieber) Gortani, *Flora Friulana* 2:222 (1906)
*S.imbricata* Bertoloni

*HISTORY & NOMENCLATURE*: Hitherto confounded with *S.caesia*, this species was first recognised as distinct by Sieber, an indefatigable and world-wide traveller and collector, who visited the South Tirol in 1820. His epithet *squarrosa*, meaning rough or shaggy with outstanding leaf-tips, draws attention to its most conspicuous difference from *S.caesia*.

---

† There may, however, be some doubt about its parentage.

*TYPE*: Not traced.

*DESCRIPTION*: S.squarrosa is like enough to S.caesia in so many features that it is best described by enumerating the differences.
(1) The leafy shoots are narrower and more crowded, giving a taller and more compact cushion.
(2) The leaves, which average 4 × 0.75mm, are oblong, not expanded at the tip, and are less markedly reflexed than in S.caesia, and only from near the tip; the marginal hairs extend to the middle or above it; the colour, though glaucous, is less markedly so than in S.caesia; the number of lime-secreting hydathodes is often only 3; and the translucent margin is more conspicuous.
(3) Although the frequency of glandular hairs on the flowering stem is variable, it is usually greatest near the base and least in the inflorescence.

*ILLUSTRATIONS*:
   Huber (1963, Figure 128)
\* Rasetti (1980, Figure 242)
\* Finkenzeller & Grau (1985, p. 107)

*RECOGNITION*: The differences from S. caesia are given above. From S.tombeanensis, S.diapensioides and the small-leaved variants of S.marginata, to which its foliage bears some resemblance, it is distinguished by the considerably smaller petals.

*VARIATION*: There is none of any consequence, apart from variation in the number of glandular hairs on the flowering stem.

*HYBRIDS*: The hybrid with S.caesia is mentioned under that species. A hybrid with S. aizoides (S. × sotchensis Engler) has once been found in the Julian Alps.

*CHROMOSOME NUMBER*: 2n = 26.

*DISTRIBUTION* (Map 18): S.squarrosa is found only in the south-eastern Alps. Its western limit lies at about 10°45′E in the Giudicarian Alps; hence it extends eastwards through the Dolomites and the Alps of the Austro-Italian border to about 15°E on the borders of Austria and Slovenia. Its northern limit is at 46°45′N in the East Tirol.

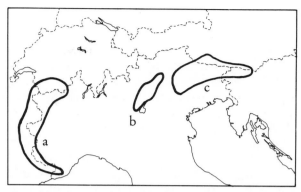

Map 18. Distribution of (a) S.diapensioides, (b) S.tombeanensis and (c) S.squarrosa

*HABITAT*: Like S.caesia, S.squarrosa is found only on limestone or dolomite, but it is much more constant on solid rock, being relatively rare on debris. It grows equally well in sun or shade. It is often accompanied by S.caesia, and its altitudinal range (1200–2500m) is similar.

*ACCESS*: This species may be conveniently seen in considerable quantity in the western Dolomites by the path which leads to the southern shoulder of the Sassolungo from the road about 3km north of the Sella pass.

*CULTIVATION*: Although some care is needed, this is easier than for S.caesia. The best results are obtained by planting in a crevice in a vertical face of limestone or tufa.

### 21. *Saxifraga marginata* Sternberg, *Revisio Saxifragarum, Supplementum I*, 1 (1822)

*SYNONYMS*: S.rocheliana Sternberg
S.coriophylla Grisebach
S.boryi Boissier & Heldreich

*HISTORY & NOMENCLATURE*: This species was brought to the notice of Tenore about 1810, and published by him over the next few years under a variety of pre-existing names; its specific identity was first recognised by Sternberg. It was at first known only from southern Italy, but its discovery in the Carpathians followed within the next 20 years. The epithet refers to the conspicuous translucent margin of the leaves.

*TYPE*: Not traced.

*DESCRIPTION*: Very variable in habit, sometimes forming low cushions with the leaves arranged in rosettes on fairly short leafy shoots; sometimes the shoots are very long and crowded together to form a large, deep cushion, their lower part clothed with the dead leaves of many years' growth. Leaves obovate to narrowly elliptical, 3–13 × 1–5mm, obtuse, flat above, bluntly keeled beneath, with a few marginal hairs towards the base, entire, with a usually conspicuous translucent margin, moderately glaucous, with 3–13 lime-secreting hydathodes on the upper surface just inside the translucent margin; calcareous incrustation variable, but usually fairly conspicuous. In large-leaved plants with short leafy shoots the leaves lie flat in rosettes; in small-leaved plants with long leafy shoots they are nearly erect and then curved sharply outwards towards the tip. Flowering stems 3–12cm, densely glandular-hairy (the glands often blackish); cauline leaves fairly numerous, linear-oblong, glandular-hairy at the base. Panicle of up to 12 flowers, but usually much fewer, short and compact. Sepals triangular, acute, densely glandular-hairy, often reddish. Petals 5–12mm, broadly obovate, white (rarely pale pink), contiguous or overlapping. Ovary ¾ inferior; styles erect. Seeds 0.8 × 0.4mm, flat on one side, strongly curved on the other, medium brown, covered with very low, rounded papillae, between which the testa is smooth. Flowering season: May to August.

*ILLUSTRATIONS*: Figure 16
* *Botanical Magazine* 109: Plate 6702 (1883)
  Fiori & Paoletti (1895, Figure 1678)
* Köhlein (1984, Plate [22])
  Horný *et al*. (1986, Figures 26–38)

*RECOGNITION*: The great variability of *S.marginata* means that there are several species with which it can be confused, though it can be distinguished from most of them by the obtuse leaves with a conspicuous translucent border. *S.scardica*, for example, which resembles some variants of *S.marginata* in general

Figure 16. *S.marginata*

habit, has sharply pointed leaves, while in *S. caesia* the leaves have only a very narrow translucent margin. Some of the smallest-leaved variants come close to *S.diapensioides* —so close, indeed, that it is difficult to key them apart. But in *S.marginata* the leafy shoots are longer, and the cushions, therefore, much bigger; the leaves are seldom quite as small as in *S.diapensioides*, and are more distinctly keeled on the lower side and recurved at the tip.

*VARIATION*: As has been implied in the description, this is very considerable, and it is not surprising that a number of varietal names have been proposed and a number of variants described as separate species. But as Engler & Irmscher (1919) rightly pointed out, the variation is quite continuous and the variants show only a very partial correlation with geographical distribution. Var. **marginata**, from which the species was described, is found only in Italy, but var. *rocheliana* (Sternberg) Engler & Irmscher, *Pflanzenreich* 69 (IV.117):564 (1919), recorded mainly from Romania but also from the Balkan peninsula, is scarcely distinguishable; both have relatively short leafy shoots and large leaves. Var. **coriophylla** (Grisebach) Engler, *Monographie der Gattung Saxifraga L.* 262 (1872), is probably the only variety worth maintaining; it designates the variants with long leafy shoots and small leaves, and is found chiefly in the Balkan peninsula. An extreme form of this, based on a single collection from a very exposed position in northern Macedonia, has been named var. *karadzicensis* (Degen & Košanin) Engler & Irmscher, *Pflanzenreich* 69 (IV.117):566 (1919), and this name has been used recently for garden plants said to come from Albania, but whether the two are identical is not clear. Moreover, although a good deal of the variation is doubtless genetically based, some of it represents a response to environmental factors (Horný *et al.* 1986, p.118).

*HYBRIDS*: No natural hybrids are known; it has been suggested that pink-flowered variants in southern Greece are hybrids with *S. sempervivum*, but no other sign of hybridity

is evident, and pink-flowered plants have also been recorded from Romania, outside the range of *S.sempervivum*. Artificial hybrids, however, are numerous; *S.marginata* has been successfully crossed with at least eleven other members of section *Porphyrion*, the best-known hybrid being the very vigorous *S.* × *apiculata* Engler (*S.marginata* × *sancta*). For details of the other hybrids see Horný *et al.* (1986).

*CHROMOSOME NUMBER*: Not known.

*DISTRIBUTION* (Map 19): *S.marginata* grows in three distinct regions of southern Europe: southern Italy, Romania and the Balkan peninsula. In Italy it extends from the Altopiano del Matese (41°25′N) to Monte Cocuzzo (39°15′N), but is rather rare and local. In Romania it is found chiefly in the mountains of Transylvania and the southern Carpathians, but has an isolated station further north in the Rodnei mountains at 47°30′N. It is widespread and fairly common in the western part of the Balkan peninsula, from northern Croatia to the Pindus range, with an outlier in the Peloponnese; it extends to eastern Serbia and northern Bulgaria, but is absent from the south-east.

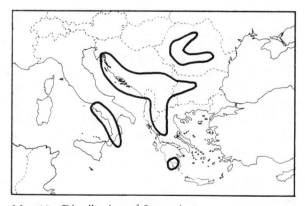

Map 19. Distribution of *S.marginata*

*HABITAT*: Limestone rocks, usually shady, mostly between 1000 and 2400m, but in a few places, as near the Iron Gates of the Danube, much lower. In the alpine region it grows on exposed rocks, but lower down it is especially characteristic of the vertical walls of river-gorges, where it can form very large cushions.

*ACCESS*: In Italy it can be seen easily enough near the summit of Monte Sant'Angelo, above Castellamare di Stabia (south of Naples). In Yugoslavia it is fairly common on the Ljuboten and other peaks of the Šar Planina in Macedonia, or on the mountain west of the lake of Plav in southern Montenegro; also, at a lower level, in the Radika Klisura, a gorge on the upper Vardar near Gostivar (Macedonia). In Romania it can be seen in the Turda gorge, south of Cluj.

*CULTIVATION*: This is fairly easy, but is more successful under glass than out of doors.

## 22. *Saxifraga diapensioides* Bellardi, *Appendix ad Floram Pedemontanum* 21 (1792)

*SYNONYM*: S.glauca Clairville

*HISTORY & NOMENCLATURE*: First recognised as distinct about 1790 by Bellardi, who found it in the Maritime Alps. It was probably known to some of his contemporaries, but confused with *S.caesia*. The epithet is based on a somewhat fanciful comparison of its foliage and habit with those of *Diapensia lapponica*.

*TYPE*: Not traced.

*DESCRIPTION*: Leafy shoots numerous, tightly crowded, giving dense, hard cushions, but the individual shoots, with a more or less rosette-like tip, remain distinct, and do not merge into a continuous mass of foliage as in *S.squarrosa* or *S.tombeanensis*. Leaves 3–5 × 1–1.5mm, oblong, entire, thick, obtuse or very shortly mucronate, glaucous, with a narrow but distinct translucent margin and with some stout marginal hairs towards the often reddish base. Lime-secreting hydathodes usually 5, situated some distance inside the margin; calcareous incrustation plentiful. Dead leaves long persistent. Flowering stems 3–8cm, densely glandular-hairy, as are the fairly numerous cauline leaves. Inflorescence a small flat-topped cyme of 3–5 flowers. Sepals 3mm, ovate-oblong, obtuse or acute, densely glandular-hairy. Petals 7–9mm, obovate, pure white. Ovary ¾ inferior; styles 3.5mm, straight. Seeds 0.65 × 0.3mm, straight on one side, curved on the other, marked by longitudinal ridges, of which those on the curved side bear long, stout, papillae; raphe very small. Flowering season: May to July.

*ILLUSTRATIONS*:
  Coste (1902, p. 136)
  Harding (1970, p. 8)
  * Rasetti (1980, Figure 239)
  * Finkenzeller & Grau (1985, p.105)
  Horný *et al.* (1986, Figure 39)

*RECOGNITION*: The species with which *S.diapensioides* is most likely to be confused are *S.marginata*, *S.squarrosa* and *S.tombeanensis*. The differences from *S.marginata* are discussed under that species. From the other two it differs in the distinctness of the leafy shoots, with perceptible gaps between them; from *S.squarrosa* also in the much larger petals and the much more densely glandular-hairy flowering stem and inflorescence; from *S. tombeanensis* also in the more glaucous foliage and the fact that the mucro of the leaf (if present) is not bent upwards.

*VARIATION*: There is virtually none which cannot be attributed to environmental factors.

*HYBRIDS*: There are no natural hybrids, but as the range of this species does not overlap that of any other in this section that is not surprising. *S. × fontanae* Sündermann was produced by crossing *S.diapensioides* with *S. ferdinandi-coburgi*. Other cultivars are ascribed to crosses with *S.aretioides* and *S.marginata*, but their parentage is not so certainly established.

*CHROMOSOME NUMBER*: $2n = 26$.

*DISTRIBUTION* (Map 18, p. 79): *S.diapensioides* is distributed over an extensive arc in the south-western and west-central Alps, running from Monte Rosa (7°50'E) in the north-east to Tende, in the Maritime Alps, without any large break. Although it descends to low altitudes in a few places it nowhere strays far from the main watershed.

*HABITAT*: Shady limestone rocks, mostly between 1700 and 2300m, but descending to 850m near Tende.

*ACCESS*: This species may be seen conveniently near Bessans (Savoie), both in the Val d'Avérol to the east of the village, and in the 'chaos' of boulders at the Col de la Madeleine, a few kilometres to the south-west. It also grows near the pass of Mont Cenis (in the gorge of the Ronce, behind the hospice) and on rocks overhanging the main road near Tende.

*CULTIVATION*: This is not very easy; the species survives, but is reluctant to increase or to flower. It is probably best sited in a fairly shady scree consisting mainly of limestone chips.

### 23. *Saxifraga tombeanensis* Boissier ex Engler, *Monographie der Gattung Saxifraga L.* 268 (1872)

*HISTORY & NOMENCLATURE*: The earliest collection of this species which we can trace is by Fleischer (mentioned by Steudel & Hochstetter 1826). Up to 1864, however, everyone who saw it considered it to belong to *S.diapensioides*, though perhaps varietally distinct; Boissier, who collected it in October 1864, was the first to recognise its specific distinctness. He seems at that time to have been too pre-occupied with the preparation of the first volume of *Flora Orientalis* to describe it himself, so he passed it on to Engler with a suggested name.

The epithet *tombeanensis* refers to Monte Tombea in Italy, where Boissier found it. The name does not often appear on modern maps; it refers to the massif which lies between the northern end of Lake Idro and Lake Garda, of which the highest summit is Monte Capione (1977m).

*TYPE*: Lombardia, dit. Brix. in rupestribus et glareosis sol. calc. alt. mt. 1–2000. 27/5/69. *Porta*. (Neotype: Kew (**K**), designated here; there is, rather surprisingly, no specimen at Geneva collected by Boissier, and whatever he sent to Engler has been destroyed.)

*DESCRIPTION*: Leafy shoots numerous, up to 5cm long, very tightly packed, so that the individual shoots do not stand out as distinct, forming a dense, rounded, moderately hard cushion. Leaves 2–4.5 × 1–1.5mm, narrowly oblong to elliptic-lanceolate, shortly mucronate, with the point on most leaves sharply bent or curved towards the upper surface, with a conspicuous translucent margin in the upper half and some stout marginal hairs towards the base, fairly dark green and only slightly glaucous; lime-secreting hydathodes 1–3; calcareous incrustation very slight or absent. Flowering stems 3–7cm; cauline leaves numerous, linear; both stems and leaves densely glandular-hairy. Flowers 1–4, in a fairly compact cyme. Sepals 2–3mm, oblong-lanceolate, acute. Petals 8–12mm, broadly obovate, contiguous, white. Ovary ¾ inferior; styles straight, more or less erect. Seeds 0.6 × 0.4mm, broadly ellipsoid, brown, with long, blackish papillae, between which are some small tubercles. Flowering season: May to July.

*ILLUSTRATIONS*: Plates 10, 11
  Huber (1963, Figures 127, 130)
* Rasetti (1980, Figure 240)
  Horný *et al.* (1986, Figure 41)

*RECOGNITION*: From all the species with which it is likely to be confused (*S.marginata*, *S.diapensioides*, *S.squarrosa*) it differs in the scarcely glaucous leaves with very little calcareous incrustation, and with a short, incurved point. From *S.squarrosa* it differs also in the much larger petals and the densely glandular-hairy inflorescence.

*VARIATION*: There is none of any consequence.

*HYBRIDS*: No natural hybrids have been reported. At least six, however, have been made by crossing with other members of the section, and most of these are in cultivation; for details see Horný *et al*, (1986).

*CHROMOSOME NUMBER*: $2n = 26$.

*DISTRIBUTION* (Map 18, p. 79): Restricted to a fairly small area of the south-eastern

Alps, centred around the Val di Ledro, near Riva di Garda. Most of the stations lie in the Giudicarian Alps, to the west of Lake Garda, but there are two on its eastern side, on the northern flank of Monte Baldo, and a few others in the southern and eastern part of the Brenta group, extending to near Bolzano. According to the detailed map given by Pitschmann & Reisigl (1959) the southern limit is at 45° 45′N and the northern limit at 46°30′N.

*HABITAT*: Vertical limestone rocks, usually but not always shady. Most of the stations lie between 1200 and 2000m, but it has been recorded as low as 600m in the Val Vestino.

*ACCESS*: No very precise directions can be given, but it should not be difficult to find on the southern slopes and shoulders of Monte Tofino (2151m, north-west of Riva), or on Monte Capione (1977m, south-east of Storo). This can be approached either from Magasa to the south, or, better, perhaps, from the Passo di Tremalzo to the north-east.

*CULTIVATION*: As for *S.diapensioides*, but perhaps a little easier. The contrast between the large white flowers and the very neat foliage makes it an attractive plant, worth some trouble.

## 24. *Saxifraga scardica* Grisebach, *Spicilegium Florae rumelicae et bithynicae* 1:332 (1843)

*SYNONYM*: *S.sartorii* Heldreich ex Boissier

*HISTORY & NOMENCLATURE*: Discovered by Grisebach in 1839 on the two main peaks of the Šar Planina (Scardus range, which is the source of the epithet) in Yugoslavia, and also on the range further to the south-east, which culminates in the peak of Kajmakčalan, on the Yugoslav-Greek border. It is curious that a species which is common on Mount Olympus at relatively low altitudes should not have been described earlier.

*TYPE*: In saxis reg. fagi Nidge ..., *Grisebach 734*. (Lectotype: University of Göttingen (**GOET**), designated here; there are also two other syntypes in this herbarium.)

*DESCRIPTION*: Leafy shoots up to 5cm long, crowded to form a hard, fairly dense cushion, but with the individual shoots clearly distinct; in the larger-leaved variants the leaves are nearly horizontal, so as to form terminal rosettes, but in the smaller-leaved variants they are more erect and the shoots more columnar. Leaves 5–15 × 2–4mm, oblong, acute or shortly mucronate, somewhat glaucous, fleshy and rather rigid, with a conspicuous translucent margin which is entire only in the upper quarter, minutely but distinctly toothed in the middle part, and produced into short, broad hairs towards the base. The lower surface is strongly convex, and distinctly keeled near the tip. Lime-secreting hydathodes 9–15; calcareous incrustation moderate. Flowering stems 4–12cm, rather densely glandular-hairy, with several oblong-oblanceolate leaves which are dark red and glandular-hairy beneath, except near the conspicuous, pale, hairless, sharply

Figure 17. *S.scardica*

mucronate tip, and a compact cyme of 5–12 flowers. Sepals 3mm, ovate, acute, glandular-hairy. Petals 7–12mm, obovate, nearly contiguous, white or pale pink, very rarely crimson. Ovary ¾ inferior; styles short, straight, erect. Seeds 0.8 × 0.45 mm, dark brown, with stout, black, fairly long papillae; raphe inconspiuous. Flowering season: May to July.

ILLUSTRATIONS: Plate 8; Figure 17
\* Botanical Magazine 135: Plate 8243 (1909)
   Harding (1970, p. 9)
\* Strid (1980, Plate 83)
   Horný et al. (1986, Figures 45–47)

RECOGNITION: The strongly mucronate leaves, keeled below near the tip, somewhat glaucous, and finely toothed at least half-way from the base, serve to distinguish this species from two others with which it might be confused—S.marginata and S.vandellii. The former has obtuse leaves, toothed only near the base; in the latter the leaves are not glaucous, and are much narrower in proportion to their length.

VARIATION: Apart from the colour of the petals, variation is seen mainly in the length of the leaves and the consequent appearance of the leafy shoots. The smallest-leaved variant, with columnar shoots and leaves c. 6mm long, has been distinguished as var. **pseudocoriophylla** Engler & Irmscher, Pflanzenreich 69 (IV,117):562 (1919), on account of its close superficial resemblance to S.marginata var. coriophylla (see p. 81). It seems very probable that var. obtusa Sprague, Botanical Magazine 132: Plate 8058 (1906), is a hybrid with S.marginata, and should therefore be named S. × wehrhahnii Horný et al.

HYBRIDS: A natural hybrid with S.sempervivum has been described from Mount Olympus as S. × gyoerffyana Wagner but has not been found since. Apart from S. × wehrhahnii mentioned above there is only one artificial hybrid of rather doubtful identity, S. × gloriana Horný. This is usually interpreted as S.lilacina × scardica, but Köhlein (1984) suggests that the second parent may really be

S.marginata, in which case it falls under S. × arco-valleyi Sündermann.

CHROMOSOME NUMBER: 2n = 26.

DISTRIBUTION (Map 20): S.scardica is found in the western and southern parts of the Balkan peninsula, from 43°10′N in northern Montenegro to 37°50′N in the northern Peloponnese. From Montenegro it extends southwards through northern Albania and the western part of Yugoslav Macedonia to Greece, where it is scattered in the mountains as far east as Dhirfis in Euboea, and as far south as Killini.

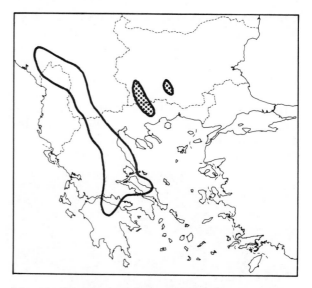

Map 20. Distribution of S.scardica (unshaded) and S.ferdinandi-coburgi (shaded)

HABITAT: Limestone rocks and screes, mostly from 1750m to 2500m, but ascending to 2900m on Mount Olympus, and descending to about 400m in ravines on Olympus and in the gorge of the Treska, south-west of Skopje. At these lower levels it requires shade, but at the higher levels it can tolerate exposure to sun and wind.

CULTIVATION: According to Harding (1970) this species is less tolerant of sun than are other members of the section, and on the whole it is probably best grown under glass, where it presents no great difficulty.

## 25. *Saxifraga spruneri* Boissier, *Diagnoses plantarum orientalium novarum* 1 (3):18 (1843)

*HISTORY & NOMENCLATURE*: Discovered by Spruner in 1842, and sent to Boissier, apparently under the impression that it was *S.sancta*. Boissier realised that it was an undescribed species and named it after its discoverer.

*TYPE*: Saxifraga sancta Grisebach [in Spruner's hand]. In cacumine montis Parnassi, *Spruner* [in Boissier's hand]. (Holotype: Boissier herbarium, Geneva (**G**).)

*DESCRIPTION*: Leafy shoots 3–7cm, slender, crowded, with blackish dead leaves extending a long way downwards from the short terminal section with living leaves, forming a deep, firm cushion. Leaves 5–7 × 3mm, oblong-spathulate to obovate-oblanceolate, obtuse or very shortly mucronate, with a translucent margin, broad near the tip, narrower elsewhere, glandular-hairy on the whole of the lower surface, and on the

margin and the basal half or ⅔ of the upper surface, somewhat fleshy, but softer and less rigid than in other species of the section; lime-secreting hydathodes usually 5, all fairly near the tip. Flowering stems 3–8cm, densely glandular-hairy, together with the linear-oblanceolate cauline leaves and the whole inflorescence. Flowers 4–15 in a fairly compact, flat-topped cyme. Sepals 1.5–2.0mm, obtuse. Petals 4–6mm, narrowly obovate, not contiguous, white. Ovary ¾ inferior; styles short, straight, erect. Seeds 0.60 × 0.35mm, dark brown, ellipsoid with pointed ends, evenly covered with rather small papillae; raphe inconspicuous. Flowering season: June to August.

*ILLUSTRATIONS*: Plate 9; Figure 18
    Engler & Irmscher (1919, Figure 116)
    Harding (1970, p. 10)
    Kuzmanov (1970, Plate 122)
    * Strid (1980, Plate 102)
    Horný *et al.* (1986, Figures 42–43)

*RECOGNITION*: S.spruneri is easily distinguishable from all other species in the section by the glandular-hairy surfaces of its leaves. It has a superficial resemblance to some species of cushion-habit in section *Saxifraga* (e.g. *S.cebennensis*), but it differs from these in the complete absence of lobed leaves, the conspicuous translucent margin to the tip of the leaf, and the presence, on at least a few of the leaves, of calcareous incrustation near the tip.

*VARIATION*: There is none that cannot be attributed to differences in the amount of shelter or exposure.

*HYBRIDS*: Wagner (1935) described from Mount Olympus a plant which he interpreted as *S.glabella × spruneri* and named *S. × degeniana*. Aldén & Strid (1986), however, regard it as merely a low-altitude variant of *S.spruneri*, larger and with a laxer habit. No other natural hybrids have been described, nor has it apparently been used in the production of artificial hybrids.

*CHROMOSOME NUMBER*: The only count is a recent one of $2n = 28$. In view of the constancy of the number 26 in other species of

Figure 18. *S.spruneri*

Plate 11.  *S.tombeanensis*

Plate 12.  *S.burseriana*

Plate 13.   *S.aretioides*

Plate 14.   *S.federici-augusti* subsp. *grisebachii*

Plate 15.   *S.media*

Plate 16.    *S.stribrnyi*

Plate 17.    *S.oppositifolia*

Plate 18.    *S.corymbosa*

Plate 19.    *S.florulenta*

Plate 20.    *S.biflora*

the section, this requires confirmation; but as *S.spruneri* is a somewhat aberrant member, it may well be correct.

*DISTRIBUTION* (Map 21): *S.spruneri* is confined to the southern part of the Balkan peninsula, and even here it is very local. It is found on the higher summits of south-central Greece, from Parnassus to Korax, and further north on Mount Olympus; further north still it re-appears in southern Bulgaria, in the northern part of the Pirin range and in the southern Rodopi near Smoljan. A record from northern Albania is mentioned in many Floras, but it is intrinsically improbable and requires confirmation.

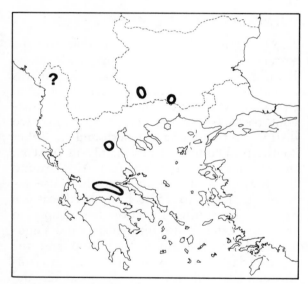

Map 21.  Distribution of *S.spruneri*

*HABITAT*: Crevices of limestone rock, more rarely on screes, mostly between 1900 and 2900m, but descending locally to 1400m.

*ACCESS*: It is fairly frequent on the eastern side of Vihren (Pirin Planina, south-west of Bansko) at 2500–2600m.

*CULTIVATION*: In spite of its numerous hairs, which are usually a danger sign, this species does not seem to be very sensitive to winter damp, and it can be grown in semi-shade in the rock-garden as well as in the alpine house.

## 26. *Saxifraga burseriana* Linnaeus, *Species Plantarum* 400 (1753)

*SYNONYM*: *Chondrosea burseriana* (Linnaeus) Haworth

*HISTORY & NOMENCLATURE*: The epithet *burseriana* commemorates Joachim Burser (1583–1639), whose herbarium found its way to Uppsala and was freely consulted by Linnaeus; it includes a specimen of this species. The epithet was originally so spelt, but from 1905 onwards the *International Code of Botanical Nomenclature* first recommended and later insisted that it be spelt *burserana*. In 1983 the authors of the *Code* in their inscrutable wisdom changed their minds, and it is now *burseriana* again.

The specimen in Burser's herbarium is annotated by him 'An hoc potius sit Sedum alpinum grandiflorum Bauh.'. This refers to the species named by Bauhin (1623) as *Sedum alpinum Saxifragae albae flore, vel grandiflorum*, which is the first printed reference that can be confidently assigned to *S.burseriana*, the synonyms cited by Bauhin all being subject to some doubt.

*TYPE*: Sheet XVI (1), 68 in the Burser herbarium, Uppsala (**UPS**) has been designated as lectotype (Stearn 1957, p.127). It comes from the Radstädter Tauern, which is the north-western part of the Niedere Tauern in Austria.

*DESCRIPTION*: Stems numerous, ascending, woody at the base, somewhat crowded, ending in short leafy shoots and forming a dense mat or low cushion of foliage. Leaves 6–12 × 1.7–2mm, mostly nearly erect, so that the foliage is built up of low 'cones' rather than rosettes. Each leaf is narrowly lanceolate, keeled beneath, tapered to a stiff, acuminate tip, and with a narrow translucent margin which usually bears near the base a few short, broad, tooth-like hairs, some of them glandular. The leaves are of a striking, glaucous, silvery-grey; each bears on its upper surface 5–7 lime-secreting hydathodes at some distance from the margin; calcareous secretion very scanty. Flowering stems 2.5–5cm, crimson, sparsely to fairly densely glandular-hairy, bearing 3–8 rather distant, erect leaves and a single terminal flower (rarely 2). Sepals and hypanthium crimson, glandular-hairy, the sepals 3–5 × 2–3mm, ovate, mucronate. Petals 7–12 × 5–10mm (larger in some cultivars), contiguous or overlapping, ovate to nearly circular, sometimes crenate in their upper half, spreading nearly horizontally, white. Ovary ¾ inferior; styles 3–4mm, straight, more or less erect. Seeds 0.6–0.8 × 0.3–0.5mm, oblong-ellipsoid, coarsely tuberculate; raphe conspicuous. Flowering season: May and June (much earlier in cultivation).

*ILLUSTRATIONS*: Plate 12
\* *Botanical Magazine* 181: Plate 747 (1977)
\* Köhlein (1984, Plate [22])
Horný *et al*. (1986, Figures 1–19)

*RECOGNITION*: The sharply pointed glaucous leaves with the solitary white flowers are quite distinctive, and it cannot be confused with any other species. Its nearest relative is *S.vandellii*, but that has dark green leaves in deeper cushions, and several flowers to a stem.

*VARIATION*: Apart from the size of the petals and the height of the flowering stems there is little variation, and both these characters vary within the same population. These variations are to some extent heritable, but they are also affected by the environment, plants from drier situations or higher altitudes having smaller petals and shorter stems. There is little to be gained, therefore, by giving for-

mal recognition to the varieties used by horticulturalists, such as *major*, *minor* and *tridentina*; variation in cultivated plants is better dealt with by the recognition of cultivars such as 'Gloria' and 'Brookside'. These are mostly variants with unusually large petals, or with two flowers on a stem, and it seems doubtful how many of the 23 cultivars listed by Horný *et al*. (1986) are really distinct.

*HYBRIDS*: No natural hybrids are known, but *S.burseriana* has been one of the most popular species among the raisers of artificial hybrids, and about a dozen are known within the section, one of them said to involve three other species. For details see Horný *et al*. (1986).

*CHROMOSOME NUMBER*: 2n = 26.

*DISTRIBUTION* (Map 22): Endemic to the eastern Alps, where it has a fairly wide range. Being confined to limestone and dolomite it is absent from much of the main central chain of the Alps, which is composed largely of siliceous rocks, so that its range falls into two distinct sections, one northern and the other southern. The former lies mainly in Austria, but includes also the Bavarian Alps around Berchtesgaden; it extends from the Kaisergebirge (12°15′E) to 15°30′E in north-eastern Styria. The southern section lies mainly in Italy, but extends also into Austria and Yugoslavia. From the Adamello group and the Giudicaria in the west (12°45′E) it runs through the Dolomites, the Karawanken and the Julian Alps to the Kamniške (Steiner) Alps north of Ljubljana (14°45′E), extending southwards to Monte Baldo and northwards to the Gailtaler Alps in south-western Carinthia.

*HABITAT*: Invariably on limestone or dolomite, where it can sometimes be seen in rock-crevices, but more often on gravelly debris, scree, or among boulders on talus-slopes. It is usually found between 1500 and 2200m, but in a few valleys it descends much lower, especially in the valley of the upper Adige, where it may be found at 230–400m about 25km north of Trento.

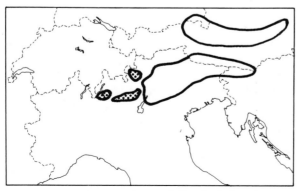

Map 22. Distribution of *S.vandellii* (shaded) and *S.burseriana* (unshaded)

ACCESS: It can be seen at the low level just mentioned under the cliffs on the eastern side of the main road from Trento to Bolzano and the Brenner pass; it grows here in shady patches among the large blocks which constitute the talus-slope. A more attractive place in which it was formerly frequent is on the western side of the Sella Nevea, a pass near the western edge of the Julian Alps, 15km south-south-west of Tarvisio. Here it was plentiful on calcareous debris at 1000m, not far from the road; the recent development of a winter-sports resort here has destroyed part of the former habitat, but it still survives at some distance from the road.

CULTIVATION: Given a little care, S.burseriana is not difficult to cultivate. It can be grown on a scree, if given plenty of water in spring and early summer, and is probably happiest in semi-shade. In view of its very early flowering season in cultivation, however, it is more easily appreciated if grown in a pan in the alpine house.

## 27. Saxifraga vandellii Sternberg, Revisio Saxifragarum 34 (1810)

SYNONYM: S.pungens Clairville

HISTORY & NOMENCLATURE: The species is called after D. Vandelli, who discovered it on the Corni di Canzo, north-west of Lecco, in 1763, and recorded it with a brief description and drawing in an unpublished diary which was forwarded to Sternberg from Padua. The first published description is as Sedum foliis compactis, plicatis, pungentibus, caule viscido paucifloro by Haller (1768). All his synonyms refer to S.burseriana, with which S.vandellii was long confused, but Haller's statement that the stem may have up to six flowers shows that it was the latter which he had in mind. In any case S.vandellii grows very close to the borders of Switzerland, while S.burseriana does not.

TYPE: Alpes Italiae superioris. Sternberg [in Hooker's hand]. Herb. Hooker, 1867 [stamp]. (Lectotype: Kew (K), designated here.)

DESCRIPTION: Leafy shoots up to 5cm, densely leafy, crowded together to form a deep, hard cushion. Leaves 7–9 × 2mm, dark green, not glaucous, narrowly triangular-lanceolate, gradually tapered to a sharp point, with an entire, translucent margin except near the base, where the margin bears stout, tooth-like hairs; lime-secreting hydathodes 5–7, well spaced out; calcareous incrustation slight and soon disappearing. Flowering stems 4–6cm, densely covered with rather long glandular hairs; cauline leaves numerous, similar to those of the leafy shoots but smaller, and glandular-hairy except at the tip. Inflorescence a compact cyme of 3–6 flowers. Sepals 2.5–3mm, acuminate, glandular-hairy. Petals 7–9mm, obovate, contiguous, white, sometimes with red veins. Ovary ¾ inferior; styles 2.5–3.5mm, straight. Seeds 0.7 × 0.3mm, oblong, bearing fairly numerous papillae; the rest of the surface very finely tuberculate; raphe inconspicuous. Flowering season: May and June.

ILLUSTRATIONS:
   Huber (1963, Figure 127)
* Rasetti (1980, Figure 238)
* Finkenzeller & Grau (1985, p.105)
   Horný et al. (1986, Figure 40)

RECOGNITION: The possession of dense cushions of sharply pointed leaves, together with fairly large white flowers, separates this species from all others except S.burseriana. This differs in having usually solitary flowers, fewer and shorter hairs on the flowering stem and very glaucous leaves.

VARIATION: There is none of any consequence.

HYBRIDS: No natural hybrids are known. Artificial hybrids (S. × clarkei Sündermann and S. × leyboldii Sündermann) have been made by crossing with S.media and S.marginata respectively.

CHROMOSOME NUMBER: $2n = 26$.

DISTRIBUTION (Map 22, p. 88): Italian Alps from 9°20' to 10°35'E. From the mountains around the eastern arm of Lake Como it extends somewhat discontinuously through the Alps of Bergamo (Arera, Presolana) to the Val Vestino (between Lake Idro and Lake Garda) and northwards to the mountains north and north-west of Bormio. There are records from Switzerland (some of them backed by specimens) and from the Pyrenees, but none of these has been confirmed in the past century, and they are probably erroneous. A distribution map is given by Pitschmann & Reisigl (1959).

*HABITAT*: Vertical limestone rocks, usually shady, from 1250 to 2300m.

*ACCESS*: S.vandellii tends to grow on cliffs that are difficult of access. Probably the easiest place to see it is on the Corni di Canzo, west of Lecco, where it is fairly frequent near the summit.

*CULTIVATION*: It has the reputation of being rather hard to establish, but once established needs little attention. It is probably best suited by a crevice in semi-shade in a vertical face of limestone or tufa. A fair proportion of the plants labelled *S.vandellii* in nurseries and private collections do not agree well with the above description and are probably hybrids.

## 28. *Saxifraga juniperifolia* Adams, in Weber & Mohr, *Beiträge zur Naturkunde* 1:53 (1806)

*SYNONYMS*: *S.pseudosancta* Janka
*S.sancta* subsp. *pseudosancta* (Janka) Kuzmanov in Jordanov, *Flora Reipublicae popularis bulgaricae* 4:680 (1970)
*S.macedonica* Degen

*HISTORY & NOMENCLATURE*: Discovered by Adams in Georgia. The epithet draws attention to the rigid, prickly leaves not unlike those of some junipers, such as *Juniperus communis* or *J.oxycedrus*.

*TYPE*: Not traced.

*DESCRIPTION*: Stems woody, freely branched below, giving rise to somewhat columnar leafy shoots aggregated to form a fairly dense cushion. Leaves very numerous, long-

persistent when dead, 9–13 × 1–2.5mm, linear to linear-lanceolate, keeled below, tapered to a narrow, rigid point, hairless, with a narrow but conspicuous translucent margin, which is entire towards the tip but furnished towards the base with numerous very small teeth (with a frequency of about 4 per mm); occasionally these extend about ⅔ of the way up the margin; lime-secreting hydathodes often only 1, near the tip, but sometimes 3–7; calcareous incrustation very inconspicuous or absent. Flowering stems 3–6cm, with numerous shaggy hairs and 4–6 cauline leaves. Inflorescence of 3–8 flowers in a dense, shortly oblong cyme. Hypanthium hairy; sepals hairless or with some marginal hairs. Petals 5–6mm, obovate, bright yellow. Stamens exceeding the petals by 1.5–2.5mm. Ovary ¾ inferior; styles 4–5mm, straight, slightly divergent. Seeds 0.7 × 0.35mm, ellipsoid, pointed at one end, truncate at the other, bearing low, rounded papillae, without tubercles; raphe inconspicuous. Flowering season: July and August.

*ILLUSTRATIONS*:
* Sternberg (1810, Plate 10)
  Engler & Irmscher (1919, Figure 113)
* *Botanical Magazine* 168: Plate 137 (1951), as *S.macedonica*
* Köhlein (1984, Plate [23]), as *S.sancta* var. *macedonica*
  Horný *et al.* (1986, Figures 64, 66)

*RECOGNITION*: The combination of bright yellow petals which are shorter than the stamens with narrow, sharply pointed leaves distinguishes this species from all other European ones except *S.sancta*. This differs most conspicuously in its completely hairless flowering stem and pedicels.

*VARIATION*: The species was described from the Caucasus, and plants from the Caucasian region differ slightly from European plants, chiefly in their longer leaves, which are sometimes less regularly arranged on the shoots, and the more boldly ciliate sepals, but the differences are hardly more than of varietal value. Among European plants an attempt was made by Degen to distinguish as *S.mace-*

*donica* some (though not all) of the plants of southern Bulgaria from those of the Stara Planina on the strength of their hairless calyx, but his article is very confused, and as intermediates are found in the Rila Planina it seems scarcely worth recognising even as a variety.

*HYBRIDS*: No natural hybrids are known, nor are any artificial hybrids attributed to this species in the literature. It may well be, however, that on account of the taxonomic confusion of the group some of the hybrids attributed to *S.sancta* are really derived from *S. juniperifolia*.

*CHROMOSOME NUMBER*: The only count recorded is of $2n = 26$, but it was made from a cultivated plant of unknown origin, and its identification cannot be regarded as certain.

*DISTRIBUTION* (Map 23): In Europe this species is known only from Bulgaria, where it is found on most of the higher mountains—Stara Planina, Rila, Pirin, Slavjanka. Kuzmanov (1970, p.683) says that it extends to Yugoslav Macedonia, but we have not discovered the basis for this statement. Outside Europe it occurs in the southern and eastern Caucasus and the adjacent regions of north-eastern Turkey.

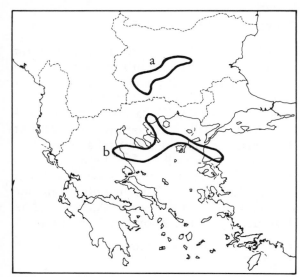

Map 23. Distribution of (a) *S.juniperifolia* (also in the Caucasus and north-eastern Anatolia) and (b) *S.sancta*

*HABITAT*: Shady rocks, usually (and perhaps always) siliceous, between 2000 and 2900m.

*ACCESS*: This species cannot be seen without some climbing. It is frequent at 2300 to 2400m about the lakes which lie south of the Vihren hut in the Pirin Planina, and under overhanging rocks north-west of the summit of Maljovica in the Rila Planina (at 2550m).

*CULTIVATION*: This is quite easy, either in the open or under glass, but flowering is apt to be rather sparse.

## 29. *Saxifraga sancta* Grisebach, *Spicilegium Florae rumelicae et bithynicae* 1:333 (1843)

*SYNONYM*: *S.juniperifolia* subsp. *sancta* (Grisebach) D.A. Webb, *Feddes Repertorium* 68:208 (1963)

*HISTORY & NOMENCLATURE*: First described by Grisebach, who discovered it on the summit of Mount Athos. The epithet refers to the name by which Athos is often known—the holy mountain.

*TYPE*: In summo cac. Ath. ..., *Grisebach 644*. (Lectotype: University of Göttingen (**GOET**), designated here.)

*DESCRIPTION*: This species is very similar to *S.juniperifolia*, and is best described by enumerating the differences:
(1) The leaves are slightly shorter (seldom more than 10mm), and the marginal teeth, which might perhaps better be described as broad-based hairs, are considerably longer (up to 0.2mm), stouter, fewer (about 0.75mm apart), and extend at least ¾ of the way to the tip.
(2) The flowering stem and the whole of the inflorescence is completely hairless.
(3) The inflorescence is shorter in proportion to its width, and is either flat-topped or nearly spherical.
(4) The stamens are only slightly, if at all, longer than the petals.
(5) The seeds have a few long, cylindrical papillae as well as the low, rounded ones.

Figure 19. *S.sancta*

These characters, though all subject to slight variation, are sufficiently well correlated to justify specific separation. It should also be noted that *S.sancta* is calcicole, and flowers in May and June, earlier than *S.juniperifolia*.

*ILLUSTRATIONS*: Figure 19
  Engler & Irmscher (1919, Figure 113)
* *Botanical Magazine* 168: Plate 137 (1951)
* Köhlein (1984, Plate [23])
  Horný *et al.* (1986, Figures 63, 65)

*RECOGNITION*: The differences from *S. juniperifolia* are given above. *S.ferdinandi-coburgi* and *S.aretioides* have obtuse or very shortly mucronate leaves, and petals clearly longer than the stamens.

*VARIATION*: None of any consequence has been described.

*HYBRIDS*: There are no reports of natural hybrids. The following artificial hybrids are known and are all common in cultivation; in some cases they are represented by several cultivars: *S.burseriana* × *sancta* (*S.* × *elizabe-thae* Sündermann); *S.ferdinandi-coburgi* × *sancta* (*S.* × *eudoxiana* Kellerer, usually known to gardeners as *S.* × *haagii*, but this is a later name); and *S.marginata* × *sancta* (*S.* × *apiculata* Engler).

*CHROMOSOME NUMBER*: Not known.

*DISTRIBUTION* (Map 23, p. 91): *S.sancta* is known with certainty in Europe only from Mount Athos and Pangaion (both in north-eastern Greece). There is, however, at Trinity College, Dublin (**TCD**), a specimen (*Aucher-Eloy 2631*) labelled as coming from Mount Olympus, and although a mistake in labelling is possible it may well be that the species once grew there, even if it might now be extinct. Outside Europe it is known only from one mountain in north-western Anatolia (Kaz Daği, perhaps better known as Mount Ida).

*HABITAT*: Crevices in marble rocks, from 1450 to 2030m.

*ACCESS*: It appears to be frequent near the summit of Mount Athos in north-eastern Greece.

*CULTIVATION*: This is easy; it can be grown either in semi-shade on the rock-garden or in a pan under glass. It flowers rather more freely than *S.juniperifolia*.

## 30. *Saxifraga ferdinandi-coburgi* Kellerer & Sündermann, *Allgemeine botanische Zeitschrift* 1901: 116 (1901)

*HISTORY & NOMENCLATURE*: It was discovered by Kellerer in 1897 in the Pirin Planina and called after Ferdinand, King of Bulgaria, of the house of Coburg, who was a keen naturalist and had suggested to Kellerer that he should undertake a collecting trip in Macedonia.

*TYPE*: Pirin, Macedonia. 1897. *Kellerer*. (Isotype: University of Vienna (**WU**), small scrap only; holotype not traced.)

*DESCRIPTION*: Leafy shoots numerous, crowded, rather short, forming dense but rather irregular and shaggy cushions. Leaves 4–8 × 1–1.5mm, oblong-lanceolate, mucronate, with the tip usually bent inwards towards the upper surface, with a narrow translucent margin, entire and hairless except for some hair-like teeth on the margin near the base, rounded or bluntly keeled beneath, flat or somewhat convex above when fresh (becoming concave on drying: hence the description of the leaves in most Floras as boat-shaped); lime-secreting hydathodes 5–13, widely spaced along the margin just in from the edge, with a conspicuous calcareous incrustation which gives the plant a greyish appearance although the actual leaf-surface is only slightly glaucous. Flowering stems 3–12cm, reddish, densely glandular-hairy; cauline leaves numerous, similar to the basal but obtuse and glandular-hairy. Inflorescence a flat-topped or somewhat elongated cyme of 3–15 flowers. Calyx red, glandular-hairy. Petals 5–8mm, broadly to narrowly obovate, bright yellow, longer than the stamens. Ovary ½ to ¾ inferior; styles 3mm, straight, erect. Seeds not seen. Flowering season: June to August.

*ILLUSTRATIONS*:
Kuzmanov (1970, Plate 122)
\* Horný & Webr (1985, Plate 3)
Horný *et al.* (1986, Figures 20–22)

*RECOGNITION*: The bright yellow flowers with stamens shorter than the petals, and the narrow, greyish leaves distinguish it from all European species except *S.aretioides*. The differences between this species and *S.ferdinandi-coburgi* are slight, and can be appreciated with certainty only on well-grown plants. Many of the distinctions made in Floras do not work out in practice, and several published descriptions contradict each other. The differences are set out under *S.aretioides*.

*VARIATION*: There is considerable variation in the height of the flowering stem and in the number of flowers in the inflorescence and the size of the petals. Varieties named *radoslavoffii* and *macedonica* have been based on these characters, but they describe individual plants rather than populations; they are not recognised in the most recent Bulgarian Flora (Kuzmanov 1970) and are best treated as cultivars.

*HYBRIDS*: No natural hybrids are known, but a large number of hybrids have been raised artificially, by crossing with other species of the section; some of these are triple hybrids. For details see Horný *et al.* (1986).

*CHROMOSOME NUMBER*: $2n = 26$.

*DISTRIBUTION* (Map 20, p. 85): Confined to a small area of eastern Macedonia, from the northern part of the Pirin Planina (Bulgaria) in the north-west to Pangaion (Greece) in the south-east. Its total range is from 40°50' to 41°50'N, and from 23°20' to 24°10'E.

*HABITAT*: Clefts in limestone rocks, from 900 to 2900m.

*ACCESS*: It is abundant at 2500–2600m on the eastern side of Vihren, in the northern part of the Pirin Planina.

*CULTIVATION*: This is fairly easy, given standard alpine treatment. It can be tried on a scree, but is probably best in the alpine house.

### 31. *Saxifraga aretioides* Lapeyrouse, *Figures de la Flore des Pyrénées* 28 (1801)

*SYNONYMS*: *Chondrosea aretioides* (Lapeyrouse) Haworth
*Saxifraga denticulata* Dulac

*HISTORY & NOMENCLATURE*: First described by Tournefort (1694) as *Saxifraga Pyrenaea lutea minima sedi foliis densissime compactis*. The epithet is based on a perhaps somewhat fanciful resemblance in habit to certain species of the Linnean genus *Aretia*, which is now included in *Androsace*.

*TYPE*: Plate 13 in *Figures de la Flore des Pyrénées* (Lapeyrouse 1801). It is a bad plate—perhaps the worst in the book—but it certainly represents this species.

*DESCRIPTION*: The resemblance to *S. ferdinandi-coburgi* is so close that *S. aretioides* is best described by enumerating the few differences:
(1) The leaves are, on the average, somewhat shorter and wider, but there is considerable overlap. More reliable, perhaps, is the fact that in *S. aretioides* many of the leaves are obtuse, while in those which are mucronate the tip is straight, not curved inwards as in *S. ferdinandi-coburgi*.
(2) Even in robust plants of *S. aretioides* there are seldom more than 5 flowers in the inflorescence, which is more compact and more consistently flat-topped than in *S. ferdinandi-coburgi*.
(3) The petals tend to be somewhat narrower in *S. aretioides*, but there is so much variation in both species that this distinction is of very limited value.

We can find no foundation for the statement by Engler & Irmscher (1919) that the translucent margin of the leaf is less developed in *S. ferdinandi-coburgi* than in *S. aretioides*, nor can we agree to the distinction given by Horný *et al.* (1986) that in *S. ferdinandi-coburgi* the petals are entire with vein-endings not sunk in pits, while in *S. aretioides* the petals are notched with vein-endings sunk in pits. This may be true of many clones common in cultivation, but a comparison of plants of *S. aretioides* from the Picos de Europa and of *S. ferdinandi-coburgi* from the Pirin showed no difference in either character.

There is little doubt that if the geographical separation were not so wide they would be treated as subspecies or varieties of the one species. We have not, however, been able to study a wide enough range of living material to suggest this rather drastic step with confidence.

*ILLUSTRATIONS*: Plate 13
   Coste (1902, p.135)
\* Bonnier (1921, Plate 203)
   Horný *et al.* (1986, Figure 23)

*RECOGNITION*: The yellow flowers, with petals longer than the stamens, and the narrow, lime-encrusted leaves in a tight cushion distinguish it from all European species other than *S. ferdinandi-coburgi*, the differences from which are set out above.

*VARIATION*: There is very little that cannot be ascribed to differences in the amount of exposure.

*HYBRIDS*: A natural hybrid with *S. media* (*S.* × *luteopurpurea* Lapeyrouse) is fairly frequent in parts of the central Pyrenees. Its status has been the subject of vigorous controversy, partly on account of its considerable variability, but its hybrid nature is now generally agreed. The variability is probably due to its fertility, and consequent segregation and

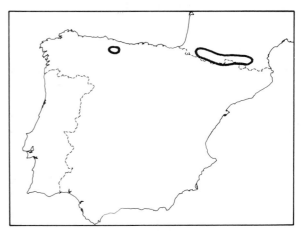

Map 24. Distribution of *S. aretioides*

backcrossing to the parents. The petals are of various shades between yellow and pinkish-purple. *S.aretioides* × *caesia* (*S.* × *saleixiana* Gaussen & Le Brun) has been recorded from the Pyrenees, growing with both parents. A number of artificial hybrids with other members of the section have also been raised, of which *S.* × *boydii* Dewar is widely cultivated; for details see Horný *et al.* (1986).

*CHROMOSOME NUMBER*: $2n = 26$.

*DISTRIBUTION* (Map 24): Endemic to the central and west-central Pyrenees, apart from one or two outlying stations in the Picos de Europa (north-western Spain). In the Pyrenees it extends from about 0°25′W to 1°30′E.

*HABITAT*: Rocks and screes, mostly calcareous, from 900 to 2700m.

*ACCESS*: This species is nowhere very common, and it is not easy to find. We can offer no detailed instructions for the Pyrenees, but it would appear that the neighbourhood of Cauterets or Eaux-bonnes is the most promising. It grows in small quantity not far from the cable-car station on the Picos de Europa above Fuente Dé.

*CULTIVATION*: This is not at all easy, for reasons that are not clear, and even experts are unable to keep it for more than a few years.

# Subsection *Engleria* (Sündermann) Gornall
## (grex *Mediae* Engler & Irmscher)

Leaves alternate, linear-oblong to spathulate, more or less glaucous, with numerous lime-secreting hydathodes and usually plentiful calcareous incrustation. Flowering stem, cauline leaves and inflorescence densely glandular-hairy, usually tinged (sometimes very strongly) with red. Sepals erect throughout the flowering and fruiting periods and usually somewhat convergent, so as to form, with the hypanthium, a broadly ellipsoid flower, in which the petals, being little, if at all, longer than the sepals, are largely concealed by them.

A very distinct group of nine species, with its centre in the Balkan peninsula, but extending to the Pyrenees, the Carpathians, Anatolia and the Himalaya.

## The *porophylla*-group

The three species included here—*S.porophylla*, *S.federici-augusti* and *S.sempervivum*—have been treated as a group for the purposes of the key, because they are not very easy to distinguish, and have been variously classified by different authors. Among the European members of the subsection these species are distinct in having stalkless flowers in a simple, unbranched, spike-like inflorescence. They are found mainly in the Balkan peninsula, but extend to Anatolia and to Italy.

Engler & Irmscher (1919) grouped them under two species (one with three varieties). Hayek (1925) also recognised two species in the Balkan peninsula, but regarded most of the plants as variants of the Pyrenean *S.media*, with only *S.sempervivum* distinct. Stapf (1928), however, recognised five species, while Aldén & Strid (1986) reduced these to two, one of them with two subspecies.

Part of this diversity of treatment arises from our rather scanty knowledge of the group, especially in Montenegro and Albania, and part from the tantalising way in which the differences between several of the group lie on the border between specific and subspecific distinction. It would not be absurd to follow Stapf in his recognition of five species; on the other hand a fair argument could be made for regarding all five as subspecies of a single variable species. We have here attempted a compromise. We follow Stapf in recognising *S.federici-augusti* (described from Montenegro) as distinct from the Italian *S.porophylla*; we agree with most authors (other than Stapf) in regarding *S.thessalica* as a variety of *S.sempervivum*; and we follow Aldén & Strid (1986), doubtless to the annoyance of gardeners, in considering *S.grisebachii* a subspecies, though we put it under *S.federici-augusti* and not under *S.porophylla*.

The three species may be distinguished thus:

1.  Leaves linear to linear-oblong, not expand-
    ed at the tip .............. *S.sempervivum*
    Leaves obovate to spathulate, expanded
    near the tip ................................. 2
2.  Leaves 4–10 × 2–3mm; flowers 4–7
    (rarely up to 12); inflorescence dull pink,
    sometimes tinged with green
    ............................... *S.porophylla*
    Leaves 12–35 × 3–8mm; flowers 10–20;
    inflorescence bright red to dark crimson
    ......................... *S.federici-augusti*

## 32. *Saxifraga sempervivum* C. Koch, *Linnaea* 19:40 (1846)

*SYNONYMS*: *S.media* var. *sibthorpiana*
Grisebach

*S.porophylla* var. *sibthorpiana* (Grisebach)
Engler & Irmscher, *Pflanzenreich* 69
(IV.117): 543 (1919)

*S.porophylla* of Boissier (in part), not of
Bertoloni

*S.thessalica* Schott

*S.media* of Sibthorp & Smith, not of Gouan

*HISTORY & NOMENCLATURE*: Des-
cribed by Koch from specimens collected by
Thirke; the locality is not stated, but it must
have been from the Bithynian Olympus (Ulu
Dağ) in north-western Anatolia; most of
Thirke's plants came from here, and it has not
been found elsewhere in Turkey. It had been
found much earlier on the same mountain by
Sibthorp, but his record was published by
Sibthorp & Smith (1823) under the name of
*S.media* Gouan. Grisebach also collected it on
Mount Athos in 1839.

The epithet indicates a rather fanciful comparison with a member of the genus *Sempervivum*, or perhaps a latinisation of the sectional name *Aizoonia*, to which Koch referred
it.

*TYPE*: Saxifraga sempervivum C. Koch. Asia
Minor. Litus aust. Pontus Euxini. *Thirke*,
determ. et misit. C. Koch 1846 (Linnaea Vol.
XIX). (Holotype: Geneva (**G**).)

*DESCRIPTION*: Rather variable in habit,
usually forming a rather loose and open
cushion, but sometimes a dense one or a mat.
Leafy shoots very variable in length, woody at
the base, freely branched, each branch terminating in a well-defined leaf-rosette. Dead leaves
do not persist, but the leaves often remain
living for over two years, giving successive
rosettes spaced out on the shoot, with bare
patches between them. Leaves 5–20 ×
1–2mm, linear to linear-oblong, acute,
glaucous, entire, with a narrow but distinct
translucent margin, hairless or with a very few
short marginal hairs, mainly at the base, with
9–19 lime-secreting hydathodes rather irregularly arranged near the margin; calcareous
incrustation present but seldom very conspicuous. Flowering stems 6–20cm, densely
glandular-hairy, dark red, with numerous
ovate to lanceolate, mucronate to apiculate
cauline leaves. Inflorescence narrow, spike-
like, with 10–20 flowers in well-developed
plants (fewer in those from exposed situations). Flowers sessile or with a pedicel not
more than 2mm long. Calyx with hypanthium
5 × 4mm, usually dark purplish-red (rarely
dull pink in plants from shaded situations),
sparsely to densely furnished with short,
glandular hairs. Sepals triangular, acute. Petals
2.5mm, elliptic-ovate to triangular-cuneate,
sometimes toothed at the tip, reddish-purple,
mostly concealed by the calyx, but a few
usually visible. Styles very short. Seeds 0.65 ×
0.4mm, ellipsoid but flattened along the side
bearing the raphe, black, with numerous short
to fairly long papillae, between which the
surface is rough but scarcely tuberculate; raphe
very inconspicuous. Flowering season: May to
July.

*ILLUSTRATIONS*:
* Sibthorp & Smith (1823, Plate 376), as
  *S.media*
  Engler & Irmscher (1919, Figure 111)
* Strid (1982, Plate 109)
* Köhlein (1984, Plate [23])
  Horný *et al.* (1986, Figures 59–62)

*RECOGNITION*: Among the red-petalled
members of this subsection, *S.sempervivum*

can be distinguished from *S.porophylla* and *S.federici-augusti* by its narrow leaves which are never widened towards the tip. From *S.stribrnyi* it differs in its unbranched inflorescence, and from *S.media* by the fact that in the latter some of the pedicels are much more than 2mm long.

*VARIATION*: Apart from general vigour and number of flowers the only variation of consequence is in the size and width of the leaves. The variants with the narrowest leaves have been distinguished as *S.thessalica* Schott, but they grade imperceptibly into the broader-leaved plants and cannot be effectively distinguished even at the level of a variety. (Such plants are sometimes known in gardens as f. *stenophylla*, a name of doubtful botanical standing.) An albino variant goes under the cultivar name 'Zita'.

*HYBRIDS*: Natural hybrids between this species and *S.federici-augusti* probably exist, but they have not been formally described. For a supposed hybrid with *S.scardica*, see under that species. Artificial hybrids have been made with *S.corymbosa* (*S.* × *gusmusii* Sündermann), *S.burseriana* (*S.* × *hofmannii* Sündermann) and with *S.stribrnyi* (*S.* × *bertolonii* Sündermann). The last is often wrongly listed as *S.porophylla* × *sempervivum*.

*CHROMOSOME NUMBER*: $2n = 12$ has been reported from south-central Greece, but the number differs so radically from all other counts for this section that it can hardly be accepted without confirmation.

*DISTRIBUTION* (Map 25): Apart from its single station in Anatolia, on the Bithynian Olympus (Ulu Dağ), *S.sempervivum* is confined to the Balkan peninsula. Here, however, it is widespread, extending from southern Greece northwards to the central Rodopi and the Rila in Bulgaria and in the west to 42°45′N in Montenegro. It is also found on the island of Thassos in the northern Aegean.

*HABITAT*: Rocks and stabilised screes, mainly, and perhaps entirely, on limestone. It ranges in altitude from 400 to 2900m, but is commonest between 1200 and 2500m.

*ACCESS*: Probably the most convenient place to see this species is in Yugoslavia at the Čakor pass, which lies on the borders of Serbia and Montenegro, on the road between Andrijevića and Peč. It is common on shady rocks about 80m above the road, on the southern side.

*CULTIVATION*: This presents no difficulty. It is probably best kept in a cold frame except in the spring, when it may be brought into the alpine house.

**33. *Saxifraga federici-augusti* Biasoletto,** *Relazione del viaggio de S.M. Federico Augusto re di Sassonia per l'Istria, Dalmalcia e Montenegro* 199 (1841)

*SYNONYMS*: *S.porophylla* of many authors, not of Bertoloni
*S.grisebachii* Degen & Dörfler
*S.montenegrina* Halácsy & Baldacci ex Engler & Irmscher

*HISTORY & NOMENCLATURE*: Discovered in rock-crevices at c.1500m in a narrow gorge not far from Cetinje (Montenegro) by Biasoletto early in June 1838. It was called after the King of Saxony, whom Biasoletto accompanied on his voyage; it should be noted,

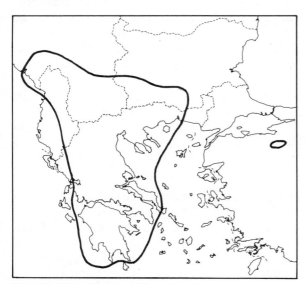

Map 25. Distribution of *S.sempervivum*

however, that the name was spelt as above (Biasoletto being influenced by the Italian spelling, Federico), and the change to *frederici* made by most modern authors is incorrect.

*TYPE*: *S.federici-augusti*. Not traced.

Subsp. *grisebachii*. In praeruptis supra fauces Treska-Schlucht ad Sisevo prope Ueskub, 28.4.1893, *Dörfler 177*. (Lectotype: Lund (**LD**), designated by Aldén & Strid (1986).) There are isolectotypes and syntypes in several other herbaria, including Kew (**K**) and Göttingen (**GOET**).

*DESCRIPTION*: Leafy stems rather few, short, terminating in flat rosettes, which are sometimes solitary but more usually 3–6 together, forming a low cushion. Leaves 12–35 × 3–8mm, obovate to spathulate, usually shortly mucronate, very glaucous, hairless except for a few short marginal hairs near the base, with a narrow translucent margin and up to 25 lime-secreting hydathodes near the margin and continuing almost to the base of the leaf; calcareous incrustation variable, but often fairly abundant. Flowering stems 7–20cm, covered densely in long glandular hairs. Cauline leaves numerous, oblong, covered in the basal ⅔ with short glandular hairs, hairless near the tip. Flowers 10–20, sessile or the lowest very shortly stalked, in a narrow, dense, spike-like inflorescence. The flowering stem, cauline leaves, bracts, hypanthium and calyx are always strongly coloured, varying from bright cherry-red to dark purplish-crimson. Calyx with hypanthium 6 × 4mm, glandular-hairy. Sepals ovate-oblong, subacute. Petals 2mm, obovate-cuneate, toothed at the tip, purplish-pink, usually concealed by the sepals. Styles very short, divergent. Seeds 0.7 × 0.4mm, ellipsoid but flattened along the side of the scarcely visible raphe, black, furnished with fairly long papillae, between which the surface is finely tuberculate. Flowering season: May to July.

*ILLUSTRATIONS*: Plate 14
Biasoletto (1841, Plate I)
Horný *et al.* (1986, Figure 51), as *S.grisebachii* subsp. *montenegrina*
* *Botanical Magazine* 136, Plate 8308 (1910)
* Strid (1980, Plate 25)
* Köhlein (1984, Plate [22])
Horný *et al.* (1986, Figures 49, 50)
All but the first two literature reference represent subsp. *grisebachii*.

*RECOGNITION*: From *S.sempervivum* this species can be distinguished by the leaves, which are always widened near the tip; from *S.porophylla* by its more numerous and much more brightly coloured flowers and by its larger leaves; from *S.media* and *S.stribrnyi* by its lack of pedicels; and from *S.corymbosa* by its purplish-pink (not yellow) petals.

*VARIATION*: There is considerable variation in the shape and size of the leaves, in the number of flowers and in the colour of the inflorescence. This permits the division of the species into two subspecies. Although subsp. *grisebachii* is usually recognised as a separate species (and universally in the horticultural literature) the arguments of Micevski & Mayer (1970) and of Aldén & Strid (1986) for including it in *S.federici-augusti* are convincing, and are borne out by a critical review of the material available at Kew.

(a) Subsp. **federici-augusti** (*S.grisebachii* subsp. *montenegrina* (Halácsy & Baldacci ex Engler & Irmscher) Micevski & Mayer). Rosette-leaves not more than 18mm, obovate-lanceolate rather than spathulate, being rather gradually widened at the tip. Inflorescence dark purplish-red, with usually not more than 15 flowers. Flowering stem fairly slender.

(b) Subsp. **grisebachii** (Degen & Dörfler) D.A. Webb, *Botanical Journal of the Linnean Society* 95:235 (1987). Rosette-leaves up to 35mm, fairly definitely spathulate, being suddenly widened at the tip. Inflorescence crimson to cherry-red, with up to 20 flowers. Flowering stem fairly stout.

*HYBRIDS*: Natural hybrids with *S.sempervivum* probably exist; see under that species. Artificial hybrids of subsp. *grisebachii* are numerous; it has been crossed by Sündermann with *S.sempervivum*, *S.stribrnyi*, *S.corymbosa*, *S.burseriana* and *S.marginata*; for details see Köhlein (1984) and Horný *et al.* (1986).

*CHROMOSOME NUMBER*: $2n = 26$ (for subsp. *grisebachii*; subsp. *federici-augusti* has not been counted).

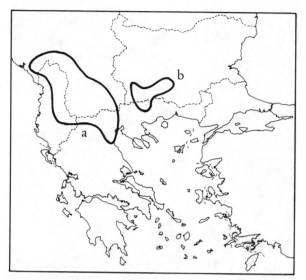

Map 26. Distribution of (a) *S.federici-augusti* and (b) *S.stribrnyi*

*DISTRIBUTION* (Map 26): The range of this species runs from central Montenegro south-eastwards through northern and eastern Albania, Yugoslav Macedonia and the western part of Greek Macedonia to reach its south-easterly limit on Mount Olympus. There is no very clear distinction between the areas occupied by the two subspecies, but subsp. *grisebachii* tends to grow at lower levels.

*HABITAT*: Limestone rocks. It grows mainly between 500 and 1700m, but has been recorded as high as 2600m.

*ACCESS*: Subsp. *grisebachii* is most easily seen in the gorge of the Treska, south-south-west of Skopje, in Yugoslav Macedonia, or, a little further west, in the Radika Klisura, about half-way along the road from Gostivar to Debar. We can give no recommendation for subsp. *federici-augusti*; all the localities we have traced are at fairly high altitude and difficult of access.

*CULTIVATION*: This is quite easy; the plants should be kept in a cold frame during autumn and winter and brought into the alpine house for spring and summer. It is almost entirely subsp. *grisebachii* which is seen in cultivation, and mainly as the cultivar 'Wisley', which has a large and particularly brightly coloured inflorescence. It is said to have come from Albania, but has doubtless been improved by selection in cultivation.

**34. *Saxifraga porophylla* Bertoloni,** *Journal de Botanique appliquée à l'Agriculture, &c.* 4:76 (1814)

*SYNONYM*: *S.media* (in part) of some authors, not of Gouan

*HISTORY & NOMENCLATURE*: Bertoloni's publication of the name is accompanied merely by a description without any localities or any information on the circumstances of its collection. In later publications (Bertoloni 1819, 1840), however, he makes it clear that he described the plant from a dried specimen collected about a century earlier by Pier' Antonio Micheli, who described it as *Saxifraga alpina parva, Sedi folio non serrato* in his catalogue of the botanic garden at Pisa.

The epithet presumably draws attention to the fairly conspicuous lime-secreting hydathodes on the leaf.

*TYPE*: Not traced.

*DESCRIPTION*: Leafy shoots short, terminating in distinct rosettes, fairly numerous and crowded together so as to form a dense cushion 4–8cm in diameter. Leaves 4–10 × 2–3mm, obovate-spathulate to oblong-oblanceolate, obtuse or shortly mucronate, glaucous, entire, with translucent margin and 5–11 lime-secreting hydathodes rather irregularly distributed near the margin; calcareous incrustation variable, but always visible on some of the leaves. Flowering stems 3–8cm, very densely clothed with long, mostly glandular hairs; cauline leaves numerous, with similar but shorter hairs over much of the surface, but hairless towards the tip. Flowers 4–7 (rarely up to 12) in a slender, spike-like inflorescence, the lowest often with a stalk up to 3mm long, the remainder sessile or with a stalk not more than 1.5mm long. Calyx with hypanthium 3–5mm, glandular-hairy, dull, rather pale pink, often tinged with green. Petals 1.5mm, obovate, sometimes minutely toothed at the tip, concealed by the calyx. Styles very short, erect. Seeds 0.6 × 0.35mm, ellipsoid but flattened on one side, with subacute ends, black, covered with short but prominent papillae, between which the surface is rough, but scarcely tuberculate; raphe inconspicuous. Flowering season: June and July.

*ILLUSTRATIONS*: Figure 20
  Fiori & Paoletti (1895, Figure 1677), as *S.media* var. *porophylla*
  Engler & Irmscher (1919, Figure 111)
* Touring Club Italiano (1958, Plate 439)
  Horný *et al.* (1986, Figure 52)

*RECOGNITION*: The species which *S. porophylla* most closely resembles are *S.media* and *S.federici-augusti*. From the former it differs in the fact that in most of the flowers the stalk is very short or absent, and also in the more definitely spathulate shape of most of the leaves. From the latter it differs in the usually smaller number of flowers and in the dull, washed-out pink colour of the calyx and hypanthium.

*VARIATION*: There seems to be very little, except in the number of flowers.

*HYBRIDS*: No natural hybrids are known, and artificial hybrids said to have *S.porophylla* as one parent are in fact to be attributed to *S. sempervivum*, *S.federici-augusti* or *S.stribrnyi*.

*CHROMOSOME NUMBER*: Although there is a report of $2n = 26$, the identity of the plant examined is uncertain because of the confused taxonomy.

*DISTRIBUTION* (Map 27): Fairly wide-spread in the central and southern Apennines. Its northern limit is at 42°50′N in the Monti Sibillini, its southern at 39°45′N in northern Calabria. It is, however, a local plant; Pignatti (1982) lists the mountains from which it has been recorded.

Figure 20. *S.porophylla*

*HABITAT*: Limestone rocks and debris, from 1100 to 2000m.

*ACCESS*: It can be seen, though not in great abundance, a short distance above the end of the road on the southern side of the Gran Sasso d'Italia. It is frequent on the summit ridge of Monte Mucchia, above Roccacaramanico (prov. Pescara), and on the northern face of Monte Alpi, near Latronico, from 1200m upwards.

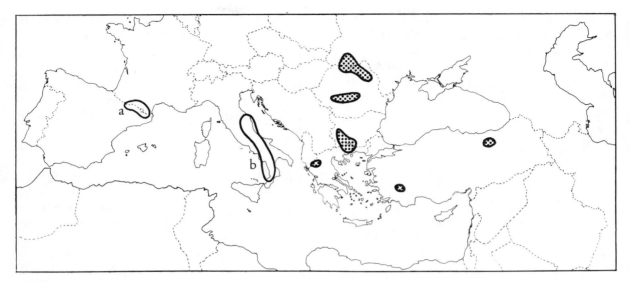

Map 27.  Distribution of (a) *S.media*, (b) *S.porophylla*, and *S.corymbosa* (shaded)

CULTIVATION: As with other members of the subsection this is quite easy, but it is not a very robust plant and is best confined to the alpine house.

## 35. *Saxifraga media* Gouan,
*Illustrationes et Observationes botanicae* 27 (1773)

SYNONYM: *S.calyciflora* Lapeyrouse

HISTORY & NOMENCLATURE: The species was discovered by Gouan in 1768 by a spring in the Val d'Eyne (eastern Pyrenees). It is difficult to interpret the epithet *media*; Gouan gave no explanation.

TYPE: Not traced.

DESCRIPTION: Stems freely branched, giving rise to short, crowded leafy shoots terminating in leaf-rosettes. New shoots arise as almost runner-like branches from the axils of the lowest leaves of the previous year's shoot, so that the pattern of growth approximates to that of section *Ligulatae*. Leaves 6–17 × 2–4mm, linear-oblong to oblance-olate, acute, somewhat glaucous, with a distinct translucent border, hairless except for short, marginal hairs in the basal half; lime-secreting hydathodes 7–17; calcareous incrustation slight to moderate. Flowering stems 3–12cm, with numerous cauline leaves, bearing a narrow raceme-like, or occasionally sparingly branched, inflorescence. Stem, cauline leaves, pedicels and flowers all densely glandular-hairy, reddish-pink, variably tinged with green. Flowers 2–12, all stalked; pedicels very variable in length, up to 25mm but often very much shorter. Flowers nodding at first, later erect. Calyx with hypanthium 7 × 4–5mm. Sepals 3.5–4mm, triangular-ovate, subacute. Petals obovate or almost circular, with a short, ill-defined claw at the base, about equalling the sepals, bright pinkish-purple. Styles very short; stigmas large. Seeds 0.65 × 0.3mm, brown, narrowly ellipsoid-oblong, ornamented with short, cylindrical papillae; raphe small but distinct, minutely tuberculate. Flowering season: May to July.

ILLUSTRATIONS: Plate 15
* Lapeyrouse (1801, Plate 12), as *S.calyciflora*
* *Botanical Magazine* 119: Plate 7315 (1893)
* Bonnier (1921, Plate 202)
  Harding (1970, p.7)
  Horný *et al*. (1986, Figure 48)

RECOGNITION: The only other species with distinctly stalked flowers of the shape characteristic of this subsection are *S.corymbosa* and *S.stribrnyi*. The former has yellow petals; the latter has somewhat larger and more spathulate leaves than those of *S.media*, but is more readily distinguished by its more freely branched panicle, of which the primary branches bear 3–4 flowers, as against 1–2 in *S.media*.

*HYBRIDS*: A natural hybrid with *S.aretioides* is discussed under that species. The only artificial hybrid recorded is with *S.vandellii* (*S.* × *clarkei* Sündermann).

*CHROMOSOME NUMBER*: The only count is of $2n = 26$, from a plant of unknown origin; it requires confirmation.

*DISTRIBUTION* (Map 27, p. 101): Confined to the eastern and central Pyrenees, from 0°20′E to 2°20′E. It is rather rare in the western part of its range, and here is recorded mainly from the French side of the chain.

*HABITAT*: Rocks, ledges and debris, usually on limestone or base-rich schists, and usually, but not always, in the shade. It ranges from 940 to 2600m. Engler & Irmscher (1919) give a record at 600m in the valley of the Aude, but this seems to have been of a plant washed down from above and not permanently established.

*ACCESS*: It can be found without much difficulty on low cliffs bordering the river Sègre above Saillagousse (Pyrénées-Orientales).

*CULTIVATION*: This is not quite as easy as with other members of the subsection; the plant survives but is slow to increase. It is best kept under glass and not attempted outside.

**36. *Saxifraga stribrnyi*** (Velenovský) Podpera, *Verhandlungen der k.k. zoologisch-botanischen Gesellschaft in Wien* 52:652 (1902)

*SYNONYMS*: *S.porophylla* var. *stribrnyi* Velenovský, *Flora bulgarica, Supplementum I*, 114 (1898)
*S.media* subsp. *stribrnyi* (Velenovský) Hayek,

*Denkschriften der kaiserlichen Akademie der Wissenschaften (math.-naturwiss. Klasse)* 94:168 (1919)

*HISTORY & NOMENCLATURE*: Discovered by Stribrný in 1893 in the central Rodopi, near Bačkovo, and sent to Velenovský. At that time all red-flowered plants of this subsection from the Balkan peninsula were usually regarded as varieties of *S.media* or of *S.porophylla*, and Velenovský put it under the latter. Four years later, however, Podpera recognised it as a distinct species, and this has been generally accepted. Its treatment by Hayek (1925), who reduced it to a subspecies of *S.media*, must be regarded as a retrograde step.

*TYPE*: S.porophylla var. stribrnyi, in rupibus calcareis m. Rhodope infra Bačkovo. *Stribrný*. (Holotype: Velenovský herbarium, Caroline University, Prague (**PRC**).)

*DESCRIPTION*: Leafy shoots numerous, crowded, terminating in well-defined leaf-rosettes. Leaves 12–25 × 3–6mm, oblanceolate or somewhat spathulate, obtuse or shortly mucronate, entire, with a conspicuous translucent margin, hairless except for a few, short, stout, tooth-like marginal hairs at the base, very glaucous, spreading horizontally or somewhat curved downwards; lime-secreting hydathodes 7–13; calcareous incrustation usually abundant. Flowering stems 3–9cm, with several cauline leaves, which, like the stem, pedicels, hypanthium and calyx, are densely glandular-hairy and deep crimson; usually branched from about the middle to form a fairly lax panicle of 8–25 flowers; pedicels variable in length, but some of the lowest usually at least 10mm. Sepals 2.5mm, triangular, obtuse. Petals 3–3.5mm, obovate-spathulate, toothed at the tip, slightly exceeding the sepals, deep violet-purple. Styles short, straight, erect. Seeds 0.75 × 0.3mm, narrowly ellipsoid, dark brown, ornamented with short, rounded, black papillae, between which the surface is irregularly roughened; raphe fairly conspicuous, very finely tuberculate. Flowering season: April to June.

ILLUSTRATIONS: Plate 16
* *Botanical Magazine* 139: Plate 8946 (1913)
Irving & Malby (1914, p.77)
Engler & Irmscher (1919, Figure 110)
Farrer (1919, Plate 38)
Horný *et al.* (1986, Figures 55-58)

RECOGNITION: Among the members of this subsection with pink or purple petals, *S.stribrnyi* is distinct in its stalked flowers in a freely branched panicle. Differences from *S. media* are given under that species.

VARIATION: A variant with white petals has been described from Slavjanka (Ali Botuš); otherwise the only variation is in size of leaves, height of flowering stem and number of flowers, which may be presumed to be dependent largely on the environment.

HYBRIDS: No natural hybrids are known, but *S.stribrnyi* has been crossed successfully with at least nine species or hybrids of section *Porphyrion*, and many of the resulting hybrids are widespread in cultivation. See Horný *et al.* (1986) for details.

CHROMOSOME NUMBER: $2n = 26$. This is an old count and requires confirmation.

DISTRIBUTION (Map 26, p. 99): Restricted to a small area of the Balkan peninsula, mainly in Bulgaria, but extending into northern Greece. In Bulgaria it extends from the Pirin to the central Rodopi, and thence southwards to Falakron in Greek Macedonia. The record from Timfi, in the northern Pindus, is erroneous, as is that from Albania.

HABITAT: Crevices of limestone rocks, usually in the shade, from 500 to 1600m.

ACCESS: *S.stribrnyi* cannot be seen without some climbing. The place of easiest access is probably the *locus classicus*, the 'red rock' on the Rodopi above the monastery at Bačkovo, south of Plovdiv.

CULTIVATION: As with other members of the subsection, this is straightforward. It can be grown on a scree, but is likely to be more successful under glass.

## 37. *Saxifraga corymbosa* Boissier, *Diagnoses Plantarum orientalium novarum* 1(3):17 (1843)

SYNONYMS: *S.luteoviridis* Schott & Kotschy
*S.chlorantha* Schur

HISTORY & NOMENCLATURE: First described by Boissier, from plants found by him in 1842 in south-western Anatolia. It was described independently eight years later by Schott & Kotschy from Romania as *S.luteoviridis*. For some years it was believed that Boissier's name was invalid, being antedated by *S.corymbosa* Lucé, a minor variant of *S.granulata* described from Estonia in 1823. It has recently been shown, however, that this was published as a provisional name and therefore has no validity, and that Boissier's name can stand.

The epithet *corymbosa* is not an altogether happy one, as the inflorescence, although it can be flat-topped, is almost as often narrow and elongated.

TYPE: Cadmi cacumen supra vallem Geyra in Caria. 1842. *Boissier.* (Holotype: Flora Orientalis herbarium, Geneva (**G**).)

DESCRIPTION: Stems sparingly branched; leafy shoots aggregated to form a fairly dense cushion. Leaves in more or less flat rosettes, 7–22 × 2.5–4mm, oblong-oblanceolate, acute to mucronate, somewhat glaucous, often tinged with pink at the base, hairless except for a few very short marginal hairs at the extreme base; translucent margin conspicuous. Lime-secreting hydathodes 9–15; calcareous incrustation slight at first but considerable on older leaves. Flowering stems 3–8cm; cauline leaves numerous, densely glandular-hairy, as is the flowering stem and the whole inflorescence. Flowers 2–12 in a somewhat crowded cyme, which varies from wide and flat-topped to narrow and elongated; pedicels mostly short, but up to 10mm. Calyx with hypanthium 8 × 5mm, ovoid. Sepals 4 × 2.5mm, triangular, subacute. Petals 3mm, shorter than the sepals and largely concealed by them, narrowly obovate, rather pale, slightly greenish-yellow. Styles very short. Seeds 0.65 × 0.4mm, dark brown, broadly ellipsoid, with numerous long papillae; raphe conspicuous, finely tuberculate. Flowering season: June to August.

Most Floras describe the flowering stem, pedicels, hypanthium and sepals as pale green, and this is true of plants growing in shade or semi-shade. In those growing in sunny situations, however, the whole inflorescence is deep crimson, as in *S.stribrnyi* or *S.sempervivum*.

*ILLUSTRATIONS*: Plate 18
   Mądalski (1962, Plate 1329), as *S.luteoviridis*
* Horný & Webr (1985, Plate 5), as *S.luteoviridis*
   Horný *et al.* (1986, Figures 53, 54), as *S.luteoviridis*

*RECOGNITION*: The combination of half-closed flowers with erect sepals and yellow petals is distinctive.

*VARIATION*: Apart from variation in the shape and colour of the inflorescence noted above, there is little, except in the shape of the leaves, which sometimes tend towards linear-oblong, sometimes towards spathulate. None of the differences is constant over distinct geographical areas, and the recognition of varieties does not seem to be justified.

*HYBRIDS*: The only natural hybrid described in *S. × paxii* Engler & Irmscher, from the southern Carpathians and interpreted as *S.corymbosa × paniculata*. No flowers were seen, and from the description it seems very doubtful that it was anything more than a very robust variant of *S.corymbosa*.

Artificial hybrids have been made with *S. stribrnyi* (*S. × schottii* Sündermann), *S.sempervivum* (*S. × gusmusii* Sündermann) and *S. federici-augusti* subsp. *grisebachii* (*S. × fleischeri* Sündermann), and are in cultivation (Horný *et al.* 1986).

*CHROMOSOME NUMBER*: The only count on record was made from a cultivated plant of unknown origin and requires confirmation; it gave $2n = 26$.

*DISTRIBUTION* (Map 27, p. 101): *S.corymbosa* occurs in the mountains of south-eastern Europe from the Ukrainian Carpathians to northern Greece, and also in two very disjunct areas of Anatolia. In the eastern Carpathians it extends from 48°30′N to 46°45′N; then after a gap it reappears in the southern Carpathians from 26° to 24°E. It is found on all the higher mountains of south-western Bulgaria, from the Rila to the central Rodopi, and extends over the border to Falakron in Greek Macedonia. It is also found much further west, on Timfi and Smolikas in the northern Pindus. Of its two stations in Anatolia, one lies in the south-west near Denizli, the other in the north-east, south of Trabzon.

*HABITAT*: Rocks and stony slopes in the mountains, usually, and perhaps always, on limestone. In Europe it ranges from 1500 to 2900m.

*ACCESS*: This species is easily found at 1600m on Pietra Arsa, the mountain on the western side of the road from Ploesti to Brasov, where it crosses the southern Carpathians north of Sinaia. It is also plentiful at 2200 to 2300m on the eastern side of Vihren in the Pirin Planina in south-western Bulgaria.

*CULTIVATION*: This presents no difficulty; it can be grown in a pan under glass or in semi-shade on the rock-garden.

## Subsection *Oppositifoliae* Hayek

Leafy shoots forming (in the European species) mats or low cushions; in some Asiatic species the cushions are rounded and dense. Leaves usually opposite. Flowers solitary or in small cymes. Sepals spreading, equalling or shorter than the petals and not concealing them. Petals pink, purple or white.

The subsection contains about 15 species, mainly in the Himalayan region, but with two species confined to Europe and one with a wide arctic-alpine distribution.

## 38. *Saxifraga oppositifolia* Linnaeus, *Species Plantarum* 402 (1753)

SYNONYMS: *Antiphylla oppositifolia* (Linnaeus) Fourreau
*Saxifraga caerulea* Persoon
*S.rudolphiana* Hornschuch
*S.murithiana* Tissière
*S.meridionalis* Terracciano
*S.pulvinata* Small
*Antiphylla pulvinata* (Small) Small
*S.blepharophylla* Kerner ex Hayek
*S.speciosa* Dörfler & Hayek

HISTORY & NOMENCLATURE: This species, although a mountain plant in central Europe, descends here and there to fairly low levels, and it can hardly have escaped the notice of the botanists of the sixteenth century. The first certain mention of it, however, is by Bauhin (1623) as *Sedum alpinum ericoides caeruleum*.

Linneaus' epithet draws attention to its most striking distinctive character, the usually opposite leaves, which it shares with only two others in Europe, though there are several species in the Himalayan region which also have opposite leaves.

TYPE: *S.oppositifolia*. The upper plant on sheet 575.32 in the Linnean harbarium, London (**LINN**) has been designated as lectotype (Webb 1987a).

Subsp. *paradoxa*. Above Héas, towards the Cirque de Troumouse, Hautes-Pyrénées, France. 22 May 1973. *D.A. Webb*. (Holotype: Trinity College, Dublin (**TCD**).)

Subsp. *rudolphiana*. Saxifraga rudolphiana mihi.—oppositifolia var. β Hohen. Auf den ... bei ... (Holotype: W.D.J. Koch herbarium, Leiden (**L**).)

Subsp. *blepharophylla*. Saxifraga blepharophylla. Stiria ... Hohenwart bei Oberwölz, 7000'. *Schiefer[?]*. (Lectotype: Kerner herbarium, University of Vienna (**WU**), designated here.)

Subsp. *speciosa*. Iter Italicum quintum. Aprutii. La Majella. In glareosis reg. alpinae. 2600-2800m. 4.VIII.1899. *G.Rigo 181*. (There are two sheets of this collection in the herbaria at the University of Vienna (**WU**); the one in the general herbarium is annotated 'S.speciosa Dörfl. & Hayek. Specim. orig.' in Hayek's hand and we designate this as lectotype. Another isolectotype may be found at the University of Göteborg (**GB**).)

DESCRIPTION: Stems woody, freely branched, usually more or less prostrate and fairly long, so as to form a rather dense mat, but sometimes shorter and semi-erect, so as to form a loose cushion. Leaves very variable in size and shape; usually 2–5 × 1.5–2mm, but sometimes up to 8 × 3mm or down to 1.5 × 0.7mm, oblong, elliptical or obovate, subacute, obtuse, or rounded at the tip, sometimes narrowed at the base to an ill-defined petiole, entire, but with stout, bristle-like hairs on the margin, at least towards the base, keeled beneath, concave above, hard and rigid, dark, dull green, usually crowded and overlapping, opposite (rarely alternate), with 1–3 (rarely 5) lime-secreting hydathodes; calcareous incrustation slight to moderate. Flowering stems 1–2cm, more or less erect, bearing a solitary flower and cauline leaves similar to those of the leafy shoots but less crowded. Sepals 2–4mm, ovate, with marginal hairs. Petals 5–12 × 2–7mm (rarely up to 20mm long), obovate to elliptic-oblong, pink to deep purple (rarely white), fading to violet. Stamens shorter than petals; filaments and anthers purple. Styles short, straight, divergent in fruit. Seeds 1.2 × 0.65mm, broadly oblong, brown, with the numerous papillae fairly short and conical in some variants, or low and dome-like with small tubercles in others; raphe inconspicuous. Flowering season: March to August, varying with altitude and latitude; the flowers usually appear within three weeks of the melting of the snow-cover.

ILLUSTRATIONS: Plate 17; Figure 21
  Reichenbach (1899, Plate 89)
  Ross-Craig (1957, Plate 15)
  Mądalski (1962, Plate 1331)
* Köhlein (1984, Plate [8])
* Moggi (1985, Plate 251)

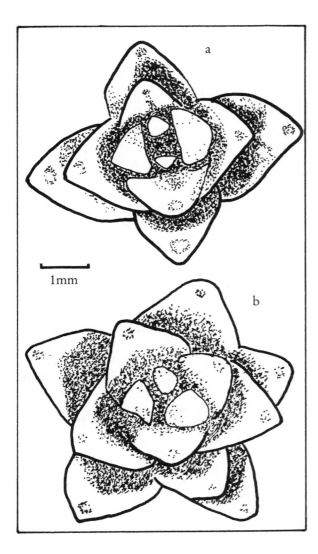

1mm

Figure 21. Apical view of leafy shoots of *S.oppositifolia*: (a) subsp. *oppositifolia*, with opposite leaves; (b) subsp. *paradoxa*, with alternate leaves

RECOGNITION: The small, crowded leaves and the solitary pink or purple flowers distinguish this species from all others in Europe except the other two members of the subsection. *S.retusa* differs in its shining leaves and the absence of marginal hairs on the sepals. *S.biflora* has soft, nearly circular leaves, narrow petals with wide gaps between them, and a conspicuous yellow nectary-disc in the centre of the flower, which is not present in *S. oppositifolia*.

VARIATION: As may be inferred from the synonymy and the description, this is a very variable species. Various attempts have been made to split it, notably by Hayek (1905), but his conclusions were trenchantly criticised by Irmscher (in Engler & Irmscher 1919). With regard to colour and size of petals, it is instructive to study the populations in such places as Mont Ventoux, in south-eastern France, where plants with every combination of light or dark with large or small may be seen growing together. Even among the small populations of north-western Ireland the contrast between the large, pale pink flowers of plants from Slieve Tooey and the small, deep purple ones from Ben Bulben, less than 50km distant, is very striking. Horticulturalists have naturally seized on large-flowered clones, which are known by various names, many of doubtful authenticity.

Nor do distinctions based on the number of lime-secreting hydathodes on the leaves, or on the presence or absence of glands on the sepal-hairs, seem able to bear the weight that is sometimes put on them.

Variation in characters of the leaf seems, however, to be more reliable, and we adopt here a division into subspecies based on leaf-characters; it follows fairly closely the scheme proposed by Engler & Irmscher (1919).

(a) Subsp. *oppositifolia*. The most widespread and most variable of the subspecies. Leaves usually oblong to narrowly obovate, but sometimes wider, with 1 (rarely 3–5) lime-secreting hydathodes; marginal hairs usually long and extending up to near the tip. Usually fairly lax in growth (except in very exposed situations) and with well developed flowering stems. Leaves all opposite, except occasionally on the upper part of the flowering stem, or, even more rarely, on single, strong-growing leafy shoots, where they may be alternate. Hairs on the margins of the sepals usually non-glandular. Petals usually 7-12mm.

(b) Subsp. *paradoxa* D.A. Webb, *Botanical Journal of the Linnean Society* 95:239 (1987). Like subsp. *oppositifolia* but leaves all alternate, except sometimes on a few very weak leafy shoots, on which they may be opposite; and often with 3 lime-secreting hydathodes. Flowers usually fairly large, variable in colour.

The contrast between this subspecies and subsp. *oppositifolia* is most easily apprehended by looking down on the tip of a leafy shoot: instead of the usual pattern of a cross the leaves form a conventional rosette (Figure 21).

(c) Subsp. *rudolphiana* (Hornschuch) Engler & Irmscher, *Pflanzenreich* 69 (IV.117):638 (1919). Leafy shoots very short, tightly compressed together to give a very dense, rather flat cushion. Leaves 1.5–2 × 0.7–1.3mm, oblong-obovate, subacute, with slender marginal hairs, often in the basal half only; all opposite. Flowering stems very short, almost obsolete. Petals 5–7mm. Sepals with glandular marginal hairs.

Very striking in its extreme form, by virtue of the minute, densely crowded leaves. Plants transitional to the typical subspecies can, however, always be found in the neighbourhood.

(d) Subsp. *blepharophylla* (A. Kerner ex Hayek) Engler & Irmscher, *Pflanzenreich* 69 (IV.117):638 (1919). Compact, often with columnar leafy shoots. Leaves 3–5mm, broadly obovate, with marginal hairs extending to the rounded tip, those at the tip being the longest; all opposite. Flowering stem short (about 5mm). Sepals with very long, non-glandular marginal hairs. Petals 5–8mm.

(e) Subsp. *speciosa* (Dörfler & Hayek) Engler & Irmscher, *Pflanzenreich* 69 (IV.117):639 (1919). Habit moderately compact. Leaves broadly obovate to almost circular, 4–5mm, with short marginal hairs mainly in the basal part; tip broad, rounded, with a wide cartilaginous margin. Flowering stem very short. Sepals with non-glandular marginal hairs. Petals 8–12mm.

Of the variants not treated as subspecies above, mention may be made of *S.murithiana* Tissière, with glandular hairs on the calyx, reported from the Pyreness, Alps, Sierra Nevada and Apennines, but always accompanied by subsp. *oppositifolia* or subsp. *speciosa*, with intermediates in which the glands on the sepal-hairs are minute or almost obsolete; also of *S.asiatica* Hayek, in which the marginal

hairs of the leaf are said to grade into teeth near the tip, but which Soviet botanists cannot distinguish reliably from subsp. *oppositifolia*; in fact many specimens from central Asia have neither hairs nor teeth on the upper part of the leaf-margin.

Mention should also be made of a curious variant described as var. *amphibia* Sündermann, *Mitteilungen der bayerischen botanischen Gesellschaft* 2:190 (1909). It formerly grew on the gravelly shores of the Bodensee (Lake Constance) at an altitude of only 400m, but now appears to be extinct. It was characterised by large flowers and leaves with usually 3 lime-secreting hydathodes. It was, however, more remarkable for its ecology than its morphology, as it flowered in March and was soon afterwards inundated by water from the melting snows, remaining under water until late summer.

The variation encountered in North America is described on p. 282.

*HYBRIDS*: The only hybrid recorded is with *S.biflora* (*S.* × *kochii* Hornung), but there are strong reasons for supposing that *S.nathorstii* Dusén, from Greenland, has been derived from the hybrid between *S.aizoides* and *S.oppositifolia* (see pp. 136, 283).

Map 28. Distribution of *S.oppositifolia*; for detailed distribution in Europe see Map 29

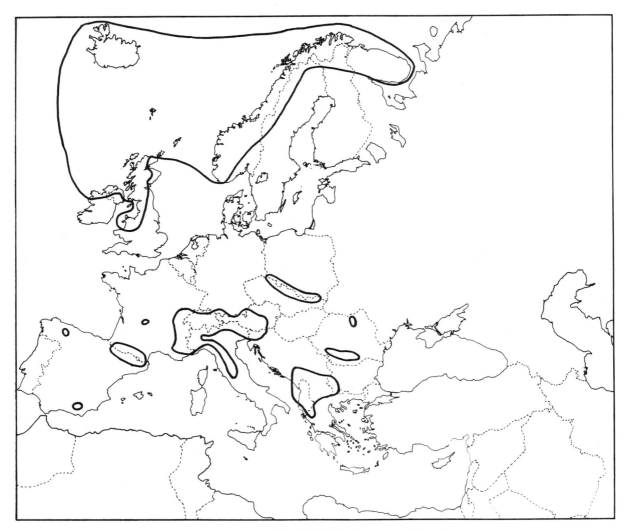

Map 29. Distribution of *S.oppositifolia* in Europe; for global distribution see Map 28

*CHROMOSOME NUMBER*: $2n = 26$ has been reported from several different parts of Europe, Greenland, North America and Wrangel Island, but there are also counts of $2n = 52$ from Spitsbergen, arctic Asia and North America, and one of $2n = 39$ from Greenland.

*DISTRIBUTION* (Maps 28, 29): This is perhaps the most widespread of all species in the genus. It has a typical arctic-alpine distribution, being almost ubiquitous in the Arctic, and appearing on the higher mountains further south in Europe, Asia and North America.

In Europe it is common in Spitsbergen, Iceland and the Faeroes, and northern and western Scandinavia, though apparently scarce in north-eastern Russia; it has, however, a few stations in the northern Ural. It extends rather locally and mainly in the mountains through Scotland, north-western Ireland and northern England to 42°N in Wales. In central Europe it is found on all the principal mountain-ranges except the Vosges, from the Riesengebirge in south-western Poland, through the Carpathians, to the whole range of the Alps and the Jura. Further south it is in the Pyrenees, the

Picos de Europa and the Sierra Nevada, and in the Apennines as far south as the latitude of Rome. It is rather scarce in the Balkan peninsula, but is found here and there from Bosnia southwards to south-western Bulgaria and north-western Greece.

In Asia it is rather sparingly distributed in the Arctic, extending southwards to Kamchatka, but it is also found in a large arc starting in the western Himalaya and running through the Tien-Shan and the Altai to the country east of Lake Baikal.

In North America it is very common in the Arctic (as also in Greenland) and it extends down the western coast to British Columbia, down the Rockies to Wyoming, and down the eastern coast to Vermont.

Subsp. *oppositifolia* is found virtually throughout the range of the species, though it is rare in parts of the Pyrenees and Apennines. Subsp. *paradoxa* is widespread in the Pyrenees, certainly from 0°25′W to 2°10′E, but seems to be absent from the two ends of the chain. Subsp. *rudolphiana* is found throughout the greater part of the Austrian Alps (though everywhere rather local), with two stations in Italy. Subsp. *blepharophylla* has a more restricted range in the Austrian Alps (12°50′ to 14°30′E). Subsp. *speciosa* is known only from the central Apennines.

*HABITAT*: In high latitudes it is found mostly in gravelly tundra, both in open and in closed communities; further south it grows mainly on mountain ledges, moraines and other gravelly rock-debris, more rarely on bare rock or in semi-open mountain grassland. It is somewhat base-demanding, but can be found on a wide variety of rocks, excluding only the poorest sandstones and quartzites. It descends to sea-level or near it as far south as north-western Ireland; in the main mountain-ranges of Europe it is commonest between 1600 and 2500m, but has been recorded as high as 3800m in the Alps, and occasionally descends river-valleys as low as 470m.

*ACCESS*: Anywhere in the Alps or Pyrenees (and to a large extent also in the West Highlands of Scotland) one can predict with confidence that on any suitable habitat where four or five other alpine plants can be seen, *S.oppositifolia* will be among them. On an alpine ascent, when the climber emerges from the woods, the first saxifrages to greet him are usually *S.paniculata* and *S.exarata* subsp. *moschata*; it is only rarely that the next 200m or so of the ascent does not yield *S.oppositifolia*.

*CULTIVATION*: This is fairly easy on a scree or in a pocket of the rock-garden, as long as the plant is given plenty of water and some shade.

### 39. *Saxifraga retusa* Gouan, *Illustrationes et Observationes botanicae* 28 (1773)

*SYNONYMS*: *S.purpurea* Allioni
*S.imbricata* Lamarck
*S.baumgartenii* Schott

*HISTORY & NOMENCLATURE*: Discovered in the eastern Pyrenees in 1770 by Costa and brought to the attention of Gouan, the species was independently found in the Maritime Alps by Allioni almost at the same time, and was published by him as *S.purpurea* a few months after Gouan's description had appeared.

The epithet *retusa* normally means 'slightly notched at the tip', but this is true neither of the leaves nor of the petals of *S.retusa*; Gouan seems to have used the word in a different sense.

*TYPE*: *S.retusa*. Not traced.
Subsp. *augustana*. Information from the herbarium at the University of Florence (**FI**) indicates that a syntype may be found there, although we have no further details.

*DESCRIPTION*: Stems woody at the base, usually short and much-branched, but occasionally long and straggling, bearing very short leafy shoots aggregated usually into a very dense and compact cushion, more rarely a mat. Leaves 2–4 × 1.5–2mm, all opposite, oblong, obtuse, entire, hairless except usually for some marginal hairs towards the base, sharply bent outwards near the middle, so that the lower half is more or less vertical, the upper half horizontal; lower half somewhat membranous, often purplish, concave on the upper (inner) side; upper half rigid and somewhat fleshy, keeled on the lower surface, the upper surface flat, of a shining dark green; lime-secreting hydathodes 3–5; calcareous incrustation sometimes prominent but often absent. Flowering stems usually rather few, 0.5–5cm, usually with a single pair of cauline leaves, usually glandular-hairy, bearing at the tip a small, umbel-like cyme of 1–3 (rarely 4–5) flowers. Sepals hairy or hairless on the lower surface, but without the stout marginal hairs seen in *S.oppositifolia* and usually in *S.biflora*, often dark reddish-purple. Petals 4–5 × 2–2.5mm, narrowly elliptical, widely separated, spreading horizontally so as to give a star-like flower, pinkish-purple. Stamens longer than the petals; filaments bright purple; anthers orange. Styles 3-5mm, straight, more or less erect. Seeds 1.1 × 0.6mm, ellipsoid, medium brown, wrinkled but otherwise smooth and without papillae or tubercles; raphe moderately conspicuous. Flowering season: May to July.

*ILLUSTRATIONS*: Plate 21
* Lapeyrouse (1801, Plate 18)
  Farrer (1919, Plate 37)
  Mądalski (1962, Plate 1332), as *S.baumgartenii*
* Moggi (1985, Plate 254)

*RECOGNITION*: The constantly opposite leaves distinguish it from all other European species except *S.biflora* and *S.oppositifolia*. From the former it is distinguished by its smaller, more rigid leaves, by the absence of marginal hairs on the sepals and by the stamens being longer than the petals. From *S.oppositifolia* it differs in its shinier leaves, by often having more than one flower on a stem, by its orange anthers and, again, by the absence of marginal hairs on the sepals.

*VARIATION*: The most conspicuous variation is in the presence or absence of hairs on the hypanthium and sepals. This is rather loosely correlated with the length of the flowering stem, the number of flowers and the habitat. It seems best to recognise two subspecies (treated by some authors as varieties and by others as distinct species).

(a) Subsp. *retusa* (var. *baumgartenii* (Schott) Velenovský, *Flora bulgarica* 194 (1891)). Hypanthium and calyx hairless. Flowering stems usually not more than 1.5 cm, with 1–3 flowers. Usually on siliceous rocks.

(b) Subsp. *augustana* (Vaccari) P. Fournier, *Les quatre flores de la France* 474 (1936) (*S.purpurea* Allioni). Hypanthium and calyx sparsely to densely glandular-hairy. Flowering stems up to 5cm, often with 3–5 flowers. Usually on limestone or other base-rich rocks.

*HYBRIDS*: None is known.

*CHROMOSOME NUMBER*: $2n = 26$.

*DISTRIBUTION* (Map 30): Widespread in the mountains of central and southern Europe, but local, and absent from large areas. It is found in seven distinct and widely separated areas: (1) eastern Pyrenees, westwards to about 1°30′E; (2) south-western and south-central Alps, from the Maritime Alps to the Val Maggia (8°45′E); (3) in a limited region of the Austrian Alps, in the provinces of Salzburg and Steiermark, from the Grossglockner region (12°55′E) to the Gosseck (14°55′E); (4) the Tatra and adjoining ranges on the border of Poland and Czechoslovakia; (5) the eastern Carpathians, in north-eastern Romania; (6) in the southern Carpathians (Transylvanian

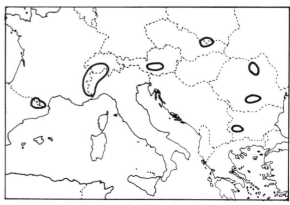

Map 30. Distribution of *S.retusa*

Alps) in south-central Romania; (7) the Rila mountains, in south-western Bulgaria. It is not found outside Europe.

Subsp. *retusa* is found almost throughout the range of the species, but is rare in the south-western Alps. Subsp. *augustana* is confined to the Alps of France and Italy, from the Maritime Alps to the Simplon region.

*HABITAT*: Rocks or scree, usually north-facing, often on exposed ridges or under the shelter of a boulder and therefore free from prolonged snow-cover, mostly between 1800 and 2500m, but descending to 1650m in the Polish Tatra, and ascending to 3150m on Monte Rosa. Subsp. *retusa* is found mainly on siliceous rocks; subsp. *augustana* on limestone or base-rich schists.

*ACCESS*: Subsp. *retusa* may be seen on north-facing slopes less than a kilometre south of the Col du Lautaret (Hautes-Alpes) in France. Subsp. *augustana* grows at the base of gneiss cliffs on the French side of the Col de la Lombarde, near the north-eastern boundary of the department of Alpes-Maritimes, and in the upper Gordalasque valley, east of St-Martin-Vésubie, in the same department.

*CULTIVATION*: This requires a little care, but is not really difficult in the alpine house. Subsp. *augustana* is said to be the easier, partly because subsp. *retusa* (unlike some other saxifrages which are calcifuge in the wild but tolerant in the garden) demands a fairly acid soil.

## 40. *Saxifraga biflora* Allioni,
*Auctuarium ad Synopsim methodicam stirpium Horti Regii taurinensis* 34 (1773)

*SYNONYMS*: S.*kochii* Bluff, Nees & Schauer
S.*macropetala* A. Kerner

*HISTORY & NOMENCLATURE*: Being very local and confined to high altitudes, this species escaped the notice of the early explorers of the Alps; it was discovered almost simultaneously by Haller in Valais and Allioni in Piedmont. Haller (1768) was the first to describe it, as *Saxifraga foliis imbricatis ovatis,*

*caulibus reptantibus bifloris*; Allioni gave it a binomial five years later, choosing the last word of Haller's description for his epithet. It is not very suitable, as the flowering stems do not always bear two flowers.

*TYPE*: S.*biflora*. Saxifraga biflora. Saxifraga caule reptante, fol. ovatis imbricatis, ramis bifloris. Hall.Em. III 189. (Lectotype: Allioni herbarium, Turin (**TO**), designated here.)

Subsp. *epirotica*. Greece, Papigno, by the river Voidomalis (to SW of Timfi Oros, prov. Ionnina). 4-6 VII 1975. *O.Polunin 13543.* (Holotype: University of Leicester (**LTR**); isotype: Trinity College, Dublin (**TCD**).)

*DESCRIPTION*: Stems woody at the base, usually prostrate; from these arise leafy shoots 3–8cm long, semi-erect or straggling, forming mats or loose cushions, hairless or sparsely to densely clothed with long, flexuous hairs. Leaves opposite, with lamina 5–9 × 3–6mm, broadly obovate or almost circular, tapered at the base to a broad petiole up to 4mm long, but often shorter. Lamina somewhat fleshy, much softer than in other members of the subsection, entire, rounded at the apex or occasionally shortly mucronate, with 1 (rarely 3–5) lime-secreting hydathodes; calcareous incrustation usually very scanty or absent. Leaves hairless on the surfaces but fringed on the margin of the petiole, and to a variable extent of the lamina, with hairs up to 1mm long. Flowers borne on the ends of shoots which in other respects resemble the sterile leafy shoots (there are no distinct flowering stems); usually 2–3 on each shoot, more rarely solitary, or very occasionally more numerous (up to 9). Calyx and hypanthium usually more or less hairy. Sepals 2–4mm, ovate, usually with some stout marginal hairs. Petals 5–10 × 1.5–6mm, oblanceolate to elliptic-obovate, dull purple or white. Nectary-disc conspicuous, yellow. Ovary half-inferior, but on passing into fruit the upper part enlarges more, so that the capsule is ⅔ superior. Seeds 0.7–1.1 × 0.35–0.55mm, oblong with obtuse ends, orange-brown, covered in low, bladder-like protuberances, between which the surface is very finely tuberculate; raphe inconspicuous. Flowering season: June to August.

*ILLUSTRATIONS*: Plate 20
* Lapeyrouse (1801, Plate 17)
* Touring Club Italiano (1958, Plate 122), as *S.macropetala*
  Huber (1963, Figure 132)
* Barnley (1967, Plate 35(5))

*RECOGNITION*: The somewhat soft and fleshy, nearly circular, consistently opposite leaves distinguish this from all other European species.

*VARIATION*: A variable species, chiefly in the number and distribution of marginal hairs on the leaves, the extent to which the leaves are crowded or spaced out below the flowers, the colour, shape and size of the petals and the number of their veins. Many Floras use these characters to distinguish from the type *S. macropetala* A. Kerner (subsp. *macropetala* (A. Kerner) Rouy & Camus), but there is no agreement as to the distribution of this taxon, nor are its supposed characters constant, at least in the western Alps. Moreover, some authors consider that most of the plants named *S.macropetala* are really *S. × kochii* Hornung (see under *Hybrids*); for more details see Webb (1987b). There is, however, a variant from Greece, and although only one plant of it is known, the differential characters are so marked and the geographical distribution so striking that its recognition as a subspecies seems justified. We therefore distinguish the following pair of subspecies.

(a) Subsp. ***biflora***. Leaves with few to many marginal hairs and with a single lime-secreting hydathode at the tip; calcareous incrustation usually absent. Lower surface of sepals and of leaves immediately below the flower sparsely to densely hairy. Flowers usually 2 or more on a stem. Pedicel very short, so that the lower part of the flower is usually overlapped by the leaves. Upper part of ovary hairless, or rarely with a single bristly hair.

(b) Subsp. ***epirotica*** D.A. Webb, *Botanical Journal of the Linnean Society* 95:237 (1987). Leaves with numerous stout marginal hairs and sometimes with 3–5 lime-secreting hydathodes; calcareous incrustation prominent. Lower surface of sepals and of leaves immed-iately below the flower hairless. Flowers all solitary. Pedicels long enough to raise most of the flowers clear of the leaves. Upper part of the ovary bearing several stout, hooked bristles.

*HYBRIDS*: Hybrids with *S.oppositifolia* appear to be fairly frequent; they are probably best called *S. × kochii* Hornung. No other hybrids have been recorded.

*CHROMOSOME NUMBER*: $2n = 26$ (subsp. *biflora*).

*DISTRIBUTION* (Map 31): Subsp. *biflora* is confined to the Alps, where it is widespread but local. It is commonest in the main chain of the central Alps, and to some extent in the south-west, but is rare in the calcareous ranges north and south of the main chain. Its southern limit in the west is on Mont Monnier, 55km north-north-west of Nice; and in the east it extends southwards to near Maloja, at the head of the upper Engadine, and to the western slopes of the Marmolada. Northwards it extends to about 47°15'N in the Allgauer Alpen and the Niedere Tauern. Its western limit is near the Col du Lautaret at 6°25'E; its eastern limit is at about 13°30'E in the Niedere Tauern.

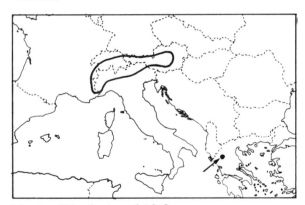

Map 31. Distribution of *S.biflora*

Subsp. *epirotica* is known only from one station in north-western Greece; for details see under *Type*.

*HABITAT*: Damp moraines and screes, usually with plenty of mud between the stones, and composed of schist, less often of limestone.

In nearly all of its habitats it is covered in snow at least until June. It is found mostly between 2000 and 3000m, but is occasionally washed down to a lower level, and it has been recorded as high as 4200m on the Matterhorn.

*ACCESS*: It can be seen in considerable quantity on the northern side of the Col de Galibier (Savoie), near the summit, immediately above the road, but is usually snow-covered until the second week in July. It can also be found on the lateral moraine of the Pasterzen glacier; this is easily accessible from the Franz-Josephs-Höhe, which is on a lateral spur of the main Grossglockner road from Lienz to Zell-am-See (Austria).

*CULTIVATION*: As with many snow-lie plants this is difficult, but perhaps not quite impossible. A plant has been successfully wintered out of doors in Dublin, but was allowed to die of drought in the spring. It should be brought under glass in the spring and watered liberally.

## Section *Ligulatae* Haworth (section *Aizoonia* Tausch)

Evergreen perennials (some species usually or occasionally monocarpic), with short, woody, usually branched rhizomes from which arise leaf-rosettes; these are usually crowded together so as to form cushions or thick mats. Leaves alternate, somewhat fleshy, leathery or stony, usually glaucous, linear to spathulate, usually without a distinct petiole, entire or finely toothed; lime-secreting hydathodes present, usually in sunken pits either in the margin or on the upper surface near the margin; calcareous incrustation usually conspicuous. Basal leaves hairless except usually for some marginal, multiseriate, non-glandular hairs at the extreme base; cauline leaves hairless or variably furnished with multiseriate, glandular or simple hairs. Flowering stems leafy, terminal; inflorescence a panicle, often large and many-flowered. Petals usually white, often with red spots,

rarely pink, yellow or orange. Ovary half-inferior to nearly fully inferior. Bulbils absent.

After flowering the rosette bearing the flowering stem dies, perennation being achieved in those species which are not monocarpic by offsets arising from the base of the flowering rosette; these offsets terminate in rosettes which flower the following year or later.

A fairly small section of ten species, almost confined to Europe (one species extends to Morocco and another to south-western Asia and to arctic and subarctic North America). Most of the species are very similar, but *S.mutata* and *S.florulenta* differ from the others in several respects, and each is placed in a separate subsection.

Many of the species and their hybrids are well known to gardeners as the 'silver' or 'encrusted' saxifrages.

## Subsection *Aizoonia* (Tausch) Schott

Leaves usually glaucous; calcareous incrustation usually evident. Petals white or pale pink, rounded at the tip. Ovary of 2 carpels.

### 41. *Saxifraga longifolia* Lapeyrouse, *Figures de la Flore des Pyrénées* 26 (1801)

*SYNONYM*: *Chondrosea longifolia* (Lapeyrouse) Haworth

*HISTORY & NOMENCLATURE*: The species was first distinguished in Sherard (1689) as *Sedum pyrenaeum pyramidatum longifolium elegantissimum*, and the epithet was taken by Lapeyrouse from this phrase. (This book is a catalogue of Tournefort's plants cultivated in the botanical garden at Paris; its author is not certainly known, but William Sherard seems the most probable. It is sometimes catalogued under the name of Tournefort, or of Hermann.)

*TYPE*: Plate 11 in *Figures de la Flore des Pyrénées* (Lapeyrouse 1801) is here designated as lectotype.

Figure 22. *S.longifolia*

*DESCRIPTION*: Stem very short, erect, woody, normally unbranched, bearing a single leaf-rosette which grows slowly but at maturity may be as much as 14cm in diameter and contain some 200 living leaves. After several years' growth a flowering stem arises from the centre of the rosette; during flowering the leaves die off, and by the time the seed is ripe the plant is dead. Very occasionally one or two lateral rosettes are produced which survive the flowering of the main rosette, but normally the plant is strictly monocarpic. Leaves rather fleshy, glaucous, and slightly convex above, pale green and bluntly keeled beneath, 6–11cm × 4–7mm, linear, sometimes slightly expanded below the tip, acute, entire; lime-secreting hydathodes numerous, situated on the margin and not on the upper surface; calcareous incrustation fairly conspicuous.

Cauline leaves and bracts similar but much smaller, and with numerous short, marginal, glandular hairs. Panicle up to 60cm long and 15cm wide, occupying, in well-grown plants, at least ¾ of the flowering stem, cylindrical, nodding; its primary branches up to 10cm long, each bearing 4–10 flowers rather crowded together at the tip; flowers usually numbering 400–800. Main axis and its branches densely glandular-hairy. Sepals obtuse, with a broad, translucent, papery margin. Petals 7 × 4.5–5.5mm, obovate, white, sometimes with crimson spots. Ovary nearly completely inferior; styles very short, divergent in fruit. Seeds 1.1 × 0.35mm, narrowly oblong with rounded ends, dark brown, uniformly covered with rather short papillae. Flowering season: June and July.

Figure 23. *S.longifolia*

*RECOGNITION*: The very large panicle combined with linear leaves distinguish this species from all others in the section except *S.callosa*. From this it differs in its lack of offsets and in its panicle branched almost from the base.

*VARIATION*: On the whole it is a very constant species; there is some variation in the extent to which the leaves are expanded at the tip and in the presence or absence of red spots on the petals, but it seems doubtful whether any variants deserve taxonomic recognition.

*HYBRIDS*: The rare Pyrenean hybrid with *S.cotyledon* is mentioned in connection with the latter. *S. × lhommei* Coste & Soulié (*S.longifolia × paniculata*) has also been described from the central Pyrenees, and might be expected to be more widespread as the two parent species often grow close together. An aritifical hybrid, raised in England in 1913 by crossing *S.longifolia* with *S.callosa* var. *lantoscana*, is deservedly popular with gardeners under the cultivar name 'Tumbling Waters'; it is sometimes called *S. × calabrica* in the gardening literature, but the name has no official status and is so inapposite that it must rest on a misunderstanding. Hornibrook (1926) also mentions hybrids with *S.cochlearis* and with *S.callosa × crustata*, but nothing is known of these beyond their mention in his article. It should be realised that the species in this section are so similar that guesswork as to parentage is extremely risky.

*CHROMOSOME NUMBER*: 2n = 28.

*DISTRIBUTION* (Map 32): *S.longifolia* is found throughout the greater part of the Pyrenean chain, from 1°W to 2°20'E. The fact that it is confined to limestone, however, means that it is absent from the central part of the main chain, and it is, in general, commoner in the subsidiary ranges, especially on the Spanish side. It is rightly regarded as the crowning glory of the Pyrenean flora, and it is very often accompanied by *Ramonda myconi*, the next most celebrated member. From the pre-Pyrenees of Catalonia it extends locally through eastern Spain (mountains of southern Catalonia, Sierra d'Aitana in Alicante province, and la Sagra in northern Granada), to reach its southern limit in the High Atlas of Morocco.

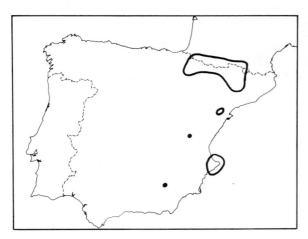

Map 32. Distribution of *S.longifolia* (also in the High Atlas of Morroco)

*HABITAT*: Limestone rocks and cliffs, mainly on vertical faces. The rosettes are pressed tight against the rock-face, and the inflorescence curves outwards and downwards in a form reminiscent of a fox's brush. The sight of a cliff with a hundred or more such inflorescences, especially towards dusk, is the most spectacular display that the genus can offer. In the Pyrenees it ranges from 800 to 2400m, but in the Atlas it ascends as high as 3500m.

*ACCESS*: One cannot travel far in the limestone country of the Pyrenees without coming across this species, but without a geological map it is difficult not to stray off the limestone. On the French side it grows near the road which ascends from Gavarnie west of the cirque. On the Spanish side there are points of easy access near Arguis (north of Huesca) and San Lorenzo de Morunys, some 40km due south of Andorra, and, much further south, on the eastern slopes of the Sierra de Miranda, north-west of Tortosa (prov. Tarragona).

*CULTIVATION*: This is quite easy, but some patience is required, as it usually takes six years or so for a seedling to reach flowering size. It might be worth while experimenting with a regime of heat in late spring and summer and cold in winter to accelerate flowering. In any case the sterile rosettes are so beautiful that one has mixed feelings in seeing them wither as flowering begins.

**42. *Saxifraga callosa* Smith, in J. Dickson, *Collection of dried plants* 3:63 (1791)**

*SYNONYMS*: *S.lingulata* Bellardi
*S.australis* Moricand
*S.lantoscana* Boissier & Reuter
*S.catalaunica* Boissier & Reuter

*HISTORY & NOMENCLATURE*: Allioni evidently knew this plant, but failed to distinguish it from *S.cotyledon*. It was left to Bellardi to do so, and he sent a specimen to Smith, whose name antedates the more familiar *S.lingulata* Bellardi by a few months. The epithet *callosa* refers to the deposits of calcium carbonate on the leaf-margins.

*TYPE*: *S.callosa*. The lectotype, designated here, is the specimen in the British Museum, London (**BM**) which accompanies Smith's description in Dickson's *Collection of dried plants*. This is a collection of dried plants bound together as a volume, each with a printed label.

Subsp. *catalaunica*. E.Bourgeau, pl.

d'Espagne, 1852. Saxifraga lingulata Bell. var. (Coss.). Mont Serrat. 11 juillet. *C.Moulin*. (Lectotype: Geneva (**G**), designated here.)

*DESCRIPTION*: Leaf-rosettes up to 16cm in diameter, rather ragged and less regular than those of *S.longifolia* or *S.cotyledon*, the flowering rosettes nearly always accompanied by smaller ones arising from offsets, and sometimes forming a crowded clump. Basal leaves 4–7cm (rarely 9cm) long, 2.5–7mm wide, linear, sometimes expanded just below the tip, hard, glaucous, entire, grooved above and keeled beneath, usually with a few long, non-glandular marginal hairs near the base; lime-secreting hydathodes numerous, sunk in the margin; calcareous incrustation slight to fairly conspicuous. Cauline leaves similar but smaller, oblong-oblanceolate, hairless except in subsp. *catalaunica*. Flowering stem 15–40cm, bearing a many-flowered but rather narrow panicle which occupies ⅖ to ⅗ of the total length of the stem. Primary branches of panicle hairless or glandular-hairy, very slender, each bearing 3–7 flowers near the tip. Sepals broadly oblong, obtuse. Petals 6–12 × 3–4.5mm, obovate to oblanceolate, sometimes with a long claw, but more usually abruptly narrowed at the base, white (turning lemon-yellow on drying), sometimes with a few crimson spots near the base. Ovary about ¾ inferior; styles short, straight. Seeds 0.85–1.15 × 0.45mm, oblong to asymmetrically ellipsoid, with one side straight, the other strongly convex, dark brown, covered with long whitish papillae, between which the surface is finely granular but scarcely tuberculate. Flowering season: May to August.

*ILLUSTRATIONS*: Figure 24
   Farrer (1911, p.216)
* *Botanical Magazine* 138: Plate 8434 (1912)
   Harding (1970, p.60)
* Köhlein (1984, Plate [14])

*RECOGNITION*: The only other members of the section with entire, linear or oblanceolate leaves are *S.longifolia*, *S.cochlearis* and *S. crustata*. From the first it differs in the constant presence of subsidiary rosettes and

Figure 24. *S.callosa*

the usually somewhat one-sided panicle, which does not extend as close to the base of the stem as in *S.longifolia*. From *S.cochlearis* it differs in the considerably greater size of the leaves and usually of the flowering stem, the greater number of flowers in the panicle (the lower branches bearing 4–7 flowers, as against 1–3, very rarely 4, in *S.cochlearis*) and the absence of leaves that can be called truly spathulate. From *S.crustata* it differs in the wider and usually longer leaves, and the much larger and more fully furnished panicle.

*VARIATION*: A rather variable species, especially in the shape of the basal leaves and the presence or absence of glandular hairs on the inflorescence. It seems best to recognise two subspecies, one of them with two varieties:
(a) Subsp. *callosa*. Inflorescence hairless or very sparsely glandular-hairy.
(i) Var. *callosa*. Leaves linear, scarcely, if at all, expanded near the tip.
(ii) Var. *australis* (Moricand) D.A. Webb, *Botanical Journal of the Linnean Society*

95: 239 (1987). Leaves oblanceolate, or linear with expanded, more or less diamond-shaped tip. This includes *S.lingulata* var. *lantoscana* (Boissier & Reuter) Engler, *Verhandlungen der k.k. zoologisch-botanischen Gesellschaft in Wien* 19:40 (1869).

(b) Subsp. ***catalaunica*** (Boissier & Reuter) D.A. Webb, *Feddes Repertorium* 68:209 (1963). Inflorescence, including the axis, bracts, pedicels and hypanthia fairly densely covered with glandular hairs. Leaves oblanceolate, fairly short.

*HYBRIDS*: Hybrids with *S.cotyledon* and *S.longifolia* are mentioned in connection with these species. A number of other hybrids, of which *S.callosa* is supposed to be one parent, are in cultivation. These include the cultivar 'Kathleen Pinsent' (probably *S.callosa × paniculata*) and a possible hybrid with *S.cochlearis*, mentioned by Köhlein (1984) under the invalid name of *S. × farreri*.

*CHROMOSOME NUMBER*: $2n = 28$.

*DISTRIBUTION* (Map 33): *S.callosa* ranges from north-eastern Spain through the south-western Alps, the Apennines and the Apuan Alps to southern Italy, Sicily and Sardinia. Subsp. *catalaunica* is confined to Spain in its typical form; it is recorded from Montserrat, north-west of Barcelona, and a few places in the pre-Pyrenees of Catalonia further north. In France subsp. *callosa* is mainly concentrated in the Maritime Alps, but it extends westwards to the ridge of Sainte-Baume, east of Marseilles,

and also to near Sisteron. These western outliers are transitional to subsp. *catalaunica* in that they bear a few glandular hairs in the inflorescence, but on the whole they come closer to subsp. *callosa*. In Italy it is found in the Maritime and Ligurian Alps, in the Apuan Alps, and fairly continuously throughout the Apennines from 44°10′ to 40°10′N. In Sicily it is recorded from a few stations in the northern mountains; in Sardinia only from near Oliena.

The plants of central and southern Italy, Sicily and Sardinia are usually assigned to var. *australis*, and those of northern Italy and the eastern part of the Maritime Alps in France to var. *callosa*. This distinction holds fairly good, if the existence of a number of transitional variants be granted. The plants of the western part of the Maritime Alps are often called var. *lantoscana*, but they differ so little and so inconstantly from plants of var. *australis* that it is difficult to maintain a taxonomic distinction. Admittedly it is rather strange that var. *callosa* should be flanked both on the west and on the south by the same variety, but specimens from Monte Alpi in the southern Apennines match those from the Maritime Alps so closely that no other conclusion seems possible.

*HABITAT*: Limestone rocks, usually more or less vertical. There are one or two records from siliceous rocks, but they require confirmation. It is found mostly between 1000 and 2000m, but it descends to 600m on Montserrat and ascends to 2500m in the Abruzzi.

*ACCESS*: Subsp. *catalaunica* is fairly common on Montserrat, and can be seen at close quarters from the cable-car which runs from the monastery to the summit; also by cautious peering over the edge from the summit plateau. Var. *callosa* can be seen in great abundance on the Italian side of the Colle de Maddalena (Col de Larche), near Argentera. Var. *australis* is frequent not far above the road on the northern side of Monte Alpi near Latronico (prov. Potenza), in southern Italy, and at 1800m on the eastern side of Monte Mucchia, above Roccacaramanico, in the extreme south of the province of Pescara (central Appennines); or again at Lantosque, due north of Nice.

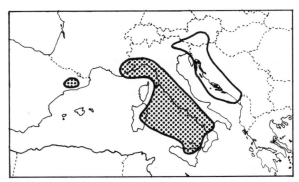

Map 33. Distribution of *S.callosa* (shaded) and *S.crustata* (unshaded)

*CULTIVATION*: As with other species of the section, this is easy. The species is not quite as decorative as *S.longifolia* or *S.cotyledon*, but is rather more regular in its flowering.

## 43. *Saxifraga cochlearis* Reichenbach, *Flora germanica excursoria* 559 (1832)

*SYNONYMS*: *S.lingulata* var. *cochlearis* (Reichenbach) Engler, *Monographie der Gattung Saxifraga L.* 237 (1872)
*S.lingulata* subsp. *cochlearis* (Reichenbach) Rouy & Camus, *Flore de France* 7:79 (1901)

*HISTORY & NOMENCLATURE*: Although it must have been known long before, Reichenbach (1832) was the first to distinguish this plant from *S.callosa*. For a long time opinion was divided as to whether it really was a distinct species, but the careful observations of Burnat (1901), who declared that he was unable to find truly intermediate plants, have convinced most modern authors that it deserves specific status.

The epithet *cochlearis* means spoon-shaped and refers to the basal leaves.

*TYPE*: Not traced.

*DESCRIPTION*: Rosettes numerous, usually rather small, 1.5–8cm in diameter, forming a dense, irregular cushion. Basal leaves up to 45 × 7mm, but usually very much less, spathulate (with a linear-oblong basal part and an expanded, almost circular tip) to oblanceolate, somewhat leathery and fleshy, hairless except for a few marginal hairs at the extreme base, which is usually red-tinted, very glaucous; lime-secreting hydathodes set in the margin, numerous, giving a conspicuous calcareous incrustation. Flowering stems 5–30cm (most often 12–20cm), reddish, branched in the upper third (rarely from below the middle) to give a fairly small, open panicle with very slender branches and pedicels; the number of flowers rarely, if ever, exceeds 60, and is more usually 15–25. The lower part of the flowering stem and inflorescence is fairly densely covered with glandular hairs, as are the small, linear-oblong cauline leaves and bracts. The upper branches and pedicels are often almost hairless, but there are usually a few very shortly stalked glands on the hypanthium. Sepals broadly oblong, obtuse. Petals oblong-obovate, 7–11 × 3–5mm, white, sometimes with crimson spots towards the base. Ovary about ¾ inferior; styles short, erect. Seeds 1 × 0.5mm, ellipsoid but with one side flat, medium brown, covered with low, rounded, blackish papillae, without tubercles; raphe fairly conspicuous. Flowering season: May to July.

*ILLUSTRATIONS*: Figure 25
* *Botanical Magazine* 109: Plate 6688 (1883)
  Harding (1970, p.60)
* Köhlein (1984, Plate [15])
* Finkenzeller & Grau (1985, p.101)

*RECOGNITION*: This species is likely to be confused only with *S.callosa*. From subsp. *callosa* it differs in the presence of glandular hairs on the inflorescence and cauline leaves, and also in the smaller size of its leaves and panicle. From subsp. *catalaunica* it differs in the scarcity of glandular hairs on the pedicels,

Figure 25. *S.cochlearis*

and in the shape of the leaves. In *S.cochlearis* the tip is always markedly expanded and rounded; in *S.callosa* subsp. *catalaunica* it is only slightly expanded and is somewhat acute.

*VARIATION*: There is a good deal of variation in leaf-shape, even on a single plant. Otherwise there is little except in stature and size of leaves. Variants known as *major* and *minor* are in cultivation, but they merely represent selected clones, and every intermediate condition can be found in wild populations.

*HYBRIDS*: The only hybrid is with *S. paniculata* (*S.* × *burnatii* Sündermann) which has once been recorded from the maritime Alps. 'Esther' is a popular cultivar probably of this parentage. Various garden cultivars have been interpreted as hybrids between *S.cochlearis* and *S.callosa* or *S.longifolia*, but the parentage is in most cases speculative, and there are no valid binomials for such crosses.

*CHROMOSOME NUMBER*: 2n =28.

*DISTRIBUTION* (Map 34): Except for a few small, outlying stations on the Portofino peninsula, south-east of Genoa, *S.cochlearis* is confined to a small section of the Maritime Alps, mostly on the French side of the frontier. From east to west it extends here over a mere 20 minutes of longitude, from the head-waters of the Rio Argentina (north-west of Triora) to the Val de Cairos, west of Saorge. Northwards it extends to near Tende, southwards to near the coast at Menton. Within these narrow limits, however, it is fairly frequent.

*HABITAT*: Shady rocks, mostly vertical, and usually on limestone. It has been seen on sandstone in a few places, but it may be that the sandstone is calcareous.

*ACCESS*: One of the best places to see this plant is in the Val de Cairos, west of Saorge in France. The rocks are separated from the road by a small river, but in any case *S.cochlearis* should not be collected from the wild in view of its very limited distribution and the fact that it is easily obtainable from nurseries.

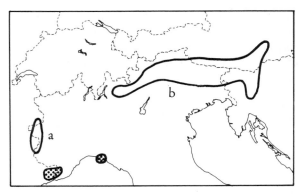

Map 34. Distribution of (a) *S.valdensis*, (b) *S.hostii* and *S.cochlearis* (shaded)

*CULTIVATION*: This is easy, and the combination of fairly large flowers, delicate red pedicels and neat foliage makes it a very attractive plant. It is best grown on a scree or in a pan under glass.

**44. *Saxifraga crustata* Vest, *Botanische Zeitung (Regensburg)* 3:314 (1804)**

*SYNONYMS*: *S.lingulata* var. *crustata* (Vest) D. Don, *Transactions of the Linnean Society* 13:391 (1822)

*S.incrustata* of several authors; the name is attributed to Vest but was not validly published by him

*S.crustacea* Hoppe

*S.longifolia* var. *minor* Sternberg, *Revisio Saxifragarum* 1 (1810)

*HISTORY & NOMENCLATURE*: As the synonymy shows, the determination of the status of this plant has been a slow process, but its recognition as a distinct species is now general. The name *S.incrustata* was published by Vest six months before *S.crustata*, but it is fairly clear that at that time he regarded it as a variety of *S.cotyledon*, and the name is therefore invalid.

The epithet *crustata* refers, of course, to the calcareous incrustation on the leaves, but this is no more marked than in several other species of the section.

*TYPE*: Not traced.

DESCRIPTION: Rosettes 2.5–8cm in diameter, numerous and crowded, forming a thick cushion. Rosette-leaves usually 10–25 × 2–3mm (rarely up to 50mm long), linear, scarcely, if at all, expanded at the tip, obtuse, entire or very obscurely crenate, curved downwards, hairless except sometimes for a few long marginal hairs at the base, glaucous; lime-secreting hydathodes numerous, sunk in the margin, usually with a heavy calcareous incrustation. Cauline leaves similar but much smaller, sometimes entire and hairless, but sometimes with glandular marginal hairs or marginal teeth or both. Flowering stem 12–35cm, glandular-hairy, branched from the middle or above it to give a small panicle of not more than 35 flowers; each primary branch bears 1–3 (rarely 4) flowers crowded together at the tip. Sepals broadly oblong or triangular, obtuse, hairless. Petals 5–6mm, obovate, white, rarely with some red spots. Ovary almost completely inferior; styles short, straight. Seeds 1.25 × 0.55mm, oblong-ellipsoid with rounded ends, brown, almost smooth but covered with slightly raised quadrangular areas; raphe inconspicuous. Flowering season: June to August.

ILLUSTRATIONS: Figure 26
* Sternberg (1810, Plate 1), as S.longifolia var. minor
  Huber (1963, Figures 125-126)
* Finkenzeller & Grau (1985, p.103)

RECOGNITION: The combination of linear, more or less entire leaves with a small panicle bearing glandular hairs and not occupying more than half the flowering stem is distinctive. It most closely resembles S.hostii subsp. rhaetica and small plants of S.callosa var. callosa, but in the former the teeth on the rosette-leaves, though low and inconspicuous, can always be seen, and the latter has a hairless panicle with more numerous flowers on each branch.

VARIATION: Apart from the length of the leaves and the flowering stem, the nature of the margin of the cauline leaves, and the presence or absence of spots on the petals, there is no variation of any consequence.

Figure 26. S.crustata

HYBRIDS: Natural hybrids with S.hostii (S. × engleri Huter) and with S.paniculata (S. × pectinata Schott, Nyman & Kotschy) have been recorded from a few places in the south-eastern Alps. The former sometimes appears in horticultural literature under the illegitimate name S.paradoxa.

CHROMOSOME NUMBER: $2n = 28$.

DISTRIBUTION (Map 33, p. 118): S.crustata has a fairly wide range in the eastern Alps and in northern and central Yugoslavia. Its western limit lies at about 11°30′E in the western Dolomites; from here it extends fairly continuously through the south-eastern Alps to Slovenia, and hence southwards through the mountains of western Yugoslavia to Montenegro and south-western Serbia. Most of its stations in the Alps are south of the main watershed, but there are a few isolated colonies in eastern Austria, reaching as far north as 47°30′N in Styria.

HABITAT: Rocks, screes and stony grassland, always on limestone or dolomite. It can range from 200m in the karst of Slovenia to 2400m in the Italian Alps.

*ACCESS*: *S.crustata* may be seen conveniently near the summit of the Passo di Pura, which is west-north-west of Ampezzo, in the province of Udine in Italy, or, further east, at 1000m on the western side of the Sella Nevea, 10km west of the Yugoslav frontier at the Passo de Predil. It is also conspicuous on the southern (Yugoslav) side of the Seeberg pass, not far from the summit.

*CULTIVATION*: This presents no difficulty, but it must be admitted that from the gardener's point of view this is one of the less decorative members of the section.

## 45. *Saxifraga hostii* Tausch, *Sylloge plantarum novarum* 2:240 (1828)

*SYNONYMS* *S.longifolia* of Host, not of Lapeyrouse
*S.elatior* Mertens & Koch
*S.besleri* Sternberg

Figure 27. S.hostii subsp. *hostii*

*HISTORY & NOMENCLATURE*: By earlier authors this species was, excusably enough, confused with *S.paniculata* and *S. crustata*, and, rather less excusably, with *S.longifolia*. Host (1827), in volume 1 of his influential *Flora austriaca*, described it as *S. longifolia*; the following year Tausch, who was the first to recognise it as a distinct species, renamed it after Host.

*TYPE*: *S.hostii*. Not traced.

Subsp. *rhaetica*. Vor der Dobretta bei Trafori in den botan. Garten verpflanzte Exe. 1872. *Kerner*. (Lectotype: Kerner herbarium, University of Vienna (**WU**), designated here; three isotypes are also in the Kerner herbarium.

*DESCRIPTION*: Rosettes 6–18cm in diameter, rather lax, separated by relatively long offsets, and thus forming a mat rather than a cushion. Basal leaves 3–10cm × 4–10mm, oblong to broadly linear, usually parallel-sided and scarcely, if at all, expanded towards the tip, very finely and sometimes rather obscurely

Figure 28. *S.hostii* subsp. *rhaetica*

toothed, hairless except for some long marginal hairs at the base, moderately glaucous, usually somewhat curved downwards towards the tip; lime-secreting hydathodes numerous, situated on the upper surface of the marginal teeth; calcareous incrustation fairly conspicuous. Cauline leaves similar but much smaller and with longer and with more acute teeth; the upper ones usually with some marginal glandular hairs. Flowering stem 25–50cm, glandular-hairy at least above, branched in the upper part (rarely from slightly below the middle) to form a lax or compact panicle, of which the lower primary branches each bear usually 5–12 (but occasionally only 2–4) flowers. Sepals 1.5–2mm, obtuse. Petals 4–8mm, elliptic-obovate, white, often with numerous purple-red spots. Ovary almost inferior; styles short, straight, divergent. Seeds 0.8 × 0.4mm, oblong with obtuse ends, dark brown, covered with low rounded papillae; raphe inconspicuous. Flowering season: May to August.

ILLUSTRATIONS: Figures 27, 28
Reichenbach (1899, Plate 78)
Huber (1963, Figures 121,122)
* Rasetti (1980, Figure 235)

RECOGNITION: The toothed leaves and the relatively short panicle mean that the only other members of the section with which this species is likely to be confused are S.paniculata and S.crustata. Subsp. hostii differs from S.paniculata in its larger size, leaves turned downwards at the tip instead of upwards, and usually by having at least 5 flowers on the lower primary branches of the panicle. In subsp. rhaetica the toothing may be so obscure that confusion with S.crustata is possible, but the former usually has wider leaves, and the lime-secreting hydathodes are on the upper surface (though very close to the margin) and not inserted in the margin itself.

VARIATION: This can for the most part be accommodated by the recognition of two fairly distinct subspecies. They overlap slightly in geographical range, but intermediates are not common.

(a) Subsp. hostii. Basal leaves up to 10cm long and usually at least 6mm wide, with a very obtuse, rounded tip; marginal teeth fairly distinct. Primary branches of panicle usually with at least 5 flowers.

(b) Subsp. rhaetica (Kerner) Braun-Blanquet in Hegi, Illustrierte Flora von Mitteleuropa 4:590 (1922). Basal leaves not more than 5cm long, 3–7mm wide, tapered to an acute tip; marginal teeth often obscure. Primary branches of panicle with 3–5 flowers.

Attempts have been made to distinguish within subsp. hostii a var. altissima (Kerner) Engler & Irmscher, Pflanzenreich 69 (IV, 117):516 (1919); it is supposedly distinguished by its larger leaves, taller flowering stem and larger panicle. It is said to be found in the northern part of the range (only in Austria). But plants conforming to these specifications can be found on Monte Grappa and elsewhere in the Italian Alps, and intermediates are frequent, so that there seems to be little to be gained by recognising the variety.

HYBRIDS: Hybrids with S.paniculata (S. × churchillii Huter) have been recorded from Italy; see under S.crustata for another.

CHROMOSOME NUMBER: 2n = 28.

DISTRIBUTION (Map 34, p.120): S.hostii is found only in the eastern Alps, where it ranges from 9°25′ to 15°10′E. Its greatest extension from north to south lies at the eastern end of its range, from the Hochshwab (47°35′N) in northern Styria to 45°35′N in the karst of Slovenia. Subsp. rhaetica occupies a limited area of the Italian Alps eastwards to 10°45′E; it comes very close to the Swiss border near the Stelvio pass, but does not seem to cross it. There is a small zone of overlap between the two subspecies in the region of the Ortles, but from here eastwards only subsp. hostii is found. It extends, mainly in the Italian Alps, but to some extent also in south-eastern Austria and northern and western Slovenia to the eastern limit of the species.

S.hostii has never been recorded from Hungary, but there are two specimens in the Rechinger herbarium at Geneva (G), labelled as *S.paniculata* or one of its synonyms, which look very like *S.hostii* (*Boros*, 12th June 1922; and *Degen*, 5th June 1927); both were collected near Lillafüred in the Bükk mountains in northern Hungary. We have also seen specimens in Budapest (**BP**) from a short distance to the west (from northern Hungary and from southern Slovakia), some of which look like typical *S.hostii*, others transitional to *S.paniculata*. The distribution of *S.hostii* in east-central Europe and the constancy of the characters which separate it from *S.paniculata* clearly demand further investigation.

*HABITAT*: Limestone or dolomite rocks, rarely on scree or debris. It is most often seen between 1400 and 2500m, but can descend locally to 400m.

*ACCESS*: A good place to see subsp. *rhaetica* is on the eastern side of the Crocedomini pass, between Bagolino and Breno in the province of Brescia, Italy. Subsp. *hostii* grows in some quantity on Monte Grappa, where the provinces of Belluno, Padova and Vicenza meet.

*CULTIVATION*: As with most members of the section, this is easy. A robust clone of subsp. *hostii* should be selected; in some gardens it is vigorous enough to form an effective edging to a border.

## 46. *Saxifraga paniculata* Miller, *The Gardener's Dictionary*, 8th edn, art. *Saxifraga*, no.3 (1768)

*SYNONYMS*: *S.aizoon* Jacquin
*Chondrosea aizoon* (Jacquin) Haworth
*S.recta* Lapeyrouse

*HISTORY & NOMENCLATURE*: Universally known as *S.aizoon* Jacquin until Fuchs (1960) showed that the earlier name *S.paniculata* Miller, previously regarded as a synonym of *S.cotyledon* Linnaeus, was really attributable to this species. Fuch's argument is in some of its details open to objection, but as it has been generally accepted it seems best not to re-open the matter now. The epithet *paniculata*, chosen by Miller, is no more descriptive of this species than of any other in the section.

Such a widespread plant, which descends to fairly low altitudes, must have been known to the botanists of the sixteenth century, but it is difficult to decide which of their polynomials refer to this species, and which to *S.cotyledon* or *S.callosa*. The earliest description and figure which seem fairly certainly to indicate *S. paniculata* are those of Valerius Cordus (1561), as *Aizoon serratum, quod foliis albicantibus et serratis montium provenit*; fischzung *aliqui vocant*.

*TYPE*: We designate as lectotype Miller's only known specimen of *S.paniculata*, which was collected from the Chelsea Garden in 1727. It is to be found in volume 244, folio 29, of the Sloane herbarium, British Museum (Natural History), London (**BM**). It is annotated by Miller "*Saxifraga sedi folio angustiore serrato* Tourn. 252. *Sedum serratum* J.B. Ray, Hist. vol.2, p.1045". Tournefort's phrase-name, unfortunately, is cited as a synonym of *S.cotyledon* by Miller in his *Gardener's Dictionary*, although Miller's own descriptions appear to conform to current concepts of the two species.

*DESCRIPTION*: Rosettes usually numerous, variable in size (1-9cm in diameter), moderately crowded, so as to give a fairly low cushion. Basal leaves very variable in size and shape, most commonly 8–35 × 4–5mm, but occasionally as small as 5 × 1.5mm or as large as 50 × 7mm, obovate-oblong to broadly linear, obtuse or somewhat acute, glaucous, stiff and somewhat fleshy; margin boldly or obscurely toothed, with whitish teeth directed towards the tip, at the base of the leaf passing into long marginal hairs. The leaves are otherwise hairless. Lime-secreting hydathodes numerous, situated on the upper surface at the base of each tooth; calcareous incrustation usually conspicuous. The leaves have a tendency to curve upwards, so that each basal cluster takes the form of a hemispherical mass rather than a flat rosette. Cauline leaves similar but smaller, and sometimes with a few glandular hairs. Flowering stem 6–40cm, branched above (very rarely below) the middle to form a fairly narrow panicle, of which the primary branches bear 1–3 (rarely 4) flowers. The stem and its branches, and the pedicels, usually bear some glandular hairs; these are very variable in frequency, length and distribution, and are occasionally absent. Sepals oblong, obtuse, hairless. Petals 3–6 × 2–4mm, elliptic-obovate, white, rarely pink or pale yellow, often with reddish-purple spots. Ovary ¾ inferior; styles short, straight. Seeds 0.9 × 0.4mm, narrowly ovoid, pointed at one end, covered with very low protuberances intermediate between papillae and tubercles; raphe conspicuous. Flowering season: May to August.

ILLUSTRATIONS: Figure 29
   Huber (1963, Figures 123,124)
 * Rasetti (1980, Plate 241)
 * Moggi (1985, Plate 252)
 * Finkenzeller & Grau (1985, p.103)

RECOGNITION: The combination of small panicle and toothed leaves distinguishes S.paniculata from all others in the section except S.hostii, from which it differs in very rarely having more than 3 flowers on any primary branch of the panicle, and in having its basal leaves markedly curved upwards. Variants with narrow leaves in which the teeth are poorly developed can be confused with S. crustata, but close examination shows that the lime-secreting hydathodes are on the upper surface of the leaf and not, as in S.crustata, set into the actual margin.

VARIATION: A variable species, but not as much as the vast synonymy would suggest. Variation in the shape and size of leaf is the most conspicuous; this has been dealt with above. There is also some variation in the shape and size of the marginal teeth and in the length of the runners giving rise to new rosettes. Variants with pink or yellow petals or with hairs on the lower surface of the leaves are, at least in Europe, very local and rare.

Figure 29. S.paniculata

In a variable species as common and as widespread as is *S.paniculata* one would expect the pattern of variation to be such as to admit the recognition of a number of subspecies, but this is not so. The only variant which is generally accorded subspecific status is subsp. *cartilaginea* (Willdenow) D.A. Webb, *Feddes Repertorium* 68:208 (1963). This is confined to the Caucasus, and does not reach Europe; it is distinguished chiefly by the more or less acuminate basal leaves (see p. 263). Plants in the Balkan peninsula, with leaves more distinctly acute than in plants from central Europe, show

some approach to it; they have been distinguished as *S.aizoon* var. *orientalis* Engler, *Monographie der Gattung Saxifraga L.* 245 (1872). One of the most distinct and attractive European variants is that known in the horticultural literature as *S.aizoon* var. *baldensis* Farrer, *Gardener's Chronicle* 49:251 (1911), from Monte Baldo in northern Italy. It has neat, closely crowded rosettes with leaves about 5 × 1.5mm.

*HYBRIDS*: Hybrids have been recorded between *S.paniculata* and all other species of

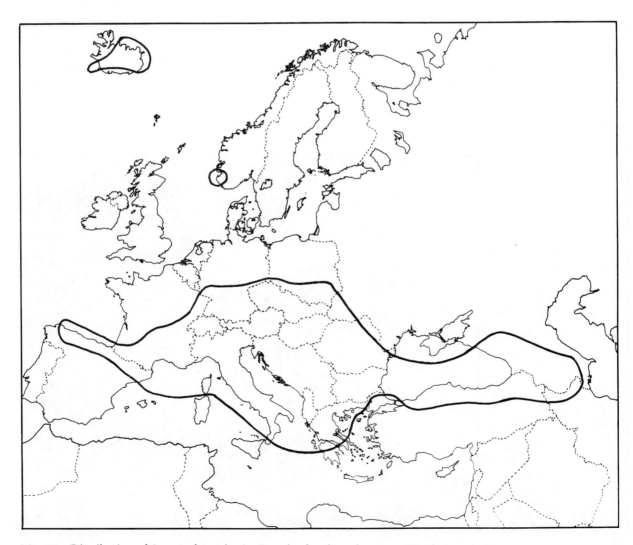

Map 35. Distribution of *S.paniculata* (also in Greenland and north-eastern North America)

subsection *Aizoonia* except *S.valdensis*. Intersectional hybrids with *S.aizoides*, *S.corymbosa*, *S.cuneifolia* and (probably) *S.spathularis* have also been reported. In all cases they are discussed in connection with the other parent.

*CHROMOSOME NUMBER*: $2n = 28$.

*DISTRIBUTION* (Map 35): This species is widespread in Europe, not only in the major mountain ranges, but also in parts of the hill-country of central Europe. From the Massif Central of France, the Rhineland, the Fichtelgebirge in north-eastern Bavaria, the hill-country of Bohemia and Moravia, the Sudeten mountains and the western Carpathians it extends southwards to northern Spain, almost the whole range of the Alps, Corsica, the Apennines southwards to Calabria, the eastern and southern Carpathians, and the mountains of the Balkan peninsula as far as the northern Peloponnese. It is also found in western Norway and Iceland, though here it is rare and local. Outside Europe it extends to Greenland and to north-eastern North America, south-westwards to Minnesota. It also grows in south-western Asia (the Caucasus, northern Anatolia and northern Iran).

*HABITAT*: *S.paniculata* is primarily a plant of rock ledges and crevices, but it can also be seen on stony grassland. In the mountains it tends to favour exposed ridges where the snow-cover is slight. It is usually reputed to be somewhat calcicole, and in many parts of the Alps is rather commoner on limestone and base-rich schists than on siliceous rocks, but there are some regions, such as the Dolomites and Pirin Planina in Bulgaria, where it is plentiful on granite or other igneous rocks but absent from the adjoining limestone. In its most northern stations it descends to low levels, but has been recorded as high as 3415m in the Alps; generally speaking it is commonest from 1200 to 2200m.

*ACCESS*: The plant is so common in the major mountain-ranges of Europe that no directions are needed for finding it. It usually grows scattered in fairly small colonies, but occasionally rises to subdominance on stony

slopes. A very striking example of this can be seen on a south-facing slope in the Val Minor, near the Bernina pass in eastern Switzerland.

*CULTIVATION*: This is a very tolerant species and can be grown in a variety of habitats. It is best seen as a large clump in a corner of the rock-garden. *S.aizoon* var. *baldensis* is worth growing in a pan.

### 47. *Saxifraga cotyledon* Linnaeus, *Species Plantarum* 398 (1753)

*SYNONYMS*: *S.pyramidalis* Lapeyrouse
*Chondrosea pyramidalis* (Lapeyrouse) Haworth
*S.montavoniensis* A. Kerner ex Kolb

*HISTORY & NOMENCLATURE*: The epithet *cotyledon* is derived from a generic name which dates back to classical times; it was variously used in the sixteenth century to denote a considerable number of succulent plants, including many now assigned to *Umbilicus* and *Saxifraga*. Linnaeus used the epithet in a wide sense, and probably included under it *S.hostii* and *S.paniculata*, but it is not easy to identify with any certainty the five varieties which he listed.

The plant, being showy and growing at moderate altitudes not too far from some of the Italian centres of learning, was known at an early date, and was established in cultivation in southern Germany by 1613. The earliest published description and figure we can trace is that of Gesner (1541, p. 27, Plate 13, Figure 28).

*TYPE*: The left-hand specimen on sheet 575.1 in the Linnean herbarium, London (**LINN**), has been designated as lectotype (Webb 1987a).

*DESCRIPTION*: The plant usually consists of a large rosette of flowering size (7–12cm in diameter), often (though not always) accompanied by small daughter-rosettes which arose from short runners the previous year. The runners themselves die off fairly early, leaving the daughter-rosettes isolated, so that large clumps of rosettes, such as are

Figure 30. *S.cotyledon*

Figure 31. *S.cotyledon*

petiole, very finely toothed except at the base, where the teeth are replaced by fairly long, non-glandular hairs, usually with a few intermediate structures at the transition. In the centre of each tooth is a lime-secreting hydathode, surrounded by a constant, but small and fairly inconspicuous calcareous incrustation. Cauline leaves similar to the basal, but much smaller, and with the teeth replaced, except near the tip, by short glandular hairs. Flowering stem up to 70cm, stout, branched often from very near the base, and always from the middle or below it, to form a pyramidal panicle up to 25cm wide at the base. Each primary branch usually has 8–40 flowers, and the total number often exceeds 1000. Inflorescence, pedicels and hypanthium glandular-hairy. Sepals 3mm, ovate-lanceolate, obtuse, more or less hairless, reddish. Petals 7–10mm, oblanceolate, narrowed to a claw-like base which often bears marginal hairs, white, occasionally with red spots or veins. Ovary almost completely inferior; styles short, erect. Seeds 0.85 × 0.4mm, ellipsoid, dark brown, covered all over with fine tubercles, and on most of the surface with low, rounded papillae. Flowering season: June and July.

*ILLUSTRATIONS*: Figures 30, 31
   Huber (1963, Figure 120)
   Harding (1970, p. 50)
\* Rasetti (1980, Plate 234)
\* Köhlein (1984, Plate [16])

*RECOGNITION*: The broad, regularly and finely toothed leaves distinguish this species from all others in the section, except perhaps *S.hostii* and *S.paniculata*. From these it differs in its panicle with much more numerous flowers and occupying at least half the flowering stem; also in its petals narrowed to a claw-like base.

*VARIATION*: There is very little, except in size of rosette and panicle, amount of red pigment in the flowers, and to some extent breadth of basal leaves. Variants are known with some of the flowers replaced by small leaf-rosettes, but they are very rare. Attempts

characteristic of *S.paniculata*, are never seen. Basal leaves firm and slightly fleshy, scarcely glaucous, 2–8cm × 6–20mm, oblong to oblanceolate or spathulate, somewhat narrowed towards the base but without a distinct

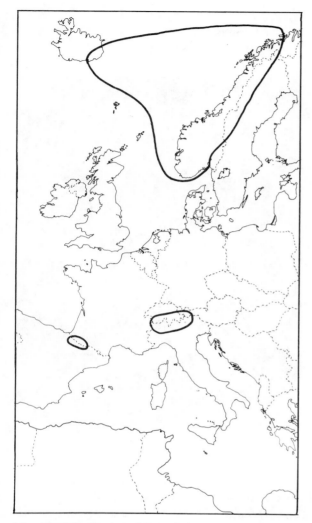

Map 36. Distribution of *S.cotyledon*

Also dubious is the alleged hybrid with *S.aizoides* in Norway.

*CHROMOSOME NUMBER*: $2n = 28$.

*DISTRIBUTION* (Map 36): *S.cotyledon* is found in three distinct regions of Europe: Scandinavia and Iceland; the central Pyrenees; and the Alps. It is frequent throughout most of Norway, mainly in the mountains, up to 1300m, but also with a number of lowland stations, and it extends locally into western Sweden. In Iceland it is local and confined to the south-east. In the Pyrenees it is rare, and extends only from Panticosa in the west to near Luchon in the east (0°15′W to 0°30′E). Records from further east are probably erroneous.

In the Alps it is found mainly in the central part, ranging from near Chamonix in the west to near Lake Garda in the east, but it is much commoner south of the main watershed than north of it. Its southern limit lies near Ivrea, in the lower part of the Val d'Aosta (45°25′N); northwards it reaches almost to 47°N in the south-eastern part of the Vorarlberg. Its stations in France, Austria and northern Switzerland are, however, few and far between.

*HABITAT*: Siliceous rocks, usually more or less vertical. It is especially characteristic of nutrient-poor rocks with a scanty flora. In the Alps it ranges from 300 to 2600m, but is commonest around 1500m.

*ACCESS*: It is common enough in Norway, and it can hardly be missed by the road up the western coast; in the Alps it is frequent and conspicuous by almost all the roads which descend into Italy from the major passes, from the Little St Bernard to the Maloja, being especially abundant in the Val d'Aosta and the Val Bregaglia (below Maloja).

*CULTIVATION*: This presents no difficulty. In spite of its calcifuge habit it will tolerate moderately calcareous soils. It seems to do better out of doors than in the alpine house, and though its leaf-rosettes are not as decorative as those of *S.longifolia* its panicle is of a splendour unequalled in the genus.

have been made to assign separate specific names to the plants of the three major areas, but they are based on very trivial and inconstant differences.

*HYBRIDS*: Hybrids with *S.paniculata* (*S.* × *gaudinii* Bruegger) are fairly frequent in the Alps; they have also been reported rarely from the Pyrenees and Norway. *S.cotyledon* × *longifolia* (*S.* × *superba* Rouy & Camus) has been reported once from the Pyrenees, and *S.callosa* × *cotyledon* (*S.* × *macnabiana* Lindsay) from the Edinburgh Botanic Garden. Photographs of the latter, however, throw some doubt on its supposed parentage.

## 48. *Saxifraga valdensis* De Candolle, in Lamarck & De Candolle, *Flore Française*, 3rd edn, 5:517 (1815)

*SYNONYM*: *S.compacta* Sternberg

*HISTORY & NOMENCLATURE*: The first mention in print of a plant that can be confidently identified with this species is by Willdenow who, in volume 2 of the fourth edition of *Species Plantarum* (Willdenow 1799), described it briefly as an unnamed variety of *S.caesia* Linnaeus; whether he had seen the plant or whence he gained his information is not clear. Its status as a species has, however, not been challenged since its adoption at specific level by Seringe (1830). The epithet, chosen by De Candolle, refers to the district (comprising part of the south-western Alps and upper Piedmont) occupied by a sect usually known as the Waldensians, after their founder Peter Waldo.

*TYPE*: Labriez à Pignerol. 17.7.[18]09. (Holotype: De Candolle herbarium, Geneva (**G**).)

*DESCRIPTION*: Rosettes very small, 1–3cm in diameter, numerous, densely crowded together so as to give a high, compact cushion of remarkably stony consistency. Rosette-leaves 3–8 × 2–3mm, obovate to oblanceolate or spathulate, obtuse, entire, hairless except for some marginal hairs towards the base, very glaucous, usually somewhat curved downwards at the tip, with several lime-secreting hydathodes set in the margin and several others scattered over the upper surface, giving the leaf a pock-marked appearance. Flowering stems 3–11cm, glandular-hairy, branched above the middle to form a usually rather compact panicle of 6–12 flowers. Cauline leaves 4–7mm, linear-oblanceolate, glandular-hairy. Sepals broadly oblong, obtuse. Petals 4–5 × 3–3.5mm, obovate, white, without red spots. Ovary nearly completely inferior; styles short, erect. Seeds 1 × 0.45mm, ellipsoid, pointed at both ends, pale brown, finely tuberculate all over; raphe inconspicuous. Flowering season: June to August.

*ILLUSTRATIONS*: Figure 32
   Harding (1970, p. 47)
\* Rasetti (1980, Plate 232)

Figure 32. *S.valdensis*

*RECOGNITION*: The species with which this is most likely to be confused are *S.caesia*, *S.marginata*, *S.diapensioides* and some small-leaved variants of *S.paniculata*. From the last it differs in its entire leaves; from *S.diapensioides* in the flatter rosettes, with reflexed instead of semi-erect leaves; from *S.marginata* in the absence of a distinct translucent margin to the leaf and usually the smaller petals; from *S.caesia* in the stouter flowering stem and generally less delicate appearance. Moreover, it differs from all in the disposition of the lime-secreting hydathodes. In *S.valdensis* some are in the actual margin with others irregularly disposed on the upper surface of the leaf; in all the other species there is a single row along each margin, but clearly on the upper surface, sometimes at a little distance from the margin.

*VARIATION*: Except for variation in the average length of leaf there is very little that cannot be ascribed to variation in the degree of exposure.

*HYBRIDS*: None has been reported.

*CHROMOSOME NUMBER*: 2n = 28.

*DISTRIBUTION* (Map 34, p. 120): Confined to a fairly small region of the south-western Alps, mostly near the Franco-Italian frontier. It is difficult to ascertain its limits very precisely, as a large proportion of the localities on herbarium labels cannot be found on the maps available to us, but its northern limit would appear to lie a little to the south of the Col d'Iseran (at about 45°20′N) and its southern limit south of Monte Viso, at about 44°30′N.

*HABITAT*: Crevices in vertical rocks, usually of limestone or calcareous schist, but sometimes, it would seem, on granite. It favours snow-free positions, often of great exposure, and seems indifferent to aspect. It often forms large cushions, very tightly wedged in a crevice by a single large tap-root. It rarely, if ever, descends below 1750m, and ascends to 2800m on Monte Viso.

*ACCESS*: It used to be conveniently accessible on rocks south and east of Bessans (Savoie), on the road leading from Lanslebourg to the Col d'Iseran, but it seems to have become much rarer there recently. It can be seen on rocks on the northern side of the Col de la Croix, a few hundred metres on the Italian side of the frontier (the *locus classicus*), some 11km north of Monte Viso. The station is most conveniently approached from the French side.

*CULTIVATION*: This is fairly easy; the plant is extremely hardy and very tolerant of drought. It is rather shy in flowering, so should be given plenty of light.

# Subsection *Mutatae* (Engler & Irmscher) Gornall

Rosette-leaves dark green; calcareous incrustation scanty or absent. Petals linear, with acuminate tips, golden-yellow or orange. Ovary of 2 carpels.

## 49. *Saxifraga mutata* Linnaeus, *Species Plantarum*, 2nd edn, 570 (1762)

*SYNONYMS*: S.demissa Schott & Kotschy S.transsilvanica Fuss

*HISTORY & NOMENCLATURE*: The first published description is that of Haller (1742), though it was known a hundred years earlier to Burser whose specimen is labelled 'In Taurero Radstatiensi. Cotyledon ?media floribus luteis'. Linnaeus gave it the epithet *mutata* (changed) because he suspected that it was a hybrid of *S.cotyledon*.

*TYPE*: *S.mutata*. Sheet XVI(1).98 in the Burser herbarium, Uppsala (**UPS**) has been designated as lectotype (Webb 1987a).

Subsp. *demissa*. Not traced.

*DESCRIPTION*: Rosettes compact, 5–15cm in diameter, often solitary, but sometimes surrounded by a few smaller ones developed from short offsets; in this case the plant behaves as a true perennial, but often it is monocarpic as the flowering rosette dies completely after flowering. Vigorous monocarpic plants may behave as biennials; more often they require 3 or 4 years from seed to flowering. Rosette-leaves 25–70 × 7–15mm, oblong-oblanceolate, widened very gradually from a narrow base to a broad, obtuse tip; margin translucent, entire at the tip, irregularly and jaggedly toothed in the middle part and frayed into fairly long hairs towards the base; rather fleshy but fairly soft, scarcely if at all glaucous, rather dark green; lime-secreting hydathodes variable in number, situated near the margin of the upper surface, but inside the translucent edge; calcareous incrustation very scanty and sometimes absent. Cauline leaves numerous, similar but smaller and usually edged with glandular hairs. Flowering stem 10–50cm, stout, densely glandular-hairy, bearing a narrow panicle, very variable in length and in number of flowers. Sepals 3–4mm, ovate, acute, bearing a few very short glandular hairs. Petals linear, 6–8mm, much longer and narrower than the sepals, tapered from a base about 1.5mm wide to a slender, acuminate tip, golden-yellow or orange. Anthers orange. Ovary about ¾ inferior; top of ovary and nectary-disc cherry-red. Seeds 0.75 × 0.35mm, ellipsoid with pointed ends, medium brown, covered with numerous fairly short papillae; testa otherwise smooth, without tubercles. Flowering season: July to September.

*ILLUSTRATIONS*: Figure 33
* *Botanical Magazine* 10: Plate 351 (1796)
  Săvulescu (1956, Plate 15)
* Huber (1963, Plate 143)
* Rasetti (1980, Figure 233)

*RECOGNITION*: It is impossible to confuse this species with any other. The long, narrow, yellow or orange petals combined with the large rosette of oblong, obtuse leaves are quite distinctive.

*VARIATION*: Apart from the presence or absence of offsets, which is probably due at least in part to environmental factors, the chief

Figure 33. *S.mutata*

variation is in the shape of the panicle and its relation to the flowering stem. This is best treated by the recognition of two subspecies, which are well separated geographically, but which show a certain amount of overlap in their morphology.
(a) Subsp. *mutata*. Flowering stem branched from the middle or above it, so that the panicle occupies not more than half its length.
(b) Subsp. *demissa* (Schott & Kotschy) D.A. Webb, *Feddes Repertorium* 68:209 (1963). Flowering stem branched from the base or very near it, so that the panicle occupies the whole of it. Sometimes the main axis is not apparent, so that an appearance is presented of several small racemes or panicles arising from one rosette.

*HYBRIDS*: The only convincing hybrid known is that with *S.aizoides* and is discussed under that species. The supposed hybrid with *S.caesia* is of doubtful authenticity; see under that species.

*CHROMOSOME NUMBER*: Recent counts from Swiss and French populations (subsp. *mutata*) have been recorded as $2n = 26$, although there is an earlier French count of $2n = 28$.

*DISTRIBUTION* (Map 37): Subsp. *demissa* is found only in the southern Carpathians, towards their eastern end, in the neighbourhood of Sinaia and Braşov (approximately from 25° to 26°E).

Subsp. *mutata* has a wide range in the Alps and some of the adjacent country, especially on their northern side; it has also been recorded from one station in the Low Tatra range in Slovakia. It is difficult to summarise accurately the limits of its distribution in the alpine area; partly because it seems to be impermanent in many of its stations, which in any case are widely scattered, with wide gaps in between, and partly because — more perhaps than for any other European species — the localities cited in Floras and monographs cannot be found on any standard maps. Broadly speaking, its range covers the greater part of Austria south of the Danube, except the extreme east, and from here it extends to a few stations in the Alps of Slovenia, and also to the Bavarian Alps and part of the 'Alpenvorland' which adjoins them on the north. In Switzerland it is mainly in the east, but there are a few stations in the Bernese Oberland. In the Italian Alps it is rather scarce, but extends from 9°E, north of Como, to 11°50′E, in the southern Dolomites. In France it is confined to two or three stations in northern Savoy and an outlying one north of Grenoble.

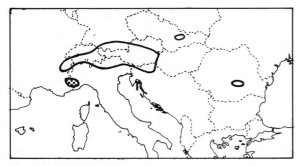

Map 37. Distribution of *S.florulenta* (shaded) and *S.mutata* (unshaded)

*HABITAT*: Sometimes on rock, but more often on debris or gravel. It is distinctly but not rigidly calcicole, and although sometimes seen on limestone or dolomite it is more often on schists, sandstones or conglomerates which are to some extent calcareous. It is less tolerant of drought than other members of this section, and is usually seen in fairly damp surroundings such as river gravels, roadside gutters, flushes or on seepage-lines. It is essentially a subalpine plant, commonest between 800 and 1800m, though it can ascend to 2200m, and it descends to 550m in some of the river-valleys north of the Alps.

*ACCESS*: The fairly small size and the relative impermanence of most of the colonies of this species make it difficult to give precise directions for the finding of it. It would seem that the Bavarian Alps, the Tirol and northern Styria provide the best hunting-grounds.

*CULTIVATION*: *S.mutata* needs a little more care than most other members of its section, but is not really difficult if given a shady and fairly moist position in somewhat sandy soil. Care must be taken to collect seed when it is ripe, but an alternative method of propagation, if several plants are available, is to pinch out the flowering stem as soon as it begins to lengthen; this will stimulate the production of runners with auxiliary rosettes.

## Subsection *Florulentae* (Engler & Irmscher) Gornall

Rosette-leaves dark green; calcareous incrustation absent. Petals oblanceolate with acute tips, flesh-pink. Ovary of 3 carpels.

### 50. *Saxifraga florulenta* Moretti, *Tentativo diretto ad illustrare la Sinonimia delle Specie del genere* Saxifraga *indigene del suolo italiano* 9 (1823)

*SYNONYM*: *Tristylea floribunda* (Dietrich) Jordan & Fourreau

*HISTORY & NOMENCLATURE*: Farrer (1919, 2:276) states that this species was first discovered by Molinari in 1820, but Molinari (or Molineri) died in 1818, and Moretti, writing in 1823, said that it was discovered *or sono molti anni*, and that the only specimen he possessed was given him by Biroli, who had received it from Bellardi, so that the date of the original discovery is likely to have been nearer 1810. It is possible that Allioni found it even earlier, but mistook it for *S.mutata*. Moretti's description is brief, and for some years the existence of the species was treated with some scepticism, but in or about 1840 an English tourist without any botanical knowledge fell in with two botanists from Nice in the mountains above Madone de Fenestre and showed them the plants which he had been collecting at random; they included some good specimens of *Saxifraga florulenta*, from which one of the botanists (Barla) made and lithographed a good painting; this established and eventually made widely known the remarkable characters of the species.

The epithet (rich in flowers) alludes to the large and dense inflorescence.

*TYPE*: Not traced.

*DESCRIPTION*: Monocarpic, consisting of a dense rosette 5–15cm in diameter, from the centre of which there arises after many years an inflorescence; the whole plant then dies. It would seem, however, that very rarely a lateral rosette can be produced; this was observed in culture at Cambridge. The leaves in the rosette are very tightly packed and very regularly arranged; even on a fairly small rosette it is easy to count 150 living leaves. The dead leaves persist so that an old plant, before flowering, may consist of a cylinder up to 7cm tall of mainly dead leaves but surmounted at the top by the rosette of living leaves, which are often strongly incurved. Leaves 3–6cm × 4–7mm, consisting of a narrowly oblong basal part, which expands above to an elliptical apical part, nearly twice the width of the basal, and ending in a short, spinose tip. There is a conspicuous translucent margin, entire near the tip, irregularly crenate below this, and in the basal half drawn out into numerous short, stout, tooth-like hairs. The leaves are otherwise hairless; the colour is a dull, rather dark green; there is a row of very inconspicuous lime-secreting hydathodes in pits near the margin on the upper surface, but no trace of calcareous incrustation. Flowering stem 10–25cm, stout, hollow, densely glandular-hairy, the basal part bearing some narrow, glandular-hairy cauline leaves, but branched from near the base to form a dense, cylindrical inflorescence of numerous flowers. Sepals erect, triangular. Petals 5–7mm, oblanceolate, flesh-pink. Ovary nearly completely inferior, in most of the flowers 3-chambered and bearing 3 styles; the terminal flower, however, usually has 5 styles and a variable number of petals and stamens in excess of 5 and 10 respectively. Seeds 0.9 × 0.35mm, oblong with rounded ends, somewhat wrinkled, covered uniformly but rather sparsely with small tubercles; raphe fairly conspicuous. Flowering season: July and August.

*ILLUSTRATIONS*: Plate 19
\* *Botanical Magazine* 100: Plate 6102 (1874)
\* Bonnier (1921, Plate 202)
  Merxmüller (1956, p. 118)
  Harding (1970, p. 59)
\* Rasetti (1980, Plates 263, 264)

*RECOGNITION*: It is impossible to confuse this with any other species. Among those with large, solitary rosettes, *S.mutata* differs in its obtuse leaves, and *S.longifolia* in its very glaucous leaves. Above all *S.florulenta* is distinguished by its 3-chambered ovary.

*VARIATION*: There is hardly any; the rosettes vary in size when they come into flower, and the colour of the petals sometimes inclines towards a deep purplish-pink.

*HYBRIDS*: None is known.

*CHROMOSOME NUMBER*: $2n = 28$.

*DISTRIBUTION* (Map 37, see p. 133): This species is known only from a restricted region of the Maritime Alps, mainly now in France, but with several stations in Italy. It is centred on the large massif, usually referred to as the Mercantour, which lies athwart the frontier, north-east of St Martin-Vésubie, and of which the principal summits are the Argentera and Mont Clapier. But from here it extends somewhat discontinuously north-westwards almost to the Col de Fer, which is on the frontier 7km due north of St Etienne-de-Tinée. Its north-western limit is at 44°20'N, 6°55'E, its south-eastern at 44°05'N, 7°30'E.

*HABITAT*: Always on vertical or overhanging cliffs of gneiss or granite, usually facing north or north-west, from 1900 to 3250m.

*ACCESS*: For the most part this species grows in wild and somewhat inaccessible country which can only be reached by those with stamina and mountaineering skill. A few plants can, however, usually be seen on the cliffs which lie not very far from the road on the left as one descends from the Col de la Lombarde on the French side, towards Isola. It may also be seen on the cliffs which overhang most of the lakes in the Mercantour massif; these include Lac des Trois Coulpes, reached from Le Boréon on the south-eastern flank of the massif, and Lac Vert, reached from St Dalmas-de-Tende, via Casterino, on the south-western flank.

It is, however, a rare plant, and in spite of the virtual inaccessibility of many of the specimens, it suffered from the depredations of collectors in the latter part of last century. It seems, moreover, also to be declining from natural causes. For these reasons, and because it is so difficult in cultivation, it should not be collected unless one is lucky enough to find, among the dead rosettes and flowering stems at the base of a cliff, a living rosette which has become detached. It is protected by law in all its Italian stations. Grey-Wilson (1985) has discussed its rarity and the need for its conservation.

*CULTIVATION*: This is very difficult. A well-rooted specimen will survive in pot-culture, but it rarely thrives and is most reluctant to flower. Boissier had some success by planting it in the crevices of a north-facing brick wall in his garden at Valleyres, and it is probable that it is likely to succeed better in a subalpine climate than in most parts of the British Isles.

## Section *Xanthizoon* Grisebach

Evergreen perennials, forming mats or cushions. Leaves fleshy, narrow, more or less entire, alternate. Lime-secreting hydathodes present, but flush with the surface, not in pits, and lime-incrustation often not evident. Glandular hairs multiseriate. Flowering stems leafy, terminal; flowers in a lax cyme. Petals yellow, orange or reddish. Ovary about half-inferior. Bulbils absent.

This section is constituted by a single, widespread species, of which the affinities are not very clear. It appears to be closely related to species of section *Porphyrion*, and also to *S.mutata*, but is sufficiently distinct to deserve treatment in a separate section.

## 51. *Saxifraga aizoides* Linnaeus, *Species Plantarum* 403 (1753)

*SYNONYMS*: *S.autumnalis* of Jacquin and several authors, but scarcely of Linnaeus
*S.atrorubens* Bertoloni
*S.crocea* Gaudin

*HISTORY & NOMENCLATURE*: The earliest mention of the plant is probably that of Valerius Cordus (1563) as *Sedula montana pulchra*; it was also known to Clusius, Bauhin and Morison. Linnaeus, who knew it from Lapland, chose the epithet *aizoides* to draw attention to its strikingly fleshy leaves (*aizoon* is the Greek equivalent of *sempervivum* (everlasting), and *aizoides* means 'looking like *aizoon*'). Some confusion was caused by the fact that he also described as *S.autumnalis* a minor variant of *S.hirculus*, but cited as a synonym a name from Haller which refers to *S.aizoides*. There is now, however, general agreement to forget about the name *S.autumnalis*; in this connection see Widder (1954).

*TYPE*: Sheet XVI(1).74 in the Burser herbarium, Uppsala (**UPS**) has been designated as lectotype (Webb 1987a).

*DESCRIPTION*: Stems numerous, ascending or prostrate, branched near the base, forming an irregular, loose cushion or thick mat. Some of the stems terminate in an erect, flowering portion, leafy up to the inflorescence; the total length of such stems varies greatly, partly in accordance with water supply, but is usually 7–20cm. Leaves medium to darkish green, not glaucous, 4–22 × 1.5–4mm, variable in size on the same plant, linear to oblong, obtuse, acute or apiculate, without a petiole, entire, or rarely with two short, tooth-like lobes near the tip, very fleshy, convex beneath, flat or somewhat convex above; margin usually furnished with stout, spinose, forwardly-directed, tooth-like hairs, which vary greatly in number and are occasionally absent. Hydathodes usually 1, near the tip, but occasionally 3 or 5, lime-secreting, but not sunk in a pit; calcareous incrustation often slight or absent, but sometimes conspicuous. Flowering stem rather densely hairy with short, stiff, slender hairs. Flowers rarely solitary, more often in short, leafy cymes of 2–15. Sepals 2.5–4mm, obtuse. Petals 3–7 × 1.5–3mm, usually yellow (often with orange spots), but sometimes orange or brick red. Ovary half-inferior, the superior part flat and disc-like in flower but increasing greatly in height as the fruit matures, greenish-yellow to deep crimson; styles 2mm, straight, divergent in fruit. Seeds 0.9 × 0.45mm, oblong-ellipsoid, rather pale brown, with the surface covered with hollow, conical, bladder-like papillae which collapse on drying, or with low, rounded papillae (see Conolly 1976; Kaplan 1981, Plate 21); raphe conspicuous. Flowering season: June to September.

*ILLUSTRATIONS*: Plates 22, 24
    Ross-Craig (1957, Plate 14)
\* Felsko (1959, p. 29)
    Mądalski (1962, Plate 1327)
\* Rasetti (1980, Plate 281)

*RECOGNITION*: The combination of soft, fleshy, more or less entire, stalkless leaves and yellow or orange petals is characteristic. In yellow-flowered members of section *Porphyrion* the leaves are harder, smaller and much more crowded.

*VARIATION*: This is a very variable species, but it is difficult to give taxonomic expression to the variation. Plants from the Arctic, the high Alps and from dry situations tend to have short stems, small leaves and few flowers; this condition is certainly in part determined by the environment, but may be partly genetic. Variation in the number of hairs on the leaf-margin, the number of hydathodes and the amount of calcareous secretion, the size, shape and colour of the petals, and the colour of the nectary-disc, is difficult to correlate with either habitat or geographical distribution. The only variant which seems perhaps worth distinguishing as a variety is var. **atrorubens** (Bertoloni) Sternberg, *Revisio Saxifragarum, Supplementum I*, 10 (1822), from the Apuan Alps. This has leaves with numerous and conspicuous marginal hairs, brick-red petals and a deep crimson nectary-

disc; it is late-flowering and grows in crevices of dry-looking rocks. All these characters can be seen elsewhere, but their constant association here makes this population fairly distinctive.

*HYBRIDS*: In view of its taxonomic isolation the facility with which this species forms hybrids is rather remarkable. Natural hybrids with *S.mutata*, *S.caesia* and *S.squarrosa* all seem to be correctly diagnosed. The first (*S.* × *hausmannii* Kerner) is fairly frequent in the northern Alps, more local in the southern; it is discussed in detail by Hamel (1957), although his chromosome counts on *S.mutata* disagree with recent work. The second (*S.* × *patens* Gaudin) is recorded mainly from the northern and western Alps, and from a few stations in the western and central Pyrenees. The third is rare, and is known only from the Julian Alps and Carinthia. A hybrid with *S.paniculata* (*S.* × *larsenii* Sündermann) has been made artificially. A supposed hybrid with *S.cotyledon* from Norway seems very doubtful, as does that with *S.umbrosa* 'Primuloides'.

    The plant described as *S.nathorstii* (Dusén) Hayek (see p. 283), known only from north-eastern Greenland, is in many respects intermediate between *S.aizoides* and *S.oppositi-*

Map 38. Distribution of *S.aizoides*; for detailed distribution in Europe see Map 39

*folia*. It has $2n = 52$, and is fertile, so that it has been generally accepted as an amphidiploid. A simple primary hybrid between the two species with $2n = 26$ has, however, never been found, and attempts to synthesise it have failed. An alternative view, therefore, is that *S.nathorstii* originated from the pollination by *S.aizoides* of a tetraploid plant of *S.oppositifolia* (such plants have been recorded from Spitsbergen, arctic Asia and arctic North America, though not hitherto from Greenland) to give a triploid hybrid closely resembling *S.oppositifolia*, and that this hybrid, partly but not entirely sterile, was then pollinated again by *S.aizoides* to give the fertile tetraploid, *S.nathorstii*. For details see Böcher (1983) and Ferguson (1972).

*CHROMOSOME NUMBER*: $2n = 26$.

*DISTRIBUTION* (Maps 38, 39): In Europe the distribution conforms to the classical arctic-alpine type. *S.aizoides* occurs in Spitsbergen, Iceland, northern and western Scandinavia, locally in north-western Russia, northern Ireland, and Britain southwards to Yorkshire, where it finds its southern limit for northern Europe. It is absent from the Harz and the Vosges, but has two stations in the

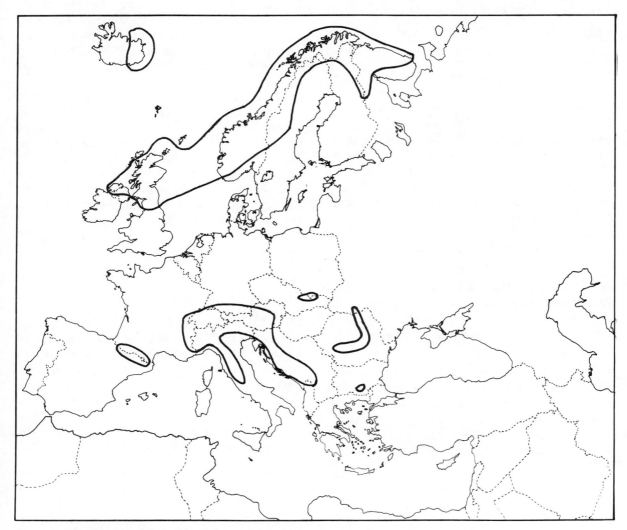

Map 39. Distribution of *S.aizoides* in Europe; for global distribution see Map 38

French Jura; it is common almost throughout the Alps, frequent in the Pyrenees and the Carpathians; and from the Alps it extends southwards to the central Apennines and through the mountains of western Yugoslavia and northern Albania to north-western Macedonia, with two outlying stations in the central Rodopi of southern Bulgaria.

Outside Europe it is found in Greenland, and is widespread in arctic and subarctic Canada, with southward extensions near the eastern and western coasts, just stopping short of the United States in the west, and just entering it in the east. In Asia it is found only in Novaya Zemlya and the polar Urals.

HABITAT: Its most characteristic habitat in Europe is on the banks of mountain streams, where it often forms conspicuous vertical yellow stripes on the sides of steep valleys. It will also grow in other situations where there is seepage of water, even in crevices of very dry-looking limestone rocks, and in the Arctic it can be found on relatively dry tundra, but the plants in these drier places are usually rather small. It has a calcicole tendency, but will tolerate any except very base-poor habitats. It ascends to 3000m in the Alps, but can also be found at low altitudes on river-gravels, where it has been washed down in floods and taken root. In northern Europe it descends to sea-level, but ascends to over 1000m in Scotland.

ACCESS: No directions are needed to find such a common and conspicuous plant in the Alps or Pyrenees; it is also very frequent in the western and central Highlands of Scotland.

CULTIVATION: It can be grown in pot-culture in a cool house if given well-drained soil and regular and generous watering, but it seldom does itself justice under these conditions. To see it at its best it should be given a scree with underground watering, or a stream with gravelly banks.

# Section *Trachyphyllum* (Gaudin) W.D.J. Koch

Evergreen perennials of somewhat diffuse habit, sometimes forming low cushions. Leaves alternate, narrow, usually lanceolate, rather stiff, entire or shortly 3-lobed at the tip, apiculate or strongly mucronate, hairless on the surfaces but with strong, broad-based, often hooked hairs on the margin. Lime-secreting hydathodes absent. Glandular hairs multiseriate. Axillary buds often prominent, but not summer-dormant. Flowering stems leafy, terminal. Flowers regular, or rarely very slightly irregular. Sepals not reflexed, even in fruit. Petals white to pale yellow, sometimes with red or orange spots or a deep yellow patch at the base. Ovary superior or nearly so.

A small section of about eight to ten species, centred chiefly in arctic and subarctic North America and north-eastern Asia; three occur in Europe, one of them with a circumpolar distribution. The recent division of the section into subsections and series by Khokhrjakov (1979) is over-optimistic in our opinion, in view of the complex patterns of variation encountered.

## 52. *Saxifraga aspera* Linnaeus, *Species Plantarum* 402 (1753)

SYNONYM: S.etrusca Pignatti

HISTORY & NOMENCLATURE: The earliest synonym given by Linnaeus is in Bauhin (1620), but the illustration in Gesner (1541), labelled *Sedum alium montanum cuius flores albi punctis sanguineis adsperguntur*, is recognisable as S.aspera. The epithet *aspera* (harsh, rough) was taken by Linnaeus from Bauhin, and is a reasonable description of the stiff leaves with strong marginal hairs.

TYPE: Sheet XVI(1).79 in the Burser herbarium, Uppsala (**UPS**) has been designated as lectotype (Webb 1987a).

DESCRIPTION: An evergreen perennial, consisting in winter of an irregular mat of compact rosettes (often with the leaves incurved so as to be nearly globular). In spring there arise from the axils of the lower leaves of these rosettes some long, prostrate leafy shoots, and from the centre of the rosette arises the flowering stem. Leaves of the prostrate leafy shoots 5–8mm long, with marginal hairs 0.75–1.25mm long, those at the base longer, broader-based, and of softer, membranous consistency. At flowering time each of these leaves has in its axil a conspicuous leafy bud, which is always considerably shorter than the leaf. The leaves are straight, at first pressed against the shoot but soon diverging, and by the end of the flowering season they are standing out almost at right angles to the shoot. Flowering stems 7–22cm, occasionally less, but usually only at high altitudes or in exposed places, furnished, rather sparsely below but more densely above, with short hairs tipped with a dark red gland. Cauline leaves numerous, similar to those of the non-flowering shoots but usually larger (up to 17 × 1.5mm), standing out from the stem nearly at right angles, without buds in their axils, often glandular-hairy with hairs similar to those on the stem, and with the marginal hairs tending to become fewer and weaker towards the top of the stem. Flowers 2–7, on long pedicels, in a lax, open cyme; rarely solitary, but then only in stunted plants. Sepals 2.5–3mm, ovate-oblong to triangular, usually strongly mucronate, rather sparsely glandular-hairy, and mainly at the base. Petals 5–7 × 3mm, occasionally less, sometimes slightly unequal in size, oblong, narrowed at the base to a very short claw, white or pale cream, often with a deep yellow patch at the base and with yellow, orange or crimson spots towards the middle. Styles short and thick, somewhat divergent. Seeds 0.6 × 0.35mm, oblong-ellipsoid, obtuse at both ends, medium brown, covered in very low, rounded papillae; raphe finely tuberculate, conspicuous. Flowering season: June to August.

*ILLUSTRATIONS*: *Sternberg (1810, Figure 8)

* Heathcote (1891, Plate 91)

Reichenbach (1899, Plate 92)
Engler & Irmscher (1919, Figure 101)

*RECOGNITION*: The narrow, entire, sharply pointed leaves with stout marginal hairs, together with the superior ovary, distinguish this from all but the other members of its section. For the differences from *S.bryoides* see under that species. From *S.bronchialis* it is best distinguished by the presence of conspicuous leafy buds in the axils of the leafy shoots at the flowering season.

*VARIATION*: There is a good deal of variation in the length of the flowering stem, the number of flowers that it bears, the size of the petals, the colour and density of their spots and the presence or absence of a deep yellow patch at the base. How much the variation in the first two characters is due to the altitude and degree of exposure can be determined only by cultivation experiments, which do not seem to have been attempted. This applies also, perhaps, to the variants with small petals which Pignatti (1969) has separated as subsp. *micrantha*. He has also described as a new species, *S.etrusca* Pignatti, the populations of the Apuan Alps and adjacent Apennines, mainly on the grounds of their having narrow, obtuse sepals (instead of broadly ovate and mucronate) and having numerous orange-yellow (instead of few crimson) spots on the petals. We do not dispute the characters which he attributes to the plants of the Apuan Alps, but we have seen plants with spots (admittedly rather fainter) of exactly the same colour from the Alpes-Maritimes, and examination of a dozen specimens from the Swiss Alps revealed sepals of exactly the same shape as those from the Apuan Alps; we have never, indeed, seen a plant with sepals of the shape which Pignatti figures as characteristic of *S.aspera* (Pignatti 1969: Figure 2, c2). It would seem that *S.etrusca* is entitled at most to varietal status.

*HYBRIDS*: None has been described, but it is possible that occasional hybridisation with *S.bryoides* may account for the plants which are to some extent intermediate and have served as the justification for some authors in uniting the two species.

*CHROMOSOME NUMBER*: $2n = 26$.

*DISTRIBUTION* (Map 40): This species is found mainly in the Alps, but there are also smaller populations in the Pyrenees, and in the Apuan Alps and the adjacent parts of the northern Apennines. In the Alps it is widespread, but its calcifuge tendency means that it is to be found chiefly in the main, central range; in the northern, mainly calcareous, subsidiary ranges it is rare, and in the similar southern ranges local. It is commonest in Switzerland and Austria, but extends south-westwards through Savoy and the Dauphiné to the Maritime and Ligurian Alps. Its northern and eastern limit is in northern Styria, near Eisenerz; its southern limit in the eastern Alps is at 45°50′N in the Giuicarian Alps west of Riva.

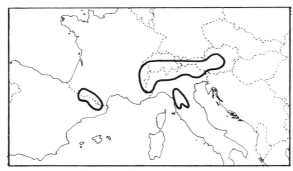

Map 40.  Distribution of *S.aspera*

In the Apuan Alps it is rather rare and local; in the Apennines to the east it is rather more frequent, but extends only from 44°05′N to 44°25′N. In the Pyrenees it is only in the east, with its western limit in or near Andorra, and nowhere is it very common.

*HABITAT*: Nearly, but not completely confined to siliceous rocks, but it will tolerate a small base-content, and in the Apuan Alps and perhaps a few stations in the southeastern Alps it ventures on to limestone. It is to be found on solid rock, but also on debris, on the banks of streams, on walls, and on mossy humus in open larch-woods. It grows

mainly between 1100 and 2200m, but has been recorded as low as 400m, and as high as 2800m.

*ACCESS*: This species is most easily seen in eastern Switzerland, in the canton of Graubünden, where it may be seen close to the road on walls in Guarda in the lower Engadin, in larch-woods above Pontresina, and on south-facing rocks on the eastern side of the Oberalp pass (east of Andermatt).

*CULTIVATION*: This is quite easy, though the prostrate shoots are slow to root, and it benefits from occasional 'settling in' to the soil. If grown out of doors it is often pulled to pieces by birds, so it is probably best kept under glass.

### 53. *Saxifraga bryoides* Linnaeus, *Species Plantarum* 400 (1753)

*SYNONYM*: *S.aspera* subsp. *bryoides* (Linnaeus) Engler & Irmscher, *Pflanzenreich* 69 (IV,117):455 (1919)

*HISTORY & NOMENCLATURE*: First noticed, it would appear, by Colonna (1616) who described it as *Sedum ejusdem alpinum quartum*; this is not very helpful, but he provided a convincing illustration. The epithet *bryoides* (moss-like) was adapted by Linnaeus from Bauhin, who called it *Sedum muscosum*, and Tournefort who described it as 'musco similis'.

*TYPE*: Sheet 575.11 in the Linnean herbarium, London (**LINN**) has been designated as lectotype (Webb 1987a).

*DESCRIPTION*: Rather compact, forming a dense mat or low cushion, composed of nearly spherical leaf-rosettes. Leaves 3.5–5 × 1–1.5mm, oblong-lanceolate, sharply incurved, mucronate or apiculate, with a distinct translucent margin, which bears, at least towards the base and sometimes up to near the tip, a number of stout, tooth-like hairs; surface hairless and shining. From the axils of a few of these leaves there develop in spring or early summer prostrate leafy shoots, usually only 1–4cm long, but occasionally up to 12cm. These bear leaves similar to those of the rosettes, but often longer (up to 8mm), and bearing in their axils conspicuous leafy buds, which are at least as long as the leaf which subtends them. The leaves are somewhat incurved and pressed against the bud, not standing out from the shoot. Through the late summer and autumn these buds develop into rosettes. Flowering stems 2–5cm, slender, usually rather sparsely glandular-hairy, with a single terminal flower and 4–12 cauline leaves, similar to those of the rosettes but smaller (2–3mm long). They are semi-erect, without leafy buds in their axils; the uppermost sometimes bear a few glandular hairs. Sepals 2.5–3.5mm, ovate, mucronate, hairless. Petals 5–7mm, elliptic-oblong to obovate, not contiguous, white, with a large patch of deep yellow at the base and usually numerous orange-yellow spots higher up. Styles very short, stout, erect. Seeds 0.65 × 0.35mm, oblong, rounded at both ends, medium brown, tuberculate all over, includ-

ing the conspicuous raphe, and with a row of fairly long papillae along the side opposite the raphe. Flowering season: June to September.

*ILLUSTRATIONS*: Plate 23; Figure 34
    Mądalski (1962, Plate 1326)
    Harding (1970, p. 124)
\* Rasetti (1980, Plate 254)

*RECOGNITION*: The only species this is likely to be confused with is *S.aspera*. It differs most obviously in its solitary flowers (though this condition is occasionally found in *S.aspera*); also in the leaves, which on both prostrate shoots and flowering stems are incurved and not standing out at right angles; moreover, the leaves on the flowering stems are very much smaller than those of *S.aspera*.

*VARIATION*: Apart from variation in the length of the leafy shoots and the flowering stems, which can be attributed largely to altitude and exposure, the only variation is in the presence or absence of glandular hairs on the flowering stems.

*HYBRIDS*: None has been recorded, but hybrids with *S.aspera* are possible; see under the latter species.

*CHROMOSOME NUMBER*: $2n = 26$.

*DISTRIBUTION* (Map 41): Widespread in the higher mountains of Europe, from the Pyrenees to Bulgaria, and northwards to the Riesengebirge (Krkonoše), on the borders of Poland and Czechoslovakia.

In the Pyrenees it is mainly in the east, but extends westwards as far as 0°25′W. It has a few stations in the volcanic mountains of south-central France. In the Riesengebirge it is confined to a single station, but is fairly widespread in the western Carpathians, extending eastwards into the Ukraine. In the eastern Carpathians of Romania it is confined to the extreme north, but it extends throughout the entire range of the southern Carpathians. In Bulgaria it is found on most of the higher peaks and extends locally into eastern Yugoslavia, but is absent from the rest of the Balkan peninsula. Finally, in the Alps it has a distribution broadly similar to that of

Figure 34. *S.bryoides*

*S.aspera*, being concentrated chiefly in the main chain and less frequent in the subsidiary and mainly calcareous ranges to the north and south. *S.bryoides* is, however, rarer than *S.aspera* in the north-eastern part of the Austrian Alps, and rather commoner in Italy. Its southern and western limits are almost the same as those of *S.aspera* (in the Alpes-Maritimes). Northwards it extends to 47°30′N in northern Tirol, eastwards to 15°E in the Koralpe, on the border between Styria and Carinthia, and in the eastern Alps southwards to 45°50′N on Monte Baldo, to the east of Lake Garda.

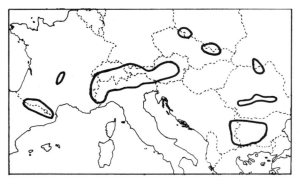

Map 41.  Distribution of *S.bryoides*

*HABITAT*: This species is strongly calcifuge, and is found only on base-poor rock and soils derived from it. It grows mainly on solid rock, but is also to be found on screes, debris and moraines. It tends to favour exposed situations, where the snow-cover does not last long. It is rare below 1800m, but from there upwards to 3000m (and locally to 4000m) it is usually frequent.

*ACCESS*: It is easy to find on most high passes through siliceous rocks, but the following places of easy access may be mentioned: on the slopes immediately south of the hotel at the Col de Lautaret (Hautes-Alpes, France); beside Lake Bianco by the Bernina pass in south-eastern Switzerland; and at the Passo di Falzarego, west of Cortina d'Ampezzo (prov. Belluno), Italy.

*CULTIVATION*: This is easy, provided that the soil is not too calcareous, but it is

difficult to obtain a good show of flowers. The best chance of this is probably in those parts of Britain which have a cold winter and a sunny summer; here the plants should be wintered out of doors, in a cold frame if necessary, and brought under glass fairly early in the spring.

### 54. *Saxifraga bronchialis* Linnaeus, *Species Plantarum* 400 (1753)

*SYNONYMS*:       *Ciliaria   bronchialis* (Linnaeus) Haworth
*Saxifraga spinulosa* Adams
*S.austromontana* Wiegand
*S.firma* Litvinov ex Lozina-Lozinskaja

*HISTORY & NOMENCLATURE*: Linnaeus cited no synonyms, and the source of his knowledge of the plant is difficult to ascertain. It seems most probable that it came from Démidov (see Savage 1945, p. vii). The only specimen of *S.bronchialis* in the Linnean collections is in London, and is labelled by Linnaeus '15. aspera'. This suggests that it was only very slightly shortly before the publication of *Species Plantarum* that Linnaeus realised that the two species were different. The epithet, according to Gmelin (1769), derives from information given to Linnaeus that the plant was used by the natives of Siberia as a cure for respiratory complaints.

*TYPE*: *S.bronchialis*. Sheet 575.37 in the Linnean herbarium, London (**LINN**) has been designated as lectotype (Webb 1987a). This choice supersedes the designation of a Gmelin specimen as neotype by Siplivinsky (1971). Our argument is that all the evidence suggests that LINN 575.37 is probably the only specimen that Linnaeus ever saw, and it seems likely that he labelled it *S.aspera* before he decided to make *S.bronchialis* a separate species (rather at the last moment) and then forgot to change his annotation.

Subsp. *spinulosa*. Not traced.

*DESCRIPTION*: Fairly compact, with short, more or less prostrate leafy shoots, forming a thick mat or low cushion. Leaves about 15 × 2mm, narrowly oblong to oblong-lanceolate, tapered at the tip to a white spine 1–1.5mm long, often reddish, hairless on the surfaces but furnished on the margin with numerous stout, often hooked, tooth-like hairs. The buds in the axils of these leaves are very small and inconspicuous during the flowering period. Flowering stems 10–20cm, hairless except in the inflorescence, bearing a few cauline leaves which are similar to those of the leafy shoots but smaller and with fewer and weaker marginal hairs. Pedicels glandular-hairy. Flowers 2–12 in a fairly compact cyme. Sepals 2.5mm, broadly elliptical, acute, hairless. Petals 5–7 × 3mm, oblong-elliptical, yellowish-white, with crimson spots in the upper half. Styles 2.5mm, stout, divergent. Seeds 0.7 × 0.3mm, ellipsoid with subacute ends, medium brown, bearing papillae of very variable length; raphe conspicuous, finely tuberculate. Flowering season: July.

*ILLUSTRATIONS*:
  Engler & Irmscher (1919, Figure 102)
  Hultén (1930, p. 15)

*RECOGNITION*: The superior ovary and narrow leaves with stout, multiseriate hairs separate it from all European species except *S.aspera* and *S.bryoides*. From both of these it is easily distinguished by the absence of conspicuous buds in the leaf-axils at flowering time.

*VARIATION*: The preceding description applies to the European plant, which most Soviet authors separate as *S.spinulosa* Adams. It is said to differ from *S.bronchialis* in having leaves that are curved beneath, instead of keeled, and which have shorter hairs, and in its smaller petals. We agree, however, with Hultén (1930) in regarding these distinctions as of only subspecific value, and follow him in designating the European plant *S.bronchialis* subsp. *spinulosa* (Adams) Hultén, *Kungliga Svenska Vetenskapsakademiens Handlingar, series 3*, 8:14 (1930). Recent treatments of the group in north-eastern Asia (Siplivinsky 1971; Khokhrjakov 1979) have led to the recognition of 14 species there, with *S.spinulosa* and *S.bronchialis* in different subsections! We

strongly suspect that we would reduce many of these to the level of subspecies or variety. Within the European populations there is no variation of any consequence.

*HYBRIDS*: None has been recorded.

*CHROMOSOME NUMBER*: No counts from European populations of subsp. *spinulosa* are known, but Siberian populations have been recorded as $2n = $ c.44 and c.80. For other subspecies, exact counts have been published of $2n = 26, 28, 48, 66, 92$ and $112$.

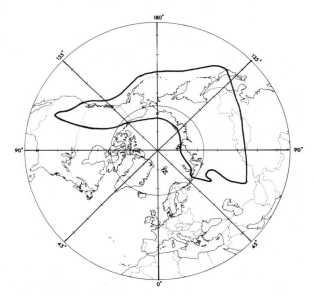

Map 42. Distribution of *S.bronchialis*

*DISTRIBUTION* (Map 42): In Europe, subsp. *spinulosa* is confined to a small part of north-eastern Russia, consisting mainly of the western slopes of the northern Ural, chiefly in the arctic and subarctic regions, but extending southwards perhaps as far as 62°N. Eastwards from here it extends through most of Siberia to Kamchatka, and southwards to north-eastern Mongolia. Subsp. *bronchialis* seems to be distributed in Siberia eastwards from the Lena River basin to the Pacific Coast, and southwards to north-eastern China. Other subspecies are found in eastern Siberia, Alaska and in the Rocky mountains southwards to New Mexico (see p. 283).

*HABITAT*: On sandy and gravelly soils, on tundra or in open coniferous woods.

*ACCESS*: The European populations are obviously difficult of access. In North America subsp. *austromontana* is fairly frequent, though mostly at high altitude, in the mountains near the border of British Columbia and Washington.

*CULTIVATION*: No information is available.

# Section *Mesogyne* Sternberg (grex *Sibiricae* Engler & Irmscher)

Perennials, usually winter-dormant, but perhaps occasionally evergreen, usually with bulbils at or just below ground level in the axils of the basal leaves, and sometimes in the axils of the cauline leaves, or replacing flowers. Basal leaves thin, scarcely fleshy, membranous when dry, with a distinct, slender petiole and semicircular to kidney-shaped lamina, usually at least as broad as long, palmately divided, not very deeply, into 5–11 lobes. Lime-secreting hydathodes absent. Hairs uniseriate. Flowering stems leafy, terminal. Flowers solitary or in a small cyme. Petals white or pink. Ovary more or less superior, but up to a quarter or a third inferior in some species.

A small section of about eight species, mainly arctic and subarctic in its distribution, but with outlying stations as far south as the southern Alps and the Aegean region in Europe, and Arizona in North America.

## 55. *Saxifraga sibirica* Linnaeus, *Systema Naturae*, 10th edn, 2:1027 (1759)

*SYNONYM*: *S.mollis* Smith ex Sprengel

*HISTORY & NOMENCLATURE*: Linnaeus gave no information as to the source from which he received the plants on which his description of the species is based, except that they came from Siberia.

*TYPE*: Sheet 575.49 in the Linnean herbarium, London (**LINN**) has been designated as lectotype (Webb 1987a).

*DESCRIPTION*: Stems solitary or forming small tufts, sometimes shortly creeping at the base. Basal leaves suberect, with a long, slender petiole and kidney-shaped lamina 5–20 × 8–30mm, divided palmately into 5–7 short, broadly ovate, more or less obtuse lobes. Both petiole and lamina vary from almost hairless to densely covered with long, woolly hairs. Bulbils in the axils of the basal leaves small, numerous. Flowering stem 5–18cm (rarely more), slender and sometimes flexuous, hairless or glandular-hairy, bearing a few cauline leaves, the lower shortly 3-lobed, the upper entire. Flowers 2–7 in a fairly compact terminal cyme, but with pedicels up to 25mm. Sepals 3–5mm, oblong, sparsely glandular-hairy. Petals 7–14 × 3.5–6mm, narrowly obovate, white. Ovary almost completely superior; styles 2mm, straight, erect. Seeds 0.8 × 0.35mm, narrowly ellipsoid with rounded ends, medium brown, covered with very low humps, scarcely to be termed papillae, each surrounded by a ring of darker tubercles; raphe inconspicuous. Flowering season: April to July.

*ILLUSTRATIONS*: Plate 25
 Sternberg (1810, Plate 25)
\* Coventry (1927, Plate 21)
\* Köhlein (1984, Plate [11])

*RECOGNITION*: Among the species with bulbils in the axils of the basal leaves (only) and a more or less superior ovary, *S.sibirica* is distinguished from other species of the section by its much larger petals.

*VARIATION*: Within Europe the chief variation is in the amount of hair on the leaves, but this has never been given any taxonomic significance. The fact that in some plants the petals are 3-veined and in others 5- to 7-veined has been used to separate the latter as *S.mollis*, but this rather trivial character does not seem to be well correlated with any other, not even with the width of the petal, and there are, according to Matthews (1972), several gatherings from Turkey in which petals with 3, 5 and 7 veins can all be found. It does not seem justifiable to recognise this distinction even at subspecific level, especially as the chief reason put forward by Kuzmanov (1970) is the unlikeliness of the same species occuring in Siberia and at low levels in the Aegean. This, however, loses much of its force when it is seen from Matthews' data that the variant with numerous veins occurs not only at low altitudes in the Aegean region, but also up to 3500m in south-eastern Turkey. Sternberg (1831) said that *S.mollis* is 'a sibirica diversissima', but the only difference of any consequence to emerge from his descriptions of the two species is that in *S.mollis* the leaves are said to be hairless, and in *S.sibirica* furnished with marginal hairs. Schönbeck-Temesy (1967) also found the supposed distinctions unreliable.

In Asia the chief variation is in the number and shape of the leaf-lobes, and several varieties have been named.

*HYBRIDS*: None is known.

*CHROMOSOME NUMBER*: $2n = 16$.

*DISTRIBUTION* (Map 43): In Europe this species is found in two widely separated areas. One is in eastern Russia, mainly in and around the foothills of the southern Urals, extending from about 53°30′ to 61°N. The other is in the eastern Rodopi range in south-eastern Bulgaria, just crossing the border into Greek Thrace, and occurring also on the island of Samothraki. Its wide range in Asia, however, serves nearly to link up the two European areas. From the Aegean it extends through Turkey, the Caucasus and northern Iran to the high mountains of central Asia on the borders of China and the USSR, and to the western Himalaya. From here it is separated only by the deserts of Transcaspia from its extensive range throughout southern Siberia, Mongolia and western and northern China.

*HABITAT*: Usually on damp rocks or screes. No reliable information is available for its range of altitude in Europe; it is probably mainly between 500 and 1500m.

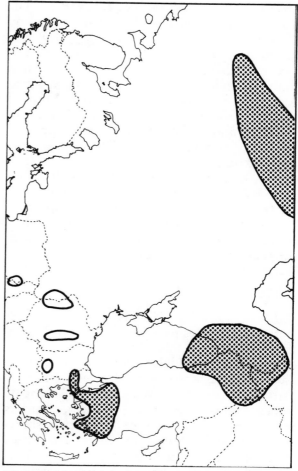

Map 43. Distribution of *S.sibirica* (shaded areas, also widely distributed in southern Siberia, Central Asia and China) and *S.carpatica* (unshaded)

*ACCESS*: We have no advice to offer under this head. Kashmir or the Aegean islands of Ikaria or Samothraki would seem to offer the best possibilities.

*CULTIVATION*: Seldom attempted; no data are available.

**56. *Saxifraga carpatica* Sternberg, *Revisio Saxifragarum, Supplementum II,* 32 (1831)**

*SYNONYMS*: S.rivularis of Townson and many later authors, not of Linnaeus
S.sibirica of Wahlenberg, not of Linnaeus
S.carpathica Reichenbach

*HISTORY & NOMENCLATURE*: The species was discovered, it would seem, by Townson (1797) in or near the Tatra, but mistaken by him for *S.rivularis*. Sternberg was the first to recognise that it was a distinct, hitherto undescribed species, but his description was overlooked in the original edition of *Index Kewensis*, an omission which was not rectified until the ninth supplement appeared in 1938. In consequence, almost all authors have attributed the name (with different spelling — *carpathica*) to Reichenbach in his *Flora germanica excursoria*, but this was published in 1832, a year later than Sternberg's work.

The epithet needs no explanation, but a caution may be given against confusing it with *carpetana*, which indicates the mountains of central Spain.

*TYPE*: Not traced.

*DESCRIPTION*: Usually forming small tufts. Basal leaves with petiole 2–4cm, slender, but with dilated, sheathing base, hairless or very sparsely glandular-hairy; lamina kidney-shaped, 5–12 × 6–16mm, hairless, with 5–9 broadly triangular-ovate, obtuse to subacute lobes. Flowering stems 5–20cm, hairless except in the inflorescence, with a few short-petioled cauline leaves, the lower 3–5-lobed, the uppermost entire. Flowers 1–4; pedicels glandular-hairy. Sepals 3–3.5mm, narrowly triangular-ovate, more or less acute, sparsely glandular-hairy. Petals 6–7mm, narrowly obovate, impure white, sometimes tinged with pink. Ovary nearly superior; styles stout, very short. Seeds 0.8 × 0.35mm, ellipsoid to oblong, dark brown, uniformly covered with fine tubercles; raphe rather inconspicuous. Flowering season: June to September.

*ILLUSTRATIONS*:
Sternberg (1831, Plate 25)
Reichenbach (1899, Plate 127)
Engler & Irmscher (1916, Figure 63)
Mądalski (1962, Plate 1318)

*RECOGNITION*: Within its section, *S.carpatica* may be distinguished from *S.sibirica* by its smaller petals, from *S.rivularis* and *S.hyperborea* by its larger petals, and from *S.cernua* by the absence of bulbils from the inflorescence.

*VARIATION*: Except for some variation in the shape of the leaf-lobes there seems to be none of any consequence.

*HYBRIDS*: None is known.

*CHROMOSOME NUMBER*: $2n = $ c.48.

*DISTRIBUTION* (Map 43, p. 145): As the name suggests, this is primarily a species of the Carpathians; elsewhere it is known only from south-western Bulgaria (Rila and northern Pirin). In the Carpathians its range is wide but discontinuous. Its western limit is in the Fatra range in Czechoslovakia, and from here it extends eastwards to the High and Low Tatra, crossing the frontier into Poland in the former. Then there is a gap, but it reappears on the higher peaks of the Ukranian Carpathians at about 24°15′E and continues into the northernmost part of the eastern Carpathians of Romania, southwards to 47°30′N. It is absent from the rest of the eastern Carpathians, but it extends through the greater part of the southern Carpathians, from 22°30′ to 25°30′E.

*HABITAT*: Damp and shady rocks or stabilised screes, usually on granite, more rarely on sandstone. It is found mostly between 1800 and 2200m, but descends to 1400m in Czechoslovakia and has been recorded as high as 2700m in Bulgaria.

*ACCESS*: We can give no recommendation based on personal experience. The Polish Tatra above Zakopane, the Rila range in Bulgaria and possibly the Transylvanian Alps in southern Romania are likely to provide the most promising hunting-grounds.

*CULTIVATION*: No information is available.

## 57. *Saxifraga rivularis* Linnaeus, *Species Plantarum* 404 (1753)

*HISTORY & NOMENCLATURE*: The species was discovered by Linnaeus in the course of his Lapland journey of 1732, and first described by him later in the same year (Linnaeus 1732) as *Saxifraga foliis palmatis, supremo cordato*. He gave it the name *rivularis* (growing by streams), as this is one of its characteristic (though by no means its only) habitats in Lapland.

*TYPE*: Sheet 174.5 in the Linnean herbarium, Stockholm (**S**) has been designated as lectotype (Webb 1987a).

*DESCRIPTION*: A delicate plant, forming small, loose tufts, or occasionally dense cushions. Like other members of the section it develops bulbils in the axils of its basal leaves during summer and autumn, but in spring most of these germinate before the flowering season to form slender runners, at the ends of which new plants develop. Basal leaves with lamina up to 20 × 30mm, but more usually 5–12 × 9–17mm, semicircular or kidney-shaped, divided, not very deeply, into 3–7 broadly ovate, obtuse lobes; petiole 2–6 times as long as the lamina, slender except for a broad, sheathing base. Leaves often completely hairless, but sometimes with hairs near the junction of lamina and petiole, and more rarely at the base of the petiole. Flowering stems 3–15cm, more or less densely glandular-hairy, at least above, usually unbranched, with a single terminal flower, but sometimes branched from about the middle, with 2–5 flowers on long, spreading pedicels. Cauline leaves few, the lower usually similar to the basal leaves, the uppermost broadly elliptical, entire. Sepals 2–3mm, obtuse, sparsely glandular-hairy, the hypanthium more densely so. Petals 4–5 × 2.5mm, obovate, white, sometimes tinged with pink. Ovary at least ⅓ inferior, less clearly superior than in other species of the section; styles very short, stout. Seeds 0.7 × 0.35–0.4mm, oblong with rounded ends, medium brown, covered all over with small, dark tubercles, including the conspicuous raphe. Flowering season: May to August.

*ILLUSTRATIONS*: Plate 26
\* Sowerby (1865, Plate 553)
 Warming (1909, Figures 27–30)
 Ross-Craig (1957, Plate 9)

*RECOGNITION*: As neither the basal bulbs nor the runners which arise from them are always easy to see, reliance must be placed on a combination of the following characters: white or pink, hairless petals not more than 5mm long; sepals erect in fruit; basal leaves divided less than half-way to the base into obtuse lobes, and with petiole slender above but with a broad, sheathing base. For the distinctions from *S.hyperborea* see page 148.

*VARIATION*: There is very little variation in Europe, except in the frequency and distribution of hairs, the number of flowers in the inflorescence and the size of the leaves.

*HYBRIDS*: It hybridises with *S.cernua* in Norway; see under that species.

*CHROMOSOME NUMBER*: $2n = 52$.

*DISTRIBUTION* (Map 44): *S.rivularis* is widespread in the Arctic, and extends southwards fairly continuously to Iceland and the Faeroes, southern Norway, Kamchatka, Montana, Newfoundland and southern Greenland. There are a few outlying stations further south, in the Scottish Highlands, California and Colorado.

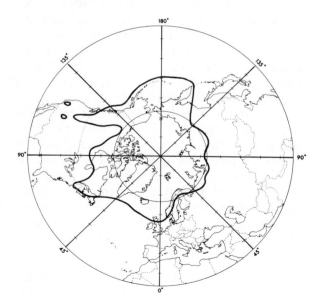

Map 44. Distribution of *S.rivularis* and *S.hyperborea*; information is insufficient to provide separate maps for these species

*HABITAT*: Always in damp situations, in wet moss, on the margins of streams, in narrow gullies or under the shelter of overhanging rocks.

*ACCESS*: It is fairly common in subarctic Norway, and should be found without difficulty near the main road along the coast.

*CULTIVATION*: Seldom attempted and probably difficult.

## 58. *Saxifraga hyperborea* R. Brown, *Chloris Melvilliana* 16 (1823)

*HISTORY & NOMENCLATURE*: The plant was described by Brown from the collection made on Melville Island, in the western part of the Canadian Arctic, in the course of Parry's voyage in search of a north-west passage. It is usually cited as having been first described in the botanical appendix to the journal of the voyage, but Brown issued this as a pre-print, entitled *Chloris Melvilliana*, a few months before the whole journal was published.

For a long time it was dismissed by Hooker, Engler and others as a rather trivial variant of *S.rivularis*. More recently, however, the apparent constancy of a chromosome number half that of *S.rivularis*, and further detailed observations on the plant in Spitsbergen, suggest that it is probably entitled to specific status. We must make it clear, however, that the data here presented refer primarily to the plant as known from the arctic regions of Europe, Asia and Greenland. In North America the name has been given to plants from as far south as New Hampshire and Colorado, probably in error. We suspect that in some cases they have been named more on the grounds of chromosome number than of morphology. For further discussion see Webb (1987b).

*TYPE*: Parry's first voyage 1819–20. 25.*Saxifraga hyperborea* Flor. [error for Chlor.?] Melv. Melville Island. *Mr James Ross*. (Lectotype: British Museum, London (**BM**), designated here.)

*DESCRIPTION*: This is best accomplished by detailing the points in which it appears to differ fairly constantly from *S.rivularis*.
(1) The whole plant is smaller, rarely more than 4cm tall.
(2) The basal leaves are also small; they are mostly 3-lobed (in *S.rivularis* usually 5-lobed), and the base of the lamina is cuneate, tapered gradually into the petiole, whereas in *S.rivularis* it is more or less cordate.
(3) The petals are red, rather than white or pink, and the whole plant is usually suffused with a red colour, which is rarely seen in *S.rivularis*, and never with the same intensity.
(4) The petals are smaller (usually about 2.5mm).
(5) There are no runners from the basal bulbils; the plant therefore forms more compact tufts.

*ILLUSTRATIONS*:
Böcher *et al.* (1968, p. 70)
The plant illustrated in Engler & Irmscher (1916, Figure 66 E–H) as *S.rivularis* f. *hyperborea* (R. Brown) Engler is wrongly named.

*RECOGNITION*: The only species which it resembles closely is *S.rivularis*, and the differences between the two are set out above.

*VARIATION*: The plant is not yet well enough known for any accurate data to be given.

*HYBRIDS*: Probably with *S.cernua*; see under that species.

*CHROMOSOME NUMBER*: $2n = 26$.

*DISTRIBUTION* (Map 44, p. 147): Widely distributed in the Arctic; occurrences reported elsewhere are subject to doubt.

*HABITAT*: In conditions similar to those favoured by *S.rivularis*; plentiful moisture is necessary, and it is particularly frequent in late snow-lies.

*ACCESS*: The data on distribution are too incomplete, and to some extent too contradictory, for us to offer any advice under this head.

*CULTIVATION*: Seldom, if ever, attempted; no information is available.

## 59. *Saxifraga cernua* Linnaeus, *Species Plantarum* 403 (1753)

SYNONYMS: *S.bulbifera* of Gunnerus and some later authors, not of Linnaeus
*S.simulata* Small

*HISTORY & NOMENCLATURE*: There is no record of this plant having been seen by the earliest explorers of the arctic regions; it appears to have been first collected by Linnaeus during his voyage to Lapland in 1732, and was published later in the same year as *Saxifraga caule simplici unifloro, foliis palmatis, alis bulbiferis* (Linnaeus 1732). He realised later (where some other authors failed) that it is quite distinct from *S.bulbifera*, particularly in its nearly superior ovary, and that it is related to *S.rivularis*. The epithet (nodding) indicates that Linnaeus noted that the flower was slightly drooping, but this is not a constant character, except perhaps in bud.

*TYPE*: Sheet 575.44 in the Linnean herbarium, London (**LINN**) has been designated as lectotype (Webb 1987a).

*DESCRIPTION*: Stems solitary or in small tufts. Basal leaves at first fairly numerous, but many of them dying off during growth of the flowering stem, each bearing in its axil at ground level a conical bulbil; lamina 5–18 × 9–25mm, kidney-shaped to semicircular, divided less than halfway to the base into 3–7 ovate to oblong, subacute lobes, hairless; petiole usually 2–3 times as long as lamina, slender and hairless above, expanded below into a sheathing base, which is sometimes clothed with long hairs. Flowering stem 3–30cm, varying from almost hairless to rather densely clothed with rather long or short hairs, usually simple, but occasionally branched from near the middle; cauline leaves numerous, the lower similar to the basal but with rather more acute lobes, showing thence a gradual transition to entire leaves, of which the lower are ovate-elliptical, the uppermost linear-lanceolate and very small. In the axil of each cauline leaf are one or more bulbils, which vary in colour from bright red to blackish-purple. Occasionally these bulbils start to germinate and produce small leaves while still attached to the stem. The stem normally bears a single, terminal flower, but quite frequently this is abortive and the stem bears nothing but bulbils; plants with a terminal flower and a branched stem may or may not bear flowers at the tips of the principal branches. The flower, when present, has shortly glandular-hairy sepals 3mm long, white petals 7–12 × 3.5–5mm, a nearly completely superior ovary (free from the hypanthium for at least ¾ of its length) with straight, erect styles about 1mm long. Seeds virtually unknown in the wild state; those produced by cross-pollination of a Scottish by a Norwegian plant in cultivation (Godfree 1979; see also below) are c.0.8 × 0.32mm, brown, with prominent tubercles in between rows of papillae. Flowering season: June to August.

*Note on reproduction in S.cernua*: The great efficiency of its vegetative reproduction by bulbils means that, even in regions of the Arctic where it is abundant, the population over quite a wide area may consist of a single clone, that is the descendants by vegetative reproduction of a single plant, and therefore with identical genetic constitution. Pollen production is apparently confined to populations north of about 66°N and, not surprisingly therefore, the rare cases of seed production in the wild all involve arctic populations (Eurola 1972; Bell & Bliss 1980). The rarity of natural seed-set, even in the Arctic, however, suggests that the species is self-incompatible. Presumably there are occasions when a pollinating insect may fly far enough to cross the boundary between one clone and another, or alternatively a bulbil may become widely dispersed by wind and germinate within the territory of another clone, when, if all goes well, there may be cross-pollination between two compatible strains and the possibility of seed production. But obviously such events are extremely rare.

It may be added that flowering plants are on the whole commoner in the Arctic than in the relict stations further south, but the correlation between latitude and production of flowers is by no means perfect.

*ILLUSTRATIONS*: Plate 27
   Warming (1909, Figures 6–9)
   Mądalski (1962, Plate 1319)
   Huber (1963, Figure 144)
* Lindman (1964, Plate 292)

*RECOGNITION*: The abundant bulbils in the axils of the cauline leaves (whether a flower is present or not) distinguish this species from all others except *S.bulbifera*. This differs in having a semi-inferior ovary, several flowers on a stem, glandular-hairy petals, hairy basal leaves and the lower cauline leaves ovate in outline.

*VARIATION*: Very variable in height and leaf-size, and in abundance of hairs on the flowering stem and lower part of the petioles of the basal leaves; also in the presence or absence of a terminal flower. None of these characters shows any obvious ecological or geographical distribution, nor is it known to what extent they are determined by environmental influences, so that no taxonomic division is practicable.

*HYBRIDS*: *S.cernua* × *rivularis* (*S.* × *opdalensis* Blytt) has been recorded from Norway and Sweden, and is locally frequent in one or two small areas. A possible hybrid with *S.hyperborea* has been reported from Spitsbergen, but requires confirmation. The recently described *S.svalbardensis* Øvstedal (2n = c.64) from Spitsbergen is morphologically intermediate between *S.cernua*, *S.rivularis* and *S.hyperborea*, and may be of hybrid origin. For further details see Borgen & Reidar (1983).

*CHROMOSOME NUMBER*: Counts of 2n = 60 and 64 have been recorded from Europe, but from other parts of the Arctic there are counts of 2n = 24, 48, 52, 56, 60, 70 and 72.

*DISTRIBUTION* (Maps 45, 46): Primarily an arctic plant, and there are no substantial areas of land north of the Arctic Circle from which it has not been recorded. Southwards it extends fairly continuously to southern Norway, to about 58°N in the Far Eastern division of the USSR, to 54°N in Labrador,

and to 46°N in the Rocky mountains. South of these limits there are, however, a number of outlying stations which extend its total range as far south as Colorado and central Japan, as well as a large arc covering the central and western Himalaya, turning northwards through the Pamirs, Tien-Shan and Altai, and then eastwards through Mongolia and south-eastern Siberia as far as the Soviet-Chinese border at 120°E.

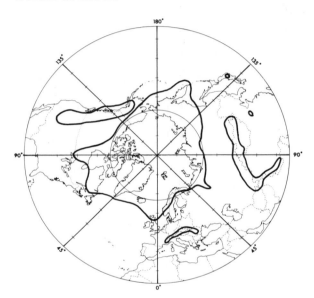

Map 45. Distribution of *S.cernua*; for detailed distribution in Europe see Map 46

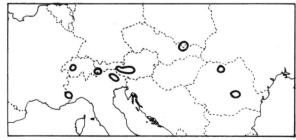

Map 46. Distribution of *S.cernua* in Europe; for global distribution see Map 45

In Europe the outlying stations are in Scotland, the Alps and the Carpathians. Everywhere it is both local and rare. A detailed survey of its distribution in the Alps is given by Chiarugi (1925, 1934). It is very rare in the Maritime Alps and the Bernese Oberland,

Plate 21.  *S. retusa*, a white-flowered variant

Plate 22.  *S.aizoides*

Plate 23.  *S.bryoides*

Plate 24.   *S.aizoides*

Plate 25.   *S.sibirica*

Plate 26.   *S.rivularis*

Plate 27.    *S.cernua*

Plate 28.    *S.granulata*

Plate 29.    *S.corsica*

Plate 30.    *S.haenseleri*

very slightly more frequent in the Alps of Styria and Carinthia, and more frequent still (though rare by ordinary standards) in the south-eastern Dolomites. In the Carpathians it is limited to three small regions: the High Tatra, the Rodnei mountains in the extreme north of Romania, and the Bucegi mountains, towards the eastern end of the southern Carpathians.

*HABITAT*: Provided that the habitat is cool and fairly moist, the plant can tolerate a good deal of variation in the substratum. Sometimes it grows in a cushion of moss, sometimes among stones under an overhanging boulder, more rarely on shady rock-faces, or on muddy or grassy tundra. It descends almost to sea-level in the Arctic; in the Alps it ranges from 1500 to 2800m.

*ACCESS*: It is not difficult to find in arctic Norway (except in the extreme north, where it is more local), and it is common around Abisko in arctic Sweden.

*CULTIVATION*: This is possible, but not easy. Good drainage is essential and conditions approximating to the arctic house at the botanical garden in Copenhagen are probably needed, although the life-cycle, at least in cultivation, apparently seldom extends beyond three years.

# Section *Saxifraga*
## including sections *Dactyloides* Seringe (*Dactylites* Tausch), *Discogyne* Sternberg, *Nephrophyllum* (Gaudin) Koch (in part), *Tridactylites* (Haworth) Grisebach and *Trachyphylloides* Huber

Mostly perennial, rarely annual or biennial. Perennial species mostly evergreen, but some are summer-dormant, perennating by bulbils at or below ground-level. Habit of perennial species very varied, usually with numerous leafy shoots forming a cushion or mat. Leaves alternate, usually fairly soft, often lobed or crenate, without lime-secreting hydathodes, usually with a distinct petiole. Hairs uniseriate. Petals usually white, more rarely pale or dull yellow, pink or red. Ovary semi-inferior to almost completely inferior.

A large section of about 70 species, centred on Europe, and especially well-represented in Spain, the Pyrenees and the Alps. About three-quarters of the species are endemic to Europe, but the range of the section extends to North Africa, Madeira, the Himalayan region, the Arctic, and North and South America.

## Subsection *Saxifraga*

Perennials, often partly or wholly summer-dormant, forming lax rosettes of basal leaves, with bulbils in their axils or in the axils of the scales on the short stock, but no summer-dormant buds of the type found in subsection *Triplinervium*. The bulbils are different from those in section *Mesogyne*; each consists of an outer series of loosely imbricate, papery scales with marginal or surface hairs, surrounding an inner series of fleshy scales. Leaves ovate to kidney-shaped, the margins variously lobed or divided, sometimes deeply so. Flowering stems terminal, bearing an inflorescence with several flowers. Petals white, rarely tinged or veined with pink. Ovary ½ or more inferior.

A small group of ten species, seven of which are endemic to Europe; three extend to North Africa and one of them also to the islands of the eastern Aegean.

## Series *Saxifraga*

Bulbils clustered together in the axils of the lower leaves or scales on the stock. They consist of a series of outer, papery scales surrounding a pair of tightly joined fleshy scales. Leaves lobed or crenate, not usually divided as far as the midvein, but if so, with lobes that are not strongly tapered at the base.

A group of seven species with the range of the subsection.

## 60. *Saxifraga granulata* Linnaeus, *Species Plantarum* 403 (1753)

SYNONYMS: *S.glaucescens* Reuter
*S.castellana* Reuter, *nomen nudum*
*S.rouyana* Magnier

HISTORY & NOMENCLATURE: This is rightly designated as the type-species of the genus, as it is the only species known to authors of the sixteenth and early seventeenth centuries to which the name *Saxifraga* was consistently applied (other species being referred to *Sedum*, *Geum*, *Cotyledon*, etc.) and served, therefore, as the nucleus around which the concept of the genus gradually crystallised. It was probably known to the medieval herbalists, but in the early printed herbals the illustration of the plant named *Saxifraga* seems to be based largely on a *Melilotus*, though with leaves more like those of a *Potentilla*. (The nitrogen-fixing root-nodules of *Melilotus* could, of course, be confused with the bulbils of *Saxifraga granulata*.) The first convincing illustration of the species is to be found in Brunfels (1530).

The 'granules' implied in the specific epithet are, of course, the underground bulbils.

TYPE: *S.granulata*. Sheet 575.43 in the Linnean herbarium, London (**LINN**) has been designated as lectotype (Webb 1987a).

Subsp. *graniticola*. Spain, near Puerto de Menga, SW of Avila. 27 April, 1959. *D.A. Webb*. (Holotype: Trinity College, Dublin (**TCD**).)

DESCRIPTION: Very variable. Basal leaves usually with the lamina 6–20 × 8–30mm, but sometimes up to 30 × 50mm, kidney-shaped, cordate at the base, crenate, or rarely toothed, with 5–13 low, usually rounded or flat-topped crenations, glandular-hairy at least beneath and often on the upper surface as well, slightly fleshy; petiole slender, hairy, up to 50mm, usually 2–5 times as long as the lamina. Each basal leaf bears in its axil, slightly below ground-level, a globular bulbil usually 3–5mm in diameter. Flowering stem usually single, usually 10–30cm, although rarely up to 50cm, branched sometimes from near the base, sometimes only in the uppermost quarter, to form a lax or moderately compact panicle of 4–30 flowers; pedicels mostly equalling the capsule in fruit, rarely longer; cauline leaves usually few but sometimes up to 7, acutely and deeply toothed, cuneate at the base with a short petiole. Sepals 3 × 2mm, oblong, hairy. Petals 7–16 × 3–7mm, obovate to broadly oblanceolate, white, occasionally with red veins, hairless. Ovary ¾ inferior; styles 4–5mm, straight, divergent in fruit. Seeds 0.5 × 0.3mm, light brown, covered with mostly very low papillae arranged in longitudinal rows, the surface between them minutely tuberculate; raphe small but fairly conspicuous. Flowering season: April to early July.

ILLUSTRATIONS: Plate 28; Figure 35
\* Sowerby (1865, Plate 555)
  Ross-Craig (1957, Plate 7)
  Mądalski (1962, Plate 1317)
  Huber (1963, Figure 147)

RECOGNITION: In spite of its great variability this species can be recognised by the combination of semi-inferior ovary, petals without glandular hairs, and bulbils in the axils of the basal leaves, which are crenate but not lobed. It is most likely to be confused with *S.corsica*, but this has basal leaves which are distinctly 3-lobed, being divided at least half-way to the base.

VARIATION: Although much of the variation in height, hairiness, nature of the leaf-margin and shape of the inflorescence can often be seen within a single population, it is possible to recognise a subspecies and a variety distinct from the type.
(a) Subsp. **granulata**. Plant robust. Basal leaves usually more than 12mm wide. Inflorescence with fairly stout, semi-erect branches. Petals usually at least 12mm long.

Figure 35. Leaf-outlines of species in series *Saxifraga*: (a) *S.granulata* subsp. *granulata*; (b) *S.granulata* subsp. *graniticola*; (c) *S.corsica* subsp. *corsica*; (d) *S.corsica* subsp. *cossoniana*; (e) *S.haenseleri*; (f) *S.dichotoma* subsp. *dichotoma*; (g) *S.dichotoma* subsp. *albarracinensis*; (h) *S.carpetana* subsp. *carpetana*; (i) *S.carpetana* subsp. *graeca*; (j) *S.cintrana*; (k) *S.bulbifera*

(i) Var. **granulata**. Leaves green, not glaucous, variably hairy. Flowering stems often with several cauline leaves.

(ii) Var. **glaucescens** (Reuter) Engler, *Monographie der Gattung Saxifraga L.* 98 (1872). Leaves more or less glaucous, usually very hairy. Stems with 0–2 cauline leaves.

(b) Subsp. **graniticola** D.A. Webb, *Feddes Repertorium* 68:207 (1963). Plant delicate, seldom more than 10cm tall. Basal leaves 8–12mm wide. Inflorescence with slender, flexuous, divergent branches. Petals 7–13mm long.

A variant of subsp. *granulata* with sterile flowers containing very numerous petals has been in cultivation since the seventeenth century ('Flore Pleno').

*HYBRIDS*: No hybrids of *S. granulata* with other species of the same subsection have been recorded, but it can form hybrids with

*S.rosacea* and perhaps with *S.cespitosa*. The first of these crosses was recorded from the Harz mountains in central Germany. In this case the *S.rosacea* parent belonged to subsp. *rosacea*, but later a cross between *S.granulata* and *S.rosacea* subsp. *sponhemica* was described from the German Palatinate and given the same *S.* × *freibergii* Ruppert. This name has priority over *S.* × *haussknechtii* Engler & Irmscher and *S.* × *potternensis* Marsden-Jones & Turrill, which must be regarded as synonyms. Marsden-Jones & Turrill (1930, 1934) produced this hybrid artificially, showed it to be partly fertile, and claimed that the F₂ gen-eration which they obtained was tetraploid, but doubt was thrown on this claim by cytological work by Philp (1934), who suggested that *S.granulata* was hexaploid, *S.rosacea* octoploid and the F₂ hybrid decaploid.

The natural hybrids from the Harz are rather variable, suggesting that some might be the result of back-crossing or segregation.

*S.cespitosa* × *granulata* has been recorded from Sweden, but requires confirmation.

*CHROMOSOME NUMBER*: Recent counts from Europe have given $2n = 52$, but a count of $2n = 30$ from a Moroccan population and

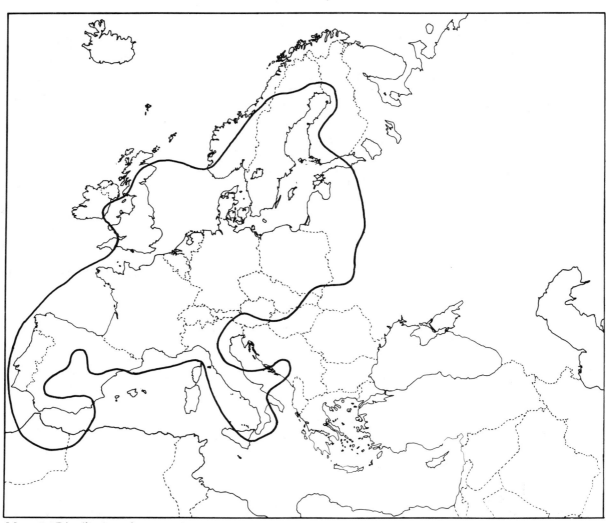

Map 47. Distribution of *S. granulata*

older counts of 32, 46 and 48 have also been published, and it seems probable that the number is not constant throughout the species.

*DISTRIBUTION* (Map 47): Next to *S. tridactylites* this is the most widely distributed species in Europe, but it is absent from most of the east. Its northern limit (as a native, as it is locally naturalised further north) runs from Scotland through southern Norway and central Sweden to south-western Finland; from here its eastern boundary runs through Estonia, western White Russia and north-western Ukraine and central Hungrary. It is absent from the Balkan peninsula, except for a few stations in Bosnia and Montenegro, from the Mediterranean islands except Sicily, and from most of the Alpine region. Even in the west it is absent from most of Ireland and from parts of central and eastern Spain. Its areas of greatest abundance are western Czechoslovakia, central and southern Germany, southern France and northern Spain.

Outside Europe it is known only from N. Africa where it extends southwards to 30°N in the Anti-Atlas.

Subsp. *graniticola* occurs in central and western Spain and eastern Portugal. Subsp. *granulata* var. *glaucescens* is almost confined to Spain, but is recorded also from the French Pyrenees and southern Portugal.

*HABITAT*: In the northern part of its range it is found almost exclusively in moderately dry grassland. Further south it is often abundant in damp meadows, but also is commonly seen on dry, rocky ground. It shows some preference for moderately base-rich soils, but cannot really be reckoned as a calcicole. Its altitudinal limit varies with latitude: in northern Europe it is mainly lowland, ascending at most to 500m, but in southern Spain it is mainly montane, ascending as high as 2250m.

*ACCESS*: This species is easy to find over large areas of western and central Europe. Particularly spectacular displays have been noted at Vassieux-en-Vercors (16km north of Die, dept. Drôme); in the western Cévennes, south-westwards from St-Affrique (depts.

Tarn and Aveyron); and in northern Spain (prov. León) on the southern side of the Cordillera Cantábrica westwards from the Puerto de Pajares. Subsp. *graniticola* is most easily seen in eastern Portugal by the River Coa, where it is crossed by the main road from Guarda to Cuidad Rodrigo; also in several places south-west of Bragança.

*CULTIVATION*: *S.granulata* is curiously intolerant of pot-culture under glass, but it can easily be grown in a deep pocket of good soil in semi-shade in the rock-garden, and would probably be easy to naturalise in a small patch of meadow, if it were not cut before early July.

**61. *Saxifraga corsica*** (Seringe) Grenier & Godron, *Flore de la France 1:642 (1849)*

*SYNONYMS*: *S.granulata* var. *corsica* Seringe in Duby, *Botanicon Gallicum* 1:211 (1828)
*S.granulata* subsp. *russii* of Engler & Irmscher, but not *S.russii* of J. Presl
*S.cossoniana* Boissier & Reuter

*HISTORY & NOMENCLATURE*: The earliest explorers of Corsica regarded this as coming under *S.granulata*, and Seringe was the first to give it varietal status; 20 years later it was established as an independent species by Grenier & Godron. By a mistake which is difficult to explain, Engler (1869) equated it with *S.russii* J. Presl, which was described from Sicily and is certainly *S.bulbifera*, *S. graeca*, or a hybrid between the two. Nevertheless, Rouy & Camus (1901), Engler & Irmscher (1916) and other authors continued to use the name (or a combination based on it) although they described the plant as endemic to Corsica and Sardinia and not occurring in Sicily.

The inclusion of *S.cossoniana* as a subspecies of *S.corsica* is based on the work of Font Quer (1927).

*TYPE*: *S.corsica*. Saxifraga orientalis, au dessus de Vivario, Corse. 1823. *M.Phil. Thomas.* (Holotype: De Candolle herbarium, Geneva (**G**).)

Subsp. *cossoniana*. Plantes d'Espagne 1852. Sax. granulata var. ramosissima (Coss.). Rochers du versant septentrional de la Sierra de S.Antonio. *Bourgeau.* [Added by Boissier: près Alcoy]. (Lectotype: Geneva (**G**), designated here; many isotypes elsewhere.)

*DESCRIPTION*: Generally similar to the smaller variants of *S.granulata*, but differing in the following features:
(1) Some at least of the basal leaves are distinctly 3-lobed, the division reaching at least halfway to the base.
(2) The flowering stems are nearly always branched from the base or near it, and are very slender, as are the pedicels, which are almost thread-like; they are mostly longer than the capsule. The branching of the inflorescence is strongly divaricate.

It must be admitted that a few specimens from Corsica and Sardinia do not show these differential characters very well developed, and could pass as *S.granulata*. It may be that there are small residual populations of *S. granulata* in these islands, which are partly hybridised with *S.corsica*.

Of the two differential characters given above the first is best marked in subsp. *cossoniana*, the second in subsp. *corsica*.

*ILLUSTRATIONS*: Plate 29; Figures 35, 36
\* Willkomm (1881–1885, Plate 68)
   Coste (1902, p. 134)
   Engler & Irmscher (1916, Figure 59)
   Font Quer (1927, pp. 33–5)

*RECOGNITION*: This species may be distinguished from *S.granulata* by the characters given earlier. It differs also in its habitat (see below). From all other species with a semi-inferior ovary and long-stalked, kidney-shaped basal leaves with bulbils in their axils, it differs in having no glandular hairs on the petals.

*VARIATION*: The species falls into two fairly well-defined subspecies.
(a) Subsp. *corsica*. Delicate. Basal leaves not very deeply lobed (not more than half-way to the base). Inflorescence branched from the base.

Figure 36. *S.corsica* subsp. *cossoniana*

(b) Subsp. **cossoniana** (Boissier & Reuter) D.A. Webb, *Feddes Repertorium* 68:203 (1963). More robust. Basal leaves deeply lobed (usually divided about ⅔ of the way to the base). Inflorescence often branched from some little distance above the base.

*HYBRIDS*: None has been reported, but, as was mentioned earlier, it is possible that there may be hybrids with *S.granulata* in Corsica and Sardinia.

*CHROMOSOME NUMBER*: $2n = 62–66$ (subsp. *corsica*); $2n = 64–66$ (subsp. *cossoniana*).

*DISTRIBUTION* (Map 48): Subsp. *corsica* is widespread in Corsica; rare in Sardinia, and mainly in the centre. Subsp. *cossoniana* is confined to a fairly small region of eastern Spain in the provinces of Valencia and Alicante. It extends from about 38°25′N to 39° 40′N, and from the coast inland to 1°W. Plants found in the Balearic Islands (Formentera) are intermediate between the two subspecies, but somewhat closer to subsp. *corsica*.

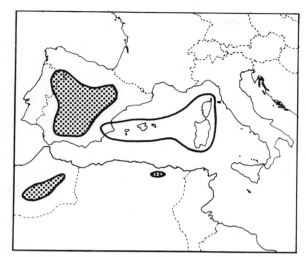

Map 48. Distribution of *S.dichotoma* (shaded) and *S.corsica* (unshaded)

*HABITAT*: Shady walls and vertical rock-faces; less often on screes. Subsp. *corsica* is found exclusively on siliceous rocks, subsp. *cossoniana* on limestone, but in neither case is the petrological diversity within their restricted areas of distribution sufficient to make it possible to say, with confidence, that the first is calcifuge and the second calcicole. The species ranges from 400 to 1500m in altitude.

*ACCESS*: Subsp. *corsica* can be found without too much difficulty above Zonza, by the road to the Col di Bavella; north of Vizzavona, by the road which descends to Vivario; and by the road leading north-eastwards below the Gorges de l'Asco. Subsp. *cossoniana* is most conveniently seen on the talus which lies below the cliff on which stands the castle of Játiva (prov. Valencia).

*CULTIVATION*: This has been tried without success at Cambridge and Dublin, but if grown from seed it should not be impossible.

## 62. *Saxifraga haenseleri* Boissier & Reuter, *Diagnoses Plantarum novarum hispanicarum* 13 (1842)

*HISTORY & NOMENCLATURE*: Discovered by Felix Haenseler, a German living in Málaga whom Boissier met on his first visit to Spain, and who put at Boissier's disposal his wide knowledge of natural history and of the countryside of southern Spain. Haenseler's specimens, from which Boissier's description was drawn up, were from the mountains above Grazalema (prov. Cádiz).

*TYPE*: Saxifraga haenseleri [in Boissier's writing]. Saxifraga. Cerro Sto Cristobal. *Haenseler* [in Haenseler's writing]. (Holotype: Geneva (**G**).)

*DESCRIPTION*: A slender plant, with something of the general aspect of *S.tridactylites* or *S.adscendens*, but in fact a summer-dormant perennial with small bulbils underground, in the axils of the basal leaves. Basal leaves with petiole up to 22mm; lamina 6–10 × 4–9mm, tapered gradually into the petiole, rather deeply divided into 3–7 oblong, obtuse segments, rather sparsely glandular-hairy. Flowering stem 8–30cm, branched from the middle or from the base, bearing 1–2 small, entire or very shortly 3-lobed cauline leaves. Inflorescence very lax and diffuse, usually with 6–12, but sometimes up to 40 flowers; pedicels 10–20mm, glandular-hairy, as are the main stem, the cauline leaves and bracts, the hypanthia and the sepals. Sepals 1.5mm, ovate, obtuse. Petals 5–6mm, narrowly obovate, white, often with glandular hairs on the basal part of the upper surface, but nearly as often hairless. Ovary almost completely inferior; styles 1mm, slender, slightly curved outwards. Seeds 0.6 × 0.3mm, ellipsoid, brown, marked by a few fine, longitudinal ribs and some very low and ill-defined papillae; raphe inconspicuous. Flowering season: May and June.

A remarkable species, suggesting a link between the subsections *Saxifraga* and *Tridactylites*.

*ILLUSTRATIONS*: Plate 30; Figure 35
Engler & Irmscher (1916, Figure 53)

*RECOGNITION*: Once the basal bulbils have been seen this species cannot be mistaken for any other. The species in this subsection to which it comes closest is *S.dichotoma*, but this has numerous cauline leaves and a small, compact inflorescence.

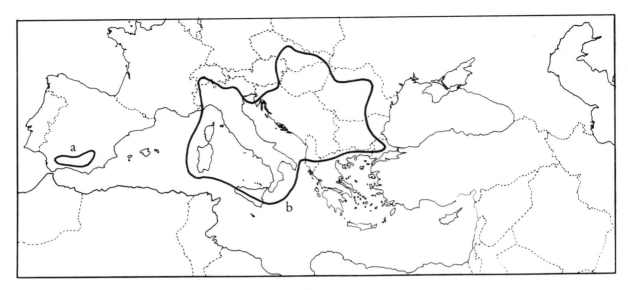

Map 49. Distribution of (a) *S.haenseleri* and (b) *S.bulbifera*

*VARIATION*: There is very little except in size and luxuriance, and in the presence or absence of glandular hairs on the petals.

*HYBRIDS*: None has been recorded.

*CHROMOSOME NUMBER*: Not known.

*DISTRIBUTION* (Map 49): *S.haenseleri* has a fairly wide range in southern Spain. Its most westerly point is in the *locus classicus* above Grazalema; from here it extends in a fairly wide arc, first eastwards and then north-eastwards, through the provinces of Málaga, Granada and Jaen to reach its north-eastern limit near Almansa, in the eastern part of the province of Albacete.

*HABITAT*: On usually shady but often fairly dry limestone rocks; also on semi-stabilised scree and limestone debris, and even on the gravelly surface of a road. The altitudinal range is from 100 to 2050m.

*ACCESS*: It may be seen in fair quantity on either side of the road near the pass by which the road from Grazalema runs northwards to Zahara; here it is found in semi-open communities on limestone debris at 1150m. It has also been seen on and beside the road near Quesada, south-west of Cazorla (prov. Jaen).

*CULTIVATION*: No information is available. It should not be too difficult if grown from seed.

**63. *Saxifraga dichotoma* Willdenow, in Sternberg, *Revisio Saxifragarum* 51 (1810)**

*SYNONYMS*: *S.arundana* Boissier
*S.kunzeana* Willkomm
*S.albarracinensis* Pau

*HISTORY & NOMENCLATURE*: Collected by Hecht in an unspecified locality in Spain, and sent by him to Willdenow, who passed on to Sternberg a description of the plant and a sketch. The epithet refers to the fact that in some plants the inflorescence is pseudo-dichotomous, the lowest axillary branch ascending parallel to the main axis and reaching to nearly the same height.

*TYPE*: *S.dichotoma*. Ex Hispania. (Holotype: No. 8415 in the Willdenow herbarium, Berlin (**B**).)
Subsp. *albarracinensis*. Not traced.

*DESCRIPTION*: Basal leaves with lamina very sparsely furnished with short glandular hairs and sometimes almost hairless, 5–18 × 7–30mm, semicircular to fan-shaped in outline with a truncate to cuneate base, deeply lobed (usually divided about ⅔ of the way to the base) into 3–7 lobes which may themselves be shortly lobed, giving 5–15 segments in all; these are obovate-cuneate, narrowed to the base and expanded towards the very blunt tip; petiole 1.5–4 times as long as the lamina, rather densely covered with long, glandular hairs. Flowering stem 6–25cm, glandular-hairy, branched above the middle (very rarely below it) to give a narrow cyme of 2–7 flowers; pedicels very variable in length; cauline leaves numbering 3–7, the lower similar to the basal but very short-stalked and glandular-hairy, the uppermost 3-lobed or entire. Sepals 2–2.5mm, triangular-oblong to ovate, glandular-hairy. Petals 5–10mm, narrowly obovate, white, often veined or tinged with pink, especially in bud, glandular-hairy (sometimes rather sparsely) on the upper surface or margins. Ovary ½ to ¾ inferior; styles very short. Seeds 0.75 × 0.4mm, prismatic, tapered from a broad, truncate end to a narrower blunt tip, pale brown, with numerous medium-length, dark papillae, between which the surface is very finely tuberculate; raphe inconspicuous. Flowering season: late March to May.

*ILLUSTRATIONS*: Figure 35
\* Sternberg (1810, Plate 21)
\* Willkomm (1881–1885, Plate 31), as *S. kunzeana*
Engler & Irmscher (1916, Figure 53)
Maire (1980, Figure 5)

*RECOGNITION*: Among the species with basal bulbils and glandular-hairy petals, *S. dichotoma* is distinct in its deeply divided basal leaves with almost hairless lamina and the frequent pink tinge to its flowers.

*VARIATION*: This mainly affects height of stem and size of leaves and flowers. It permits the division of the species into two fairly well-defined subspecies. Intermediates occur, but they are not very common except in a few districts.
(a) Subsp. *dichotoma*. Robust; stem 12–25cm, fairly stout. Basal leaves usually at least 12mm wide, often with 7 or more segments. Inflor-

escence often occupying ⅓ or more of the height of the stem, with some of the pedicels long. Petals 7–10mm.
(b) Subsp. *albarracinensis* (Pau) D.A. Webb, *Feddes Repertorium* 68:207 (1963) (*S.dichotoma* var. *hervieri* Engler & Irmscher, *Pflanzenreich* 67 (IV.117):238 (1916)). Delicate; stem seldom more than 15cm, slender. Basal leaves not more than 12mm wide, usually with 5 narrow segments. Inflorescence short and compact, with short pedicels. Petals 5–8mm.

*HYBRIDS*: None is known.

*CHROMOSOME NUMBER*: $2n = 32 + 2B$ (subsp. *dichotoma*).

*DISTRIBUTION* (Map 48, see p. 157): *S.dichotoma* is fairly widely distributed in Spain, and is found also in Morocco and Algeria. It is found mainly in the mountains, but is absent from the north. It extends from the neighbourhood of Calatayud in the province of Zaragoza southwards and then westwards through the provinces of Teruel, Cuenca, Valencia, Albacete, Granada and Málaga to the neighbourhood of Ronda. It is also found in the Sierra de Gredos and the Sierra de Guadarrama and a few other regions of central Spain, just extending into north-eastern Portugal in the region of Bragança. On the whole, subsp. *dichotoma* is prevalent in the southern part of the range, subsp. *albarracinensis* in the northern part.
In Morocco it is found in the High and Middle Atlas. In Algeria it has been recorded from the Kabylie region east-south-east of Algiers.

*HABITAT*: This is rather varied, ranging from dry, exposed rocky slopes without much other vegetation to closed communities in medium-dry grassland. It exhibits no strong preference for calcareous or siliceous soil. Data on altitudinal range are rather scanty; it certainly extends from 700 to 1700m and perhaps rather further.

*ACCESS*: Subsp. *dichotoma* is frequent at about 1000m by the main road which ascends the northern side of the Sierra Nevada from

Granada. Subsp. *albarracinensis* is more elusive, but can be seen not far from the Madrid–Barcelona road on the northern side of the Puerto del Cavero, a few kilometres north-east of Calatayud.

*CULTIVATION*: This seems to be difficult. Plants established at Dublin and at Kew died within a year.

## 64. *Saxifraga carpetana* Boissier & Reuter, *Diagnoses Plantarum novarum hispanicarum* 12 (1842)

*SYNONYMS*: *S.atlantica* Boissier & Reuter
*S.veronicifolia* Dufour
*S.graeca* Boissier & Heldreich
*S.granulata* var. *graeca* (Boissier & Heldreich) Engler, *Monographie der Gattung Saxifraga L.* 98 (1872)
*S.granulata* subsp. *graeca* (Boissier & Heldreich) Engler & Irmscher, *Pflanzenreich* 67 (IV.117):254 (1916)
*S.blanca* Willkomm

*HISTORY & NOMENCLATURE*: As can be seen from the synonymy the species is here interpreted in a wide sense. As subsp. *graeca* it was probably known to Dioscorides, and may have been one of the numerous and diverse elements around which his 'Saxiphragion' was based. It was first collected by Sibthorp, but mistaken by Smith for *S.granulata*. It was first recognised as a distinct species by Reuter, who collected it at Colmenar-viejo, which lies about half-way between Madrid and the Sierra de Guadarrama, and was given the epithet *carpetana* after the old name Montes Carpetani which was used collectively for the mountains of central Spain.

*TYPE*: *S.carpetana*. Colmenar viejo in pascuis. 1841. *Reuter*. (Holotype: Geneva (**G**).)
 Subsp. *graeca*. In sylvis abietinis in Parnethos Atticae. 27 mai 1852. Herb. *Heldreich 1978*. (Lectotype: Flora Orientalis herbarium, Geneva (**G**), designated here; many syntypes elsewhere.)

*DESCRIPTION*: Basal leaves variable in shape. The first-formed are usually circular to kidney-shaped, cordate, crenate, and with a long, slender petiole. In subsp. *graeca* all the basal leaves conform more or less to this pattern, but in subsp. *carpetana* the later ones are ovate, short-stalked, and cuneate or rounded at the base. All are provided rather sparsely with short glandular hairs on the lamina; the hairs on the petiole are more numerous and longer. Many of the basal leaves bear in their axil an underground bulbil, but the number of such bulbils tends to be smaller than in other species of the subsection. Flowering stem 12–25cm, branched in the upper part (rarely from as low as the middle) to form a compact cyme of 4–13 flowers; pedicels mostly very short but sometimes (especially in subsp. *graeca*) up to 20mm; cauline leaves 4–10, sessile, the lower leaves more or less pinnately lobed with 2–4 somewhat forwardly directed lobes on each side, the upper leaves very small and undivided. Sepals 2–3mm, ovate-oblong, glandular-hairy. Petals 8–12mm, narrowly obovate, pure white, glandular-hairy on the upper surface. Ovary ¾ inferior; styles very short. Seeds 0.45–0.5 × 0.3–0.35mm, ovoid, brown, with longitudinal rows of rather low papillae, between which the surface is finely to fairly coarsely tuberculate; raphe inconspicuous. Flowering season: May and June.

*ILLUSTRATIONS*: Plate 31; Figure 35
\* Willkomm (1881–1885, Plate 7), as *S. blanca*
 Engler & Irmscher (1916, Figures 54, 58)
 Maire (1980, Figure 6), as *S.veronicifolia*

*RECOGNITION*: The combination of glandular-hairy petals, fairly numerous cauline leaves, of which the lower are more or less pinnately lobed, and the absence of bulbils in their axils is distinctive.

*VARIATION*: There is little, except in the shape of the basal leaves. As this is partly correlated with geographical distribution it permits the recognition of two subspecies.
(a) Subsp. **carpetana**. Basal leaves mostly short-stalked, truncate, rounded or cuneate at

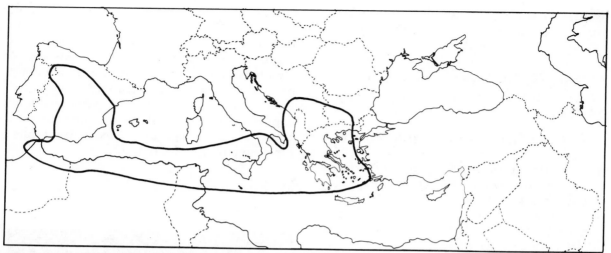

Map 50. Distribution of *S.carpetana*

the base, ovate, with a prominent terminal tooth or crenation and showing some approach in shape to the lower cauline leaves. Inflorescence compact. Sepals usually c. 2mm long.

(b) Subsp. *graeca* (Boissier & Heldreich) D.A. Webb, *Botanical Journal of the Linnean Society* 95:243 (1987). Basal leaves all semicircular or kidney-shaped, cordate, equally crenate. Inflorescence often laxer than in subsp. *carpetana* and with more numerous flowers. Sepals usually c. 2.5–3mm long.

*HYBRIDS*: Possibly with *S.bulbifera*; see under that species.

*CHROMOSOME NUMBER*: $2n = 20$ (subsp. *carpetana*); $2n = 64$ (subsp. *graeca*).

*DISTRIBUTION* (Map 50): Widely distributed in southern Europe and north-western Africa. Its range may be conveniently divided into four areas. (1) Central and eastern Spain, just extending into north-eastern Portugal. Its northern limit here lies at 40°45′N, just south of the Cordillera Cantábrica in the province of Palencia; (2) Morocco, Algeria and Tunisia, mostly fairly near the Mediterranean coast; (3) northern Sicily and south-western Italy, northwards to 40°10′N; (4) the Balkan peninsula, from Montenegro and south-western Bulgaria southwards, and in many of the Aegean islands.

In Spain and Portugal subsp. *carpetana* is in almost exclusive possession, although a few plants here and there show some approach to subsp. *graeca*. In North Africa subsp. *carpetana* is widespread, but subsp. *graeca* is found in several parts of Algeria. The plants of Italy belong to subsp. *graeca*; those of Sicily are somewhat intermediate but mostly nearer subsp. *graeca*. In the Balkan peninsula and the Aegean islands subsp. *graeca* alone is represented.

*HABITAT*: Usually in rather dry pastures; more rarely in wet meadows or in scrub or open woodland. It is found mainly between 800 and 2000m but in the Balkan peninsula it is also found at low levels, down to 100m. It has no obvious soil-preference.

*ACCESS*: Subsp. *carpetana* can be seen in abundance very near its northern limit, in wet meadows by the River Carrion, about 7km north of Guardo, near the western boundary of the province of Palencia, Spain. Subsp. *graeca* is common at the margin of beechwoods at 1400m on Monte Alpi, near Latronico in the province of Potenza, Italy.

*CULTIVATION*: Subsp. *carpetana* is apt to die out after a year or two, but subsp. *graeca* can be grown with fair success in potculture under glass. It would probably be hardy at least in the milder parts of the British

Isles and should be tried in a shady pocket in the rock-garden.

## 65. *Saxifraga cintrana* Willkomm, *Oesterreichische botanische Zeitschrift* 39:318 (1889)

SYNONYMS: *S.bulbosa* Hochstetter, *nomen nudum*

*S.granulata* var. *hochstetteri* Engler, *Verhand- lungen der k.k. zoologisch-botanischen Gesellschaft in Wien* 19:537 (1869)

*S.granulata* subsp. *hochstetteri* (Engler) Engler & Irmscher, *Pflanzenreich* 67 (IV.117): 253 (1916)

HISTORY & NOMENCLATURE: First collected, it would seem, by Hochstetter in 1838; he labelled his specimens *S.bulbosa*, but did not publish the name. It was published by Engler in 1869, with description, but only in synonymy, as Engler preferred to treat it as a variety of *S.granulata*. Twenty years later Kuzinsky sent some plants to Willkomm, suggesting that it be called *S.willkommii*; Willkomm, however, more modestly named it after Sintra, the town north of Lisbon where it was first discovered.

TYPE: Not traced.

DESCRIPTION: Basal leaves very variable in shape; lamina 7–16 × 8–25mm circular, rhombic or semicircular, crenate (sometimes obscurely), furnished on the upper surface and margin densely, on the lower surface more sparsely, with short glandular hairs; petiole slender or stout, 2–3 times as long as the lamina, with longer glandular hairs. Bulbils present in the axils of the basal leaves, one of them often much larger than the others. Flowering stem 10–18cm, stout or slender, branched sometimes from the base but more often only in the upper part to give a moderately lax cyme of 4–25 flowers; pedicels 2–10mm; cauline leaves 0–5, the lowest rather like the basal leaves, the upper rhombic-oblanceolate, tapered to a short stalk, 3-toothed at the tip. Pedicels, hypanthia and sepals densely glandular-hairy. Sepals 3mm, ovate-

oblong, obtuse. Petals 8–11 × 5–7mm, oblanceolate to obovate, glandular-hairy on the upper surface. Ovary ¾ inferior; styles short, divergent; stigmas large. Seeds 0.9 × 0.6mm, oblong, truncate at one end, bluntly pointed at the other, brown, ornamented rather sparsely and irregularly with fairly low papillae, between which are minute tubercles, which also cover the fairly conspicuous raphe. Flowering season: March to May.

ILLUSTRATIONS: Figures 35, 37
Engler & Irmscher (1916, Figure 57), as *S. granulata* subsp. *hochstetteri*

Figure 37. *S.cintrana*

RECOGNITION: Despite its variability this species is easy to recognise. Among the other species with glandular-hairy petals, semi-inferior ovary and bulbils in the axils of the basal leaves, *S.dichotoma* differs in its deeply divided basal leaves, *S.haenseleri* in the same way and also in its very long and slender pedicels, *S.bulbifera* in the possession of bulbils in the axils of the cauline leaves and bracts, and *S.carpetana* in having at least the lower cauline leaves pinnatifid and sessile.

*VARIATION*: It seems possible that the plants from Sintra and its neighbourhood have stouter and more freely-branched flowering stems than those from further north. The number of plants examined, however, has been so few and the total range of the species so small that it would be rash to give taxonomic recognition to this difference, which may, in any case, be due partly to differences in habitat.

*HYBRIDS*: None is known.

*CHROMOSOME NUMBER*: Not known.

DISTRIBUTION (Map 51): Limited to a small area of central Portugal north of Lisbon. From Sintra in the south it extends rather discontinuously to Bombarral and the Sierra de Montejunto, the whole range covering less than half a degree of latitude.

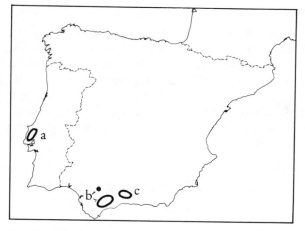

Map 51. Distribution of (a) *S.cintrana*, (b) *S.gemmulosa* and (c) *S.biternata*

*HABITAT*: In and around Sintra it is found mostly on walls and rock-faces, but further north it grows mainly in semi-open vegetation on level or gently sloping outcrops of limestone fully exposed to the sun. It ranges from about 80 to 540m in altitude.

*ACCESS*: This species is most easily seen on walls in the village of S. Pedro de Sintra, which lies to the east of Sintra. It is rare, and should not be collected here.

*CULTIVATION*: No information is available. It should not be too difficult if grown from seed.

### 66. *Saxifraga bulbifera* Linnaeus, *Species Plantarum* 403 (1753)

*HISTORY & NOMENCLATURE*: First described by Colonna (1616), who observed it in southern Italy, and named it *Saxifraga bulbosa altera bulbifera montana*—a not very helpful description, which is, however, accompanied by a good figure which leaves no doubt as to the identity. The epithet chosen by Linnaeus refers, of course, to the bulbils in the axils of the cauline leaves.

*TYPE*: The illustration on p. 317 of *Minus cognitarum rariorumque nostro coelo orientium stirpium Ecphrasis* (Colonna 1616) has been designated as lectotype (Webb 1987a).

*DESCRIPTION*: A summer-dormant perennial, similar in general aspect to *S.granulata* and *S.carpetana*, and not easily distinguishable from them unless an inflorescence is present. Basal leaves usually rather few, each bearing in its axil slightly below ground-level a small bulbil similar to those of *S.granulata*; petiole slender, hairy, 3–6cm long; lamina 8–18 × 10–24mm, kidney-shaped, crenate, densely hairy on the margin and sparsely on the upper surface but hairless beneath; hairs mostly non-glandular. Flowering stem 15–50cm, densely clothed in very short glandular hairs, branched only at the top; cauline leaves usually 10–15, the lowest shortly stalked but mostly sessile, diminishing greatly in size upwards, the lower ovate, deeply toothed or lobed, with obtuse to subacute, upwardly pointing teeth, the uppermost linear-lanceolate, entire. Most of the cauline leaves and the bracts (which are similar to the upper cauline leaves) bear in their axil an ovoid, pointed, reddish-brown bulbil about 3mm long. Inflorescence a small and usually very compact cyme of 3–8 (very rarely up to 20) flowers. Pedicel of the terminal flower very short, of the others up to 20mm. Sepals 2.5mm, ovate, obtuse, densely glandular-hairy, as is also the hypanthium. Petals 6–10 × 2–4.5mm, obovate-oblong, glandular-hairy on the upper surface, white. Ovary ¾ inferior; styles very short. Seeds 0.35–0.45 × 0.25mm, rather pale brown, ovoid, pointed at one end, covered with fine tubercles and a few low, rounded papillae; raphe prominent. Flowering season: May and June.

*ILLUSTRATIONS*: Figure 35
   Sternberg (1810, Plate 12)
   Fiori & Paoletti (1895, Figure 1654)
   Reichenbach (1899, Plate 17)
\* Bonnier (1921, Plate 204)

*RECOGNITION*: The numerous axillary bulbils on the flowering stem distinguish it from all except *S.cernua*; this differs in its smaller size, in never having more than one flower, in the nearly superior ovary, and in the fact that the bulbils are usually bright red. Plants in the later stages of flowering may have lost all the bulbils from the cauline leaves, as they are very easily detached, but they persist for longer in the axils of the bracts. In any case the compact inflorescence and the numerous cauline leaves help to distinguish such plants from *S.carpetana* subsp. *graeca*, with which they might otherwise be confused.

*VARIATION*: The only obviously variable character, apart from general size and vigour, is in the compact or lax nature of the inflorescence and the number of flowers it contains. *S.bulbifera* var. *pseudogranulata* Lacaita, *Nuovo Giornale botanica*, series 2, 25:53 (1918) (*S.pseudogranulata* (Lacaita) Fenaroli), seems to consist partly of plants of *S.bulbifera* that have lost their bulbils, partly of *S.carpetana* subsp. *graeca* and partly, very probably, of hybrids between the two.

*HYBRIDS*: None has been described, but it seems probable that in southern Italy and Sicily there is hybridisation with *S.carpetana* subsp. *graeca*. The two have been seen in Sicily growing in very close juxtaposition.

*CHROMOSOME NUMBER*: $2n = 28$.

*DISTRIBUTION* (Map 49, p. 158): *S. bulbifera* is endemic to Europe. It is found in the central Mediterranean region, in parts of central Europe and in the northern part of the Balkan peninsula. Westwards it extends to Sardinia and south-western Switzerland; eastwards to European Turkey. Its northern limit is in central Czechoslovakia, its southern in central Sicily.

*HABITAT*: It is found mainly in rather dry grassland, sometimes on rocky slopes or in open scrub. It ranges from 100 to 2000m in altitude.

*ACCESS*: It is abundant on Monte S. Vergine, near Avellino, Italy, in grassland not far from the summit. It can also be seen near Naples, on shady banks and walls at 800m on the northern side of Monte Sant'Angelo, above Castellamare; and in northern Italy, around Garessio (prov. Cuneo), on shady banks and in meadows, both near the town and near the Colle San Bernardo to the south of it.

*CULTIVATION*: This seems to be fairly easy. The plants should be put out of doors in June, when flowering is finished, and left in a sunny spot till late September, when the appearance of new leaves can be expected; then brought in under glass and given reasonably liberal watering till the flowering stems appear.

# Series *Biternatae* (Engler & Irmscher) Gornall

Bulbils in the axils of the basal leaves consisting of a loosely imbricate series of outer papery, or sometimes leafy, scales which grade into a series of increasingly fleshy ones. In species with prostrate stems the bulbils are spaced out, not clustered together. Leaves divided as far as the midvein (or nearly so), forming three primary lobes which are strongly narrowed at the base, often so as to resemble leaflets; the lobes themselves are nearly always divided further into segments.

A small series of three species, all from southern Spain.

## 67. *Saxifraga gemmulosa* Boissier, *Bibliothèque universelle des Sciences, Belles-lettres et Arts (Partie des Sciences)*, nouvelle Série, 13:409 (1838)

*HISTORY & NOMENCLATURE*: Discovered by Boissier in 1837 in the Sierra d'Estepona (Sierra Bermeja) to the south of Ronda in southern Spain. There is a pre-print, entitled *Notice sur l'Abies pinsapo*, of Boissier's article in the journal cited above, which would have priority over the article, were it not that it is so rare that it cannot be assumed it was distributed to botanical institutions sufficiently to constitute effective publication under the *International Code of Botanical Nomenclature*. Boissier published a somewhat altered description a few months later in his *Elenchus*. The epithet (bud-bearing) refers to the leafy bulbils which arise in the axils of the basal leaves, and are unfolding at the season when Boissier first saw it (early May).

*TYPE*: Saxifraga gemmulosa Boiss. El. no. 76. In fissuris umbrosis rupium S. d'Estepona. Alt. 3000'–4000'. Mai 1837. *Boissier*. (Lectotype: Geneva (**G**), designated here; two further sheets from the original gathering are also at Geneva.)

*DESCRIPTION*: A delicate, apparently evergreen perennial, forming a small tuft, with numerous, long-stalked basal leaves and several delicate flowering stems, diffusely branched. In the axils of the basal leaves are small bulbils, consisting of brown, scale-like leaves with stout marginal hairs, but most of these, instead of remaining dormant through the summer as in other members of the subsection, start into growth in spring, producing leaves which eventually take on the appearance of the basal leaves, so adding another rosette to the tuft. A few bulbils which have failed to germinate can usually be found at ground-level in early summer, but whether these germinate later is not known. Basal leaves, including petiole, 6–35mm, slender, moderately hairy; lamina semicircular in outline, varying greatly in size but usually 8–12 × 11–20mm, very deeply divided into 3 primary lobes, each of which has a stalk-like base 2–7mm long; above this base each lobe is expanded into a partial lamina, and is variously divided into elliptic-ovate, obtuse segments, of which the total number in a leaf is usually 11–13. The lamina is sparsely to moderately densely furnished with fairly long glandular hairs. Flowering stems 5–18cm, very slender, repeatedly branched, usually from near the base, but sometimes only in the upper half, rather sparsely furnished with short glandular hairs; lower cauline leaves similar to the basal ones, the upper much smaller and less divided. Flowers 1–5 on each primary branch of the inflorescence, in lax, open cymes with long pedicels. Sepals 2–2.5mm, broadly oblong, obtuse, sparsely glandular-hairy, the hypanthium more densely so. Petals 5.5–8 × 3.5–4.5mm, not contiguous, white, with a narrow, greenish, claw-like base. Ovary nearly inferior; styles short, erect. Seeds 0.55 × 0.25mm, narrowly ellipsoid, medium brown, covered all over, including the conspicuous raphe, with relatively coarse tubercles. Flowering season: April and May.

*ILLUSTRATIONS*: Figure 38
   Boissier (1839–1845, vol. 1, Plate 64)
\* Casas & Jimenez (1982, p. 178)

*RECOGNITION*: The only other species with leaves as deeply divided into three primary lobes are *S.biternata* and *S.bourgaeana*. The former differs greatly in its much larger flowers, with petals up to 20mm, and in its generally coarser habit, with prominent leafy shoots. From *S.bourgaeana* the differences are not so obvious, and many herbarium specimens of the latter are labelled *S.gemmulosa* and *vice versa*. Generally speaking *S. bourgaeana* is larger in all its parts, but stunted specimens of it can rather closely resemble luxuriant speciments of *S.gemmulosa* in general appearance. The best distinction lies in the fact that the leafy stems of *S.bourgaeana* are prostrate at the base, the lower part becoming slightly woody and often clothed with the petioles of dead leaves; in the axils of these are abundant bulbils which remain dormant until autumn, or at any rate throughout the

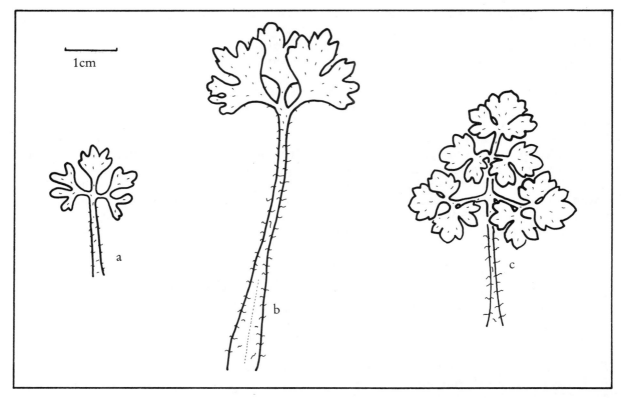

Figure 38. Leaf-outlines of species in series *Biternatae*: (a) *S.gemmulosa*; (b) *S.bourgaeana*; (c) *S.biternata*

flowering period. There is also a difference in habitat, *S.gemmulosa* growing invariably on basic or ultrabasic igneous rocks, and *S. bourgaeana* on limestone.

*VARIATION*: There is little, except in size and vigour. Plants exposed to the sun develop red colour in their leaves and stem in early summer.

*HYBRIDS*: None has been recorded.

*CHROMOSOME NUMBER*: $2n = $ c.64.

*DISTRIBUTION* (Map 51, see p. 163): Known only from the Sierra Bermeja (Sierra d'Estepona), which lies north of Estepona (prov. Málaga), in southern Spain, and from one outlying station more than 60km to the north-west; this is the hill called Esparteros, which is 5km south-west of Morón de la Frontera (prov. Sevilla). It is probable that *S.gemmulosa* grows mainly in the north-

western half of the Sierra Bermeja; the south-eastern half is largely composed of acid, siliceous rocks.

*HABITAT*: Crevices of basic or ultrabasic igneous rocks, rarely on rock debris. Usually, but not invariably, in the shade. The habitat, even when shaded, is usually rather dry. The species ranges from about 450 to 1200m in altitude.

*ACCESS*: *S.gemmulosa* is very frequent near the road which crosses the Sierra Bermeja between Ronda and the coast west of Marbella, especially near the summit. Coming from Ronda, the first 21km are all through limestone, but then there is a change to ultrabasic rock, and over the next 10km *S.gemmulosa* is frequent in suitable habitats. It is also abundant on the Esparteros; the plants on the north-north-eastern face are the most luxuriant.

*CULTIVATION*: This is difficult; it has survived for a year at Dublin but did not thrive. Until more is known of its annual cycle it is difficult to suggest the best treatment. Unfortunately, all herbarium specimens and all observations are taken during the flowering period in late spring.

## 68. *Saxifraga bourgaeana* Boissier & Reuter, in Boissier, *Diagnoses Plantarum orientalium novarum* 3(2):71 (1856)

*SYNONYMS*: *S.boissieri* Engler

*HISTORY & NOMENCLATURE*: This name has long been a mystery. It was based on specimens cultivated at Geneva, derived from seed sent by Bourgeau, allegedly from an unspecified place in the eastern part of the kingdom of Granada. The old 'kingdom' of Granada was more extensive than the modern province of the same name, but even if we extend it into the province of Almería there is no locality in its eastern part where any saxifrage remotely resembling *S.bourgaeana* can be found. The type-specimen corresponds well enough to the descriptions given by Boissier & Reuter and by Engler (1872), but it is a poor scrap, and its interpretation has been made more difficult by having a label pasted across its middle part. There are, however, in the herbarium at Geneva other, later and much better specimens cultivated by Boissier or Reuter under the name of *S.bourgaeana*, which match perfectly recent collections from Grazalema of the plant hitherto known as *S. boissieri*. Moreover, there is in the Reuter herbarium at Geneva a sheet from Grazalema originally labelled 'Reuteri Boiss.'; this has been deleted and replaced by 'gemmulosa Boiss. var.', which in turn has been deleted and replaced by 'bourgaeana' (in Boissier's hand); and there is another sheet (which is probably the type of *S.boissieri* Engler), also from Grazalema, again originally labelled 'Reuteriana Boiss.' by Reuter, and at a later date changed by him to 'Bourgaeana Boiss. & Reut.'. These facts make it fairly clear that *S.bourgaeana* Boissier & Reuter and *S.bois-*

*sieri* Engler are identical, and that Boissier would probably have realised this had it not been for the unfortunate muddle between *S. reuteriana* and the Grazalema plant, which is discussed under *S.reuteriana*. The alleged origin from 'eastern Granada' must arise from a change of labels on the part of either Boissier or Bourgeau.

*TYPE*: S.bourgaeana ex hort. Valeyres 1854. (Holotype: Boissier herbarium, Geneva (**G**).)

*DESCRIPTION*: An evergreen perennial. Stems woody at the base, which is often clothed with the petioles of dead leaves, in the axils of which are rather large bulbils; these remain dormant through the flowering season and probably do not germinate until autumn. From this woody base arise the leafy stems of the current year, up to 15(–20)cm, most of which terminate in an inflorescence; they are diffuse, ascending, slender, freely branched and somewhat intertwined, bearing hairs which vary widely both in length and density. Lower leaves with a slender petiole up to 5cm, with a bright pink expanded base up to 3mm wide. Lamina semicircular in general outline, divided to the base into 3 primary lobes, each of which is narrowed into a stalk-like base (longest in the central lobe); each primary lobe is divided, much less deeply, into 3–7 oblong, obtuse segments, the total number of which varies from 11 to 21. The primary lobes are well separated at the base but converge and often overlap at the top. The lamina is fairly densely glandular-hairy on both surfaces. Further up the stem the leaves become progressively smaller and with fewer segments, but they are all deeply divided into 3 primary lobes which are narrowed at the base. Some of these bear axillary buds which are initially somewhat bulbil-like, but they have no prolonged period of dormancy and are showing normal green leaves at the time of flowering. Flowers in lax, ill-defined, leafy cymes; pedicels long and slender. Sepals 1.5–2mm, oblong-ovate, obtuse, glandular-hairy. Petals 5–8mm, broadly elliptic-ovate, almost contiguous, without a claw at the base, white. Ovary nearly inferior; styles very short, divergent. Seeds 0.5 × 0.3mm, broadly ellipsoid, subacute at both ends, medium brown, covered all over with fine tubercles, including the moderately conspicuous raphe. Flowering season: April to June.

*ILLUSTRATIONS*: Plate 33; Figure 38
Engler & Irmscher (1916, Figure 61), as *S. boissieri*
\* Casas & Jimenez (1982, p. 176), as *S.boissieri*

*RECOGNITION*: The leaves, divided into 3 primary lobes, each with a narrow, stalk-like base, distinguish this species from all others except *S.gemmulosa* and *S.biternata*. For differences from the former see under that species. From *S.biternata* it is distinguished by the much smaller petals, the summer-dormant axillary bulbils usually confined to the lowest leaf-axils, and the fact that the primary lobes of the leaf are palmately divided, not very deeply, into usually more than 3 segments, whereas in *S.biternata* they are deeply divided into 3 secondary lobes which are narrowed at the base.

*VARIATION*: The only variation is in size and general vigour; this is correlated with the dampness or exposure of the habitat.

*HYBRIDS*: Plants from the Sierra del Pinar (near Grazalema) have been named as *S.boissieri × globulifera* (*S. × camboana* Font Quer). This diagnosis might be correct, but there is nothing in the description or in the specimens at Barcelona (**BC**) to prevent one from regarding them as stunted plants of *S.bourgaeana*. The habit is cushion-like, but the inflorescence is very diffuse, and the flowers like those of *S.bourgaeana*.

*CHROMOSOME NUMBER*: 2n = 64.

*DISTRIBUTION* (Map 52): If we dismiss as an error the supposed origin of Bourgeau's seed from eastern Granada, the area in which *S.bourgaeana* is found is a small one in the mountains of Cádiz and Málaga provinces, in south-western Spain, a short distance to the west of the territories of *S.gemmulosa*, *S. biternata* and *S.reuteriana*, but falling largely within the limits of the territory occupied by

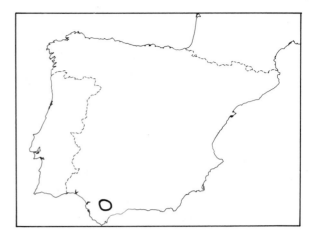

Map 52. Distribution of *S.bourgaeana*

*S.globulifera*. This area is centred around the town of Ronda and the village of Grazalema, to the west of Ronda. Its western and southern limit is on the Sierra de Algibe, 35km south-west of Grazalema, its northern limit on the Sierra del Pinar, and its eastern limit at the western end of the Sierra de las Nieves, south-east of Ronda. Within the territory so delimited it is nowhere very abundant, but well over a dozen distinct stations are known.

*HABITAT*: Always on limestone rocks, often vertical, always shaded and often fairly damp. Data on altitudinal limits are scanty, but most of the known stations lie at a height of between 500 and 1100m.

*ACCESS*: There is a well-known station scarcely 2km above Grazalema, on the left-hand side of the steep road which leads to Zahara; here it grows on a vertical rock-face kept constantly damp by a trickle of water. It can also be seen near Villaluenga del Rosario, by the road from Ubrique to Grazalema; and also very close to the provincial boundary but just on the Málaga side, some 10km from Ubrique by the road to Cortes de la Frontera.

*CULTIVATION*: This is not very easy; it has been kept going for 18 months in Dublin but never looked like thriving. As with *S. gemmulosa* we do not understand its annual cycle well enough to provide it with the conditions that suit it best, but a well-drained soil under glass, with fairly liberal watering most of the year, seems most likely to succeed. It is not likely to be hardy.

## 69. *Saxifraga biternata* Boissier, *Voyage botanique dans le Midi de l'Espagne* 2:231 (1840)

*HISTORY & NOMENCLATURE*: Discovered in about 1839 by Pablo Prolongo, a resident of Málaga whose acquaintance Boissier made in 1837, and described by Boissier from specimens sent to him by Prolongo. They were collected in El Torcal, a few kilometres south of Antequera (prov. Málaga), which remained for many years its only known station. On his next visit to Spain in 1849, Boissier visited the site, accompanied by Reuter, and collected specimens. The second known station, near Villanueva de Rosario, which is 25km east-north-east of El Torcal, was not discovered until 1919. The epithet draws attention to the most striking feature of the plant, the deeply and doubly 3-lobed leaves.

It should be noted that material sent out under the name of *S.biternata* by several collectors, and notably by Reverchon and by Font Quer, is really *S.bourgaeana*.

*TYPE*: Torcal d'Antequera. *P.* [in Boissier's hand]. (Holotype: Geneva (**G**).)

*DESCRIPTION*: Stems sprawling or nearly prostrate, woody below and often bearing persistent petioles of dead leaves; from these stems arise the leafy shoots, which may be up to 15cm long, and give rise to a somewhat diffuse habit, scarcely compact enough to be described as a cushion. All green parts of the plant are rather densely covered with glandular hairs of medium length; this gives a rich, velvety appearance to the upper surface of the leaves; the lower surface, though hairy, is paler and somewhat shining. The leaves vary greatly in size and shape according to their position on the leafy shoot and the general vigour of the plant. In their fullest development the lamina is 40 × 45mm, boldly and deeply divided into 3 primary lobes, each

narrowed to a stalk-like base which is long and narrow enough to suggest at first glance that the leaf is compound; these primary lobes are in turn 3-lobed, with the secondary lobes narrowed at the base to a much shorter stalk, and in their upper part variously crenate or even divided into segments. A few such leaves can always be found on a healthy and well-grown plant, but some of the leaves lower down on the shoot and all the leaves in less vigorous plants show reduced division of the primary lobes, and often consist simply of a lamina with 3 distinctly stalked, crenate lobes. The petioles are narrow above, but expanded to a broad, somewhat sheathing base. Summer-dormant axillary bulbils inconspicuous until flowering has begun, but attaining by late June a size of 8 × 6mm; the outer scales of the bulbil are membranous to somewhat fleshy, consisting of the expanded leaf-base, some of them bearing at the tip a minute petiole and 3-lobed lamina. In late September they unfold and start growing into new leafy shoots. Flowering stems are both terminal and axillary, up to 10cm tall, bearing usually 2–6 (rarely up to 15) funnel- to bell-shaped flowers in a lax cyme; cauline leaves and bracts few and small. Sepals 3–5.5mm, oblong to broadly elliptical. Petals 12–20 × 6–9mm, broadly oblanceolate to obovate, white with fairly conspicuous green veins. Ovary almost entirely inferior; styles 4–5mm, straight, erect at first, divergent in fruit. Seeds 0.7 × 0.4mm, ovoid, very dark brown, entirely covered with low, rounded papillae; raphe conspicuous, finely tuberculate. Flowering season: late May and June.

*ILLUSTRATIONS*: Figure 38
\* Boissier (1839–1845, vol. 1, Plate 64a)
Harding (1970, p. 20)
\* *Botanical Magazine* 180: Plate 670 (1974)
\* Casas & Jimenez (1982, p. 175)

*RECOGNITION*: The only other species with leaves consisting of 3 stalked lobes are *S.gemmulosa* and *S.bourgaeana*; see under those species for the differences.

*VARIATION*: As has been mentioned earlier, differences in the habitat give rise to differences in size and shape of leaves, number of flowers and size of petals; there is no evidence, however, of significant genetically determined variation.

*HYBRIDS*: None is known.

*CHROMOSOME NUMBER*: $2n = 66$.

*DISTRIBUTION* (Map 51, p. 163): Known only from two small areas south of Antequera (prov. Málaga) in southern Spain. El Torcal d'Antequera, the better known, lies to the west of the central of the three roads which lead from Antequera to Málaga, a short distance south of the summit. This has recently been developed into a tourist attraction, but the threat to the saxifrage flora does not appear to be very serious. The second station is more remote; it is in the Sierra Gordo, which lies between the village of Villanueva del Rosario and the main road from Loja to Málaga.

*HABITAT*: In both the stations the limestone rocks are horizontally bedded and much broken up by weathering into isolated blocks separated by ravines. The plant grows mainly in horizontal fissures in the vertical walls of these blocks, between the bedding planes, often protected from the mid-day sun by an overhanging ledge, but sometimes in exposed vertical fissures. In both stations the altitude is 1000–1100m, but it is possible that careful search might extend this range slightly.

*ACCESS*: There is no difficulty in finding the plant in El Torcal. In the more easterly station it is most easily seen on an isolated block lying between the north-facing cliffs of the Sierra Gordo and the village of Villanueva.

*CULTIVATION*: This is not very difficult in an alpine house; it is not likely to be possible out of doors. For the best display of foliage the plant should be well fed and protected from too much sun; for free flowering, a poorer soil and more sunshine are recommended. It is a splendid plant, which should be more widely grown.

## Subsection *Triplinervium* (Gaudin) Gornall

Biennials or evergreen perennials often forming mats or cushions, but sometimes of diffuse habit with lax rosettes of basal leaves. Bulbils absent, but summer-dormant, axillary buds present on the leafy shoots of some species. Leaves obovate to kidney-shaped with the margins variously lobed or crenate, or linear to lanceolate with the margins entire. Flowering stems terminal, occasionally axillary, bearing flowers singly or in small cymes or lax panicles. Petals white to greenish-yellow, sometimes tinged or veined with red. Ovary 2/3 or more inferior.

A large group of about 50 species with the geographical range of the section, although about 70 per cent of them are to be found in Europe.

## Series *Gemmiferae* (Willkomm) Pawłowska

Evergreen perennials forming loose mats or cushions, without bulbils but usually with summer-dormant buds in the axils of the leaves on the leafy shoots. Leaves herbaceous, lobed or entire, usually less than 4cm long (including petiole), with petioles longer or shorter than the laminae. Wavy hairs present on the leaves of the summer-dormant buds. Flowering stems terminal. Petals white, rarely tinged with pink. Ovary inferior or nearly so.

A small group of seven species in Europe, of which five are endemic and two extend to North Africa, where there are a further four or five species.

**70. *Saxifraga globulifera* Desfontaines,** *Flora Atlantica* 1:342 (1798)

*SYNONYMS*: *S.granatensis* Boissier & Reuter
*S.gibraltarica* (Seringe) Boissier & Reuter

*HISTORY & NOMENCLATURE*: Discovered by Desfontaines, apparently in the High Atlas of Morocco, some years before 1798, and named by him *globulifera* to draw attention to the more or less spherical summer-dormant axillary buds, which are a conspicuous feature of the plant. Discovered in Europe by Boissier on 12 May 1837, on the Sierra de Mijas, south-west of Málaga. The European populations are fairly uniform, but in North Africa there are several taxa more or less similar to Desfontaines' plant which have been variously held to be varieties or subspecies of it, or even independent species. On these questions we do not feel qualified to express a confident opinion (see p. 259); they cannot be satisfactorily solved from herbarium specimens alone, and many more observations on living plants, both in the wild and in cultivation, are necessary. We believe, however, that the European plants differ, if at all, from Desfontaines' type only at the varietal level, and that the separation of *S. granatensis* and *S.gibraltarica* as distinct species cannot be justified. See in this connection Ball (1878, pp. 447–8).

*TYPE*: Saxifraga globulifera. Herbier de la Flore Atlantique donné au Muséum par M. Desfontaines. (Holotype: Paris (**P**).)

*DESCRIPTION*: Leafy stems varying greatly in length in accordance with the degree of exposure, but normally 4–8cm, more or less erect, freely branched, forming a large but not very densely packed cushion. A few of the leaves at the base of each season's growth are oblanceolate-spathulate, without a distinct petiole, but most of them have a rather broad petiole 2–3 times as long as the lamina, which is semicircular in outline, rather deeply 5-lobed, with elliptical, acute lobes; both petiole and lamina are fairly densely glandular-hairy. In the largest leaves the lamina may be up to 8 × 17mm and the petiole 25mm, but in many plants, especially those from dry, sunny habitats, the dimensions are scarcely a third of these. Summer-dormant buds numerous and conspicuous, 3–4 × 2.5–3.5mm, obovoid,

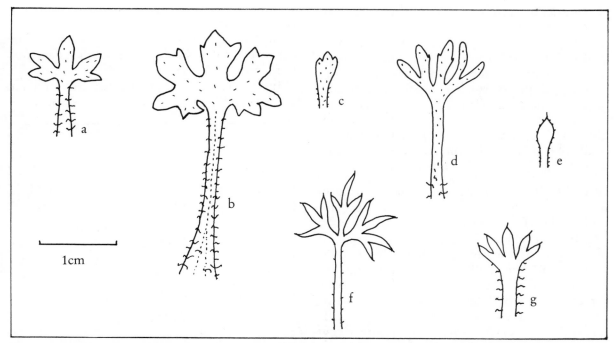

Figure 39. Leaf-outlines of species in series *Gemmiferae*: (a) *S.globulifera*; (b) *S.reuteriana*; (c) *S.erioblasta*; (d) *S.rigoi*; (e) *S.conifera*; (f) *S.continentalis*; (g) *S.hypnoides*

shortly obconical or nearly globular, stalked; the length of the stalks varies greatly, those at the base of each year's growth being up to 15mm, those near the tip considerably shorter; but here again there is great variation in accordance with habitat, and in dwarfed or congested plants the buds can be almost sessile. Flowering stems 5–15cm, slender, glandular-hairy, bearing 2–3 very small cauline leaves and a cyme of 2–7 (rarely up to 11) flowers. Sepals 2mm, obtuse. Petals 5–7mm, narrowly obovate, white. Ovary inferior; styles short, straight, erect. Seeds 0.65 × 0.35mm, ellipsoid, brown, without papillae but uniformly covered with rather conspicuous tubercles; raphe small. Flowering season: April to June.

*ILLUSTRATIONS*: Plate 38; Figure 39
    Desfontaines (1798, Plate 96)
    Engler & Irmscher (1916, Figures 80, 81)
    Maire (1980, Figure 11)
\*  Casas & Jimenez (1982, p. 174)

*RECOGNITION*: The only other species with summer-dormant axillary buds which are nearly as broad as long are *S.erioblasta* and *S.reuteriana*; similar leafy bulbils are also found in *S.bourgaeana* and *S.biternata*. *S. globulifera* differs from the first in its normally 5-lobed leaves and absence of long, cottony hairs on the axillary buds; from *S. reuteriana* in its smaller sepals and petals, which remain flat; from *S.bourgaeana* in its compact, cushion-like habit and its less deeply lobed leaves, with the lobes not narrowed to a stalk-like base; and from *S.biternata* in this last character and in the much smaller petals.

*VARIATION*: There is very little variation in Europe. Plants exposed to the sun are rather dwarf and tend to turn dark red in summer. The plants from Gibraltar tend to have many of the leaves 3-lobed rather than 5-lobed, and the axillary buds more shortly stalked and longer in proportion to their breadth. This perhaps justifies their recognition as var. **gibraltarica** Seringe in De Candolle, *Prodromus Systematis universalis Regni vegetabilis* 4:31 (1830). In Africa there is much more variation, but it is not clear to

what extent some variants such as *S.oranensis* Munby and *S.trabutiana* Engler & Irmscher should be treated as separate species or as variants of *S.globulifera* (see p. 259).

*HYBRIDS*: A supposed hybrid with *S. bourgaeana* is discussed under that species.

*CHROMOSOME NUMBER*: 2n = 66. The only counts available are from Morocco.

*DISTRIBUTION* (Map 53): Apart from the outlying station on the rock of Gibraltar, *S.globulifera* is confined in Europe to a limited area of southern Spain centred on Ronda. Its western limit is near Ubrique (5°27′W), south-east of Grazalema. From here it extends through all the mountains around Grazalema and Ronda eastwards to near Carratraca and southwards through the Sierra Bermeja and the Sierra Blanca to the Sierra de Mijas, where it reaches its eastern limit at 4°35′W.

On Gibraltar (which is separated from the main area by only about 45km) it is now very rare, and perhaps on the verge of extinction. Much of its habitat has been concreted over to provide catchment for rainwater, and the area where it is said to survive is under military control and difficult to visit.

In North Africa it is fairly widespread in Morocco, southwards to the High Atlas, and in northern Algeria.

It is interesting to note that the area which it occupies in Spain abuts on but does not over-

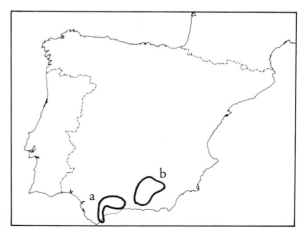

Map 53. Distribution of (a) *S.globulifera* (also in North Africa) and (b) *S.erioblasta*

172

lap that occupied by the closely related *S. reuteriana*. If one makes allowance for various misidentifications on herbarium sheets it becomes clear that the Rio Guadalhorce separates the two, *S.globulifera* lying to the west of it and *S.reuteriana* to the east.

*HABITAT*: Limestone rocks, most commonly on vertical faces. It is commonest on north-facing rocks, but not confined to them. It ranges from 300 to 1500m above sea-level.

*ACCESS*: Within its restricted geographical range *S.globulifera* is quite common, especially by the road leading south from Ronda, on the northern side of the Sierra Bermeja, and in several places near Grazalema, especially on the hillside just above the village.

*CULTIVATION*: This is quite easy under glass, but annual repotting is advisable. It survives out of doors in Dublin on a sunny ledge on the rock-garden but does not thrive. It might have a better chance in semi-shade in south-western England.

## 71. *Saxifraga reuteriana* Boissier, *Voyage botanique dans le Midi de l'Espagne* 2:730 (1845)

*HISTORY & NOMENCLATURE*: According to Boissier's original description, it was sent to him by Haenseler from the mountains above Grazalema in 1839. This date would explain its relegation to the appendix of the *Voyage*, as the part in which most species of *Saxifraga* are described was published in 1839. But there are two difficulties in accepting the statement at its face value. The first is the fact that no specimen which agrees with Boissier's description has been recorded from the neighbourhood of Grazalema since 1839; all specimens in the herbaria of London, Kew, Paris, Barcelona, Madrid and Coimbra come from the neighbourhood of Antequera, as detailed below. Mr B.E. Smythies, who lived at Marbella for some years and scoured the neighbouring mountains diligently, assures us that the western limit for *S.reuteriana* is south of Gobantes, on the eastern side of the Rio

Guadalhorce, more than 55km to the east of Grazalema. The second difficulty lies in the fact that in many herbaria there are specimens sent out by Boissier & Reuter, collected on their *Iter Algeriensi-Hispanicum* of 1849 from the Serrania de Ronda (which would include Grazalema), and there is one in Paris (**P**) labelled 'In fissuris rupium supra Grazalema. Juin, 1849. *Reuter*', all of them labelled *S.reuteriana*, but all, without any doubt, the plant which was later named *S.boissieri* by Engler, but which we here include under *S.bourgaeana*. It is pardonable to confuse *S.reuteriana* with *S.globulifera*, or to confuse *S.bourgaeana* with *S.gemmulosa* or *S.biternata*, but the most superficial examination is enough to distinguish *S.reuteriana* from *S.bourgaeana*. We conclude, therefore, that Boissier, who doubtless received many other plants from Haenseler at the same time, made an error in labelling his specimen of *S.reuteriana* and that the *idée fixe* that Grazalema was the home of *S.reuteriana* made him and Reuter give this name to the saxifrage which they found there in abundance.

Reuter seems eventually to have realised that a mistake had been made, as there is in the Reuter herbarium at Geneva (**G**) one of the sheets from the 1849 collection at Grazalema originally labelled as *S.reuteriana* Boiss., but this has been crossed out by Reuter and '*Bourgaeana* Boiss. & Reut.' substituted.

*TYPE*: Grazalema. [Without date or collector's name.] (Holotype: Geneva (**G**).)

*DESCRIPTION*: Leafy shoots mostly 2–3cm, arising from a short, branched, woody stock, erect or ascending, moderately densely crowded, so as to give a fairly compact hemispherical cushion. Leaves varying greatly in size according to the luxuriance of the plant; lamina usually 6–10 × 10–15mm, semicircular in outline, rather deeply 3-lobed, the lateral lobes nearly always divided into 2–4 segments, the central more rarely into 3, so as to give 5–11 subacute segments in all; petiole considerably longer than the lamina, grooved and rather stiff. Whole leaf densely covered with glandular hairs; those at the base

Figure 40.  *S.reuteriana*

Figure 41.  *S.reuteriana*

ILLUSTRATIONS: Plate 32; Figures 39, 40, 41
\* Casas & Jimenez (1982, p. 175)

RECOGNITION: The large, globular summer-dormant buds and the large flowers with petals reflexed at the margins characterise this species without any fear of confusion with another.

VARIATION: There is a good deal of variation in size, luxuriance and number of flowers, but this can all be related to conditions of the habitat, plants in the damper and shadier positions being best developed. A striking variation is seen also in the colour of the foliage at the flowering season, which varies from fresh green to deep crimson, the latter being associated with sunnier and drier situations. Red and green plants can sometimes be seen side by side, in which case one must assume that the difference arises from differences in the development of the roots and their efficiency in reaching seepage-cracks in the rock.

of the petiole over 1mm long. Summer-dormant buds numerous, conspicuous, globular to obovoid, 4–6mm across, the outer leaves herbaceous but undivided. Flowering stems 2–5cm, covered with long and short glandular hairs, bearing usually 2 small, lanceolate cauline leaves and 1–3 (rarely 4) flowers. Sepals 4 × 3mm, broadly ovate, subacute. Petals 8–10 × 7–8mm, elliptical, but with the margins reflexed towards the tip, slightly greenish-white. There is a wide nectary-disc on top of the ovary so that the flower is usually at least 20mm in diameter. Ovary inferior; styles straight, erect. Seeds 0.5 × 0.35mm, variable and irregular in shape, brown, rather sparsely ornamented with low, rounded papillae; raphe inconspicuous. Flowering season: May to June.

*HYBRIDS*: None has been reported.

*CHROMOSOME NUMBER*: Not known.

*DISTRIBUTION* (Map 54): Limited to an area scarcely 60km wide from east to west (and much less from north to south) in the mountains south and east of Antequera, in the provinces of Málaga and Granada in southern Spain. Within this area it is, however, frequent, and in places abundant. Its western limit lies in the Sierra del Valle, south-south-east of Gobantes, a village 20km west-south-west of Antequera. Its eastern limit is in the Sierra de Loja (between Loja and Alhama de Granada).

*HABITAT*: Vertical limestone rocks, mostly between 600 and 1200m.

*ACCESS*: This species grows in great abundance near its western limit, towards the eastern end of the northern face of the Sierra del Valle; this can be approached easily from the road to the relatively new railway-station of Gobantes. It is also very abundant on the cliffs east of Villaneuva del Rosario, which is 17km east of Antequera. It can be seen in fair quantity in an even more accessible station, on cliffs about 5km from Antequera by the road which leads to El Torcal and to Villaneuva de la Concepción.

*CULTIVATION*: This is not difficult, though a little vigilance is needed. It is best

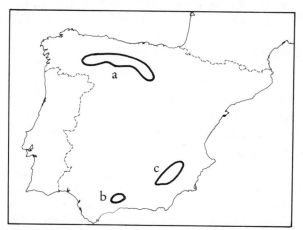

Map 54. Distribution of (a) *S.conifera*, (b) *S.reuteriana* and (c) *S.rigoi* (also in the Rif mountains of Morocco)

grown in a wide pan, in soil with plenty of limestone chippings in a sunny spot in the alpine house. It is not likely to be hardy out of doors. When well grown it gives a striking and handsome display.

## 72. *Saxifraga erioblasta* Boissier & Reuter, in Boissier, *Diagnoses Plantarum orientalium novarum* 3(2):67 (1856)

*SYNONYMS*: *S.spathulata* var. *erioblasta* (Boissier & Reuter) Engler, *Monographie der Gattung Saxifraga L.* 193 (1872)
*S.globulifera* var. *erioblasta* (Boissier & Reuter) Engler & Irmscher, *Pflanzenreich* 67 (IV.117):352 (1916)

*HISTORY & NOMENCLATURE*: First collected by Boissier on the Sierra Nevada in southern Spain in 1837, and considered by him at the time to be identical with the North African *S.spathulata* Desfontaines; later he changed his mind and decided that it was specifically distinct, and in this opinion we follow him. The epithet (with woolly buds) draws attention to the most characteristic feature of the plant.

*TYPE*: Saxifraga spathulata Desf. In rupibus calcar. Sierra Tejeda et Nevada. Juin 1837. Alt. 4500'–6700'. (Lectotype: Boissier herbarium, Geneva (**G**), designated here.)

*DESCRIPTION*: Leafy shoots numerous, more or less erect, freely branched, forming a compact, but usually fairly small cushion; somewhat woody below, and clothed in long-persistent dead leaves, the uppermost 8–15mm green and bearing living leaves. Leaves 4–7mm, oblong-oblanceolate to spathulate, entire or shortly 3-lobed, obtuse, narrowed towards the base but seldom with a distinct petiole, rather densely covered with very short glandular hairs. Summer-dormant buds numerous and conspicuous, 1.5–3mm in diameter, obovoid, shortly stalked, their outermost leaves similar to the smaller simple leaves of the leafy shoots, but with longer marginal hairs, their inner leaves broader, largely membranous and translucent, and with very long, cobweb-like marginal hairs. Towards midsummer the axillary buds open up to some extent so that these long hairs become very conspicuous and give the whole plant a white colour. Flowering stems 4–7cm, sparsely glandular-hairy, bearing 1–3 minute cauline leaves and a small cyme of 1–4 flowers. Sepals 2.5mm, obtuse. Petals 3.5–5mm, obovate, nearly contiguous, white at first but later changing to bright cherry-pink. Ovary inferior; styles 1.5mm, straight, slightly divergent. Seeds 0.65 × 0.3mm, oblong, brown, without papillae, the surface slightly wrinkled and very minutely tuberculate; raphe small but conspicuous. Flowering season: May and June.

ILLUSTRATIONS: Plate 39; Figures 39, 42
* Willkomm (1881–1885, Plate 67)
  Engler & Irmscher (1916, Figure 82)
* Casas & Jimenez (1982, p. 177)

RECOGNITION: In summer the abundance of dormant buds with white cottony hairs, together with the change in colour of the petals from white to pink, makes this species quite unmistakable. In winter and early spring its general appearance is not so distinctive, but there can always be found among the foliage some of the broad, membranous, translucent leaves fringed with long white hairs which formed part of the previous summer's dormant buds, and they are unlike the leaves of any other species.

VARIATION: There is none of any consequence.

HYBRIDS: None is known.

CHROMOSOME NUMBER: $2n = 34$.

DISTRIBUTION (Map 53, p. 172): S. erioblasta is found in the mountains of southern Spain. It extends from the Sierra Tejeda and Sierra de Loja (4°05′W) in the west to the Sierra Nevada and the Sierra de Baza (2°50′W) in the east. Its northern limit is at about 37°25′N.

HABITAT: Calcareous rocks, usually on ledges or inclined slopes rather than vertical faces, mainly north-facing, but often with considerable exposure to the sun in summer. In altitude it ranges from 1300 to 2250m.

ACCESS: It is most easily seen by the main road which ascends the eastern part of the Sierra Nevada towards the Valeta. Here it is frequent between 1500 and 2000m.

CULTIVATION: This needs a little care, but it can be grown in a pan in the alpine house, where its very distinctive appearance makes it well worth a place. It is not very likely to succeed out of doors.

### 73. Saxifraga rigoi Porta,
Atti della I.R. Accademia roveretana di Scienze, Lettere ed Arti degli Agiati 9:26 (1891)

HISTORY & NOMENCLATURE: Discovered by Freyn and Porta in 1890 on the Sagra Sierra in the north-eastern corner of Granada province, Spain, and named after G. Rigo, Porta's companion on many collecting expeditions.

Figure 42. S.erioblasta

*TYPE*: Porta & Rigo. Iter II Hispanicum 1890. Saxifraga rigoi Freyn et Porta nov. sp. Granate in rupium fissuris Sagra Sierra sol. Calcareo 2000–2500 m.s.m. Jul. (Lectotype: Kew (**K**), designated here.)

*DESCRIPTION*: Leafy shoots numerous, forming a lax or fairly dense cushion. Leaves up to 25mm long, including the petiole, which is very variable in length. Lamina up to 8 × 12mm, semicircular in outline, deeply 3-lobed, the lateral lobes usually and the central lobe sometimes divided, so as to give 5–7 linear-oblong, subacute segments. Leaves, stems, pedicels, hypanthia and sepals densely covered in very short glandular hairs; some longer hairs are often present towards the base of the petiole. Summer-dormant buds 5–8 × 2.5–4mm, stalked, not very tightly packed, the outer leaves entire, linear, herbaceous, edged with conspicuous, long, cobweb-like hairs. Flowering stems 7–13cm, with 4–7 cauline leaves, mostly narrow and entire, but the lowest 1 or 2 usually lobed. Flowers 2–5 in a fairly compact cyme. Hypanthium globular; sepals 5mm, narrowly oblong. Petals 12–20mm, oblanceolate, more or less erect, so that the flower is narrowly bell-shaped. Ovary inferior; styles 6mm, straight, erect. Seeds 0.7 × 0.3mm, brown, oblong, uniformly covered with low, rounded papillae; raphe inconspicuous. Flowering season: May and June.

*ILLUSTRATIONS*: Plate 34; Figure 39
*Bulletin de la Société botanique de France* 75: 788 (1928)

*RECOGNITION*: The combination of long, narrow petals and stalked, narrow, summer-dormant buds is distinctive.

*VARIATION*: There is little or none in Europe. The African population differs in its shorter petals and sepals, less clearly stalked summer-dormant buds and some other features, and has been separated as subsp. *maroccana* Luizet & Maire (see p. 260).

*HYBRIDS*: None is known.

*CHROMOSOME NUMBER*: Not known.

*DISTRIBUTION* (Map 54, p. 175): This species is confined in Europe to a fairly small area of south-eastern Spain from the Sagra Sierra (prov. Granada) in the east to the Sierra de Cazorla (prov. Jaen) in the west, including the Sierra la Cabrilla, which lies on the border between the two provinces. There are specimens collected by Reverchon labelled 'Sierra Grimona', but, as with so many of this collector's localities, we have been unable to locate this range on any map.

Outside Europe, it is known (as subsp. *maroccana* Luizet & Maire), from a single station in the Rif mountains of northern Morocco. It seems probable, however, that *S.tricrenata* Pau & Font Quer, recorded from other stations in the Rif, should be reduced to a subspecies or variety of *S.rigoi* (see p. 260).

*HABITAT*: Shady rock ledges and vertical rock-faces, always on limestone, from about 1250 to 2600m.

*ACCESS*: This species is most conveniently seen, accompanied by *Geranium cataractarum*, on vertical rocks near the source of the Guadalquivir, towards the southern end of the Sierra de Cazorla, south-south-east of the town of Cazorla.

*CULTIVATION*: No information is available. It is a handsome species, well worth trying, and should not be very difficult.

**74. *Saxifraga conifera* Cosson & Durieu,** *Bulletin de la Société botanique de France* 11:332 (1864)

*HISTORY & NOMENCLATURE*: Discovered by Bourgeau in 1864 on calcareous rocks on the Pico de las Corvas, which is near the Puerto de Pajares, half-way between Oviedo and León in northern Spain. He passed on one of his specimens to Cosson, who described it, with Durieu, as a new species in the same year. The epithet refers to the conspicuous, conical summer-dormant buds.

*TYPE*: Plantes d'Espagne. S.conifera Cosson & Durieu, sp. nov. Fentes des rochers calcaires de la région sous-alpine du Pico de las Corvas, près le Combento de Arvas, prov. de León. 8 juill. 1864. *E. Bourgeau 2727*. (Lectotype: Paris (**P**), designated here; several isotypes elsewhere.)

*DESCRIPTION*: Leafy shoots prostrate, 1–4cm, numerous, forming a dense mat. Leaves 3–10mm, linear-lanceolate, entire, apiculate or strongly acuminate, pale silvery-green, somewhat shining, conspicuously 3-veined, hairless on the surface, but provided on the margin with hairs which vary greatly in length, nature and abundance; those on the outer leaves of the summer-dormant buds, and therefore at the base of the next season's growth, being abundant, very slender, wavy, cobweb-like, non-glandular and up to 1.5mm long; higher up the shoot the hairs become progressively fewer, shorter, slightly stouter and mainly glandular. Summer-dormant buds numerous, 9–12 × 3–4mm, spindle-shaped to obconical, broadest a short distance below the bluntly pointed tip, gradually tapered at the base to a leafy stalk 4–10mm long. Flowering stems 4–8cm, with 3–7 very small cauline leaves; both stem and leaves sparsely furnished with very short glandular hairs. Stem branched near the top to form a compact panicle of 3–7 flowers. Pedicels and sepals densely glandular-hairy. Sepals 1.5–2mm, ovate, obtuse to mucronate. Petals 3–4mm, narrowly obovate, white. Ovary inferior; styles 1.5mm, straight, erect. Seeds 0.7 × 0.35mm, oblong, brown, densely covered with small tubercles, with occasionally a few, low rounded papillae among them; raphe fairly conspicuous. Flowering season: May and June.

*ILLUSTRATIONS*: Plate 35; Figure 39
  Leresche & Levier (1880, Plate 2)
  Engler & Irmscher (1916, Figure 77)

*RECOGNITION*: In summer the combination of short, prostrate shoots, narrow, entire leaves, small petals and prominent, obconical summer-dormant buds renders this species quite unmistakable. Even in winter, when the buds are not present, its mat-like habit and the form of its leaves distinguish it

from all other species other than *S.tenella*; in this, however, the hairs on the margins of the leaves are always sparse and short, and nothing like the long, cobweb-like hairs on at least some of the leaves of *S.conifera* are present.

*VARIATION*: There is none of any consequence.

*HYBRIDS*: None has been recorded.

*CHROMOSOME NUMBER*: Not known.

*DISTRIBUTION* (Map 54, p. 175): Endemic to a fairly small region of northern Spain, in and to the south of the Cordillera Cantábrica. It extends from the western margin of the province of León to the eastern margin of the province of Burgos.

*HABITAT*: Horizontal or gently inclined rock-faces, or gravelly debris; nearly always on limestone. Its altitudinal range extends from about 1000 to 2400m.

*ACCESS*: It may be seen in fair frequency on the level ground near the top of the cable-car at Fuente Dé, in the Picos de Europa. It can also be found at the Puerto de Piedrasluengas on the border of the provinces of León and Cantábria.

*CULTIVATION*: This appears to be difficult, for reasons which are not apparent.

**75. *Saxifraga continentalis*** (Engler & Irmscher) D.A. Webb, *Proceedings of the Royal Irish Academy* 53B:222 (1950)

*SYNONYMS*: *S.hypnoides* of many French and Iberian authors
*S.hypnoides* subsp. *continentalis* Engler & Irmscher, *Pflanzenreich* 67 (IV.117): 342 (1916)

*HISTORY & NOMENCLATURE*: It is difficult to trace the early knowledge of this species, as some of the synonymy in the works of earlier authors is obviously mistaken. It was certainly in cultivation in Montpellier early in the eighteenth century, the plants being presumably derived from the Cévennes, but we do not know who collected them.

The epithet, coined by Engler & Irmscher at subspecific level, emphasises the fact that this species grows only on the continent of Europe, in contrast to *S.hypnoides*, which is mainly on the off-shore islands.

TYPE: Rochers à Tournoy (Ardèche). 30 mai 1857. *Gandoger*. [Labelled *Saxifraga hypnoides* L.] (Lectotype: M. Winkler herbarium, Wroclaw (**WRSL**), designated here; this is one of the few specimens cited in the protologue which was not destroyed in Berlin.)

DESCRIPTION: Leafy shoots prostrate, mostly 4–10cm, rarely up to 15cm, forming a fairly compact mat. Leaves on these shoots entire to 5-lobed, usually 5-lobed only at the base and mainly entire near the tip; 3-lobed leaves are mainly in the middle portion but can occur mixed in with other types. Entire leaves 10–20mm, linear, sometimes almost thread-like, tapered to a long, fine point, without a clearly defined petiole; 3-lobed leaves usually slightly shorter, consisting of a long, slender petiole and a shorter lamina deeply divided into 3 linear to linear-lanceolate lobes; 5-lobed leaves shorter still, with petiole not much longer than the lamina and lobes lanceolate to elliptical. In all cases the lobes are strongly apiculate. Summer-dormant buds 7–11mm, narrowly ellipsoid, shortly stalked, numerous, conspicuous and always present; they are formed in April or May and remain dormant until September. The leafy shoot terminates in a similar bud. Outer leaves of the buds lanceolate, membranous and translucent except for the prominent midrib, which is continued as a slender point; margin fringed with long, wavy, non-glandular hairs. As the bud unfolds in autumn these are followed by the leaves which form the winter rosettes; they are very variable, usually with a long petiole and a lamina more or less semicircular in outline, divided into 3 primary lobes which are variously further lobed so that the total number of segments ranges from 5 to 13; they vary from elliptical to oblong-lanceolate, but are always apiculate. Most of the leaves (other than those on the outside of the summer-dormant buds) are hairless to sparsely hairy on the lamina, but glandular-hairy on the petiole. Flowering stems 8–25cm, slender, hairless below, sparsely glandular-hairy above, bearing 1–3 entire or 3-lobed cauline leaves, branched in the upper half (rarely from the middle) to give a small, open panicle of 4–11 flowers. Sepals 2mm, glandular-hairy, shortly apiculate. Petals 4–8mm, elliptical, white, not contiguous. Ovary ¾ inferior; styles 1.5mm, straight, erect. Seeds 0.6 × 0.25mm, narrowly oblong, brown, with fairly numerous moderately short papillae between which the surface is covered in dark tubercles; raphe rather inconspicuous. Flowering season: April to July.

ILLUSTRATIONS: Figure 39
* Lapeyrouse (1801, Plate 32), as *S.hypnoides* Engler & Irmscher (1916, Figure 77)

RECOGNITION: The only other species with long and narrow summer-dormant buds are *S.conifera*, *S.rigoi* and *S.hypnoides* (in some of its variants). From the first it differs in having numerous lobed leaves; from *S.rigoi* in its much smaller petals; and from *S.hypnoides* most clearly in the almost entirely membranous and translucent outer leaves of the summer-dormant buds. The buds are also more numerous than in *S.hypnoides* and consistently present; the leaves have usually more numerous segments and the petals are smaller.

VARIATION: This is considerable, mainly in the shape of the rosette-leaves. Following Engler & Irmscher (1916) we recognise two varieties.
(i) Var. **continentalis** (var. *pungens* Engler & Irmscher). Leaves with very narrow segments, the outer ones usually strongly recurved.
(ii) Var. **cantabrica** (Boissier & Reuter ex Engler) D.A. Webb, *Botanical Journal of the Linnean Society* 95:245 (1987). Leaves with broader segments, for the most part forwardly-directed.

As with *S.hypnoides* the foliage of plants in dry, sunny situations often turns bright red in summer.

HYBRIDS: The only natural hybrids known are with *S.babiana*, *S.pedemontana* subsp.

prostii and S.cuneata; see under those species. S. × schraderi Sternberg, described from the botanical garden at Göttingen, where it had already long been in cultivation in 1811, is still often seen in cultivation (frequently under the name S.trifurcata), and is probably S.continentalis × trifurcata. A hybrid with S.geranioides (S. × cuspidata Schleicher) has also been described from a garden specimen; whether it survives in cultivation is doubtful.

CHROMOSOME NUMBER: 2n = 26, 52.

DISTRIBUTION (Map 55): S.continentalis occupies two regions in south-western Europe separated by the main chain of the Pyrenees. The more westerly comprises north-western and west-central Spain and northern Portugal, with its southern limit at about 40°30′N in the Sierra d'Estrela and the mountains south-west of Avila, and its eastern limit at 2°40′W in the Sierra Cebollera. The easterly region lies wholly in France, largely in the Massif Central and the Cévennes. Its northern limit is at about 45°45′N in Auvergne; hence it extends southwards to the department of Tarn-et-Garonne in the west and to the department of Var in the east. It appears probable that it formerly grew in the Pyrénées-Orientales, but has not been seen there for many years.

Throughout France, and in the northern and eastern parts of the Spanish range of the species, only var. continentalis is to be found. Var. cantabrica is found in Portugal and in western Spain, but in much of the Spanish range transitional plants are frequent.

HABITAT: Rocks and walls, rarely on screes. It is usually in sole possession of the habitat, and is never found in closed vegetation, in contrast to S.hypnoides. In nearly all its stations the rock is siliceous or basaltic, but there are a few places where it is abundant on limestone. This is all the more surprising as in many parts of northern Spain it is abundant on siliceous rocks but stops abruptly at the boundary of the limestone. Most of the recorded stations lie between 700 and 1700m in altitude.

ACCESS: Within the greater part of its two areas of distribution, S.continentalis is easy to find in suitable habitats. It may be helpful, however, to indicate a few localities where the species is particularly abundant and conspicuous. (1) On limestone rocks on the northern face of Mont Ste Baume, 30km east of Marseille, in France; (2) by the head-waters of the rivers Lot and Altier, between Mende and Villefort (dept. Lozère), also in France; (3) south-east of Riaño (prov. León), by the road to Guardo and Palencia, in Spain; (4) in the gorge of the Rio Sabor, west of Vimioso, Tras-os-Montes, in Portugal.

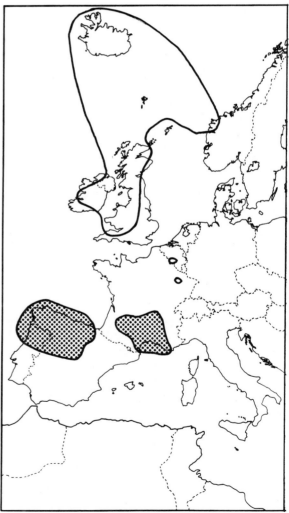

Map 55. Distribution of S.hypnoides (unshaded) and S.continentalis (shaded)

CULTIVATION: This is fairly easy under glass; it would probably be hardy out of doors in at least the milder parts of the British Isles.

## 76. *Saxifraga hypnoides* Linnaeus, *Species Plantarum* 405 (1753)

SYNONYMS: *S.leptophylla* of D. Don and others, but scarcely of Persoon
*S.platypetala* Smith
*S.elongella* Smith
*S.sponhemica* of British authors, not of Gmelin

HISTORY & NOMENCLATURE: The first undoubted mention of this species is by Parkinson (1640, p. 739) as *Sedum Alpinum laciniatis Ajugae foliis*; it was sent to him from the 'mountains of Lancashire' (probably the English Lake district) by Mr Hesketh. Many of the references to early authors given by Linnaeus are erroneous. Linnaeus' concept of the species included *S.continentalis*.

The epithet indicates a superficial resemblance to *Hypnum* and other pleurocarpous mosses.

TYPE: Sheet 575.62 in the Linnean herbarium, London (**LINN**) has been designated as lectotype (Webb 1950b).

DESCRIPTION: Leafy shoots more or less prostrate, very variable in length, but usually 6–12cm, almost hairless, bearing fairly widely-spaced leaves which are mostly undivided and linear-lanceolate, but usually some are 3-lobed with linear-lanceolate segments. The shoots terminate in a bud which in late summer expands into a rosette of 3- to 7-lobed leaves, from which may arise a flowering stem and prostrate axillary shoots the following year. The plant thus forms an extensive, rather loose mat. Occasional plants, however, have very short prostrate shoots and are much more compact in habit. All leaves have the lamina hairless or with very sparse marginal hairs; the petiole, however, is fairly densely hairy. The segments (and the lamina of the undivided leaves) terminate in a stiff, bristle-like tip 0.5–0.75mm long. The leaves

with 5 or 7 lobes have the lobes directed more or less forwards, so as to be fan-shaped in outline. Summer-dormant buds 5–10 × 2–4mm, sometimes present in the leaf-axils of the prostrate leafy shoots; they are commonest in plants growing in dry or warm habitats, but can occur in those on shady mountain ledges. Plants without such buds are, however, at least as common. The outer leaves of these buds have broad, scarious margins, but a green, herbaceous centre. Flowering stems 5–20cm, branched in the upper half (occasionally from the middle) to form a loose panicle of 2–7 flowers; stems hairless below, but glandular-hairy in the inflorescence. Flower-buds nodding. Sepals 2–3mm, acuminate. Petals 7–10mm (rarely up to 12mm) elliptical, white, not contiguous. Ovary ¾ inferior; styles 2mm, straight, slightly divergent. Seeds 0.65–0.8 × 0.35–0.5mm, oblong, black, with fairly numerous, low, rounded papillae; the rest of the surface, including the prominent raphe, tuberculate. Flowering season: late April to July.

ILLUSTRATIONS: Figure 39
* Sowerby (1865, Plate 562), as *S.eu-hypnoides*, var. *gemmifera*
Reichenbach (1899, Plate 106)
Engler & Irmscher (1916, Figure 79)
Ross-Craig (1957, Plate 10)

RECOGNITION: Of the species with which *S.hypnoides* might be confused, *S. tenella* and *S.conifera* differ in having all their leaves entire and in their much smaller petals; *S.rosacea* subsp. *rosacea* in the obtuse to mucronate, but never apiculate leaves, the absence of entire leaves and the erect flower-buds; and *S.rosacea* subsp. *sponhemica* in the last two characters. For the differences from *S.continentalis* see under that species.

VARIATION: There is a good deal of variation in size and robustness of the whole plant, and Marshall, *Journal of Botany (London)* 56:67 (1918), distinguished as var. *robusta* the large plants from Black Head, Co. Clare, in Ireland, but they intergrade so smoothly with the type that the variety is difficult to sustain. There is also a good deal of variation in the presence or absence of summer-dormant buds and the proportion of entire to 3-lobed leaves on the prostrate leafy shoots. Both these characters seem to be partly under environmental, and partly under genetic control, but there is little correlation between them, and all attempts to give taxonomic recognition to these variants have broken down. In plants growing in dry situations most of the foliage turns bright red in summer.

*HYBRIDS*: Several hybrids mentioned in the literature as derived from *S.hypnoides* are really hybrids of *S.continentalis*. Hybrids of *S.hypnoides* with *S.rosacea*, *S.granulata* and *S.tridactylites* are, however, known. All three have been produced artificially, but the first and (more doubtfully) the third have been recorded in the wild in southern Ireland and northern England respectively.

*CHROMOSOME NUMBER*: An extensive series of recent counts from various parts of Britain and Ireland have given consistently $2n = 26$ or $52$. No consistent morphological difference between the diploid and the tetraploid can be discerned. There are, however, earlier, differing, approximate counts for Ireland and one of $2n = 48$ for Iceland.

*DISTRIBUTION* (Map 55, p. 180): *S.hypnoides* is confined to north-western Europe. It is widespread in Iceland and the Faeroes, frequent in western Scotland, northern England and Wales, with an isolated station in south-western England (Cheddar), and is thinly scattered over a good deal of Ireland. On the continent it is known only from a few localities in western Norway, from a short stretch of the valley of the Meuse, partly in the Belgian province of Namur and partly in the finger-like projection of the French department of Ardennes which extends northwards, surrounded by Belgium. Finally, it is recorded from an outlying station further south in the Vosges, near Gérardmer, but it does not seem to have been seen there in recent years.

*HABITAT*: This is rather variable; the recorded habitats include stream-sides, damp, mossy ledges, screes, dry, rocky grassland and sand-dunes. It has a slight calcicole tendency, but grows freely on siliceous rocks in many places if there is some flushing. It is better able than most species of the genus to survive the competition of closed vegetation, and is often seen mingled with a continuous carpet of moss, both in dry and damp situations. It ranges from near sea-level to 1300m.

*ACCESS*: In Britain it is most conveniently seen in the limestone dales of the southern Pennines, especially in western Derbyshire. In Ireland it is easy to find in the central part of the Burren district of Co. Clare, especially around Carran and to the south of it.

*CULTIVATION*: This is easy, either in pot-culture or on a ledge in semi-shade in the rock-garden.

# Series *Cespitosae*
## (H.G.L. Reichenbach) Pawłowska

Evergreen perennials, forming cushions, usually without axillary summer-dormant buds. Leaves herbaceous to slightly fleshy, less than 2.5cm long (including petiole), the lamina divided into lobes and usually longer than or equalling the petiole. Hairs not wavy. Flowering stems terminal. Petals white to dull yellow, sometimes tinged or veined with red. Ovary 2/3 or more inferior.

A group of about 12 species, five of which are endemic to western Europe, one is circumpolar, and one ranges from northern Spain to the Caucasus. One species is endemic to North Africa (see p. 260) and about four more are confined to South America (see p. 286).

**77. *Saxifraga rosacea* Moench**, *Methodus Plantas Horti botanici et Agri Marburgensis a Staminum Situ describendi* 106 (1794)

*SYNONYMS*: *S.petraea* of Roth, not of Linnaeus
*S.decipiens* Ehrhart ex Sternberg

Plate 31.   *S.carpetana*

Plate 32.   *S.reuteriana*

Plate 33.   *S.bourgaeana*

Plate 34.   *S.rigoi*

Plate 35.   *S.conifera*

Plate 36.    *S.pubescens*

Plate 37.    *S.hariotii*

Plate 38.  *S.globulifera*

Plate 39.  *S.erioblasta*

Plate 40.  *S.nevadensis*

S.*palmata* Smith
S.*sternbergii* Willdenow
S.*hirta* of Smith, not of Haworth
S.*hibernica* Haworth
S.*affinis* D. Don
S.*incurvifolia* D. Don
S.*cespitosa* subsp. *decipiens* (Sternberg) Engler
   & Irmscher
S.*drucei* Marshall
S.*hartii* D.A. Webb

*HISTORY & NOMENCLATURE*: Although it is frequent in lowland Germany this species was not distinguished until 1789, when Roth, in the second volume of his *Tentamen Florae germanicae*, gave a description (under the name S.*petraea* L.) which is based, at least in part, on the plant which we now call S.*rosacea*. (In the first volume, although he said that S.*petraea* grows in the Harz mountains, his description is applicable only to the true S.*petraea* of the southern Alps.) Next year Ehrhart (1790) pointed out that a plant he had received from the Harz was not S.*petraea* L., but a new species, which he called S.*decipiens*; he gave no description, however, so that this remains a *nomen nudum*. It was not until 1794 that Moench gave an adequate description.

His epithet (meaning like the flower of a rose) refers not to the flowers, but to the rosettes which terminate the leafy shoots.

*TYPE*: S.*rosacea*. Ex herb. Gay. Saxifraga decipiens Ehrh. Rauhe Alb in Würtenburg. Endres misit, Aug. 1828. [Note added by N.E. Brown: S.*decipiens* Ehrh. Compared with type-specimen Oct. 8, 1890.] (Neotype: Kew (**K**), designated here; none of Moench's types has survived.)

Subsp. *sponhemica*. Saxifr. sponh. Gmelin. Rchb. Fl. germ. sub 2. 3596. E loco classico! Felsen der Nahegebirge bei Kirn, Burgsponheim, Bockenau usw. 1888. *C.Bogenhard*. (Neotype: British Museum (**BM**), designated here; no types of Gmelin are known.)

Subsp. *hartii*. Saxifraga hartii Webb. Ex hort. Co. Dublin. Root from Arranmore Island, W. Donegal. 17/5/[19]50. *D.A. Webb*. (Lectotype: Trinity College, Dublin (**TCD**), designated here; no type was indicated in the original description.)

*DESCRIPTION*: A very variable species. Leafy shoots 1–10cm, arising in some cases from straggling, somewhat woody prostrate stems, erect, spreading or prostrate, forming a dense or loose cushion or a thin mat. In the latter part of the summer, each shoot forms a fairly well-defined terminal rosette, which lasts through the autumn, winter and early spring. Rosette-leaves 6–25 × 5–17mm, including the usually fairly well-defined petiole, which is flat and relatively broad, measuring 2–12 × 2–4mm; it may be longer or shorter than the lamina. Lamina 4–13 × 6–17mm, divided usually fairly deeply but sometimes not much more than half-way into 3–5 primary lobes, which may be entire or further divided so as to give up to 11 ultimate segments. The segments vary from broadly elliptical to linear-oblong (1–5mm wide) and from obtuse to apiculate; they are not furrowed. There are always some hairs on the petiole, usually fairly long, but the lamina varies from completely hairless to densely hairy. Except in subsp. *hartii* the hairs are predominantly (and usually exclusively) non-glandular, or with the terminal gland so poorly developed as to be almost invisible. The leaves on prostrate shoots below the rosette are always 3-lobed. Flowering stems 4–25cm, fairly stout, furnished, often sparsely below but more densely above, with mainly glandular hairs, and with 1–4 cauline leaves, the lower 3-lobed, the upper entire. Flowers 2–6 in a fairly open cyme, erect in bud. Sepals 2–3.5mm, broadly ovate, acute to apiculate, sparsely glandular-hairy. Petals 6–10 × 3–7mm, obovate, pure white. Ovary ⅔ inferior; styles 1.5–3mm, straight, slightly divergent. Seeds 0.8 × 0.55mm, broadly ellipsoid with rounded ends, dark brown, covered with fine tubercles, in some variants without papillae, in others with frequent, fairly long papillae interspersed between the tubercles; raphe fairly conspicuous. Flowering season: May to July.

*ILLUSTRATIONS*: Figures 43, 44
* Sowerby (1865, Plate 557), as *S.decipiens*
  Webb (1950b, Figures 1–3)
  Ross-Craig (1957, Plate 12)
  Mądalski (1962, Plate 1324), as *S.decipiens*

*RECOGNITION*: The partially inferior ovary, leaves hairy at least on the petioles, and with plane, not furrowed, segments, white petals usually at least 6mm long, absence of bulbils and of prominent summer-dormant buds on the leafy shoots separate *S.rosacea* from other European species except *S.cespitosa*, *S.hypnoides*, *S.irrigua*, *S.geranioides* and *S.pedemontana*. From *S.cespitosa* most variants are distinguished by the non-glandular leaf-hairs; subsp. *hartii*, in which they are glandular, differs in its flatter rosettes, usually with more than 5 lobes on some of the leaves, and in its pure white petals, which are usually larger than those of *S.cespitosa*. From *S.hypnoides*, *S.rosacea* differs in the erect (not nodding) flower-buds, and in the absence of entire leaves from the leafy shoots. *S.irrigua*, *S.geranioides* and *S.pedemontana* all have petals normally exceeding 10mm and more numerous flowers in the inflorescence; in *S.irrigua* and *S.pedemontana* the sepals are long and narrow, and in *S.geranioides* the leaf-hairs are usually much shorter and the leaves round or kidney-shaped with very numerous segments.

*VARIATION*: The list of synonyms and the details of the description show that this is a very variable species, but a large part of the variation cannot find taxonomic recognition, as it is shown in small populations, in which very different-looking plants grow side by side and obviously interbreed, giving a new recombination of characters in each generation. The regions in which this state of affairs is most marked are south-western Ireland and Czechoslovakia. Engler & Irmscher (1916), who treated the species as a subspecies of *S. cespitosa*, recognised within it ten varieties, two of them divided into subvarieties, and below this a bewildering array of forms and

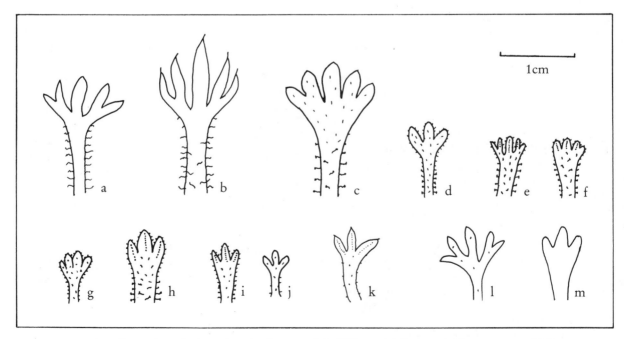

Figure 43. Leaf-outlines of species in series *Cespitosae* and *Axilliflorae*: (a) *S.rosacea* subsp. *rosacea*; (b) *S.rosacea* subsp. *sponhemica*; (c) *S.rosacea* subsp. *hartii*; (d) *S.cespitosa*; (e) *S.pubescens* subsp. *pubescens*; (f) *S.pubescens* subsp. *iratiana*; (g) *S.nevadensis*; (h) *S.cebennensis*; (i) *S.exarata* subsp. *exarata*; (j) *S.exarata* subsp. *moschata*; (k) *S.hariotii*; (l) *S.praetermissa*; (m) *S.wahlenbergii*

subforms. Any attempt at a simpler and more realistic division of the species inevitably introduces an arbitrary quality, by drawing boundary-lines in what is nearly a continuous pattern of variation, but the two lines which we draw represent regions in this pattern where transitional plants are relatively rare. We may therefore recognise the following subspecies.

(a) Subsp. *rosacea*. Leaf-segments obtuse, acute or shortly mucronate, but not apiculate, usually relatively broad. Leaf-hairs predominantly non-glandular. Seeds variable.

(b) Subsp. *sponhemica* (Gmelin) D.A. Webb, *Feddes Repertorium* 68:210 (1963). Leaf-segments apiculate, narrow. Leaf-hairs predominantly non-glandular. Seeds coarsely papillose.

(c) Subsp. *hartii* (D.A. Webb) D.A. Webb, *Botanical Journal of the Linnean Society* 95: 246 (1987). Leaf-segments subacute, broad. Leaf-hairs predominantly glandular. Seeds finely tuberculate.

Figure 44. *S.rosacea*

It will be seen that within the limits of *S. rosacea*, which is in many respects intermediate between *S.cespitosa* and *S.hypnoides*, subsp. *hartii* comes closest to *S.cespitosa* and subsp. *sponhemica* to *S.hypnoides*.

*HYBRIDS*: Hybrids with *S.hypnoides* have been reported from Ireland, but they are rare. They have also been produced artificially by Webb (1950b) and Marsden-Jones & Turrill (1956). Hybrids with *S.granulata* have been recorded in the wild in Germany, and have also been synthesised (see under that species).

*S.rosacea* has certainly been a major contributor in the parentage of the 'mossy saxifrages' common in cultivation and usually referred to as 'arendsii-hybrids'. The other species involved can only be the subject of speculation, as the origin of the hybrids is not properly documented, but they probably include *S.hypnoides*, *S.granulata* and *S.exarata* subsp. *moschata*.

*CHROMOSOME NUMBER*: Numbers as various as $2n = 50, 52, 56$ and 64 have been recorded, but recent work suggests that $2n = 52$ (in all subspecies) is the most likely to be correct.

*DISTRIBUTION* (Map 56): *S.rosacea* occurs in Iceland and the Faeroes, in western and south-central Ireland, in a single station in North Wales, where it is probably extinct (last seen in 1963 and repeatedly searched for since then), and in a region of west-central Europe extending from 4°45′E in the French Ardennes to 16°45′E on the borders of Poland and Czechoslovakia, southwards to 46°45′N in the French Jura and northwards to 52°N in central Germany. This area includes part of eastern France, south-eastern Belgium, Luxembourg, much of southern and central Germany, the western half of Czechoslovakia and a small part of south-western Poland. From south-central Czechoslovakia it just crosses the border into Austria at one point; other records for Austria are probably based on garden escapes. Records for southern Greenland are, according to Löve & Löve (1961, p. 53), based on lax variants of *S.cespitosa*, but the possibility that *S.rosacea* subsp.

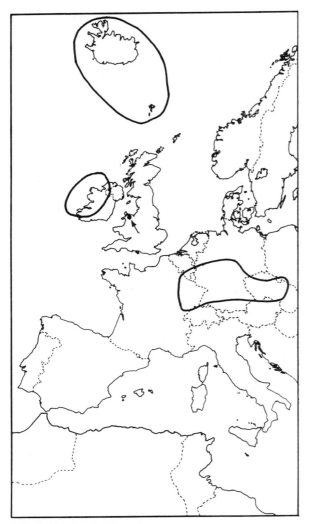

Map 56. Distribution of *S.rosacea*

*HABITAT*: On rocks and screes; also among grass and shady mountain ledges. In Ireland it ranges from sea-level to 960m. It is equally at home on limestone and sandstone.

*ACCESS*: Subsp. *rosacea* is most conveniently seen in Ireland about 1.5km south of Black Head, Co. Clare; here it grows in abundance just above the storm-beach, with *Armeria maritima* and *Parietaria judaica*. This is a slightly unusual variant, with mucronate leaf-segments; more typical plants require some mountain-climbing, but can be seen in fair abundance on the cliffs above Coomloughra, on the north-western face of MacGillycuddy's Reeks, Co. Kerry. The plant can also be seen in France in the Cirque de Baume, east of Lons-le-Saunier (dept. Jura); here it grows on limestone talus near the far end of the cirque, on the left.

Subsp. *sponhemica* is easy to find in the Grand-Duchy of Luxembourg, near Vianden, at Goebelsmühle in the valley of the River Sure, and in several other places by the road which follows the valley of this river northwards from Ettelbruck. In Belgium it can be seen in the valley of the river Amblève (south-south-east of Liège, near and around Aywaille).

To see subsp. *hartii* the hunter must be prepared to search all the gullies in the cliffs on the northern and western coasts of Arranmore Island, Co. Donegal.

*CULTIVATION*: This presents no problem; it grows easily both out of doors and under glass.

*hartii* occurs in Iceland or southern Greenland is not to be excluded.

Subsp. *rosacea* is found in Iceland and the Faeroes, Ireland, much of central and southern Germany, with outlying stations in the Vosges and the French Jura. Subsp. *sponhemica* occurs in two separate areas: the western one covers Belgium, Luxembourg and the Rhineland, with two stations in the French Jura; the eastern area is in Czechoslovakia, Poland and Austria. Subsp. *hartii* is known only from Arranmore Island, Co. Donegal, in Ireland.

## 78. *Saxifraga cespitosa* Linnaeus, *Species Plantarum* 404 (1753)

*SYNONYMS*: *S.groenlandica* Linnaeus
*S.sileneflora* Sternberg ex Chamisso
*S.uniflora* R. Brown

*HISTORY & NOMENCLATURE*: Linnaeus can hardly have failed to see this species during his voyage to Lapland in 1732, but for some reason he did not describe it until 1753. Meanwhile Dillenius (1732) had described from cultivated specimens sent to him from Greenland *Saxifraga tridactylites groenlandica caulibus valde foliosis*. This was called *S.groenlandica* by Linnaeus, but it was eventually agreed, after some rather bitter opposition from the botanists of Central Europe, that *S.groenlandica* and *S.cespitosa* were identical, and Linnaeus united them under the latter name. The species was, however, for long confused by Linnaeus and later authors with variants of *S.exarata* from the Alps, and also with *S.cebennensis*. The three synonyms cited by Linnaeus from Swiss or Italian authors derive from this confusion.

The epithet indicates 'closely tufted' or 'sod-forming', and is reasonable enough as a description of plants from high latitudes or exposed positions. The spelling 'cespitosa' was adopted deliberately by Linnaeus, and its alteration to 'caespitosa' by many later authors is not justified.

*TYPE*: Sheet 575.57 in the Linnean herbarium, London (**LINN**) has been designated as lectotype (Webb 1987a).

*DESCRIPTION*: Leafy shoots numerous, usually densely packed, forming a tight cushion, but occasionally longer and somewhat straggling. Leaves 4–15mm, consisting of a broad petiole, often scarcely distinct from the lamina, and a short lamina, elliptic-obovate in outline, usually divided into 3 oblong-elliptical, obtuse lobes, the upper surfaces of which are flat, not furrowed; usually a few leaves are 5-lobed, and in depauperate plants a few are undivided, but 3-lobed leaves always predominate. The margin of the petiole and lamina is fairly densely furnished with short, glandular hairs, the surface usually more sparsely, but sometimes densely. Flowering stems 2–10cm, with 1–4 cauline leaves, with are either 3-lobed with narrow lobes or linear-oblong and undivided. Flowers 1–5, in a fairly open cyme. Stem, pedicels, hypanthium and calyx glandular-hairy, often tinged with dark red. Sepals 2mm, ovate, obtuse. Petals 5.5–6.5mm, obovate, white, but usually with a slight greenish or yellowish tinge. Ovary ⅔ inferior; styles 1.5–

2mm, slightly curved, divergent. Seeds 0.8 × 0.5mm, broadly oblong with truncate to rounded ends, dark brown, uniformly covered with small, black tubercles; raphe fairly conspicuous. Flowering season: June to August.

*ILLUSTRATIONS*: Figure 43
   Warming (1909, Figures 12–16), as *S.groenlandica*
\* Lindman (1964, Plate 293)

*RECOGNITION*: *S.cespitosa* may be distinguished from other European species by the following combinations of characters: petals whitish, mostly at least 5mm long; ovary semi-inferior; plant without bulbils or prominent summer-dormant buds; leaves mostly 3-lobed, with obtuse segments not furrowed above, and with numerous glandular hairs, most of them over 0.2mm long. From *S. exarata* subsp. *exarata* it differs in the absence of furrows on the leaf-segments, and from all subspecies of this species by its larger petals. Depauperate specimens have been confused with *S.pubescens* subsp. *iratiana*, but here again *S.cespitosa* is distinguished by the absence of furrows on the leaf. It comes close to *S.rosacea* subsp. *hartii*, but the latter has larger petals of a pure white, and most of the leaves with more than 3 and often more than 5 lobes.

*VARIATION*: In Europe there is very little except in the characters obviously related to differences in the habitat—compactness of the cushions, length of flowering stem and number of flowers. In North America it is much more variable (see p. 285).

*HYBRIDS*: The hybrid with *S.granulata* has been recorded from Sweden but requires confirmation.

*CHROMOSOME NUMBER*: Most recent counts agree on $2n = 80$, but one recent worker has recorded $2n = 78$ from ten different localities.

*DISTRIBUTION* (Map 57): This species is found almost throughout the arctic regions. In Europe it extends southwards to about 59°N in southern Norway and in the central Urals; also to a few isolated stations in the Scottish

Highlands and one in North Wales. In North America its range is wider. On the eastern coast it extends to 48°30′N in Quebec province; in the west it runs from the Aleutian Islands and southern Alaska down the Rocky mountains and adjacent ranges as far as California and New Mexico. Populations from the west, however, differ from the arctic plant in several respects (see p. 285).

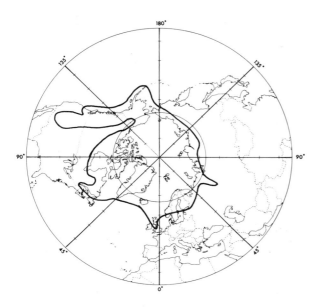

Map 57. Distribution of *S.cespitosa*

*HABITAT*: Usually in rock-crevices or on scree, gravel, stony tundra or shingle beaches. It can tolerate moderately dry conditions and also exposure to salt-spray. It can be found on a wide variety of rocks, from limestone to granite.

*ACCESS*: It is common in a large part of arctic and subarctic Norway.

*CULTIVATION*: As with most arctic plants this is rather troublesome, but by no means impossible. It should be given well-drained soil, kept out of doors in autumn and winter, protected from the rain but if possible exposed to snow and frost, and brought in to the alpine house for spring and summer.

## 79. *Saxifraga pubescens* Pourret, *Mémoires de l'Académie de Toulouse* 3:327 (1788)

*SYNONYMS*: *S.mixta* Lapeyrouse
*S.iratiana* F.W. Schultz
*S.melaena* Boissier
*S.groenlandica* of Lapeyrouse and many later authors, but not of Linnaeus

*HISTORY & NOMENCLATURE*: This species was doubtless seen by earlier travellers (perhaps including Clusius), but none of them described it in terms clear enough to distinguish it from related species. Its discovery may, therefore, be fairly attributed to Pourret, who probably first found it in the Val d'Eyne, in the eastern Pyrenees, in 1781.

The epithet refers to the conspicuous covering of short, glandular hairs on the leaves.

*TYPE*: *S.pubescens*. Saxifraga pubescens P., e Pyrenaeis hispan. et eynes [in Pourret's hand]. [In another hand] Collection de l'Abbé Pourret, extrait de l'herbier légué par M. le Dr Barbier, 1847. (Lectotype: Paris (**P**), designated here.)

Subsp. *iratiana*. Herbarium normale, Cent. 9. 858 Saxifraga iratiana. Fentes des rochers au bord des neiges du Pic de Midi. Rec. Irat. 17 juillet 1849. *F. Schultz*. (Lectotype: Paris (**P**), designated here.)

*DESCRIPTION*: Leafy shoots variable in length; if short, forming fairly flat rosettes, but sometimes long, slender and columnar. Leaves usually rather dark green, densely covered (as is the whole plant) with glandular hairs mostly about 0.25mm long (excluding the gland), but up to 0.6mm on the petioles. Basal leaves up to 18mm long, including the petiole, but often much less; lamina divided into 5–9 oblong, obtuse lobes, usually 2–3 times as long as wide, most of them furrowed on the upper surface. Flowering stem terminal, but soon over-topped by leafy shoots arising below it, so as to appear axillary, 3–10cm, usually with 1 cauline leaf which, like the lower bracts, is deeply 5-lobed; upper bracts 3-lobed to entire. Inflorescence fairly compact, flat-topped, usually with 5–9 flowers. Sepals 3mm, elliptical. Petals 4–6 × 3.5–5.5mm, broadly obovate to nearly circular, contiguous or overlapping, white, rarely veined with red. Ovary nearly fully inferior; styles very short, straight. Seeds 0.65 × 0.35mm, ellipsoid with pointed ends, dark brown, densely covered with fine tubercles; raphe rather inconspicuous. Flowering season: June to August.

Figure 45. *S.pubescens*

*ILLUSTRATIONS*: Plate 36; Figures 43, 45
* Lapeyrouse (1801, Plate 14), as *S.groenlandica*
Engler & Irmscher (1916, Figures 92, 93)

*RECOGNITION*: The densely glandular-hairy leaves, mostly with 5 or more segments and at least some of them furrowed, make this species fairly easy to recognise. Of those with which it might be confused, *S.exarata* is less densely hairy, usually with narrower petals, and with undivided cauline leaves; this last character, together with the lighter colour of the foliage and the smaller number of leaf-segments, helps to distinguish *S.cebennensis* from *S.pubescens*. *S.cespitosa* and *S.nevadensis* have none of the leaf-segments furrowed, and the leaves are mostly 3-lobed.

*VARIATION*: The species is certainly variable; this is in part due to introgressive hybridisation with *S.exarata* subsp. *moschata*, and partly to variation in the habitat. There is, however, enough intrinsic variation which is preserved in cultivation to permit the recognition of two subspecies.
(a) Subsp. *pubescens*. Habit relatively lax, with short leafy shoots on which the dead leaves do not persist for long. Leaf-segments about 3 times as long as wide, somewhat divergent. Petals pure white. Anthers yellow. Top of ovary green.
(b) Subsp. *iratiana* (F.W. Schultz) Engler & Irmscher, *Pflanzenreich* 67 (IV.117):401 (1916). Of very compact growth, with small leaves and long, slender, columnar shoots on which the dead leaves persist for many years. Leaf-segments about twice as long as wide, nearly parallel. Petals sometimes veined with red. Anthers and top of ovary reddish.

*HYBRIDS*: Hybrids with *S.exarata* subsp. *moschata* are common and apparently fertile, giving rise to hybrid swarms. A hybrid with *S.hariotii* is discussed under that species. One with *S.geranioides*, though rare, seems to be well-attested; but that with *S.pentadactylis* is more speculative.

*CHROMOSOME NUMBER*: $2n = 26, 28$.

*DISTRIBUTION* (Map 58): Found only in the Pyrenees. The eastern limit lies on or

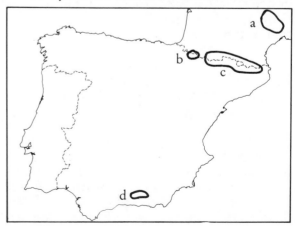

Map 58. Distribution of (a) *S.cebennensis*, (b) *S.hariotii*, (c) *S.pubescens* and (d) *S.nevadensis*

near the Canigou; the western limit at 0°40′W, west of the Col du Somport near Gèdre. Within this range the two subspecies show only a small overlap, for subsp. *pubescens* is confined to the eastern part, and is probably not found west of Andorra, while subsp. *iratiana* extends from the Puigmal (2°05′E) to the western end of the range.

*HABITAT*: Rocks and screes, mostly above 2400m, though subsp. *pubescens* descends much lower in one or two places. Subsp. *pubescens* grows mainly on screes, often with snow-cover; subsp. *iratiana* on exposed rocks. Both are found mainly, and perhaps entirely, on siliceous rocks.

*ACCESS*: Subsp. *pubescens* can easily be found in the Val de Llo, south of Fort-Romeu; it grows in small quantity in the gorge above the village, and more abundantly on the higher slopes. Subsp. *iratiana* grows in fair quantity on the frontier ridge at the Port de Vénasque, south of Bagnères-de-Luchon. It can also be seen near Héas, east of Gavarnie, on large boulders by the road leading up to the dam, with *S.intricata*, and also at 2600m at the top of the cliffs which form the Cirque de Troumouse nearby.

*CULTIVATION*: Subsp. *pubescens* presents no great difficulty if given careful alpine-house treatment. It is a pretty plant, well worth growing. Subsp. *iratiana* is much more difficult; it has never survived for long at Dublin, and, although it survives at Cambridge, it does not thrive.

## 80. *Saxifraga nevadensis* Boissier, *Diagnoses Plantarum orientalium novarum* 3(2):67 (1856)

*SYNONYMS*: *S.mixta* of Boissier, not of Lapeyrouse
*S.mixta* var. *nevadensis* (Boissier) Engler, *Monographie der Gattung Saxifraga L.* 182 (1872)
*S.pubescens* subsp. *nevadensis* (Boissier) Engler & Irmscher, *Pflanzenreich* 67 (IV.117): 402 (1916)

*HISTORY & NOMENCLATURE*: Discovered by Boissier near the summit of the Sierra Nevada in 1837. He at first believed that it fell under *S.mixta* of Lapeyrouse, a name which we now consider to be a later synonym of *S.pubescens* Pourret, and he confused it also with the plant of the high Pyrenees which he later described as *S.melaena* but later realised was the *S.groenlandica* of Lapeyrouse (but not of Linnaeus), and which we now know as *S.pubescens* subsp. *iratiana* (F.W. Schultz) Engler & Irmscher. All these confusions are very understandable if one is dealing with dried plants, and it was only after studying the Sierra Nevada plant in cultivation that he decided that it was specifically distinct. We agree with him in this decision, but it is sufficiently similar to *S.pubescens* subsp. *iratiana* for it to be not unreasonable to include it under *S.pubsecens* as a third subspecies, as was done by Engler & Irmscher (1916).

*TYPE*: Sax. mixta Lap. in summis Sierra Nevada alt. 9000′–10500′. (Holotype: Boissier herbarium, Geneva (**G**).)

*DESCRIPTION*: Leafy stems usually with densely packed, columnar leafy shoots 2–8cm long, with dead leaves persistent for many years, forming a small to medium-sized, compact cushion; plants sheltered from wind and sun may, however, show a laxer growth, with the shoots longer and less densely packed. Leaves usually with a fairly clearly defined petiole 3–4mm long; lamina 4–7 × 5–8m, with usually 3, more rarely 5, oblong, obtuse, plane segments, not furrowed on the upper surface and with veins of dried leaves prominent in the petiole but scarcely visible in the lamina, densely glandular-hairy with hairs mostly 0.3–0.4mm long, those on the petiole fewer but longer. Flowering stems 3–9cm, densely glandular-hairy, with 0–2 entire or 3-lobed cauline leaves, and bearing a very compact cyme of up to 6 flowers. Sepals 2mm, deep purplish-red. Petals 5–6 × 4–4.5mm, broadly obovate, contiguous, white, usually with 3 prominent red veins but sometimes pure white. Anthers bright red or orange before dehiscence. Ovary inferior; styles

1.5mm, divergent. Seeds 0.65 × 0.4mm, ellipsoid with truncate to subacute ends, medium brown, covered all over with fine tubercles, including the conspicuous raphe. Flowering season: May to July.

*ILLUSTRATIONS*: Plate 40; Figure 43
   Engler & Irmscher (1916, Figure 93)
\* Casas & Jimenez (1982, p. 172)

*RECOGNITION*: The conspicuously red-veined petals of many plants are sufficient in themselves for recognition. White-flowered plants can be distinguished from *S.pubescens*, *S.cebennensis* and some subspecies of *S. exarata* by the complete absence of furrows on the leaf-segments; from other subspecies of *S.exarata* by the longer and more abundant glandular hairs and the more deeply divided leaves.

*VARIATION*: There is none, except in the amount of red pigment in the petals, that cannot be accounted for by variation in the habitat.

*HYBRIDS*: None is known.

*CHROMOSOME NUMBER*: $2n = 58$.

*DISTRIBUTION* (Map 58, p. 189): Known only from the upper regions of the Sierra Nevada range in southern Spain.

*HABITAT*: Schistose rocks and stabilised screes, mostly north-facing. It is frequent from 3000 to 3400m, and occasional below this, down to 2450m. Most plants are snow-covered until late May.

*ACCESS*: It is most easily seen on the path to the summit of the Veleta, from 3000m upwards.

*CULTIVATION*: This is difficult in the British Isles, but perhaps not impossible, given sufficient care. This is especially so in regions with cold winters, where it is best kept out of doors, except for a few months in spring and early summer, which can be spent in the alpine house.

## 81. *Saxifraga cebennensis* Rouy & Camus, *Flore de France* 7:55 (1901)

*SYNONYMS*: *S.pubescens* var. *prostiana* Seringe in De Candolle, *Prodromus Systematis universalis Regni vegetabilis* 4:28 (1830)
*S.prostiana* (Seringe) Luizet

*HISTORY & NOMENCLATURE*: This species was first noticed by Gouan, who found it as a young man on the Pic St Loup, near Montpellier where he lived. He corresponded with Linnaeus, and it is presumably his discovery that is responsible for Montpellier being mentioned by Linnaeus in *Species Plantarum* among the localities for *S.cespitosa*, for at that time many species from the mountains of southern and central Europe were believed to be identical with the arctic and subarctic *S.cespitosa*. The first person to recognise *S.cebennensis* as distinct was T.-C. Prost, who was postmaster of Mende (dept. Lozère) in the early nineteenth century. He brought it to the attention of De Candolle when the latter was at Montpellier, and he in turn passed it on to Seringe, who described it in the *Prodromus* as a variety of *S.pubescens*. (The first publication of this name is often ascribed to Bentham (1826), but as Bentham gave no description, his mention of the name is of no nomenclatural consequence.) It was not until 1901 that it was given the status of an independent species; Rouy & Camus chose the epithet *cebennensis* to indicate its habitat in the Cévennes (using the term in the wide sense so as to include the Causses). They wisely avoided the epithet *prostiana* at specific rank for fear of confusion with *S.prostii* Sternberg.

*TYPE*: Not traced.

*DESCRIPTION*: Leafy shoots numerous, forming a fairly large, domed, soft cushion of light green foliage. Leaves on well-grown plants mostly 3- to 5-lobed, but on the weaker shoots or on starved plants many of them are entire. Petiole about 6mm; lamina 6 × 5mm, with obtuse lobes furrowed on the upper surface, covered rather densely with short, glandular hairs, those on the petiole somewhat longer. Flowering stems numerous, 5–8cm, slender, often reddish, densely glandular-hairy, with 3–4 cauline leaves, which are mostly entire but the lowest sometimes 3-lobed, and 2–3 flowers. Sepals 2.5mm, triangular-ovate. Petals 6–8 × 4.5–6mm, broadly obovate, contiguous. Ovary inferior. Seeds 0.8 × 0.35mm, dark brown, oblong, pointed at one end, uniformly covered with fine tubercles; raphe inconspicuous. Flowering season: May and June.

ILLUSTRATIONS: Figure 43
\* Rouy (1901, Plate 386)
  Coste (1902, p. 143)
\* Köhlein (1984, Plate [5])

RECOGNITION: This species is not always to be distinguished easily from S. pubescens on the one hand and from S.exarata on the other. There is no possibility of confusion with S.pubescens subsp. iratiana; from subsp. pubescens, S.cebennensis differs in the lighter green of the leaves, the smaller leaf-rosettes terminating the leafy shoots (10–15mm in diameter, against 20–25mm in S. pubescens) and the more numerous and mainly entire cauline leaves. From S.exarata it differs mainly in the longer and more numerous hairs on the leaves, the bigger, often hemispherical cushions of foliage, and the longer and broader, contiguous petals.

VARIATION: There is a fair amount of variation dependent on the season and type of habitat, but none that calls for taxonomic recognition.

HYBRIDS: None has been reported.

CHROMOSOME NUMBER: 2n = 26, 32.

DISTRIBUTION (Map 58, p. 189): Endemic to a fairly small area of southern France in the departments of Aveyron, Gard, Hérault and Lozère, extending from the Pic St Loup, north of Montpellier, for about 100km northwards and westwards to near Mende and Millau. This is the region of the 'Causses', bare limestone plateaux intersected by deep gorges, and it is mainly on the sides of these gorges that the plant is to be found. Its range falls exactly half-way between the ranges of the two species to which it is most closely related, S.exarata subsp. exarata in the western Alps, and S.pubescens in the eastern Pyrenees.

HABITAT: On limestone rocks, usually shaded and vertical, ranging from 600 to 1600m in altitude.

ACCESS: In many of its stations S.cebennensis is by no means abundant. It grows, however, in fair quantity near Ste Enimie, near the middle of the Gorges du Tarn, and may be seen on the rocks flanking either of the roads which lead out of the gorge, one northwards to Mende and the other southwards to Meyrueis.

CULTIVATION: This is fairly easy, given reasonable care in the alpine house. The compact, hemispherical cushions of foliage and the abundance of pure white flowers make it well-suited to the show-bench, and it is a favourite with gardeners who otherwise confine their interest to section Porphyrion.

## 82. *Saxifraga exarata* Villars, *Prospectus de l'Histoire des Plantes de Dauphiné* 47 (1779)

SYNONYMS: S.cespitosa of many earlier authors, not of Linnaeus
S.hypnoides of Allioni, not of Linnaeus
S.moschata Wulfen
S.muscoides of Wulfen and other authors, not of Allioni
S.ampullacea Tenore
S.adenophora Koch
S.planifolia of Lapeyrouse, not of Sternberg
S.varians Sieber
S.carniolica Huter ex Hayek
S.fastigiata Luizet
S.lamottei Luizet
S.tenuifolia Rouy & Camus

HISTORY & NOMENCLATURE: As can be seen from the list of synonyms (which could be extended to at least twice its present length) this is a species which has been very variously interpreted. It is here treated in a wide sense, so as to include *S.moschata*. For a justification of this procedure see Webb (1987b); it is sufficient here to say that no Flora or monograph has, to our knowledge, indicated a clear distinction between *S.exarata* and *S.moschata* which takes full account of the wide variation shown by both. Moreover, many subspecies or varieties originally established under *S.exarata* have been transferred to *S.moschata* and *vice versa*.

The species so defined is very abundant in the Alps at moderate altitudes, and must certainly have been seen by some of the botanists of the sixteenth century. It was, however, so often confused with other species and given such a cursory description that it is difficult to say who first described it. It is almost certainly the *Sedum tridactylites alpinum minus* of Bauhin (1620), and his citation as a synonym of the *Sedum vii vel alpinum ajugae folio* of Clusius (1583) may well be correct. Nothing earlier than this can be cited with any confidence.

Linnaeus confused it with the northern *S. cespitosa*, and it was left to Villars to draw the distinction. His epithet (ploughed up) refers to the conspicuous furrow on the leaf-segments of subsp. *exarata* and some other variants.

TYPE: *S.exarata*. Not traced.

Subsp. *pseudoexarata*. Not traced.

Subsp. *moschata*. Not traced.

Subsp. *lamottei*. Cantal: Roc des Ombres. 9/7/[19]12. *Coste et Soulié 526*. (Lectotype: Paris (**P**), designated here.)

Subsp. *ampullacea*. Information from the herbarium at the University of Florence (**FI**) indicates that a type may be found there, although we have no further details.

DESCRIPTION: Leafy shoots 0.5–4cm, numerous, more or less erect, crowded, forming a compact cushion. Leaves 4–20mm, usually with a fairly distinct petiole, which may be shorter or longer than the lamina, usually sparsely to densely glandular-hairy with fairly short hairs, but occasionally almost hairless, soft, rarely somewhat fleshy. Lamina most often 3-lobed, but sometimes entire or 5-lobed, rarely 7-lobed; lobes oblong, obtuse, furrowed or flat on the upper surface. Flowering stems 3–10cm (less in plants dwarfed by exposure), branched in the upper third (rarely from the middle) to give an often somewhat flat-topped cyme, or rarely bearing a single flower. Cauline leaves 0–4, 3-lobed or entire. Pedicels, bracts and hypanthia usually bearing very short glandular hairs, but sometimes almost hairless. Sepals 2mm, oblong, obtuse. Petals 2.5–6 × 1.5–4mm, oblong or narrowly elliptical to broadly obovate, white to dull, sometimes greenish, yellow, occasionally tinged with red. Ovary inferior; styles very short. Seeds 0.7 × 0.3mm, oblong-ellipsoid, medium brown, covered all over with rather coarse tubercles; raphe fairly conspicuous. Flowering season: May to September.

ILLUSTRATIONS: Plates 41, 42; Figure 43
   Mądalski (1962, Plate 1325), as *S.moschata*
 * Rasetti (1980, Plate 256)
 * Finkenzeller & Grau (1985, p. 107)

RECOGNITION: With such a variable species it is difficult to give simple criteria for distinction from other species. Those with which it might be confused are *S.cebennensis*, *S.hariotii*, *S.italica*, *S.muscoides*, *S.nevadensis*, *S.pubescens*, *S.seguieri* and *S.intricata*. From all of these except the last the differential characters are given in the account of the species concerned. From *S.intricata*, *S.exarata* differs in its softer, paler green foliage with longer hairs, and in its narrower petals, which are never quite contiguous.

VARIATION: An extremely variable species; some 10 species and 14 subspecies, as well as innumerable varieties, have been described from among the plants here grouped together as *S.exarata*. Most of these are local populations which differ from their immediate neighbours, but have no characters which differentiate them constantly if the range of variation of the whole complex is taken into account. One of the most important differences between the original *S.exarata* and *S. moschata* was said to be the presence of furrows on the upper surface of the leaf-segments of the former and their absence from the latter. Unfortunately these furrows disappear on drying, except in leaves which are detached and dried separately and very carefully, and as most of the taxonomy has been worked out from herbarium material our knowledge of the distribution of this important character is very defective. It is said, with a fair amount of truth, that the former presence of furrows can be deduced from the prominence of the veins, but the correlation is far from perfect. It used to be thought that furrowed leaf-segments were accompanied by relatively broad petals of a white or very pale cream colour, while flat segments were on plants of which the petals were dull yellow or reddish. This is true of much of the Alps, but the correlation breaks down elsewhere.

The division into five subspecies we have adopted here, based on Webb (1987b), must be regarded as tentative, and can probably be improved when more observations have been made on living plants, but we believe it to be more workable than any scheme which has hitherto been published. It ignores a few peculiar variants of extremely limited distribution.

(a) Subsp. *exarata*. Leaf-segments furrowed. Petals white or pale cream, 4–6mm long, broadly obovate, about 1.5 times as long as broad, nearly contiguous. Leaves with 3–5 lobes (occasionally 7), which are usually widely divergent.

(b) Subsp. *pseudoexarata* (Braun-Blanquet) D.A. Webb, *Botanical Journal of the Linnean Society* 95:247 (1987). Leaf-segments furrowed. Petals pale, dull yellow, 3.5–4.5mm long, oblong to narrowly elliptical, twice as long as broad, widely separated. Leaves mostly with 3 lobes, not very widely divergent.

(c) Subsp. *moschata* (Wulfen) Cavillier in Burnat, *Flore des Alpes Maritimes* 5:81 (1913). Leaf-segments not furrowed. Petals yellowish, sometimes tinged with red, 3–4mm long, oblong to narrowly elliptical, twice as long as broad, widely separated. Leaves 3-lobed or entire, sparsely to fairly densely hairy.

(d) Subsp. *lamottei* (Luizet) D.A. Webb, *Botanical Journal of the Linnean Society* 95: 248 (1987). Leaf-segments not furrowed.

Petals white, 4–5mm long, obovate, usually less than twice as long as broad, nearly contiguous. Leaves not fleshy, entire to 5-lobed, usually with a fairly distinct petiole, sparsely hairy to almost hairless.

(e) Subsp. *ampullacea* (Tenore) D.A. Webb, *Botanical Journal of the Linnean Society* 95: 248 (1987). Like subsp. *lamottei* but leaves fleshy, entire or with 3 very short, parallel lobes, and a petiole not distinct from the undivided part of the lamina; also the inflorescence usually has 1–3 flowers, as opposed to the usual 3–5 in subsp. *lamottei*.

*HYBRIDS:* Eleven natural hybrids of *S. exarata* with other species have been reported, and although some of them require confirmation others are certainly correctly diagnosed, and in some cases fairly common. They are particularly frequent in the eastern Pyrenees, where *S. × jouffroyi* Rouy (*S.exarata × pubescens*) forms extensive hybrid swarms, *S. × costei* Luizet & Soulié (*S.exarata × geranioides*) is fairly frequent, as is *S. × ciliaris* Lapeyrouse (*S.exarata × praetermissa*), which is found also in the central Pyrenees. The hybrid with *S.hariotti* is discussed under that species. In the Alps, *S. × wettsteinii* Brügger (*S. exarata × muscoides*) and *S. × vetteri* Burnat (*S.exarata × pedemontana*) are occasional to locally frequent in the west-central and south-western parts of the chain respectively. Three hybrids described by Luizet & Soulié (*S. exarata × pentadactylis* and *S.exarata × intricata* from the Pyrenees, and *S.continentalis × exarata* from Auvergne) are rare and require confirmation, as does a plant described by the same authors from the east-central Pyrenees as *S. × miscellanea* and diagnosed, perhaps somewhat optimistically, as a triple hybrid involving *S.exarata*, *S. geranioides* and *S.pentadactylis*. A report of *S.exarata × androsacea* (*S. × gentyana* Bouchard) from the French Alps is not very convincing.

Artificial hybrids with *S.rosacea* have been raised from about 1870 onwards, and have been backcrossed, selected and re-crossed with *S.hypnoides*, *S.granulata* and possibly other species to give the 'mossy saxifrages' of gardens, which are usually referred to as 'arendsii-hybrids'. Their parentage is mostly unknown and their nomenclature confused. For details see Engler & Irmscher (1916, pp. 441–43) and Köhlein (1984, pp. 133–7).

*CHROMOSOME NUMBER*: Counts of $2n = 20, 22, 24, 26, 28, 32, 34, 36, 44, 48$ and 52 have been published since 1950. No clear correlation with morphology or geographical range is as yet apparent. Some of the variation in chromosome number might possibly be explained by the presence of supernumerary chromosomes, which have been recorded from an Italian population, and which may be present in others but mistaken for 'A' chromosomes; but even so the species clearly has a number of cytological races.

*DISTRIBUTION* (Map 59): Widespread in the mountains of central and parts of southern Europe, from the Riesengebirge (Krkonoše) and western Carpathians, on the borders of Poland and Czechoslovakia, southwards to northern Spain and the Pyrenees, the central Apennines and the northern Peloponnese. It is absent from the mountains of central and southern Spain, southern Italy and Sicily, and is rather local in the Balkan peninsula. Outside Europe it is found in the Caucasus, Anatolia and north-western Iran.

The distribution of the subspecies, as far as it is known, is as follows:

(a) Subsp. *exarata*. Widespread in the western and central Alps, but probably not found east of 11°20′E. Locally in the Balkan peninsula, from Montenegro to southern Greece. Probably in the Caucasus and Anatolia.

(b) Subsp. *pseudoexarata*. Alps, mainly in the east, but also in the south-centre; northern Apennines; Balkan peninsula from east-central Greece to Yugoslav Macedonia, and perhaps further north.

(c) Subsp. *moschata*. Throughout most of the major mountain ranges of Europe, but probably absent from the Apennines and the southern part of the Balkan peninsula; recorded also in the Caucasus and Anatolia.

(d) Subsp. *lamottei*. Known only from south-central France (Auvergne), but perhaps to be found elsewhere.

(e) Subsp. *ampullacea*. Higher peaks of the central Apennines.

*HABITAT*: Rocks, screes and mountain slopes with semi-open vegetation. It is found mainly between 1500 and 3000m, but can extend above and below these limits. Subsp. *ampullacea* is known only from limestone and subsp. *lamottei* from basalt; subsp. *exarata* grows mainly on granite or gneiss, occasionally on other siliceous rocks; subsp. *moschata*

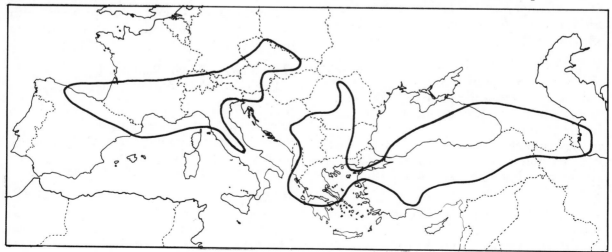

Map 59. Distribution of *S.exarata*; within the limits shown on the map the species is found only on mountains, but these are so numerous that to indicate them would make the map too confused

is somewhat calcicole, but is by no means confined to limestone; subsp. *pseudoexarata* seems to be indifferent to the nature of the rock or soil.

*ACCESS*: Subsp. *moschata* is so common in the Alps and Pyrenees that no special directions are needed for its discovery; as soon as one has reached the subalpine zone and seen the first plants of *S.bryoides*, *S.oppositifolia* or *S.paniculata* one is almost certain to have passed a few plants of *S.exarata* subsp. *moschata*. Subsp. *exarata* is most conveniently seen in the Maritime Alps, in the upper valley of the Gordalasque (east of St Martin Vésubie), or at the Col de la Lombarde. Subsp. *pseudoexarata* is common on the southern (Italian) side of the Grand St Bernard pass. Subsp. *ampullacea* can be found not very far from the end of the road at the 'Blockhaus' on the north-eastern flank of Monte Maiella, Italy. Subsp. *lamottei* is most likely to be found by the streams and waterfall above Mont-Dore (dept. Puy-de-Dôme) or on or around the Puy Mary (dept. Cantal), in France.

*CULTIVATION*: This presents no difficulty; plants may be grown under glass or in a rock-garden or scree.

## 83. *Saxifraga hariotii* Luizet & Soulié, *Bulletin de la Société botanique de France* 58:638 (1912)

*HISTORY & NOMENCLATURE*: First collected by Soulié in 1909 on the Pic d'Anie and Pic d'Orrhy in the western Pyrenees and named by him as *S.muscoides* Wulfen. Later Luizet convinced him that it was a new species, and they named it after their friend P.A. Hariot, whose interests were mainly in cryptogams, but who had also published some local floras in France.

*TYPE*: [In Coste's hand] Saxifraga muscoides Wulf. Basses-Pyrénées, Pic d'Anie, 2000m. 19 août 1909. [Added in Luizet's hand] Saxifraga hariotii Luiz. et Soul.! sp. nov. Foliis sulcatis, lobis ± acutis mucronatis. *D. Luizet*. Lecto-

type: Coste herbarium, Montpellier (**MPU**), designated here.)

*DESCRIPTION*: Leafy shoots up to 6cm but often considerably less, erect or somewhat inclined, forming a dense to fairly lax cushion. Leaves 5–9mm, mostly 3-lobed, but some undivided; basal part variable in width but seldom forming a distinct petiole; lobes 2–3 × 0.75mm, oblong, mostly mucronate, but a few apiculate and a few obtuse, conspicuously furrowed on the upper surface, in some leaves pointing forwards and nearly parallel, but in others, especially near the base of the flowering stems, the lateral lobes diverge almost at right angles. The leaves are sometimes almost hairless, but are usually thinly furnished with short glandular hairs. Flowering stems 3–7cm, slender, fairly densely glandular-hairy, with or without a single cauline leaf, branched above (rarely from near the base) to give a narrow panicle of 3–12 flowers. Sepals 1.5–2mm, obtuse, acute or shortly mucronate. Petals 3.5–4 × 1.75mm, oblong, not contiguous, dull creamy-white, usually with reddish-brown veins. Anthers yellow, flushed with red. Ovary inferior; styles 1.5mm. Towards the end of flowering the filaments, styles and top of the ovary usually turn crimson. Seeds 0.85 × 0.4mm, ellipsoid, rounded to subacute at both ends, covered with very low but fairly broad papillae in groups of 3 or 4; raphe conspicuous, with similar papillae but single, in rows. Flowering season: June to August.

*ILLUSTRATIONS*: Plate 37; Figure 43 Engler & Irmscher (1916, Figure 100)

*RECOGNITION*: Although similar in general aspect to some variants of *S.exarata*, the combination of mucronate, conspicuously furrowed, sparsely glandular leaf-segments with narrow, off-white petals is distinctive.

*VARIATION*: Apart from the laxity or compactness of the cushions, which depends largely on exposure, there appears to be none. The development of red colour in the later stages of flowering is to some extent dependent on exposure to the sun.

HYBRIDS: Hybrids with S.exarata subsp. moschata (S. × richteri Luizet & Soulié) and with S.pubescens subsp. iratiana (S. × darrieuxii Luizet & Soulié) have been reported from a few kilometres west of the Col du Somport, just on the Spanish side of the frontier.

CHROMOSOME NUMBER: 2n = 34.

DISTRIBUTION (Map 58, p. 189): Confined to a small part of the western Pyrenees, from 0°30′W to 1°05′W, on both sides of the frontier.

HABITAT: Limestone rocks and stabilised limestone screes, from 1600 to 2500m.

ACCESS: This species is most easily seen on the French side of the Col de la Pierre St Martin, which lies on the frontier at 0°45′W. Here it is frequent on north-facing limestone bluffs not far from the road at about 1600m.

CULTIVATION: This is not very difficult, given some care and with normal 'alpine' treatment.

# Series *Axilliflorae*
## (Willkomm) Pawłowska

Evergreen perennials of straggling habit, forming loose mats of long, slender, prostrate, leafy shoots from which arise actually or apparently axillary flowering stems. Leaves herbaceous, usually shorter than 15mm (including petiole), divided into 3–5 main lobes, with the petiole more or less equalling the lamina. Hairs short. Petals white. Ovary almost completely inferior. Capsule unusually long and narrow.

A small group of two species endemic to Europe.

**84. *Saxifraga praetermissa* D.A. Webb,** *Feddes Repertorium* 86:204 (1963)

SYNONYMS: S.ajugifolia of Lapeyrouse and many authors, but not of Linnaeus
S.chamaepityfolia Bubani, illegitimate name
S.axillaris of Dulac, not of Kitaibel

HISTORY & NOMENCLATURE: Linnaeus (1755) described as S.ajugifolia a plant which had been sent to him from the south of France; he gave Galloprovincia as its source. He used this term to cover eastern Languedoc as well as Provence, but he would not have used it to denote a station in the Pyrenees. Forty years later, Lapeyrouse came across in the Pyrenees a plant which agreed well enough with the short Linnaean diagnosis, and sent a specimen to J.E. Smith, asking him to compare it with the Linnaean type (which is sheet 575.47 in the Linnaean herbarium in London). Smith, unfortunately, assured him that they were identical, so that throughout the nineteenth century the plant here described (which is known only in the Pyrenees and the Cantabrian range of northern Spain) passed under the name of S.ajugifolia. Rouy (1901, p.52) was the first to draw attention to the error, but his attempt to save the epithet ajugifolia is inconsistent with the present nomenclatural code. Engler & Irmscher (1916) passed over the matter in silence, so that it was necessary when the account of Saxifraga for Flora Europaea was being prepared to give the plant a new name (praetermissa, meaning overlooked) and a new description.

S.ajugifolia of Linnaeus is the plant now generally known as S.pedemontana subsp. prostii (Sternberg) D.A. Webb. To revive the epithet ajugifolia for it would cause intolerable confusion, and it was therefore dismissed as an ambiguous name.

Although the phrase ajugae foliis was used by Parkinson (1640) and some other early writers in their description of a saxifrage, it seems unlikely that they had ever seen this species. Lapeyrouse, therefore, must be considered its discoverer.

TYPE: NE side of Pic de Coutende, near the Pic d'Anie, Basses-Pyrénées, France, c.1750m. 7 August 1959. D.A. Webb. (Holotype: Trinity College, Dublin (**TCD**).)

DESCRIPTION: Stems more or less prostrate, slender, forming loose mats; on each shoot there can be recognised alternating zones, some where the leaves are small and widely spaced (representing the first part of a season's growth), and others (representing the later part) where the leaves are larger and crowded. Leaves up to 15 × 10mm, including the petiole, sparsely hairy, at least on the margins of the petiole; lamina 3- to 5-lobed, with divergent, oblong to oblanceolate, obtuse, acute or shortly mucronate lobes. Flowering stems slender, 10–15cm, arising from leaf-axils in the prostrate part of a shoot, usually 4–7cm behind its upturned tip. Cauline leaves few, very small, entire or 3-lobed. Flowers on each stem 1–3. Sepals 2mm, ovate, acute. Petals 4–5mm, oblong-elliptical, white. Styles straight, divergent. Capsule 6 × 4mm. Seeds 0.6 × 0.35mm, broadly ellipsoid, dark brown, uniformly covered with small tubercles; raphe fairly inconspicuous. Flowering season: June to August.

*ILLUSTRATIONS*: Figures 43, 46
\* Lapeyrouse (1801, Plate 31), as *S.ajugifolia*
Coste (1902, p.141), as *S.ajugifolia*

Figure 46. *S.praetermissa*

*RECOGNITION*: The habit of a well-grown plant is extremely characteristic, with erect flowering stems arising from prostrate shoots some distance from the upturned tip. The only European species with a similar appearance is *S.wahlenbergii*, but in this the petioles are hairless, the leaf-segments all obtuse (in *S.praetermissa* there are always some that are acute or mucronate), the flowering stem less than 10cm, and arising from the terminal tuft of foliage.

*VARIATION*: There is none of any consequence.

*HYBRIDS*: Hybrids with *S.aquatica* (*S.* × *capitata* Lapeyrouse) are common; see under that species. Hybrids with *S.exarata* subsp. *moschata* (*S.* × *ciliaris* Lapeyrouse) are locally frequent.

*CHROMOSOME NUMBER*: $2n = 44$. There is also an old count of $2n = 66$.

*DISTRIBUTION* (Map 60): *S.praetermissa* is found, although somewhat discontinuously, throughout the length of the main chain of the Pyrenees, from 2°30′E to 0°45′W. It is also found much further west, in the Picos de Europa, in north-western Spain.

*HABITAT*: Fine screes and rock-debris, usually in late snow-lies and in all cases irrigated by a trickle of water. It is usually on siliceous rocks, but is not rigidly calcifuge. It is commonest between 1600 and 2000m, but Gaussen (1937) records it as high as 2800m.

*ACCESS*: A convenient place to see this species is by the path which leads from the

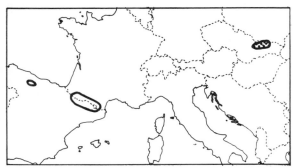

Map 60. Distribution of *S.praetermissa* (unshaded) and *S.wahlenbergii* shaded

Hospice de France, south of Bagnères-de-Luchon, to the Port de Vénasque. About half-way up there is a cliff on the left of the path, and at the base of this cliff, covered in snow at least till late June, there is plenty of *S.praetermissa*.

*CULTIVATION*: As with many snow-lie plants, this is difficult. It has failed at Cambridge and Dublin, and although it flourished for a year or so out of doors at Kew, it did not persist. It is an interesting species, but scarcely a showy one.

## 85. *Saxifraga wahlenbergii* J. Ball, *Botanische Zeitung* 4:401 (1846)

*SYNONYMS*: *S.perdurans* Kitaibel
*S.ajugifolia* of Kitaibel, not of Linnaeus or Lapeyrouse

*HISTORY & NOMENCLATURE*: First discovered, it would seem, by Mauksch, who sent it to Kitaibel. Kitaibel gave it the name *perdurans*, and sent a manuscript description of it to Wahlenberg, who published the name in his *Flora Carpatorum* (Wahlenberg 1814), but without a description and as a synonym of *S.ajugifolia*; the name is, therefore, doubly invalid. It was published validly much later by Kanitz from Kitaibel's manuscripts after his death, but meanwhile Ball had recognised that it was different from the Pyrenean plant (despite Wahlenberg's extremely emphatic statement that they were identical). His criteria for distinguishing the two are not entirely correct, and he rather surprisingly said that *S.wahlenbergii* is intermediate between *S.androsacea*, *S.exarata* and *S.controversa* (this last name indicating *S.adscendens*); his description, however, leaves no doubt as to the identity of the plant to which he gave the name *S.wahlenbergii*.

*TYPE*: Zakopane, N. Carpathians. Aug.[18]43. *J. Ball*. (Lectotype: Kew (**K**), designated here.)

*DESCRIPTION*: Perennial, with nearly prostrate stems forming a loose mat or low cushion. The whole plant is hairless except for a few very peculiar hairs on the inflorescence and the lower surface of the leaves. These may be described as 'worm-like'; they have the form of rather stout cylinders consisting of a row of 8–10 cells, with an obtuse, non-glandular tip, and they lie more or less flat. When mature, the cuticle separates from the rest of the cell-wall, and the intervening space fills with an ethereal oil. They have been described in detail by Pawłowska (1953, 1966). Leaves, including the broad, not very distinct petiole, $10 \times 5mm$, with 3 (rarely 5) oblong, obtuse lobes, directed forwards and nearly parallel. Along most of the stem of each year's growth the leaves are small and well spaced out; at the upturned tip they are larger and crowded together into a tuft or irregular rosette. From this rosette arises a slender flowering stem 4–8cm tall, bearing 1 or 2 small cauline leaves and a single flower (occasionally 2 or 3). The leafy stem produces a continuation from the axil of one of the leaves just below the flowering stem; this often grows onwards while the flowering stem is growing, and gives the impression that the latter is axillary, whereas it is really terminal. Sepals 1.5mm, broad, obtuse. Petals 4–5mm, narrowly obovate, white. Hypanthium elongating in fruit, so that the capsule is longer than wide, $3.5 \times 2$–2.5mm. Styles short, straight, thickened at the base. Seeds $0.8 \times 0.35mm$, ellipsoid with pointed ends, brown, ornamented with numerous small tubercles, some stout, short, black papillae, and some longer, soft, transparent papillae. Flowering season: July and August.

*ILLUSTRATIONS*: Figure 43
Sternberg (1831, Plate 26), as *S.ajugifolia* var. *carpatica*.
Mądalski (1962, Plate 1323), as *S.perdurans*

*RECOGNITION*: The small, lobed leaves and prostrate stems distinguish this species fairly clearly from all others except *S.continentalis*, *S.hypnoides* and *S.praetermissa*. From the first two it differs in its much smaller petals, obtuse leaf-segments and absence of hairs of the usual type. For the distinction from *S.praetermissa* see under that species.

*VARIATION*: As might be expected of a species with such a limited range, there seems to be none worth taxonomic recognition. Ball, in his original description, named two varieties (*subglaberrima* and *latifolia*), but their characters can be seen combined on the same plant. The same probably holds good for varieties based on characters of the seed-coat recognised by Pawłowska (1953, 1966).

*HYBRIDS*: A plant named *S. × thrinax* Rechinger was interpreted as *S.androsacea × wahlenbergii*.

*CHROMOSOME NUMBER*: $2n = 66$.

*DISTRIBUTION* (Map 60, p. 198): Endemic to a fairly small part of the western Carpathians, mainly in the Tatra and Fatra ranges. Most of the stations are in Czechoslovakia, but it extends into Poland on the northern slopes of the High Tatra.

*HABITAT*: Given shade and plenty of moisture, this species can be found in a fairly wide range of habitats. It is commonest on wet rocks, but extends to stabilised screes and even to wood-margins. It is found on both calcareous and siliceous rocks. It grows mainly between 1000 and 1800m, but can ascend as high as 2500m.

*ACCESS*: It grows in fair abundance in the Polish Tatra on the northern side of the peak called Giewont, which is only some 5km south of Zakopane. Here it is to be found on grassy banks and stabilised scree from 1130 to 1300m.

*CULTIVATION*: This is very difficult, for no very obvious reason; it has failed not only at Cambridge and Dublin, but even at Cracow. It is an interesting species of rather doubtful affinities, but it has little decorative value.

# Series *Ceratophyllae* (Haworth) Pawłowska

Evergreen perennials. Stems more or less woody at the base, bearing leafy shoots which form dense or fairly lax cushions; without bulbils or axillary, summer-dormant buds. Leaves lobed, often rather stiff and leathery,

usually less than 7cm long (including petiole), with petiole longer than or about equalling the lamina; usually with very short glandular hairs or sessile glands. Flowering stems terminal or axillary, bearing flowers in fairly compact cymes. Petals white. Ovary inferior or nearly so.

A group of 14 species mainly in Spain and the Pyrenees; one species is widespread in southern Europe and extends into North Africa, and two are endemic to Madeira.

## 86. *Saxifraga pedemontana* Allioni, *Flora pedemontana* 2:73 (1795)

*SYNONYMS*: *S.cymosa* Waldstein & Kitaibel, invalid name
*S.cervicornis* Viviani
*S.pedatifida* of many French authors, not of Smith
*S.prostii* Sternberg
*S.ajugifolia* Linnaeus, ambiguous name

*HISTORY & NOMENCLATURE*: Described by Allioni in 1785 from the Maritime Alps; he cited no synonyms and there is no evidence that the species had been recognised by any earlier author. A few years later it was discovered in the eastern Carpathians by Kitaibel; it was described as *S.cymosa* by Waldstein & Kitaibel (1799–1802), but they made it clear that they considered it identical with *S.pedemontana*, and their name is therefore invalid as superfluous. In 1825 Viviani described from Corsica under the name of *S.cervicornis* a plant which later authors have agreed to regard as a variety or subspecies of *S.pedemontana*. Finally Sternberg (1831) described as *S.prostii* a plant from the Cévennes which Webb (1963) added to *S.pedemontana* as a fourth subspecies.

*TYPE*: *S.pedemontana*. Saxifraga pedemontana All. Fl. Ped. (Lectotype: Allioni herbarium, Turin (**TO**), designated here.)
  Subsp. *cymosa*. Not traced.
  Subsp. *cervicornis*. Not traced.
  Subsp. *prostii*. Herb. J.Gay. Mende, La Lozère. Majo 1825. *Prost*. (Lectotype: British Museum (**BM**), designated here.)

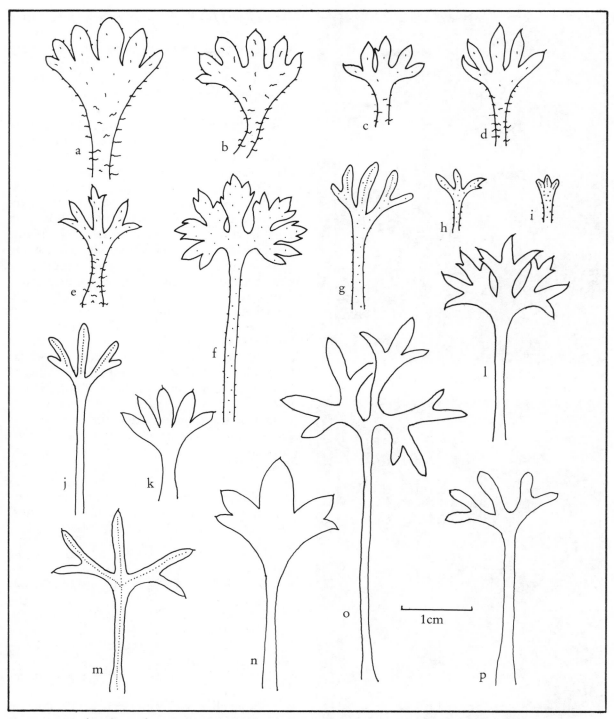

Figure 47. Leaf-outlines of species in series *Ceratophyllae*: (a) *S.pedemontana* subsp. *cymosa*; (b) *S.pedemontana* subsp. *pedemontana* (c) *S.pedemontana* subsp. *cervicornis*; (d) *S.pedemontana* subsp. *prostii*; (e) *S.babiana*; (f) *S.geranioides*; (g) *S.moncayensis*; (h) *S.vayredana*; (i) *S.intricata*; (j) *S.pentadactylis*; (k) *S. camposii*; (l) *S.trifurcata*; (m) *S.canaliculata*; (n) *S.cuneata*; (o) *S.fragilis* subsp. *fragilis*; (p) *S.fragilis* subsp. *valentina*

Figure 48. *S.pedemontana* subsp. *pedemontana*

Figure 49. S.pedemontana subsp. *cervicornis*

DESCRIPTION: Stems branched to form rather numerous, fairly long leafy shoots aggregated into loose cushions. Leaves usually somewhat fleshy or leathery, varying considerably in shape and size; petiole 6–18 × 1.5–3mm; lamina 8–15 × 9–20mm, divided palmately into 3–9 segments, which are narrowly elliptical to linear-oblong, obtuse, acute or mucronate, and not furrowed on the upper surface. Lamina with numerous very short glandular hairs, those on the petiole much longer (up to 3mm), of which the longest are usually non-glandular. In subspecies *pedemontana* and *cervicornis* the young leaves on non-flowering shoots, especially on plants growing in rather dry situations, are usually closely incurved at flowering time; they straighten out as the plant passes into fruit. Flowering stems 5–18cm, terminal, sparingly branched in the upper half to form a rather narrow panicle of 2–12 flowers; cauline leaves few, often absent. Pedicels and hypanthium densely covered with very short glandular hairs. Sepals 4–7 × 1.5–3mm, linear-lanceolate, much longer than the hypanthium. Petals 9–21 × 2.5–8mm, pure white, rarely red-veined or tinged with red at the base, oblanceolate, the basal part erect and the upper part outwardly curved, giving a funnel-shaped flower. Styles 5–7mm, straight, nearly erect. Seeds 0.6–0.75 × 0.35mm, irregularly ellipsoid-oblong, wrinkled, very minutely tuberculate, almost smooth; raphe inconspicuous. Flowering season: May to September.

ILLUSTRATIONS: Plates 43–45; Figures 47–50

Coste (1902, p.140) (subsp. *cervicornis*), as *S.cervicornis*

Mądalski (1962, Plate 1323a) (subsp. *cymosa*), as *S.cymosa*

* *Botanical Magazine* 180: Plate 687 (1975) (subsp. *prostii*)

* Rasetti (1980, Plate 259) (subsp. *pedemontana*)

* Finkenzeller & Grau (1985, p.113) (subsp. *pedemontana*)

RECOGNITION: The long, rather narrow petals and the long styles distinguish *S.pede-*

*montana* from most of the species with which it might be confused. From *S.geranioides* it differs in the much smaller number of leaf-segments and the long hairs on the petiole; from *S.corsica* in the absence of bulbils; from *S.rigoi* in the absence of true summer-dormant buds enclosed in entire, papery outer leaves; from *S.irrigua* in its spreading stems and cushion-like habit.

*VARIATION*: The considerable variability of this species is best treated by the recognition of five subspecies, corresponding to the five disjunct regions in which the plant is found: subsp. *cymosa* from the Carpathians and Balkan peninsula; subsp. *pedemontana* from the south-western Alps; subsp. *cervicornis* from Corsica and Sardinia; subsp. *prostii* from the Cévennes; and subsp. *demnatensis* from Morocco. The difficulties of the treatment are, however, illustrated by the fact that on the one hand all five were originally described as distinct species, while on the other hand there is little agreement among Flora-writers on the criteria by which they are to be distinguished. Each subspecies shows in well-grown plants a *facies* which makes recognition easy, but each shows a range of variation, partly seasonal, partly environmental, but partly, it would seem, genetic, which blurs the distinctions and makes the construction of an honest key very difficult.

The European subspecies are described below reading from east to west, but this is also the order in which each subspecies is most closely related to those which follow and precede it.

(a) Subsp. *cymosa* Engler in Engler & Prantl, *Pflanzenfamilien* III, 2a:55 (1890). Leaves softer and thinner than in other subspecies, fairly densely hairy, with the lamina tapered gradually into a wide petiole; segments short and wide, forwardly directed, obtuse. Flowering stem seldom more than 8cm. Petals 9–15 × 3–5mm.

(b) Subsp. *pedemontana*. The most robust of all the subspecies and usually largest in all its parts. Leaves somewhat fleshy, fairly densely hairy, with the lamina tapered rather gradually into a narrow petiole; segments short and fairly

Figure 50. S.pedemontana subsp. *prostii*

wide, subacute. Flowering stem up to 18cm. Petals 15–21 × 6–8mm, sometimes tinged with pink at the base.

(c) Subsp. *cervicornis* (Viviani) Engler in Engler & Prantl, *Pflanzenfamilien* III, 2a:55 (1890) (*S.cervicornis* Viviani). Very variable. Leaves somewhat sparsely hairy, slightly fleshy or leathery, with the lamina usually tapered rather abruptly into a narrow petiole; segments numerous, narrow and fairly long, forwardly directed or diverging, obtuse, acute or mucronate. Flowering stem up to 15cm. Petals 10–13 × 4–5mm. The young leaves on non-flowering shoots are usually incurved in this subspecies, which gives it a characteristic appearance, but this can also be seen on some plants of subsp. *pedemontana*.

(d) Subsp. *prostii* (Sternberg) D.A. Webb, *Feddes Repertorium* 68:205 (1963) (*S.prostii* Sternberg; *S.pedatifida* of French authors, not of Smith). Leaves somewhat leathery, usually densely hairy, with the lamina tapered somewhat abruptly into a fairly narrow petiole; segments broader than in subsp. *cervicornis* but narrower than in the other two, acute to strongly mucronate. Flowering stem up to 18cm. Petals 9–12 × 2.5–4mm.

A note on the North African subsp. *demnatensis* may be found on p. 261.

HYBRIDS: A hybrid of subsp. *pedemontana* with *S.exarata* subsp. *exarata* (*S.* × *vetteri* Burnat) has been described from several stations in the Maritime Alps.

CHROMOSOME NUMBER: Counts of 2n = 42 are recorded for subsp. *pedemontana*; of 2n = 26, 42 and 44 for subsp. *cervicornis*; and 2n = 32 for subsp. *prostii*.

DISTRIBUTION (Map 61): Each subspecies has its well-defined territory. Subsp. *cymosa* is widespread in the mountains of Bulgaria (just extending into northern Greece), eastern Serbia and southern Romania; further north it reappears on the borders of Romania and Ukraine. There is a record of the species for Albania which, if correct, would presumably refer to subsp. *cymosa*, but it requires confirmation. Subsp. *pedemontana* is found in the south-western Alps, both in France and Italy; it extends from about 45°30′N in the Gran Paradiso southwards to the neighbourhood of Tende. Records for Switzerland are

erroneous. Subsp. *cervicornis* occurs almost throughout Corsica, and in east-central Sardinia. Subsp. *prostii* grows rather sparingly in the Cévennes, from the Montagne Noire (on the borders of the departments of Aude and Tarn) in the south-west to the department of Ardèche in the north-east.

HABITAT: All subspecies grow exclusively on siliceous rocks or screes, nearly always in shade. The altitudinal range is considerable: subsp. *cymosa* ranges from 1850 to 3000m; subsp. *pedemontana* from 1500 to 2700m; subsp. *cervicornis* from 700 to 2700m; and subsp. *prostii* from 250 to 1400m.

ACCESS: Subsp. *cymosa* is abundant on shady rocks from 2250 to 2900m by the path which leads up the northern side of Musala, the highest peak of the Rila mountains, in Bulgaria. Subsp. *pedemontana* is most conveniently seen on the French side of the Col de la Lombarde, 16km north-west of St Martin Vésubie in the Maritime Alps. Subsp. *cervicornis* is common on most of the mountains of Corsica from 1200m upwards; it may be seen at low level in the Gorges de la Restonica, south-west of Corte. Subsp. *prostii* is fairly common in ravines on the northern side of Mont Carroux (west of Bédarieux, dept. Aude).

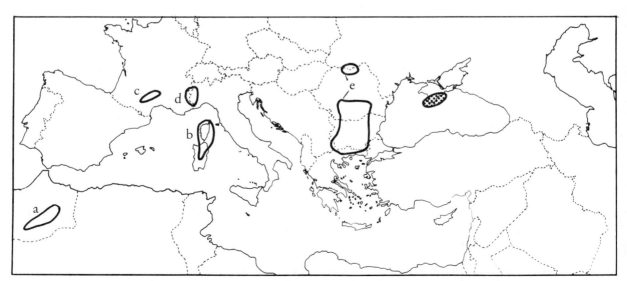

Map 61. Distribution of *S.pedemontana* (unshaded): (a) subsp. *demnatensis*, (b) subsp. *cervicornis*, (c) subsp. *prostii*, (d) subsp. *pedemontana* and (e) subsp. *cymosa*; and *S.irrigua* (shaded)

CULTIVATION: This is fairly easy, either in semi-shade on the rock-garden or in an alpine house. Subsp. *prostii* is the easiest out of doors; the other three are happier under glass. Subsp. *pedemontana* is much the most handsome; if it is given full sun at flowering time the older leaves turn bright red, and the contrast between these and the fresh green of the young leaves and the large, pure white flowers makes a splendid display.

## 87. *Saxifraga babiana* Diaz & Fernandez Prieto, *Anales del Jardín Botánico de Madrid* 39:249 (1983)

HISTORY & NOMENCLATURE: It is remarkable that this very distinct species was not discovered (or at least recognised as distinct) before 1980. Admittedly it is confined (as far as our present information goes) to an area of 45 × 30km in a little-visited area of northern Spain, but several of its stations are on rocks beside a road and must have been passed over by dozens of botanists. Its variety *septentrionalis* can easily be mistaken for *S.trifurcata* at a distance, but var. *babiana*, with its grey-hairy foliage, is very distinct.

It is named from Babia, which indicates the district south of the Puerto de Somiedo.

TYPE: Truébano de Babia (León), 1260m, 14.viii.1980. *Diaz & Fernandez Prieto 7750.* (Holotype: Malaga (**MGC**).)

DESCRIPTION: Leafy shoots numerous, erect, crowded, forming a fairly dense, green to greyish-green cushion; the young leaves are erect, forming a bush-like tuft. Leaves up to 37mm long, but mostly about 25mm, densely covered, at least on the lower part of the petiole, and sometimes all over, with rather long glandular hairs, those on the lamina 0.5–0.75mm long, those on the petiole up to 1.5mm or more. Lower surface of the petiole crimson at least in the lower part. Lamina divided almost to the base into 3 primary lobes which are flat, not furrowed; these are usually further divided each into 3 short, sometimes almost tooth-like, apiculate segments ending in a transparent point 0.3–0.4mm long. Flowering stems 10–20cm, very slender, ascending, arising from the axils of the upper leaves of the previous year's growth; cauline leaves about 5, the lower with a long petiole and 3 small lobes, the uppermost linear-oblong, entire; both stem and cauline leaves sparsely glandular-hairy. Flowers 5–9 in a fairly compact cyme; pedicels and hypanthium with a few very short glandular hairs or subsessile glands. Sepals 2.5mm, oblong-lanceolate. Petals 6–8 × 3–3.5mm, narrowly obovate, white. Styles short, outwardly curved. Seeds 0.8 × 0.5mm, with very low, rounded tubercles; raphe inconspicuous. Flowering season: May to July.

ILLUSTRATIONS: Figure 47
*Anales del Jardín Botánico de Madrid* 39: 250–252 (1983)

RECOGNITION: The combination of compact, cushion-like habit, leaves with 7–9 apiculate segments, hairy and crimson-tinted at least at the base of the petiole and slender axillary flowering stems, is found in no other species.

VARIATION: The authors also described a variety of the species in their original account. This is var. *septentrionalis* Diaz & Fernandez Prieto, *Anales del Jardín Botánico de Madrid* 39:253 (1983). It differs from var. *babiana* in having the hairs and the crimson coloration confined to the lower part of the petiole; the lamina and upper part of the petiole are green and hairless. Intermediates can be found, in which the upper part of the petiole, and sometimes the lamina, are sparsely hairy.

HYBRIDS: In the same paper as that in which they described the species, the authors described a hybrid, *S. × somedana* Diaz & Fernandez Prieto (*S.babiana × continentalis*).

CHROMOSOME NUMBER: Not known.

DISTRIBUTION (Map 62): Known so far only from a small area in the north-western part of the province of León in Spain, with a few stations in the adjacent part of the province of Cantábria. It extends from 42°57'N to 43°07'N, and from 5°43'W to 6°17'W. Var. *septentrionalis*, as its name implies, is found mainly in the northern part of this range, on both sides of the main Cantabrian watershed; var. *babiana* is mainly to be found in the valley of the River Luna.

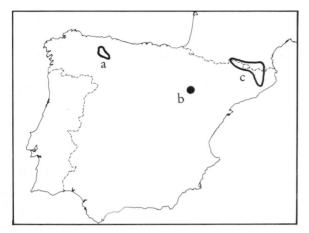

Map 62. Distribution of (a) *S.babiana*, (b) *S.moncayensis* and (c) *S.geranioides*

*HABITAT*: Limestone bluffs and cliffs; rarely also on siliceous rocks (perhaps base-rich). Var. *babiana* seems mostly to favour shaded habitats, but var. *septentrionalis* is more tolerant of sun. The species ranges from 1050 to 1720m in altitude.

*ACCESS*: Var. *septentrionalis* can easily be seen at various places on the descent from the Puerto de Somiedo to the village of Piedrafita de Babia, and grows in profusion in the village on a wall just to the west of the road-junction. We have found var. *babiana* more elusive, but it can certainly be seen on a west-facing cliff by the road about 6km north-west of La Pola de Gordon, which is on the León-Oviedo road 25km north of León.

*CULTIVATION*: It is growing well in Dublin under glass after a year: it has not yet been tried out of doors.

## 88. *Saxifraga geranioides* Linnaeus, *Centuria Plantarum* 1:10 (1755)

*SYNONYM*: *S.palmata* of Lapeyrouse, not of Smith

*HISTORY & NOMENCLATURE*: This species is represented in the Burser herbarium at Uppsala, and the specimen there was the source of Linnaeus' description. For some reason it became confused with *S.fragilis* (which has similar flowers but very different leaves and habitat), and until quite recently the latter was treated as a variety or subspecies of *S.geranioides*.

The epithet refers to the leaves, which in their general outline resemble fairly closely some species of *Geranium* such as *G.molle*.

*TYPE*: No. XVI(1).86 in the Burser herbarium, Uppsala (**UPS**) has been designated as lectotype (Webb 1987a).

*DESCRIPTION*: Stems bearing lax cushions of light green foliage. Petiole up to 40mm, slender; lamina about 15 × 25mm, semicircular in outline, divided rather deeply into 3 primary lobes, which are further lobed and toothed, so that the total number of ultimate segments amounts to 17–25; the segments are acute and not furrowed. Surface of the lamina covered with extremely short glandular hairs, giving a finely warty rather than downy appearance; the hairs, like those of *S.vayredana* and *S. moncayensis*, have a stalk of 1–2 cells, not longer than the diameter of the terminal gland. On the petioles and in the inflorescence there are hairs of this type, but also some others slightly longer (up to 0.35mm long). Flowering stems 15–25cm, terminal, usually branched from near the middle, with or without a single cauline leaf. Flowers up to 20, in a fairly lax cyme; bracts very variable in shape and size. Sepals 4.5–5mm, linear-lanceolate, acuminate, enlarging in fruit up to 7mm. Petals 12 × 4mm, oblanceolate, white. Styles up to 5mm, straight. Seeds 0.75 × 0.45mm, ellipsoid, shortly pointed at one end, truncate at the other, dark brown, uniformly covered with very small tubercles; raphe inconspicuous. The flowers have a faint but distinct scent like that of the primrose; we know of no other European species with scented flowers. Flowering season; May to August.

*ILLUSTRATIONS*: Figures 47, 51
\* Lapeyrouse (1801, Plate 43)

Engler & Irmscher (1916, Figure 73)
* Bonnier (1921, Plate 205)
* Moggi (1985, Plate 247)

*RECOGNITION*: The leaf-shape is distinctive, with its long petiole and semicircular lamina with numerous, acute segments. The only species with somewhat similar leaves are *S.irrigua*, *S.aquatica* and *S.petraea*. In all these the hairs are much longer than those of *S. geranioides*; moreover, in *S.petraea* the petals are conspicuously notched and usually unequal; *S.aquatica* has shorter petals and much stouter flowering stems; *S.irrigua* has the leafy stems arranged in a compact tuft, and they are not woody at the base.

*VARIATION*: A plant similar to *S.geranioides* in many characters, but dwarf, and with greyish, obviously downy leaves, was described by Lapeyrouse (1801) under the name of *S.palmata*; he did not realise that this name had already been used by J.E. Smith in 1798 for a variant of *S.rosacea*. In 1815 De Candolle dismissed it as a variety of *S.geranioides*, and it was formally described as *S.geranioides* var. **palmata** by Engler & Irmscher, *Pflanzenreich* 67 (IV.117):327 (1916); they indicated that it was only to be found at high altitudes, mostly above 2350m. The only specimen we have seen which corresponds to this is one collected by B.E. Smythies in 1975 near Caldas de Bohi at relatively low altitude (1800m); it has hairs on the lamina 2–3 times as long as those of typical plants. This plant is rather disconcerting in view of the constancy elsewhere in this series of the nature of the leaf-hairs; it needs further investigation.

*HYBRIDS*: A large number of hybrids has been attributed to *S.geranioides*. It is difficult without observation in the field to be sure that all these have been correctly diagnosed, but most of them seem fairly convincing. It must be remembered, however, that in the diagnosis of all these hybrids, *S.geranioides* was interpreted so as to include *S.fragilis*, and it is possible that in some cases the latter may be the parent. The following have been described as natural hybrids:

Figure 51. *S.geranioides*

*S.geranioides × vayredana* (*S. × cadevallii* Luizet)

*S.geranioides × exarata* subsp. *moschata* (*S. × costei* Luizet & Soulié)

*S.geranioides × pentadactylis* (*S. × lecomtei* Luizet & Soulié)

*S.geranioides × pubescens* (*S. × obscura* Grenier & Godron)

*S.geranioides × intricata* (*S. × yvesii* Neyraut & Verguin ex Luizet)

Mention must be made here of the rather mysterious *S.ladanifera* Lapeyrouse. It was described as a species, but the description is inadequate and somewhat confused, and according to Luizet (1913) the name was applied by Lapeyrouse to several different hybrids of *S.geranioides*. His plate is strongly suggestive of *S.fragilis* Schrank, but it does not agree well with the description, and in many of the localities which he cited *S.fragilis* does not grow. The name is impossible to typify and is probably best forgotten.

Two garden plants have been interpreted as hybrids of *S.geranioides*: these are *S.* × *trifurcatoides* Engler & Irmscher, supposedly *S.geranioides* × *trifurcata*, but more probably a variant of the latter, and *S.* × *cuspidata* Schleicher, which is perhaps *S.continentalis* × *geranioides*.

It would be of considerable interest to attempt to synthesise all these hybrids by controlled pollination. None of them is now in cultivation, and herbarium material is scanty.

*CHROMOSOME NUMBER*: 2n = c.52.

*DISTRIBUTION* (Map 62, p. 206): Eastern and, more sparingly, east-central Pyrenees, on both sides of the international frontier, with southern outliers on the Sierra de Montseny and other granitic ranges on the borders of the provinces of Barcelona and Gerona. The eastern limit lies on or near the Canigou; the western at 0°50′E, near the border between the departments of Ariège and Haute-Garonne.

*HABITAT*: Siliceous rocks, usually granite, and usually but not always shaded, from 1200 to 2850m.

*ACCESS*: It can be seen in considerable abundance on the northern side of the Canigou, on rocks and stabilised scree, and large clumps of it overhang the rather adventurous road which ascends the lower slopes of the mountain. It can also be seen about 20km north of Mont-Louis, on the eastern side of the road which leads to Axat.

*CULTIVATION*: This is fairly easy, though it seldom shows the same luxuriance as on its native ground. The long, narrow petals give to the flowers a certain elegance.

## 89. *Saxifraga moncayensis* D.A. Webb, *Feddes Repertorium* 68:201 (1963)

*SYNONYM*: *S.pentadactylis* subsp. *moncayensis* (D.A. Webb) Malagarriga, *Plantae Sennenianae IV. Saxifraga (T.)L.* 7 (1974)

*HISTORY & NOMENCLATURE*: The Sierra de Moncayo, after which the species is named, is situated on the borders of the provinces of Zaragoza and Soria in north-eastern Spain; it may be regarded as a somewhat isolated south-eastern outlier of the Cordillera Ibérica. It has often been visited by botanists, but mainly at a time when the differences between *S.intricata*, *S.pentadactylis* and *S.pubescens* were not properly understood. Willkomm (1874) recorded *S.pentadactylis* from the mountain; he later (1893) changed the identification to *S.willkommiana* Bossier ex Willkomm, but that is now generally regarded as a variety or subspecies of *S.pentadactylis*. It is quite true that this plant grows on the upper part of the mountain, but on rocks and walls around the hermitage (which stands at about 1500m on the eastern side of the mountain) there grows in abundance a saxifrage which differs from *S.pentadactylis* in several characters (see below). This was noticed by Webb on his first visit to the mountain in 1959; later visits in 1967 and 1969 confirmed his earlier observations, and a search for intermediates indicated that they were very few and could reasonably be interpreted as hybrids. *S.moncayensis* seems, on the whole, to be at least as closely related to *S.vayredana* as it is to *S.pentadactylis*.

*TYPE*: Sierra de Moncayo (Zaragoza): abundant at 1500–1600m, near the hermitage, 5 April 1959. *D.A. Webb.* (Holotype: Trinity College, Dublin (**TCD**).)

*DESCRIPTION*: Leafy shoots long and very numerous, forming fairly dense, soft, deep cushions of foliage up to 1.5m across. Whole plant rather densely covered with very short glandular hairs, mostly 0.15–0.2mm long, with a stalk of 2 cells, though on the petioles hairs up to 0.35mm long can be found. Foliage with a slightly spicy scent, but not as strong as in *S.vayredana*. Petiole 8–13 × 2mm, somewhat dilated at the whitish base; lamina 8–11 × 9–15mm, deeply divided into 3 primary lobes, which are narrowly oblong to oblanceolate, obtuse and conspicuously furrowed on the upper surface. In many leaves these lobes are entire, but in a fair number the lateral lobes bear on their outer side a short secondary lobe about 3mm long; these secondary lobes are not furrowed. The leaves are of a light, fresh green. Flowering stems 5–10cm, terminal, but with their base soon overtopped by axillary shoots arising below them; cauline leaves usually 1 or 2, similar to those of the leafy shoots but with a shorter petiole. Inflorescence branched from about half-way up the stem, with 3–7 primary branches, each bearing 3–5 flowers. Lower bracts 3-lobed, the upper entire. Flower-buds long, pointed, nodding, slightly flushed with red on the calyx and hypanthium. Sepals 3mm, oblong, obtuse. Petals 6–7 × 3.5–4mm, broadly oblong, narrowed at the base but without a distinct claw, pure white, sharply bent slightly below the middle, with the lower part vertical, giving a cup-like centre to the flower, and the upper part spreading horizontally. Nectary-disc bright yellow, surrounding the short, emergent part of the almost inferior ovary; styles 1.5mm, straight, slightly divergent. Seeds 0.6 × 0.25mm, oblong, brown, minutely tuberculate or almost smooth; raphe conspicuous. Flowering season: May to July.

Figure 52. *S.moncayensis*

*ILLUSTRATIONS*: Plate 48; Figures 47, 52

*RECOGNITION*: It is only likely to be confused with *S.pentadactylis*, *S.vayredana*, *S.intricata* and *S.pubescens*. From the first it differs in having short hairs instead of sessile glands, also in its longer petals and greater number of leaves with the lateral lobes undivided. From *S.vayredana* it differs in its furrowed, more obtuse and fewer leaf-segments. From *S.intricata* it differs in its much more vigorous growth, lighter green foliage and narrower, not contiguous petals. These characters distinguish it also from *S.pubescens*, which in addition has considerably longer hairs.

*VARIATION*: As might be expected from a narrow endemic there is none of any consequence.

*HYBRIDS*: Probably with *S.pentadactylis*, but these have not been fully investigated.

*CHROMOSOME NUMBER*: 2*n* = 60.

*DISTRIBUTION* (Map 62, p. 206): Known only from the Sierra de Moncayo, in north eastern Spain.

*HABITAT*: Sandstone rocks, mostly east-facing, at 1500–1600m.

*ACCESS*: It is particularly abundant on the retaining wall of the broad terrace in front of the hermitage.

*CULTIVATION*: This presents no difficulty; it can be grown in semi-shade on the rock-garden or in a pan in the alpine house. It gives rise to fair-sized cushions and flowers freely, but it is not quite as vigorous as *S.vayredana*.

**90. *Saxifraga vayredana*** Luizet,
*Bulletin de la Société botanique de France*
60:413 (1913)

*HISTORY & NOMENCLATURE*: First mentioned by Colmeiro (1846) under the name of *S.groenlandica*. Later collected by Vayreda in 1875, and named by him *S.exarata* var. *intricata*. Luizet, who saw plants collected by Soulié in 1913, realised that it was specifically distinct and named it after Vayreda.

*TYPE*: Société pour l'étude de la flore franco-helvétique, No.2228. Catalogne: entre Gualba et Santa Fé, éboulis siliceux vers 700m. 2 juin 1913. *Soulié*. (Lectotype: Paris (**P**), designated here.)

*DESCRIPTION*: Leafy shoots numerous, forming very large, fairly dense cushions. Leaves, flowering stems and inflorescence covered with very short (0.15–0.2mm) glandular hairs similar to those of *S.moncayensis* and *S.intricata*, the stalk, usually consisting of 2 cells, being scarcely longer than the diameter of the gland. Petiole 7–15mm, usually longer than the lamina; lamina 5–9 × 8–13mm, deeply divided into 3 primary lobes, which are sometimes entire but more often shortly lobed, giving 5–9 segments which are acute and flat, not furrowed, on the upper surface. The foliage has a strong, pleasant, spicy or balsamic odour; this can be noticed also in a few other species of this series, but in all cases in far lesser intensity than in *S.vayredana*. Flowering stems 7–12cm, terminal, bearing 1–2 cauline leaves, similar to the others but smaller. Flowers 3–9, in a compact, rather narrow panicle. Sepals 2.5mm, ovate, subacute. Petals 6–7 × 4.5mm, obovate, pure white, almost contiguous. Styles 2mm, curved, divergent. Seeds 0.65 × 0.35mm, oblong-ellipsoid, somewhat pointed at one end, dark brown, bearing longitudinal rows of low, broad, rounded papillae, longest at the longest at the back and diminishing towards the fairly conspicuous, finely tuberculate raphe. Flowering season: June and July.

*ILLUSTRATIONS*: Figure 47
Engler & Irmscher (1916, Figure 76)

*RECOGNITION*: The very short hairs and relatively small petals distinguish this species from all others except *S.moncayensis* and *S. intricata*. From both of these it differs in the absence of furrows on the leaf-segments. The strong scent of the foliage is also characteristic.

*VARIATION*: There is none of any consequence.

*HYBRIDS*: The hybrid with *S.geranioides* (*S.* × *cadevallii* Luizet) is fairly frequent. No other natural hybrid is possible, as *S.geranioides* is the only species which grows within the distribution area of *S.vayredana*. No artificial hybrids have been reported.

*CHROMOSOME NUMBER*: $2n = $ c.64.

*DISTRIBUTION* (Map 63): Known only from the Sierra de Montseny, a small range which lies some 50km north-north-east of Barcelona.

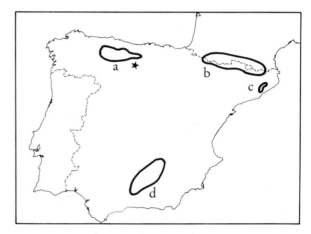

Map 63.  Distribution of (a) *S.canaliculata*, (b) ★*S.intricata*, (c) *S.vayredana* and (d) *S.camposii*

*HABITAT*: Schistose and granitic rocks from 700 to 1600m.

*ACCESS*: There is no difficulty in finding this species, especially by the road which leads up the southern side of the range to the hermitage of Santa Fé.

*CULTIVATION*: Like many narrow endemics, *S.vayredana* is surprisingly easy to cultivate, either in semi-shade on the rock garden, where it spreads to form very large cushions, or in the alpine house. It is free-flowering, but the flowers are rather too small to make an impressive show. It is worth growing in a pan, however, for the delicious scent of its foliage.

## 91. *Saxifraga intricata* Lapeyrouse, *Figures de la Flore des Pyrénées* 58 (1801)

SYNONYMS: *S.nervosa* Lapeyrouse, invalid name

*S.exarata* var. *intricata* (Lapeyrouse) Engler, *Monographie der Gattung Saxifraga L.* 180 (1872)

HISTORY & NOMENCLATURE: First described by Lapeyrouse, who chose the epithet *intricata* to describe the interwoven young leaves of some plants. He described at the same time as a separate species *S.nervosa*, but this must be regarded as, at best, a trivial variety, and as a specific epithet the name is invalid since he cited *S.exarata* Villars as a synonym.

TYPE: Plate 33 in *Figures de la Flore des Pyrénées* (Lapeyrouse 1801) is here designated as lectotype.

DESCRIPTION: Stems bearing short leafy shoots which form rather small tufts or low cushions. Plant covered with very short glandular hairs, similar to those of *S.moncayensis* and *S.vayredana*; they are always less than 0.1mm long except on the lower part of the petiole, where they may be as much as 0.25mm. Leaves rather rigid, fairly dark green, mostly 3-lobed, but varying from entire to 9-lobed. In the 3-lobed leaves the angle of divergence of the lobes is very small and the lamina passes very gradually into the petiole, but in leaves with more numerous lobes the lamina may be almost semicircular in outline. Lamina 5–7mm long; petiole 3–10mm; leaf-segments obtuse, furrowed on the upper surface (sometimes only faintly on the lateral segments). Flowering stems 7–10cm, terminal, usually branched from near the base, but occasionally only near the top, so as to give a panicle with 2–5 primary branches, each bearing 2–3 flowers; cauline leaves (if present) and bracts varying from entire to 5-lobed. Sepals 1.5mm, elliptical, obtuse. Petals 5–6 × 4–5mm, very broadly elliptic to almost circular, contiguous, speading horizontally, white. Styles short, somewhat curved, divergent. Seeds 0.6 × 0.35mm, brown, uniformly covered with small tubercles; raphe inconspicuous. Flowering season: June to August.

ILLUSTRATIONS: Plate 47; Figure 47
* Lapeyrouse (1801, Plates 33,39), the latter as *S.nervosa*
Coste (1902, p.142)

RECOGNITION: The rather rigid and darkish green leaves covered with very short, wart-like hairs, together with the very wide petals, are characteristic. Of the species with similar hairs, *S.geranioides* has much larger leaves of a different shape; *S.vayredana* lacks the furrows on the leaf-segments; *S.moncayensis* shows much more vigorous growth, forming large cushions of softer, paler foliage, and has narrower petals, which are not contiguous.

VARIATION: Lapeyrouse separated *S. nervosa* as a species distinct from *S.intricata* on the grounds that in the latter the young leaves were interwoven into an erect, brush-like structure, whereas in *S.nervosa* they remain free. This character, however, is possible to observe only in the early summer, and does not seem to be correlated with any other, so that it is doubtful if it has any taxonomic significance. The only other variation is between well-grown plants and those stunted from drought or exposure.

HYBRIDS: Hybrids have been described with *S.geranioides* (*S.* × *yvesii* Neyraut & Verguin ex Luizet), *S.pubescens* subsp. *iratiana* (*S.* × *wilczeckii* Verguin & Neyraut ex Luizet) and *S.exarata* subsp. *moschata* (*S.* × *baregensis* Rouy & Camus). The first seems to be locally frequent, the other two very rare.

CHROMOSOME NUMBER: Two recent counts agree on $2n = 34$; an earlier one of 20 requires confirmation.

DISTRIBUTION (Map 63, p. 210): *S.intricata* is fairly widespread in the eastern and central Pyrenees. Its eastern limit is not clearly established; it certainly extends to Andorra (Losa & Montserrat 1950), and it has been recorded from the Canigou, but this last record is subject to some doubt and has not been confirmed recently. Its western limit in the Pyrenees is at the Col de Somport (0°30′W), but it re-appears much further west in the Cordillera Cantábrica. Here it is found, not like other Pyrenean species such as *S.aretioides* or *S.praetermissa* in the Picos de Europa, because these are largely calcareous, but on siliceous rocks on the Peña Prieta, which lies to the south-east of the Picos, at the junction of the provinces of Santander, Palencia and León (Losa 1957).

*HABITAT*: Siliceous rocks from 1400 to 2600m, often in dry, exposed situations where few other plants are to be seen. Its calcifuge nature is well shown on the Pic de la Sagette, which lies half-way between Laruns and the Col du Pourtalet; here it is abundant on a small outcrop of siliceous rock surrounded by limestone, from which it is completely absent.

*ACCESS*: *S.intricata* can be seen in some abundance on large boulders near Heás.

*CULTIVATION*: This is not very difficult, but it is not a strong grower and needs some care. It can survive on a scree out of doors, but is better in the alpine house.

## 92. *Saxifraga pentadactylis* Lapeyrouse, *Figures de la Flore des Pyrénées* 64 (1801)

*SYNONYMS*: *S.willkommiana* Boissier ex Willkomm
*S.caballeroi* Camara & Sennen
*S.losae* Sennen

*HISTORY & NOMENCLATURE*: Although it was doubtless seen by earlier collectors it was confused with *S.intricata* and *S.exarata*, and it was first effectively distinguished by Lapeyrouse. His epithet *pentadactylis* (five-fingered) is apt enough, for although leaves with three or seven segments are not uncommon the majority have five, and the segments, being narrowly oblong and obtuse, can reasonably be compared with fingers.

*TYPE*: *S.pentadactylis*. Plate 40 in *Figures de la Flore des Pyrénées* (Lapeyrouse 1801) is here designated as lectotype.
   Subsp. *willkommiana*. Not traced.

   Subsp. *losae*. Losa: S. de Barrio (Alava), 1200m. *Sennen 7297*. (Lectotype: British Museum (**BM**), designated here.)
   Subsp. *almanzorii*. Avila: Paredes Negras, Picos de Gredos, Hoyos de Espino, 30T UK 085597, 1950m, fissuras graníticas. *Luceño & Vargas*. [Herbarium sheet no. MA 343083.] (Holotype: Madrid (**MA**).)

*DESCRIPTION*: Stems rather brittle, sparingly branched to give small, usually open cushions of leafy shoots. Completely hairless, the green parts covered with sessile glands and often sticky. Leaves with petiole up to 20mm long, usually longer than the lamina, which is divided almost to the base into 3 primary lobes; the lateral lobes are usually divided into 2 segments, the central one occasionally into 3; segments 3–10 × 0.5–1.5mm, linear to oblong, obtuse, furrowed on the upper surface. Flowering stems 7–17cm, terminal, slender; cauline leaves 1–2, small. Inflorescence a dense to very lax cyme of 5–50 flowers. Sepals 2–3mm, narrowly triangular to oblong, obtuse. Petals 3.5–5 × 1.5–3mm, usually white, obovate to oblong. Styles 1.5–2.5mm, curved, divergent. Seeds 0.65 × 0.3mm, dark brown, oblong, covered all over with minute tubercles arranged in longitudinal rows; raphe inconspicuous. Flowering season: June and July.

*ILLUSTRATIONS*: Figure 47
* Lapeyrouse (1801, Plate 40)
* Flahault (1912, Plate 80)
   Engler & Irmscher (1916, Figure 90)

*RECOGNITION*: Among the hairless species with divided leaves *S.pentadactylis* is distinguished by its relatively small petals and its narrow, parallel-sided, obtuse, furrowed leaf-segments. Of the species with which it might be confused, *S.fragilis* and *S.canaliculata* have larger petals, and the former has the leaf-segments flat, while the latter has them pointed. *S.intricata* comes closest to it in general habit, but its leaf-segments are covered with very short hairs, and its petiole is usually shorter.

*VARIATION*: A variable species in which several subspecies have been described. Our information is, unfortunately, too fragmentary to assign with confidence subspecific or varietal rank to some of the variants; nor has their geographical range been accurately determined. It seems best, therefore, for the time being to recogise four subspecies.

(a) Subsp. *pentadactylis*. Cushions small, rather loose. Leaves dark green, hard and rigid; petiole usually much longer than the lamina, but scarcely, if at all, wider than the widest segments, which are long, narrow and divaricate. Panicle usually with not more than 8 flowers. Petals c.4.5 × 2.5mm, usually contiguous, pure white.

(b) Subsp. *willkommiana* (Boissier ex Willkomm) Rivas Martinez, *Anales del Instituto Botánico A.J. Cavanilles* 21:228 (1963). Cushions fairly large and fairly compact. Leaves medium green, fairly soft; petiole often equalling or slightly shorter than the lamina, scarcely, if at all, wider than the widest segments, which are 1.5–2mm wide and divaricate. Panicle usually with at least 8 flowers. Petals c. 5 × 3mm, contiguous, pure white.

(c) Subsp. *losae* (Sennen) D.A. Webb, *Botanical Journal of the Linnean Society* 95:249 (1987). Cushions small, very compact, often with more or less columnar leafy shoots. Leaves hard and rigid; petiole about equalling the lamina, much wider than any of the segments, and sometimes nearly as wide as the lamina; segments short and forwardly directed. Panicle usually small; the published description and the available material are insufficient for a description of the flowers.

(d) Subsp. *almanzorii* Vargas, *Anales del Jardín Botánico de Madrid* 43:457 (1987). Petiole considerably longer than the lamina, much wider than the segments, which are short, 0.5–1mm wide and slightly divaricate. Panicle with up to 6 flowers. Petals 3.5 × 1.5mm, not contiguous, greenish-yellow.

Subsp. *pentadactylis* is found chiefly in the Pyrenees, but occasional plants of identical appearance occur, together with intermediates, among populations of subsp. *willkommiana* in the northern and eastern parts of the range of the latter. The geographical separation of the two subspecies is not nearly as clear as Will-

komm (1893) and Rivas Martinez (1963) suggested. The morphology and the geographical range of subsp. *losae* need to be more clearly defined, but in spite of this its recognition as a subspecies seems justified by its distinctive habitat. Subsp. *almanzorii* seems to have been described from a fairly small population, in a range otherwise occupied by subsp. *willkommiana*; it might, perhaps, be better given rank as a variety.

It is clear that much more observation of living plants, if possible in cultivation, is needed before the variation in this species is fully understood.

*HYBRIDS*: S.geranioides × pentadactylis seems to occur in several places in the eastern Pyrenees. It seems probable that this hybrid forms at least one element of the *S.ladanifera* of Lapeyrouse, but this name is so uncertain in its application that Luizet & Soulié (in Luizet 1910) gave a new binomial, *S. × lecomtei*, to the hybrid (see also Luizet (1913)). The hybrid with *S.exarata* is discussed under that species.

*CHROMOSOME NUMBER*: S.pentadactylis (subspecies not given) has been recorded as $2n = 16$ with up to 5 supernumerary chromosomes; subsp. *willkommiana* has $2n = 32$.

*DISTRIBUTION* (Map 64): Eastern Pyrenees and mountains of northern and central Spain. In the Pyrenees it ranges from the Canigou westwards to about 0°30′E

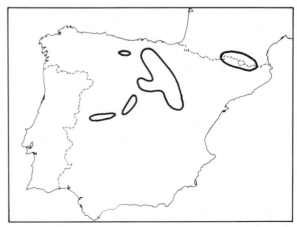

Map 64.  Distribution of *S.pentadactylis*

(possibly to 0°10'W, but this requires confirmation). Further south it is to be found on most of the higher summits of the Cordillera Ibérica, in the provinces of Soria, Logroño and Burgos, and also on the limestone hills to the east of this range, from the province of Álava possibly as far south as the province of Teruel. It is also in the Sierra de Guadarrama, the Sierra de Gredos and adjacent ranges, and in a few isolated stations on the siliceous mountains south of the Picos de Europa.

Subsp. *pentadactylis* is found mainly in the Pyrenees, but plants indistinguishable from it have been collected in the Cordillera Ibérica and the Sierra de Guadarrama. Subsp. *willkommiana* is reported from all the siliceous mountains south of the Pyrenees within the range of the species. Subsp. *losae* was first described from the southern part of the province of Álava (near Miranda de Ebro and Haro), but has since then been reported from several stations eastwards to 1°W (prov. Zaragoza) and southwards to about 41°50'N (south of the Sierra Cebollera). Subsp. *almanzorii* is known only from the central part of the Sierra de Gredos.

*HABITAT*: Except for subsp. *losae*, which is calcicole, plants of this species are to be found on siliceous rocks, usually shady but often dry. In the Pyrenees it is seldom seen below 2000m, but in the mountains further south it is frequent down to 1750m. Subsp. *losae*, on the other hand, is known only from limestone, usually at an altitude of about 1000m.

*ACCESS*: The most convenient place to see this species in some quantity is in the Sierra de Guadarrama, north-west of Madrid. The road to Segovia crosses the range at the Puerto de Navacerrada, and on any north-facing slope near the pass the plant can be seen in abundance on vertical rocks, ledges and stabilised screes. In the Pyrenees it is rather elusive, but it is fairly frequent on shady rocks at 2050m south-south-west of Lac de Lanoux, which lies near the extreme western edge of the department of Pyrénées-Orientales, not far from the Col de Puymorens.

*CULTIVATION*: Subsp. *pentadactylis* from the Pyrenees seems to be difficult to maintain. Plants so labelled abound in botanic gardens, but they all belong to some other species. Subsp. *willkommiana* is easier, and responds to ordinary 'alpine' treatment, but it must be confessed that the species has little decorative value and is not worth a great deal of trouble.

### 93. *Saxifraga fragilis* Schrank, *Plantae rariores Horti Academiae Monacensis*, Plate 92 (1821)

*SYNONYMS*: *S.paniculata* of Cavanilles, not of Miller
*S.trifurcata* subsp. *paniculata* Pau, *Notas botanicas a la Flora española* 6:53 (1895)
*S.corbariensis* Timbal-Lagrave
*S.geranioides* subsp. *corbariensis* (Timbal-Lagrave) Rouy & Camus, *Flore de France* 7:50 (1901)
*S.geranioides* var. *obtusiloba* Seringe in De Candolle, *Prodromus Systematis universalis Regni vegetabilis* 4:30 (1830)
*S.valentina* Willkomm

*HISTORY & NOMENCLATURE*: As the rich synonymy indicates, this plant has been very variously interpreted. Admittedly it belongs to a somewhat critical group, but although it is pardonable to confuse it with *S.camposii* it is fairly easy to distinguish it from *S.trifurcata*, and why it should have been considered a variant of *S.geranioides* by Seringe, by Rouy & Camus and by Engler & Irmscher (1916) is hard to understand. Part of this confusion must be attributed to Cavanilles, who first described it in 1803 (unless the enigmatic *S.ladanifera* of Lapeyrouse (1801) belongs here; the plate strongly resembles *S.fragilis*, but neither the description nor the localities accord well); for both the sheets in the Madrid herbarium labelled by Cavanilles as *S.paniculata* consist of mixtures of *S.fragilis* with *S.trifurcata*. Fortunately no problem of typification arises, as Cavanilles' name is a later homonym of *S.paniculata* Miller. Timbal-Lagrave correctly distinguished it from the other species with which it had been confused but, pardonably enough, overlooked Schrank's earlier description. Schrank obtained the plant from the Mainz botanic garden, where it had come from Strasbourg, but beyond that its history cannot be traced. Schrank's plate, however, is a good one and, together with his type-specimen, leaves no doubt as to the identity of the plant. His epithet refers to the leaves which, especially in subsp. *fragilis*, are easily broken at the base or top of the petiole.

*TYPE: S.fragilis.* What must be regarded as the holotype is a sheet at Munich (**M**), with a printed label 'Herbarium regium monacense. Herbarium Schreberianum'; then in MS 'Saxifraga trifurcata Schrader'. The sheet is annotated by Schrank at great length, partly in scarcely legible German, partly in Latin, of which the relevant parts are:
Saxifraga fragilis nob. Saxifragae hypnoidis nomine in H. Argent. 1791 Mayo falso … Non est S.petraea … Non est S.groenlandica … Definiri poterit sequenti modo. Saxifraga fragilis, foliis rigidis, caulinis inferioribus trifidis, laciniis lateralibus divaricatis subbifidis, superioribus axillaribus integris, caule ramoso, flexuoso. Moguntia allata ab hortulano 1790, ubi postea periit a nobis iterum expedita.
    Subsp. *valentina*. Not traced.

*DESCRIPTION*: Stem sparingly branched, giving fair-sized, rather lax cushions of foliage; on account of the finer division of the leaves these appear more open than those of *S. cuneata*, which it resembles in general habit. Hairless, but with numerous sessile glands on leaves, stems and inflorescence, but usually only slightly sticky. Leaves medium green, rigid and somewhat leathery; petiole usually 10–25mm, sometimes up to 55mm; lamina 10–17 × 10–30mm, usually semicircular in outline, divided almost to the base into 3 primary lobes, of which the lateral ones are nearly always, and the central one sometimes, divided into 2–3 segments, giving 5–9 in all (rarely up to 13); segments flat, narrowly oblong, obtuse to subacute. Flowering stems 10–22cm, terminal, usually with 1–3 small,

Figure 53. *S.fragilis* subsp. *valentina*

entire or 3-lobed cauline leaves, branched above to give a fairly lax cyme of 5–20 flowers. Sepals 3mm, triangular-lanceolate, subacute. Petals 7–14 × 4–7mm, obovate to oblanceolate, sometimes slightly notched at the tip, pure white. Styles 3mm, straight, strongly divergent in fruit. Seeds 0.85 × 0.5mm, ellipsoid, rounded at both ends, dark brown, covered, except on the prominent raphe, with minute tubercles, and over part of the surface also with blackish, low, rounded papillae. Flowering season: April to July.

*ILLUSTRATIONS*: Plate 49; Figures 47, 53
\* Schrank (1821, Plate 92)
    Engler & Irmscher (1916, Figure 73), as *S. geranioides* subsp. *corbariensis*
\* *Botanical Magazine* 180: Plate 701 (1975)

*RECOGNITION*: Among the hairless species with palmately lobed leaves *S.fragilis* differs from *S.cuneata* in its much narrower leaf-lobes; from *S.trifurcata*, *S.canaliculata* and *S.camposii* in having all the leaf-segments obtuse or subacute, not apiculate or mucronate; and from *S.pentadactylis* in its much longer petals and its flat, not furrowed, leaf-segments.

*VARIATION*: The plants in the northern part of the range of this species differ sufficiently from those in the southern part to justify the discrimination of two subspecies, though there is a fairly wide zone in the middle of the range where plants of intermediate appearance are found.

(a) Subsp. *fragilis* is the northern subspecies. It has larger leaves, usually with longer petioles, and with 5–11 segments to the lamina; its petals are seldom less than 10mm long, and the stamens exceed the sepals by at least 3mm during the flowering period.

(b) Subsp. *valentina* (Willkomm) D.A. Webb, *Botanical Magazine* 180:186 (1975), from the south, is smaller in most of its parts and of more compact growth; the leaves have 3–7 segments; the petals are 7–11mm long, and the stamens do not exceed the sepals by more than 1mm.

*HYBRIDS*: None is known, but some of the hybrids attributed to *S.geranioides* may possibly be hybrids of this species.

*CHROMOSOME NUMBER*: 2n = 60–66, perhaps usually 64.

*DISTRIBUTION* (Map 65): *S.fragilis* occurs mainly in eastern Spain, but it extends also into France in the Corbières (dept. Aude) and the limestone hills that lie between these and the eastern Pyrenees. In Spain it is found in the

pre-Pyrenees of Catalonia, and extends southwards through the provinces of Teruel, Castellon, Cuenca and Valencia to the Sierra d'Aitana in Alicante province; it also has an isolated station some distance to the southwest in the Sierra de Cazorla (prov. Jaen). Its western limit (apart from the Sierra de Cazorla) lies at about 1°30′W, near the southern end of the Montes Universales; its northern and eastern limit is on Mont Alaric, between Carcassonne and Narbonne. The integradation of the two subspecies makes it difficult to assign definite limits to either, but broadly speaking specimens from north of 42°N are referable to subsp. *fragilis*, and south of 40°30′N to subsp. *valentina*; between these parallels intermediate plants are common.

*HABITAT*: Predominantly on limestone; Mateo (1983) says that it occurs on triassic sandstone but without citing a locality. Possibly the sandstone is calcareous. It is commonest on vertical rock-faces, especially in river-gorges; it can stand a good deal of desiccation but is seldom seen in full sun. It ascends as high as 2000m (albeit in a rather pinched and starved-looking condition) on the summit of the Javalambre, but most of its stations are below 1000m, and it descends to about 400m in the Corbières.

*ACCESS*: Subsp. *fragilis* is most easily seen in the gorge of the River Aude south of Axat, in France, where it grows on and off for several kilometres on vertical rocks above the road or river. It is also frequent in the Gorges de Galamus, which lie 20km to the east and slightly to the north of Axat. Subsp. *valentina* can be seen on the walls of the very narrow gorge through which the river Guadalaviar makes its rather dramatic entry into the village of Albarracín, west-north-west of Teruel, in Spain.

*CULTIVATION*: Although it will survive in the open in Dublin it does not flourish, but if grown in a pan in the alpine house in well-drained but not too poor soil it makes a fine display. Subsp. *fragilis* is from every point of view preferable to subsp. *valentina* as an ornamental plant.

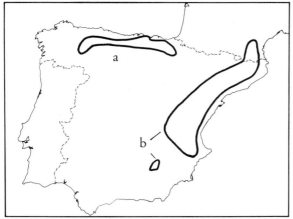

Map 65. Distribution of (a) *S.trifurcata* and (b) *S.fragilis*

**94. *Saxifraga camposii* Boissier & Reuter, *Pugillus plantarum novarum* 47 (1852)**

*HISTORY & NOMENCLATURE*: Named after its discoverer, Don Pedro del Campo, who found it in 1849 in the Sierra de Loja, which on modern maps indicates a small range 12km south-south-east of Loja (prov. Granada, Spain), but in Boissier and Reuter's day probably included the adjacent Sierra de Gorda.

*TYPE*: Sierra de Loja, ubi eam detexit el *Pedro Campos* fin. Jun. 1849. [flowering specimen] (Lectotype: Geneva (**G**), designated here; also at Geneva, with the same annotation, is a fruiting specimen which may be considered as an isotype.)

*DESCRIPTION*: Stems clothed in dead leaves, branching to form loose, rather hard cushions of dark green, rather rigid foliage. Plant hairless, covered with sessile glands but rarely very sticky. Leaves more or less erect when young, spreading later; petiole up to 20mm, usually longer than the lamina; lamina divided, sometimes deeply, sometimes only half-way to the base, into 3–5 flat, rather broad, acute to mucronate or shortly apiculate lobes, some of which occasionally bear lateral teeth, so that there may be as many as 9 ultimate segments on the leaf, but there are never more than 5 well-developed lobes. Flowering stems up to 15cm, terminal, with several cauline leaves which are mostly undivided. Flowers 6–15 in a rather compact cyme. Sepals 4–6mm, narrowly oblong-lanceolate, mucronate. Petals 8–12 × 3.5–4.5mm, narrowly obovate, tapered to an ill-defined claw, white. Styles 3–3.5mm, straight, divergent. Seeds 0.85–1 × 0.45mm, oblong-ellipsoid, pointed at one end, dark brown, bearing longitudinal rows of very low, rounded, blackish papillae, the rest of the surface, including the conspicuous raphe, covered with minute, paler tubercles. Flowering season: May to July.

*ILLUSTRATIONS*: Figure 47
\* Willkomm (1881–1885, Plate 32)
  Engler & Irmscher (1916, Figure 74)

The illustrations in *Botanical Magazine* 108: Plate 6640 (1882) and in Nicholson (1886, p.371) named as *S.camposii* represent a quite different species—perhaps *S.corsica* subsp. *cossoniana* or one of its hybrids.

*RECOGNITION*: Among the hairless species with divided leaves *S.camposii* comes closest to *S.fragilis* subsp. *valentina*, but it differs in having at least some of the leaf-segments mucronate and in the rather more rigid texture of its leaves. From *S.canaliculata* it differs in its wider leaf-segments, which are flat, not channelled; and from *S.trifurcata* in its fewer leaf-segments, which never overlap, as well as in its terminal flowering stems.

It must be confessed that the difference between *S.fragilis* subsp. *valentina* and *S. camposii* var. *leptophylla* is often less clear than one would wish, and it might, perhaps, be wise to include *S.camposii* under *S.fragilis* as a third subspecies. We do not, however, feel justified in doing this without further study of *S.camposii* both in the wild and in cultivation.

*VARIATION*: There is little variation except in the shape of the leaf, but by this a fairly readily recognisable variety may be distinguished. In the typical variety, var. **camposii**, the petiole is 2.5–3mm wide, gradually expanded at the top to a lamina with segments about 2mm wide. Plants collected by Willkomm as early as 1845 from the Sierra de Maria (prov. Almería) have, however, a petiole only 1mm wide, which is expanded suddenly into a semicircular lamina with segments 1mm wide, many of them scarcely or very obscurely mucronate. This was first labelled *S.almeriensis*, but was published as *S.camposii* var. **leptophylla** Willkomm in Willkomm & Lange, *Prodromus Florae Hispanicae* 3:112 (1874). It was raised to the rank of a subspecies by Webb (1963, p.204), but examination of a wider range of material makes us think that this was a mistake. It is best treated as a variety.

*HYBRIDS*: None has been described, though it seems possible that some of the variation in the species arises from introgression by *S.fragilis* subsp. *valentina*.

*CHROMOSOME NUMBER*: $2n = 64$.

*DISTRIBUTION* (Map 63, p. 210): Mountains of southern and south-eastern Spain. Its north-easterly limit lies in the Sierra de Alcaraz, in the western part of Albacete province; hence it extends fairly continuously southwards and westwards through the provinces of Jaen, Almería, Granada and Málaga, where it finds its western limit south-east of Archidona. There is a record by Reverchon from the Serrania de Ronda, much further west, but like many of Reverchon's records it is open to suspicion, and has not been confirmed since. On the whole the plants from the south-western end of the range belong to var. *camposii*, and those in the central and north-eastern parts to var. *leptophylla*, but there is a good deal of overlap and interpenetration.

*HABITAT*: Mainly on shady, more or less vertical limestone rocks or cliffs, more rarely on screes. It ranges from about 900 to 2100m.

*ACCESS*: It is plentiful on north-facing cliffs on the Sierra de la Sagra, in the north-eastern tip of the province of Granada, from 1800 to 2050m. It may also be seen in fair quantity at 1000m on the northern side of the Cerro Jabalcón north of Baza (prov. Granada). It might perhaps be possible to see it closer to a road at the Puerto de los Alazores, the highest point on the road from Loja to Málaga.

*CULTIVATION*: This is rather difficult; it has not succeeded for more than two years at Kew, Cambridge or Dublin, partly because cuttings are difficult to root. It could, no doubt, be kept going in an alpine house with sufficient care, but it is not worth a great deal of trouble, being less attractive than most of the related species.

### 95. *Saxifraga trifurcata* Schrader, *Hortus Gottingensis* 13 (1809)

*SYNONYM*: S.ceratophylla Dryander

*HISTORY & NOMENCLATURE*: This species was first described in 1809 by Schrader from a cultivated specimen in the botanic garden of Göttingen, where it was said to have been long in cultivation. A year later it was independently described as *S.ceratophylla* by Dryander in the second edition of Aiton's *Hortus Kewensis*. Schrader knew that it came from Spain, as did Sims, who published an account of the species in the *Botanical Magazine* (Sims 1814), but neither gave a more precise locality nor any indication of who collected and distributed the plant. Sims stated that it was introduced to Britain in 1804, and was already stocked by a nurseryman in 1814. It may have come from the Madrid botanic garden, as the specimens of Cavanilles labelled *S.paniculata* are a mixture of *S.fragilis* and *S.trifurcata*. Don (1822, p.416) mentioned a specimen in the Lambert herbarium which came from Pavon and was named by him *S.petraea*; this must have been collected in the latter years of the eighteenth century.

It is not clear from Schrader's description whether he meant his epithet to mean 3-lobed or 3-times forked; either is applicable to the larger leaves.

*TYPE*: Not traced.

*DESCRIPTION*: Stems branched so as to form large, fairly open cushions of dark, shining green foliage. Hairless, but covered with sessile glands; usually scarcely, if at all, sticky. Leaves rigid; petiole usually longer than the lamina, which is up to 20 × 30mm but often much less, more or less semicircular in outline, divided about ¾ of the way to the base into 3 primary lobes, which in all but the smallest leaves are further divided, so that in the larger leaves the number of segments is seldom less than 9 and may be as high as 17; segments triangular, mostly apiculate, concave above, some of the lateral ones strongly recurved, giving a characteristic antler-like appearance to the lobes. In the larger leaves the segments are widely spaced, but in many of the smaller ones they are crowded and overlapping. Flowering stems up to 30cm, arising from an axil of one of the upper cauline leaves of the previous season's growth; cauline leaves small, usually few. Flowers 5–15, in a lax cyme. Sepals 2–2.5mm, narrowly triangular, acuminate. Petals 8–11 × 5mm, elliptic-oblong, white. Styles 3mm, straight, erect. Seeds 0.7–0.85 × 0.3mm, oblong, rather angular, rounded or truncate at the ends, dark brown, covered with black papillae of very varying length, the rest of the surface, including the conspicuous raphe, very minutely tuberculate. Flowering season: May to July.

*ILLUSTRATIONS*: Figures 47,54
    Schrader (1809, Plate 7)
\* *Botanical magazine* 40: Plate 1651 (1814)
    Nicholson (1886, Figure 436)

*RECOGNITION*: Among the hairless species of similar habit, *S.trifurcata* is easily distinguished by the axillary origin of the flowering stems, and by the characteristic antler-like appearance of the leaves, with numerous short, triangular, apiculate or mucronate, often overlapping segments.

*VARIATION*: There is none that cannot be ascribed to environmental influence, except for the presence or absence of viscidity in the leaves (in most plants they are scarcely viscid, but occasionally they can be as sticky as in *S.canaliculata*). The difference in appearance

Figure 54. *S.trifurcata*

between luxuriant and starved plants can, however, be very striking.

*HYBRIDS*: *S.* × *schraderi* Sternberg, described from a plant of unknown origin in the botanical garden at Göttingen, was diagnosed by Engler & Irmscher (1916) as *S.hypnoides* × *trifurcata*, and this seems plausible, if one interprets their use of the epithet *hypnoides* to indicate *S.continentalis* (which they regarded as a subspecies), although it resembles the second parent more closely than the first. It is still frequent in cultivation, usually under the name of *S.trifurcata*. *S.* × *trifurcatoides*, described by Engler & Irmscher in 1916 from a plant observed in the Munich botanic garden in 1872, was diagnosed by them as *S.geranioides* × *trifurcata*, but this seems much less plausible; it was probably only a variant of the latter. It is no longer in cultivation.

No natural hybrids are known.

*CHROMOSOME NUMBER*: $2n = 28$.

*DISTRIBUTION* (Map 65, p. 216): Confined to northern Spain, where it is rather widely distributed through the western pre-Pyrenees and the Cantabrian chain. Its eastern limit is at 1°30′W, south-west of Roncesvelles; from here it extends somewhat discontinuously through the Cantabrian range to 7°W in the north-eastern tip of the province of Orense. Its area, though wide from east to west, is narrow from north to south; nowhere, except near its western limit, is it to be found more than 100km from the coast. Most of its stations lie north of the main watershed, but it is to be found on the southern side in a few places.

*HABITAT*: Almost exclusively on limestone rocks, but in several towns (notably Oviedo) it has spread on to walls and roofs. The walls are usually mortared, but it can be seen on tiled roofs without any source of lime. It can tolerate full sun, but is more often seen in shaded situations. It is commonest between 700 and 1300m, but it ascends to 2000m in the Picos de Europa, and apparently it can descend almost to sea-level (at Santona, according to sheet *52584* in the herbarium of the Madrid botanic garden).

ACCESS: *S.trifurcata* may be seen in some quantity by the road that leads up to Lake Enol from Covadonga, on the northern side of the Picos de Europa. It may also be seen on the northern side of the Puerto de Pajares on the main road from Ovideo to León.

CULTIVATION: This is very easy. It is perfectly hardy, and can form large tufts in the rock-garden, preferably in semi-shade. It is also effective in a pan in the alpine house.

## 96. *Saxifraga canaliculata* Boissier & Reuter ex Engler, *Monographie der Gattung Saxifraga L.* 169 (1872)

HISTORY & NOMENCLATURE: First collected, it would seem, by Boissier in 1858 in the mountains near Reinosa in northern Spain (prov. Santander), but confused by him with his still undescribed *S.willkommiana*. It was collected again by Bourgeau in 1864 at Arvas (between Oviedo and León), and again labelled *S.willkommiana*. It was later recognised as a distinct species by Bossier & Reuter, who suggested the name *S.canaliculata* but did not publish it; this was left to Engler in 1872. The name was suggested by the deeply channelled leaf-segments. It was overlooked by Willkomm (1874), who equated it with *S.camposii* var. *leptophylla*, but he corrected his mistake later (Willkomm 1893). Leresche & Levier (1880, p.190) gave a good account of the species and its distinctive characters.

TYPE: Bourgeau, Plantes d'Espagne, 1864. Saxifraga willkommiana Boiss. mscr. herb. Rochers au Pic de las Corvas, près la Combento de Arvas, Prov. de León. 10 juillet. *E.Bourgeau 2647*. (Lectotype: Geneva (G), designated here; isotypes exist in many other herbaria, and the second of the two collections cited by Engler is also at Geneva.)

DESCRIPTION: Stems freely branched so as to form large, fairly lax cushions of foliage. Whole plant hairless, but covered with sessile glands and very sticky, especially in spring and summer. Petiole up to 14mm, slender, expanded gradually into a fan-shaped to nearly semi-circular lamina up to 12 × 18mm, which is deeply divided into linear, deeply channelled, apiculate segments, varying in number from 3 to 11, but usually 5–7. Flowering stems 8–15cm, terminal, with 2–3 entire to 5-lobed cauline leaves. Flowers 5–12 in a usually very compact cyme. Sepals 3.5–4mm, linear-lanceolate. Petals 8–10 × 5–7mm, broadly obovate, contiguous, often recurved at the tip in the later stages of flowering, white. Styles 3.5mm, straight, erect. Seeds 0.85 × 0.5mm, dark brown, truncate at one end, bluntly pointed at the other, with numerous irregularly disposed, very low, rounded papillae; between these the surface is rough, but without definite tubercles; raphe inconspicuous. Flowering season: May to July.

ILLUSTRATIONS: Plate 46; Figures 47, 55
   Leresche & Levier (1880, Plate 3)
 * Willkomm (1881–1885, Plate 32)

RECOGNITION: Among the hairless species with deeply divided leaves *S.canaliculata* can be distinguished by the linear, apiculate, deeply channelled leaf-segments, the terminal flowering stems and by the very broad, often reflexed petals.

HYBRIDS: A hybrid with *S.cuneata* was discovered in 1914 by Font Quer in the rather narrow zone of overlap between the areas of the two species (near Cervera de la Pisuerga, prov. Palencia), and it was described in 1924 by Pau as *S.* × *fontqueri*.

CHROMOSOME NUMBER: $2n = 52$.

DISTRIBUTION (Map 63, p. 210): Like *S.trifurcata* this species is confined to northern Spain, but it occupies a much smaller area. It is essentially a plant of the Picos de Europa and the adjacent parts of the Cantabrian range, but, in contrast to *S.trifurcata*, it is commoner on the southern side of the watershed than on the northern. It extends from 4°05′W, near Reinosa, to 6°20′W, south of the Puerto de Somiedo, in the province of León. Guinea (1949, p.173) has recorded it from much further east, on the Sierra de Gorbea (2°45′W), but this station is not marked on the distri-

Figure 55. *S.canaliculata*

bution-map of Diaz & Fernandez Prieto (1983) and requires confirmation.

*HABITAT*: Mainly on limestone rocks, but there are a few records from igneous rocks; whether these are base-rich or not is not known. It is equally common in sunny or in shaded situations. It ranges from 600 to 2100m, but is mainly to be found between 1000 and 1700m.

*ACCESS*: S.canaliculata can be seen easily at the Puerto de Pontón, north of Riaño (mainly on the southern side of the pass); also a few kilometres to the east, by the roadside below the Puerto de Pandetrave, and further east still at the Puerto de Piedrasluengas.

*CULTIVATION*: This species is as easy to cultivate as is *S.trifurcata*. Thanks to its broader petals and therefore fuller flowers it is rather more showy, but it loses, perhaps, a little in delicacy.

**97.** *Saxifraga cuneata* **Willdenow,** *Species Plantarum*, 4th edn, 2:658 (1799)

*SYNONYM*: S.cuneifolia of Cavanilles, not of Linnaeus

*HISTORY & NOMENCLATURE*: First distinguished by Cavanilles, and published by him in 1795 as *S.cuneifolia* in the third volume of his *Icones et Descriptiones Plantarum*, oblivious, apparently, of the fact that Linnaeus had used this name over 30 years earlier for a very different plant. The epithet was therefore changed to *cuneata* by Willdenow, who cited the diagnosis, description and figure of Cavanilles. The diagnosis is not full enough to distinguish it from some other species, but the figure is entirely characteristic of the plant which we call *S.cuneata* today. The only difficulty arises from the fact that Cavanilles gave as the locality Castellfort. This is a name which might well be duplicated in several parts of Spain, but the only occurrence on modern maps is for a village in the western part of the province of Castellón, far to the south of the known range of *S.cuneata*. Nobody has reported it from this region since, and Mateo (1983), in his detailed report on the saxifrages of this region, does not mention the species. It seems clear that the figure was drawn from a cultivated plant, and that there was a confusion of labels. This does not, however, invalidate the status of Cavanilles' illustration as the type.

*TYPE*: Plate 248 in volume 3 of *Icones et descriptiones plantarum* (Cavanilles 1795) is the holotype.

*DESCRIPTION*: Stems not easily rooting, covered with dead leaves, fairly freely branched so as to form large, loose tufts of leafy shoots. Plant hairless, but usually somewhat sticky from an abundance of sessile glands. Leaves rather stiff and leathery; petiole very variable in length according to the luxuriance of the plant; lamina up to 22 × 26mm, rhombic to fan-shaped in general outline, divided about half-way to the base into 3 primary lobes, which are broadly triangular to ovate and 3–8mm wide at the base, obtuse but usually mucronate, very shortly secondarily 3-lobed on the larger leaves. Flowering stems 7–30cm, arising from the axils of the leaves of the previous year's growth, slender, branched above the middle to give a narrow panicle of 7–15 flowers; cauline leaves 3–6, linear-lanceolate or shortly 3-lobed. Sepals 2.5–3mm, oblong-lanceolate, acute. Petals 5–8 × 3–5mm, obovate, more or less contiguous, pure white. Styles short, slightly curved outwards. Seeds 0.55–0.7 × 0.4–0.45mm, broadly ellipsoid, shortly pointed at one end, black, rather thickly covered in obtuse, cylindrical papillae which diminish in height towards the smooth, conspicuous raphe. Flowering season: May to July.

ILLUSTRATIONS: Plate 50; Figure 47
  Cavanilles (1795, Plate 248), as *S.cuneifolia*
  Engler & Irmscher (1916, Figure 74)
  Farrer (1919, p.264)
* Casas & Jimenez (1982, p.164)

RECOGNITION: Among the hairless species with palmately lobed leaves this species is quite distinctive in the width of the leaf-lobes; all others have leaves more finely divided and usually with more numerous segments.

VARIATION: There seems to be none that cannot be ascribed to environmental conditions.

HYBRIDS: *S.urbionica* Losa, although described as a new species, seems most probably to be a hybrid between *S.continentalis* and *S.cuneata*. It was discovered in 1932 in the Sierra de Neila, in the eastern part of the province of Burgos. It was accompanied by both parent species. For the hybrid with *S. canaliculata* see under that species.

CHROMOSOME NUMBER: 2n = 26, 28.

DISTRIBUTION (Map 66): Confined to northern Spain, with one station in south-western France. It extends from the calcareous mountains of the western Pyrenees through the Spanish Basque country to the central part of the Cantabrian range, nearly, but not quite as far as the Picos de Europa. It is found almost entirely to the south of the main watershed,

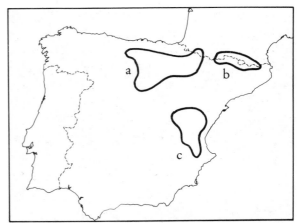

Map 66. Distribution of (a) *S.cuneata*, (b) *S.aquatica* and (c) *S.latepetiolata*

and it extends southwards to 41°N. Its eastern limit lies at about 0°45′W, in the Valle de Ansó on the Spanish side of the Pyrenees and north of the Pic d'Anie on the French side; westwards it reaches 4°45′W in the north-western corner of the province of Palencia.

HABITAT: Limestone rocks and walls, usually on vertical rock-faces, but sometimes on boulders or scree. It can tolerate very dry conditions, but is commoner on shaded rocks than on those exposed to the sun. It ascends as high as 1900m; its lower limit is probably at about 750m.

ACCESS: *S.cuneata* may be seen conveniently in abundance at Aguilar de Campoo, a village in the north-eastern part of the province of Palencia, some 30km south of Reinosa. It is frequent in the small gorge which lies to the west of the village, and also on the walls of the convent nearby. It can also be seen in the gorge of the Ebro north of Oña, in Burgos province.

CULTIVATION: This presents no difficulty. *S.cuneata* is reasonably hardy, and robust enough to fill a pocket in the rock-garden. But like many Spanish species it does itself better justice in the alpine house. In spite of its coarse foliage it is an attractive plant in flower; the slender flowering stems (red if grown in full sun) together with the well-spaced pure white flowers give the inflorescence a delicacy reminiscent of *S.cochlearis*.

# Series *Aquaticae* (Engler & Irmscher) Pawłowska

Biennials or evergreen perennials, of rather coarse growth. Leaves large, usually more than 4cm long (including petiole), with petiole longer than the lamina, which has numerous lobes. Hairs, at least on the petioles, long and wavy. Flowering stem leafy, tall and rather stout. Petals white. Ovary ⅔ or more inferior.

A small group of three species endemic to Europe.

## 98. *Saxifraga aquatica* Lapeyrouse, *Figures de la Flore des Pyrénées* 53 (1801)

*SYNONYMS*: *S.adscendens* of Willdenow, D. Don and others, not of Linnaeus
*S.petraea* of Gouan, not of Linnaeus

*HISTORY & NOMENCLATURE*: There is a specimen of this species in the Burser herbarium at Uppsala, and it is probably the plant intended by no.2 on p.131 in Bauhin (1620). Bauhin (who collected it in the Pyrenees and sent a specimen to Burser) described it by comparing it with *S.petraea*, and Linnaeus in his manuscript list of the Burser herbarium identified it as *S.adscendens*. In consequence these three very different species were for long confused together, and Lapeyrouse was the first to make clear the distinctive characters of *S.aquatica*.

The name is very apt, as it is the only European species which nearly always has its roots in running water.

*TYPE*: Plate 28 in *Figures de la Flore des Pyrénées* (Lapeyrouse 1801) is here designated as lectotype.

*DESCRIPTION*: A rather coarse perennial, spreading by short stolons, so as to give rise to dense mats of foliage up to 2m across. Basal leaves with petiole up to 35mm and lamina up to 25 × 35mm, more or less semicircular in outline, divided nearly to the base into 3 primary lobes, which are again repeatedly though not very deeply lobed; the ultimate segments vary in number from 15 to 27, and in shape from ovate to narrowly triangular; they are often overlapping. Lamina rather sparsely, and petiole densely, furnished with medium to long hairs. Cauline leaves numerous, similar to the basal but smaller and with shorter petioles. Flowering stems 25–60cm, usually 2–3mm (sometimes up to 5mm) in diameter, arising from the axils of leaves on more or less prostrate stems, some distance behind the apex. Inflorescence a rather narrow panicle occupying the upper half of the flowering stem, and consisting of a large apical cyme, and several smaller lateral cymes spaced out below it. Within each cyme the pedicels are short and the flowers rather crowded. Sepals 4–6mm, narrowly oblong. Petals 7–9 × 3.5–4mm, narrowly obovate, white (rarely pale yellow). Ovary ¾ inferior; styles straight, nearly erect. Seeds 0.8 × 0.3mm, oblong, brown, uniformly covered in minute tubercles; raphe inconspicuous. Flowering season: June to August.

*ILLUSTRATIONS*: Plate 51; Figure 56
\* Lapeyrouse (1801, Plate 28)
\* Bonnier (1921, Plate 205)
\* Moggi (1985, Plate 240)

*RECOGNITION*: The very robust flowering stems and the large mats of coarse, deeply dissected leaves make this species easy to recognise, apart from its invariable habitat in swift mountain streams. The only species with which it might be confused is *S.irrigua*, but this has closely tufted flowering stems without any stolons; the flowering stems are terminal, shorter and slenderer; and the petals are longer and narrower.

*VARIATION*: There is considerable variation in leaf-shape, but most of the range can often be found on a single plant.

*HYBRIDS*: The hybrid with *S.praetermissa* is the only one known, but it is fairly common. It was described as a species by Lapeyrouse under the name of *S.capitata*, but its hybrid status is now generally agreed. It is intermediate between the parents, though tending to resemble *S.aquatica* more closely. It is fertile, but far less free-flowering than *S. aquatica*, so that if, as often happens, the two

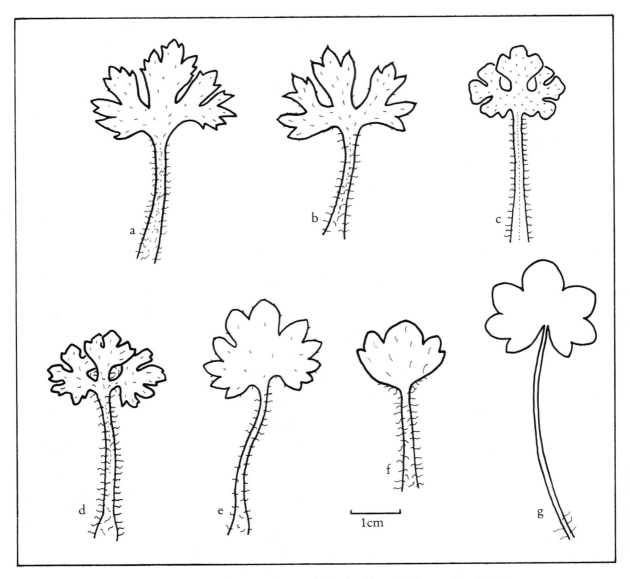

Figure 56. Leaf-outlines of species in series *Aquaticae* and *Arachnoideae*: (a) *S.aquatica*; (b) *S.irrigua*; (c) *S.latepetiolata*; (d) *S.petraea*; (e) *S.berica*; (f) *S.arachnoidea*; (g) *S.paradoxa*

are growing side by side the hybrid stands out not only by its smaller and more finely dissected leaves, but also by its fewer flowering stems.

*CHROMOSOME NUMBER*: $2n = 66$.

*DISTRIBUTION* (Map 66, p. 222): Confined to the eastern and central Pyrenees, where it ranges from the Canigou in the east almost to Gavarnie in the west.

*HABITAT*: On the banks of fast-flowing streams from 1500 to 2400m, probably always on siliceous rocks.

*ACCESS*: It may be seen most conveniently half-way between Barèges and the Col du Tourmalet; it is abundant here by streams not far above the road.

*CULTIVATION*: It seems impossible to grow this species in pot-culture; it demands flowing, non-calcareous water. If planted by a suitable stream in one of the cooler parts of the British Isles it should survive. An attempt was made to establish it by a stream at about 250m in Co. Wicklow; it was growing fairly well, but after nine months was eaten by a sheep.

## 99. *Saxifraga irrigua* Marschall von Bieberstein, *Flora Taurico-Caucasica* 2:460 (1808)

*SYNONYMS*: *S.aquatica* of Bieberstein, not of Lapeyrouse

*S.petraea* of Russian authors, not of Linnaeus

*S.ranunculoides* Haworth

*S.geranioides* var. *irrigua* (Bieberstein) Seringe in De Candolle, *Prodromus Systematis naturalis Regni vegetabilis* 4:16 (1830)

*HISTORY & NOMENCLATURE*: First discovered about 1784 by Hablizl, a German botanist who spent most of his life in Russia. He described it in a general account of the Crimea (Hablizl 1785), which had been added to the Russian empire only a few years previously. He named it *S.petraea* Linnaeus—a name which at that time was still widely misunderstood. Marschall von Bieberstein published it in the first volume of his *Flora Taurico-Caucasica* as *S.aquatica* Lapeyrouse, but admitted that he was to some extent guessing, as he had not seen Lapeyrouse's description. In the next volume he corrected his error, pointing out the differences between the two species and giving to the Crimean plant the name *irrigua*, because he saw it beside mountain streams, though in fact it is often found in fairly dry habitats.

*TYPE*: Inter rupes ad fontem Salghir. In muscosis rupibus ad fontem riv. Salghir et in excelsis Jaillae. *Pallas*. (Apparent isotype: British Museum (**BM**); presumed holotype in Leningrad (**LE**) not found.)

*DESCRIPTION*: Perennial, forming a compact tuft of short, erect, leafy shoots, of which the larger produce flowering stems in late spring. Basal leaves semicircular, kidney-shaped or almost circular in outline, usually about 25–30 × 35–40mm, divided nearly to the base into 3 subequal primary lobes, which are themselves further divided to a variable extent, the total number of ultimate segments varying from 11 to 35; ultimate segments oblong-lanceolate, subacute to apiculate. Petiole 40–70mm, very broad at the base, narrow and deeply channelled above. Cauline leaves few, similar to the basal but with shorter petioles and fewer, longer lobes. All leaves and stems with rather abundant, glandular but only slightly sticky hairs, mostly about 1mm long, but up to 3.5mm on the petioles. Flowering stems 10–20cm, terminal, usually unbranched in the lower part and bearing at the top a more or less flat-topped cyme of 5–12 flowers. Buds narrow, drooping. Sepals 3–4.5mm, narrowly triangular, acute, longer than the hypanthium. Petals 12–16 × 4.5–5.5mm, oblanceolate, subacute, without a distinct claw, of a delicate, somewhat translucent white. Ovary ⅔ inferior; styles slender, straight, divergent; stigmas very small. Seeds 0.75 × 0.35mm, medium brown, ellipsoid, straight on the side of the inconspicuous raphe, curved on the opposite side, bearing 12 or more rows of low but fairly broad papillae, between which are minute tubercles. Flowering season: May and June.

*RECOGNITION*: The coarse, perennial habit, broad, glandular-hairy leaves divided into numerous segments and long, narrow petals distinguish this species from all except *S.geranioides* and *S. aquatica*, with both of which it has been confused. *S.geranioides* differs in its somewhat woody, spreading stems, much shorter hairs and smooth, broader seeds. *S.aquatica* differs in its taller and stouter flowering stems, with a narrow, not at all flat-topped panicle, its shorter and much less numerous hairs, and its stoloniferous habit, with new rosettes at some distance from the flowering stems. For the differences from *S.latepetiolata* see under that species.

*ILLUSTRATIONS*: Figure 56
\* *Botanical Magazine* 48: Plate 2207 (1821)
Marschall von Bieberstein (1843, Plate 73)

*VARIATION*: There is some variation in the size of the leaves and in the point of origin of the lowest branch of the inflorescence; it is occasionally quite low down, so that the flat-topped character of the inflorescence is lost.

*HYBRIDS*: The geographical isolation of the species makes the occurrence of natural hybrids impossible, and we know of no attempt to produce artificial ones.

*CHROMOSOME NUMBER*: $2n = 44$.

*DISTRIBUTION* (Map 61, p. 204): Endemic to the Crimea, where it is widespread in the mountains which fringe its southern coast. This geographical isolation is remarkable, and what is equally remarkable is that in the Crimean mountains it is in sole possession; the Caucasian element, so prominent here in most groups, does not include any species of *Saxifraga*, and indeed in the whole Crimea the only other species recorded is *S.tridactylites*.

*HABITAT*: Rocky woods and shady cliffs, boulders or screes, always on limestone, from 500 to 1250m.

*ACCESS*: We have no first-hand information. Mr A.O. Chater tells us that he found it without difficulty in a clearing in pinewoods 10km north-north-east of Yalta, by the road from Massandra to Krasnij Kamen at 700m.

*CULTIVATION*: This is very easy. *S. irrigua* is hardy in most of the British Isles, and succeeds well in a rock-garden without much attention. It should be planted in clumps to fill large pockets, as the individual plants seem to be fairly short-lived. It is perhaps a useful, rather than a choice plant, the foliage being rather too coarse for the size of the inflorescence.

## 100. *Saxifraga latepetiolata* Willkomm, in Willkomm & Lange, *Prodromus Florae Hispanicae* 3:120 (1874)

*SYNONYM*: *S.geranioides* var. *irrigua* Willkomm, *Botanische Zeitung* 5:431 (1847)

*HISTORY & NOMENCLATURE*: Discovered by Willkomm in 1844, and first taken by him as identical with the Crimean *S.irrigua*, which was at that time regarded as a variety of *S.geranioides*. He realised later that it was a separate species known only from Spain, and gave it an epithet which draws attention to its broad petioles.

*TYPE*: In rup. cacum. Cerro de Sta Maria montis Sierra de Chiva cum S.paniculata sed rarissime. 2.6.1844. *Willkomm*. (Lectotype: Willkomm herbarium, Coimbra (**COI**), designated here.)

*DESCRIPTION*: Biennial, rather densely covered with sticky glandular hairs; those on the stem and petioles long, those on the leaf-lamina, pedicels and hypanthium somewhat shorter. Basal leaves numerous (over 100 in a well-grown plant), arranged regularly in a domed, almost hemispherical group up to 6cm tall, which can scarcely be termed a rosette; these persist for a year and begin to wither as the flowers open. Lamina 8–15 × 10–27mm, kidney-shaped to semicircular in outline, more or less cordate at the base, divided half-way to the base into 5–7 obovate-cuneate, truncate (but sometimes shortly mucronate) lobes, which in the larger leaves may themselves be divided into 3 segments; petiole 15–50mm, stiff and rather brittle, 3–4mm wide at the base, narrower and deeply channelled above. Lowest cauline leaves and bracts similar, becoming progressively smaller upwards and with fewer and more acute lobes, and with the base truncate or cuneate. Flowering stem 15–25cm, terminal, produced in the second year, rather stout, reddish, freely branched, usually from near the base, to form a narrow pyramidal panicle 15–20cm long, of which the lower branches each bear 3–10 flowers. Sepals 2.5–3.5mm. Petals 7–10 × 3–5mm, narrowly obovate, white. Ovary nearly fully inferior; styles 2mm, erect in flower, divergent in fruit. Seeds 0.8 × 0.4mm, ellipsoid, rounded or truncate at one end, covered with low, rounded papillae, except for the finely tuberculate, fairly conspicuous raphe. Flowering season: April to June.

*ILLUSTRATIONS*: Plate 56; Figures 56, 57
\* Willkomm (1881–1885, Plate 6)
\* *Botanical Magazine* 115: Plate 7056 (1889)

Figure 57. *S.latepetiolata*

RECOGNITION: If seen alive, especially before the basal leaves have withered, this species cannot be confused with any other. Among biennials it differs from *S.adscendens* and related plants by its greater size and larger petals, and in its leaves, which are wider than long and with long, distinct petioles; from *S.petraea* in its entire petals and stout flowering stem with compact panicle. From *S.geranioides* it differs in its truncate leaf-lobes and much longer hairs. The species with which it is most frequently confused today is *S.irrigua*, and many plants of the latter species in botanic gardens are labelled *S.latepetiolata*. This confusion is based on imperfect specimens and poor descriptions, for if seen side by side the two species are obviously different. Apart from its perennial habit, with several stems in a compact tuft, *S.irrigua* has much larger petals, and more deeply divided leaves with acute segments.

VARIATION: Apart from some variability in size the species seems to be very constant.

HYBRIDS: None is known.

CHROMOSOME NUMBER: $2n = 66$.

DISTRIBUTION (Map 66, p. 222): Endemic to a fairly small region of eastern Spain, mostly in the provinces of Valencia and Cuenca, but extending into the adjacent parts of the provinces of Castellón and Teruel. Its northern limit lies in the Sierra de Albarracín at about 40°25′N, and its southern limit lies some 15km south-west of Gandía, at 38°50′N. Westwards it extends to 2°05′W, north of Cuenca, and eastwards to 0°20′W, east of Castellón. A map and a partial list of localities is given by Mateo (1983).

HABITAT: Almost always on vertical limestone cliffs and rock-faces, usually shaded, but often fairly dry. It ranges in altitude from 800 to about 1500m.

ACCESS: It should not be too difficult to find in suitable habitats in the valley of the river Júcar, north of Cuenca, especially in and around the 'Ciudad Encantada'. It grows in fair quantity (mostly on inaccessible cliffs) at 850–950m on the Rincón del Peñon del Moro, a hill of 1003m which lies immediately south-west of Ayora, in the south-western part of the province of Valencia.

CULTIVATION: Apart from the inconvenience common to all biennials, this presents no great difficulty. Hooker (1889) described it as hardy, but it is probably wiser to give it the protection of a frame or cool house. It should be watered fairly freely in the early stages of growth, but dried off some time before flowering is expected and at the same time given as much light as possible. This encourages the development of red pigment in the inflorescence. It is a striking plant, well worth a place in any considerable collection.

# Series *Arachnoideae*
## (Engler & Irmscher) Gornall

Biennials or evergreen perennials of diffuse habit, with straggling or ascending leafy stems. Leaves often longer than 4cm (including petiole), soft, thin, crenate or lobed, usually with petiole longer than lamina. Hairs, at least on petioles, long. Flowers solitary, axillary, or forming a lax, leafy panicle. Petals white or pale greenish-yellow. Ovary inferior or nearly so.

A group of four species endemic to the eastern Alps and adjacent regions, and adapted to life in the entrance to caverns and other very shady habitats.

## 101. *Saxifraga petraea* Linnaeus, *Species Plantarum*, 2nd edn, 578 (1762)

*SYNONYMS*: *S.ponae* Sternberg
*S.rupestris* Willdenow
*S.geranioides* of Host, not of Linnaeus

*HISTORY & NOMENCLATURE*: There is a sad history of confusion behind the name, dating from confusion in the mind of Linnaeus himself, for he used the name as a substitute for his second variety (*alpina*) of *S.tridactylites* in the first edition of *Species Plantarum*, and the synonyms and localities which he cited for this show that he based it partly on *S.petraea* and partly on *S.adscendens* (although he gave an independent description of the latter on the following page). It is surprising that although he added an asterisk (indicating approval of a good description) to his citation of the *Saxifraga alba petraea* of Pona (1601) (described from Monte Baldo in the Italian Alps), he gave only Lapland and the Pyrenees as the native places of the variety. In the second edition of *Species Plantarum* he partly resolved the confusion by setting up this variety as an independent species under the name of *S.petraea*, and his addition of the phrase *caule ramosissimo laxo* to the description and Monte Baldo to the localities shows that it was Pona's description which he had principally in mind. This appears to be the first record of the plant in print under its present name. The name has, however, been used by various authors for plants which we now know as *S.adscendens*, *S.aquatica*, *S.hypnoides*, *S.irrigua* and *S.rosacea*.

The epithet is taken from Pona, and is apposite enough to indicate the usual habitat of the plant on solid rock.

*TYPE*: The lower figure on p.cccxxxvii in *Plantae . . . quae in Baldo Monte . . . reperiuntur* (Pona 1601; usually bound up as a supplement to the *Historia Plantarum* of Clusius) has been designated as lectotype (Webb 1987a).

*DESCRIPTION*: Biennial, covered with soft, rather long, sticky, glandular hairs. Leaves varying greatly on the same plant; those of the basal rosette, formed in the first year, having a petiole 15–55mm long, expanded at the base and channelled above, and a lamina 12–30 × 22–35mm, semicircular to diamond-shaped in general outline, but deeply divided into a narrow central lobe and 2 broader lateral lobes, the former 3- to 5-toothed, the latter variously toothed and lobed, the total number of ultimate segments being usually 19–23. Of the leaves borne on the flowering stem in the second year, the lowest are somewhat similar to the basal, but with fewer segments and tapered to the petiole; these differences are increased further up the stem, so that the upper cauline leaves are nearly stalkless, obovate, with 3–7 triangular lobes; these in turn grade into entire, oblong-lanceolate bracts. Flowering stems up to 35cm, slender, erect to spreading, brittle, freely branched with widely spreading branches which form an intricate mass from which it is difficult to extract individual stems without fracture. Flowers up to 18mm in diameter, in small, lax, leafy cymes; pedicels 3–8mm, very slender; hypanthium small, spherical, hairy. Sepals 2–4mm, oblong-elliptical, obtuse. Petals up to 11 × 6mm on the largest flowers, but often much less, usually somewhat unequal in the same flower (the smallest being about ⅘ the size of the largest), conspicuously notched at the tip, pure white. Ovary almost completely inferior; styles slender, straight, divergent. Seeds 0.45 × 0.35mm, broadly ellipsoid, covered over the whole surface except the raphe by long, conical, truncate papillae, between which are fine tubercles; raphe rather small, bearing fine tubercles. Flowering season: April to July.

*ILLUSTRATIONS*: Plate 52, Figure 56
* *Botanical Magazine* 57: Plate 3026 (1830)
  Huber (1963, Figure 141)
* Rasetti (1980, Plate 257)
* Köhlein (1984, Plate [11])
* Finkenzeller & Grau (1985, p. 115)

*RECOGNITION*: The intricately branched stems and the large, deeply notched petals distinguish this species from all others except *S.berica*; for the differences between the two see under *S.berica*. First-year plants have some similarity to those of *S.latepetiolata*, but the leaf-rosettes of *S.petraea* are flatter, less domed, and the leaves have more numerous, narrower and more acute lobes.

*VARIATION*: Although the appearance of the plant changes greatly during its life-cycle, giving to herbarium specimens a great appearance of diversity, there is little difference between whole plants that cannot be ascribed to differences in habitat.

*HYBRIDS*: None is known.

*CHROMOSOME NUMBER*: $2n = 64$.

*DISTRIBUTION* (Map 67): *S.petraea* is confined to a fairly limited region of north-eastern Italy and north-western Yugoslavia, mainly in the foothills of the eastern Alps. Its western limit is on the Corni di Canzo, near Lake Como; from here it ranges through the Giudicarian Alps, Monte Baldo, the southern Dolomites and the Julian Alps to north-eastern Slovenia, Istria and northern Dalmatia, southwards to about 44°50′N in the Mala Kapela range. The record from Albania (Demiri 1981) cannot be accepted without confirmation.

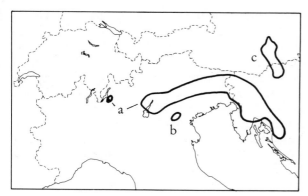

Map 67. Distribution of (a) *S.petraea*, (b) *S.berica* and (c) *S.paradoxa*

*HABITAT*: Shady limestone rocks, especially at the entrance to caves, or where heavy shade and protection from rain is provided by trees or overhanging rocks. It is for the most part a lowland species, but is occasionally found as high as 1900m in the western part of its range.

*ACCESS*: *S.petraea* is local and nowhere very common, so that in spite of its fairly wide range it is not very easy to find. It can be seen on the slopes of Monte Tombea (Capione) in the Giudicarian Alps, east of Lake Idro, at 1350–1400m, near the headwaters of the Val Vestino; but perhaps the most convenient place to see it is in western Slovenia, a few kilometres south of Kobarid (formerly Caporetto), where it grows in fair quantity at the entrance to two caverns on the western side of the road to Tolmin and Gorizia.

*CULTIVATION*: This presents no difficulty, provided the plant is protected from severe frost or excessive damp in winter and from drying up in summer. It is best to pot up half-a-dozen plants in a large pan, in a soil with some leaf-mould and plenty of limestone chips. The combination of the very fresh green foliage and the chalky-white flowers is striking, and makes an attractive, and indeed a showy pot-plant. It is unlikely to do well out of doors except in the most favoured districts.

## 102. *Saxifraga berica* (Béguinot) D.A. Webb, *Feddes Repertorium* 68:202 (1963)

*SYNONYM*: *S.petraea* var. *berica* Béguinot, *Bulletino della Società botanica italiana* 1904:384 (1904)

*HISTORY & NOMENCLATURE*: First discovered, it would seem, by Béguinot, who was then Professor at Modena, and was collecting data for his Flora of the province of Padua. His reference of the plant to *S.petraea* as a variety is understandable, as the two species have many characters in common, and cultivation is needed to show up the differences clearly. Its elevation to the rank of species has been generally accepted.

The specific epithet is derived from the Colli Berici, south of Vicenza, its only known habitat.

Figure 58.  *S.berica*

*TYPE*: Colli Berici (prov. di Vicenza). M. tra Longare e Costozza. 8 iv [19]04. *Béguinot*. (Lectotype: Padua (**PAD**), designated here; there are several syntypes also in this herbarium.)

*DESCRIPTION*: Perennial, usually short-lived, with numerous short, leafy shoots crowded together into a small tuft, more or less glandular-hairy, but with hairs shorter than those of *S.petraea*, especially on the upper part of the plant. Lamina of basal leaves 14–20 × 18–23mm, kidney-shaped, often tinged with brown, divided for about ⅓ of the way to the base into 11–21 broadly ovate or nearly square lobes, which are entire except that the central one may itself be slightly 3-lobed; petiole 20–35mm, slightly expanded at the base. Cauline leaves rather more deeply divided into fewer lobes, which are longer and more acute; in the uppermost the base is truncate and the general outline triangular-ovate; bracts entire, oblong-lanceolate. Flowering stems 15–20cm, consisting largely of a very diffuse cyme with strongly divaricate branches; pedicels 10–30mm. Hypanthium small, subglobose, hairy. Sepals 1.5mm, obtuse. Petals up to 7 × 4mm but often much less, usually markedly unequal in the same flower (the smallest being ½ to ¾ of the size of the largest), distinctly notched at the tip, pure white. Ovary largely inferior; styles straight, fairly short. Seeds similar to those of *S.petraea* in shape and size, but with a less conspicuous raphe and completely lacking the long papillae, the whole surface being uniformly covered in fine tubercles. Flowering season: late March to June.

*ILLUSTRATIONS*: Figures 56, 58. There appear to be no published illustrations.

RECOGNITION: This species can be confused only with *S.petraea*, from which it differs in its perennial habit, smaller and more markedly asymmetrical flowers, shorter hairs (those on the hypanthium being only about 0.5mm long, while those in *S.petraea* are often 1.5mm), brownish tint to the leaves and smoother seeds.

VARIATION: A well-grown plant in culture looks very different from most of those seen in their native habitat, but there appears to be no variation of any consequence with a genetic basis.

HYBRIDS: None is known.

CHROMOSOME NUMBER: Not known.

DISTRIBUTION (Map 67, p. 229): Confined to the Colli Berici, a small limestone ridge rising to a height of 444m which interrupts the Venetian plain a few kilometres south of Vicenza. It seems to have been recorded only from the northern end of the chain (all the stations known to us are within 10km of Vicenza), but it may be that the southern end has not been thoroughly explored. The nearest station for *S.petraea* is on Monte Baldo, some 60km to the north-west.

HABITAT: In shady hollows under overhanging limestone rocks at 200–300m. The hills have a generally dried-up appearance in summer, and the plant probably depends on shade from shrubs as well as from rocks to maintain a sufficiently moist micro-climate. It seems probable that quite small modifications of the habitat could bring about its extinction. Details of the habitat and associated vegetation are given by Lausi (1967).

ACCESS: The place where it is most easily found is above the village of Costozza, on the north-eastern flank of the hills. It is a rare plant and should not be collected.

CULTIVATION: Although it is perennial it seems to be short-lived; it should be repotted each autumn and seeds sown when available. It might be hardy out of doors in a sheltered and shady situation in one of the milder counties, but is best grown in a cool house, where it can form a very attractive plant. It does well in chinks in a block of tufa in the alpine house at Cambridge and seeds itself there.

### 103.  *Saxifraga arachnoidea* Sternberg, *Revisio Saxifragarum* 23 (1810)

SYNONYM: *S.sibirica* of Pollini, not of Linnaeus

HISTORY & NOMENCLATURE: Discovered by Sternberg in 1804 not far from the road in the Val d'Ampola (west-south-west of Riva di Garda), and described by him in 1810. The epithet indicates the cobweb-like hairs with which the plant is covered.

TYPE: Not traced.

DESCRIPTION: Perennial, with very slender stock and poorly developed root-system. All parts of the plant except the older stems are densely covered with slender, wavy glandular hairs, which on the stems and petioles are often 5–10mm long; those on the pedicels and leaf-laminae are rather shorter. These hairs, thanks to the sticky secretion which spreads along them, adhere together tenaciously, to form a structure which resembles not so much a cobweb, as the specific epithet suggests, as very loosely woven cotton-wool, from which the laminae and inflorescence emerge. Under any but the most careful handling this tangled mass of hairs mats together into a felt or strings, so that most herbarium specimens give a very poor idea of the habit and general appearance of the plant. Leaves very variable in size and shape, the largest with laminae up to 20 × 30mm, but most of them about 12 × 14mm, fan-shaped, circular or elliptical in general outline, the apical half usually divided into 3–5 broadly ovate, obtuse lobes. Most of the petioles are very short, but those of the lowest leaves may be up to 10mm long. Bracts similar to the upper leaves, but with more acute lobes. Flowering stems ascending, slender, fragile, 10–20cm. Flowers seldom more than 5 on each stem, in a very lax cyme; pedicels 8–35mm, very slender. Hypanthium hemispherical, hairy. Sepals 1.5mm, broadly oblong, obtuse. Petals 2.5–3mm, oblong, not contiguous, entire, of a translucent and impure white, sometimes tending towards cream, but never really yellow as is stated in many of the descriptions. Ovary completely inferior, surmounted by a nectary-disc, on the margin of which are inserted the expanded bases of the filaments; styles short, straight, divergent. Seeds rather few, 0.8–0.55mm, broadly ellipsoid, smooth and shining; raphe conspicuous. Flowering season: July and August.

*ILLUSTRATIONS*: Plate 53; Figure 56
* Sternberg (1810, Plate 15)
  Huber (1963, Figure 140)
* Rasetti (1980, Plate 257)
* Finkenzeller & Grau (1985, p. 115)

*RECOGNITION*: The combination of abundant long hairs, diffuse stems and small, off-white petals renders this species quite unmistakable. It has been confused with *S.petraea* and *S.sibirica*. The former, though somewhat similar in habit and to some extent in leaf-shape, is a much more robust plant, with notched, pure white petals 2–4 times as long as those of *S.arachnoidea*. *S.sibirica* also has large, pure white petals; moreover it is nearly hairless, the ovary is almost superior, and there are bulbils at the base of the plant.

*VARIATION*: As might be expected from an endemic of such narrow range, there is no variation of any consequence.

*HYBRIDS*: None is known.

*CHROMOSOME NUMBER*: $2n = 56$ and $66$.

*DISTRIBUTION* (Map 69, p. 236): Endemic to the Giudicarian Alps, the mountains that lie to the west of the northern part of Lake Garda in northern Italy. It is a region rich in endemics, of which many are presumed to be Tertiary relics, and this is probably true of *S.arachnoidea*. Its total range appears to span some 28km from east to west and 16km from north to south. Its most westerly stations are on the Corna Blacca, west of Lake Idra; its most easterly a short distance west of Lake Ledro. None of the known stations is more than 18km from the village of Storo.

*HABITAT*: The habitat is as peculiar as the plant itself; it grows almost without exception in limestone dust under an overhanging rock, sheltered alike from rain and sun. The soil is not as dry as it sometimes seems, as there is often seepage through cracks in the rock, but the reduced root-system suggests that much of the absorption of water takes place through the hairs. Many of the hollows or caverns in which it is found are used as roosts by small mammals, and the soil tends, therefore, to have a high nitrogen content (Linskens 1964). It ranges from 600 to 1850m above sea-level.

*ACCESS*: This is not a very easy species to find, as the mountains in which it lives, though not very high, are steep, densely wooded, and with few paths. There was for many years a fine colony in the Val Lorina, which joins the Val d'Ampola on its southern side not far above Storo; here it grew beside the path on the right bank of the stream, but the path seems to have been changed. The upper part of the Val Vestino would seem to be the region in which it is commonest, but in 1985 it was seen in three places beside the rather adventurous road which descends from the Passo di Tremalzo to Tremosine and Limone di Garda. Detailed localities are given by Arietti & Fenaroli (1972).

*CULTIVATION*: This is difficult, but not quite impossible if sufficient care is given to reproduce conditions similar to those of the natural habitat. It is almost impossible to transplant, so it must be grown from seed. A fine-grained soil, absence of sunlight and a constant, fairly high humidity are the conditions needed. Watering should be done from below, or by syringing the surroundings of the plant rather than the plant itself. It lacks conventional beauty, but will always attract attention as a curiosity.

**104. *Saxifraga paradoxa* Sternberg, *Revisio Saxifragarum* 22 (1810)**

*SYNONYM*: *Zahlbrucknera paradoxa* (Sternberg) Reichenbach

HISTORY & NOMENCLATURE: This species was brought to the attention of Sternberg by a Herr Lindaker, who had discovered it some years previous to 1810. The epithet *paradoxa* draws attention to the peculiar arrangement of its petals. This, together with its prominent nectary-disc, led Sternberg (1831) to create a special section for it, section *Discogyne*, and Reichenbach (1832) was sufficiently impressed by these characters to set up for it a separate genus, *Zahlbrucknera*. But recent authors, who consider that the species only shows in an extreme form characters to be found in other species of *Saxifraga*, treat it as belonging to this genus. For discussion see Schwaighofer (1908) and Brath (1948).

TYPE: Saxifraga paradoxa Sternberg. *Sternberg* [in Hooker's hand]. (Stamped 'Herbarium Hookerianum 1867'). (Lectotype: Kew (**K**), designated here.)

DESCRIPTION: A delicate perennial, probably short-lived, hairless except for some cottony hairs at the base of the stem and of the petioles of the basal leaves and some very short glandular hairs on the hypanthium. Leaves with very slender petioles up to 10cm long. Lamina kidney-shaped, 15–20 × 25–40mm, cordate at the base, very thin, shiny and almost translucent, with 5–9 shallow lobes usually broader than long, obtuse, each with a very inconspicuous hydathode. Cauline leaves similar to the basal, but becoming smaller and more shortly stalked upwards. Flowering stems very slender and brittle, up to 20cm, scarcely projecting above the basal leaves. Flowers in irregular, few-flowered, leafy cymes; pedicels long and slender. Flower 8mm in diameter, the centre occupied by a large nectary-disc covering the inferior ovary. Sepals 2 × 1.2mm, broadly oblong, obtuse. Petals 1.5mm, linear, green, not narrowed at the base and appearing to be inserted on the calyx. Stamens as long as the petals; anthers bright reddish-pink. Ovary inferior; styles 1–1.5mm, slightly curved. Seeds 0.5 × 0.35mm, broadly ellipsoid with pointed ends, dark brown, covered with rather widely spaced dark tubercles; raphe inconspicuous. Flowering season: June to August.

ILLUSTRATIONS: Figures 56, 59
\* Sternberg (1810, Plate 14)
   Reichenbach (1899, Plate 128), as *Zahlbrucknera paradoxa*
   Huber (1963, Figure 162)

RECOGNITION: The combination of long-stalked, broad, shining, slightly lobed leaves, greenish flowers and inferior ovary distinguishes it from all other species. In habit it is similar to members of section *Cymbalaria*, but these have a largely superior ovary and yellow or white flowers. From *S.arachnoidea* it differs in being almost hairless.

VARIATION: There appears to be little or none.

HYBRIDS: None has been recorded.

CHROMOSOME NUMBER: $2n = 64$.

DISTRIBUTION (Map 67, p. 229): Restricted to a small area of the south-eastern Alps in south-eastern Austria and northern Slovenia.

Figure 59. *S.paradoxa*

It is centred on the hill-country around the Koralpe, south-west of Graz, mostly in western Styria, but extending into eastern Carinthia, and southwards to the Pohorje mountains in Slovenia, west of Maribor. Its northern limit is at about 47°10′N, and its total range extends for only 90km north to south and 55km east to west. It is clearly a Tertiary relic, but its range lies further to the north than that of most other species which are so regarded.

*HABITAT*: Very shady and usually fairly damp recesses or caverns in siliceous rocks (mainly gneiss or mica-schist). Although it frequents the skirts of the mountains, it is a lowland plant with most of its stations below 500m.

*ACCESS*: A convenient place to find this species is by the path which leads up to the Koralpe from St Gertraud, a village north of Wolfsberg in eastern Carinthia. Here it may be seen in shady recesses in two or three places on the southern side of the path. It is a rare species, and should not be collected except sparingly as seed.

*CULTIVATION*: This is not very easy, but is possible if the plant is kept in fairly deep shade and given plenty of water in the growing season. It is short-lived, but comes fairly easily from seed.

## Subsection *Holophyllae* Engler & Irmscher

Evergreen perennials, usually of small size. Leafy shoots erect to prostrate, forming cushions or mats. Leaves entire or shortly 3-lobed at the tip. Bulbils and summer-dormant buds absent. Flowering stems terminal, bearing flowers singly or in small cymes of up to 8. Petals white or pale greenish-yellow, entire or notched at the tip. Ovary inferior or very nearly so.

A group of eleven species, ten endemic to Europe (mainly in the Alps) and one found also in Siberia.

## The *androsacea*-group

This consists of four closely related species, S.androsacea, S.seguieri, S.italica and S.depressa. They have in common a habit and manner of growth which contrasts with that of other species of the same subsection, to which they bear a fairly close resemblance in other respects. Even the larger plants of this group are not cushion-forming; their foliage forms a rather thick, close mat of limited height and width. This is because their flowering stems are terminal, and vegetative growth of the following year has its origin in axillary buds towards the base of the previous year's growth. It follows from this that the leaves appear to be all basal or very nearly so. This is in contrast to the commoner condition as seen in species such as S.exarata, S.muscoides and S.rosacea in which the leafy stems can attain a considerable length, giving either a deep cushion or (if the axillary shoots are more or less prostrate) an extensive loose mat.

Within the group, S.androsacea may be distinguished by the predominance of entire leaves, at least on some plants, with hairs much longer than those of the other species, and confined to the margin and occasionally the upper surface; S.seguieri by its small, dull yellow petals and entire leaves with short glandular hairs on both surfaces; S.italica by its small size (flowering stems less than 4cm; leaves not more than 4mm wide), constantly 3-lobed leaves and abundance of short glandular hairs; S.depressa by its robust habit, constantly 3-lobed leaves mostly 7mm or more wide, and more numerous flowers than in the other species (usually 3–5 on each stem, rarely up to 7).

## 105. *Saxifraga androsacea* Linnaeus, *Species Plantarum* 399 (1753)

*SYNONYM*: S.pyrenaica Scopoli

*HISTORY & NOMENCLATURE*: First figured by Colonna in his *Ecphrasis* of 1616, under the rather noncommital name of *Sedum alpinum tertium*. The epithet (suggested to Linnaeus by Haller) refers to the close superficial resemblance of the saxifrage to certain species of *Androsace*, especially *A.obtusifolia* Allioni.

*TYPE*: The last figure in Plate LXVII in *Minus cognitarum rariorumque nostro coelo orientium stirpium Ecphrasis* (Colonna 1616) has been designated as lectotype (Webb 1987a).

*DESCRIPTION*: Leafy shoots usually forming fairly small tufts, occasionally dense mats up to 2cm tall and 10cm wide. Leaves 7–30 × 3–6mm; the lamina is relatively constant in size, the variation in length being due mainly to the variable development of a rather ill-defined petiole, which may be virtually absent or may be over 10mm long. Lamina linear-oblong to narrowly obovate, usually entire with an obtuse or subacute tip, but sometimes with 3 short, subacute teeth. Plants with most of the leaves 3-toothed occur interspersed with others in which all or nearly all are entire. The leaves bear on the margin hairs of very variable length, most of them terminating in a small and inconspicuous gland; they range in length from 0.4mm or less to 2mm, and although they consist of only a single row of cells are relatively stout. Similar hairs are sometimes found on the upper surface of young leaves, but they disappear with age. Flowering stems 2–8cm, rather densely glandular-hairy, bearing 1 or 2 cauline leaves and 1–2 (rarely 3) flowers. Sepals 1.5–2mm, obtuse. Petals oblong or narrowly obovate, 4–7 × 2.5–3.5mm, not contiguous, white. Styles c. 1.5mm, straight, erect at first, later divergent. Seeds 0.6 × 0.35–0.45mm, broadly ellipsoid, truncate at one end and sometimes almost pear-shaped, the whole surface covered with fine tubercles; raphe inconspicuous. Flowering season: May to August.

*ILLUSTRATIONS*:
* Touring Club Italiano (1958, Plate 201)
  Mądalski (1962, Plate 1322)
  Harding (1970, p. 78)
* Rasetti (1980, Plate 247)

*RECOGNITION*: For distinction from other members of the group, see p. 234.

*VARIATION*: There is very little, except in the proportion of entire and of 3-lobed leaves. Plants from the most exposed habitats are somewhat dwarfed.

*HYBRIDS*: Hybrids with *S.seguieri*, *S.depressa* and *S.wahlenbergii* have been described, and are probably correctly diagnosed; see under those species. Supposed hybrids with *S.muscoides* and *S.exarata* are very doubtful.

*CHROMOSOME NUMBER*: This is extremely variable; precise counts have been recorded of $2n = 16, 66, 88, 124, 150$ and $198$, and there are approximate counts of up to 220, the highest number in the genus.

*DISTRIBUTION* (Map 68): Widespread in the mountains of Europe, but rare except in the Alps and Carpathians; there are also some very distant outliers in Siberia. West of the Alps it is thinly scattered through the eastern and central Pyrenees as far west as Gèdre, and has (or had) a station in the Auvergne (Puy Mary). It occurs throughout the entire range of the Alps and is frequent in most regions; it is also fairly frequent throughout the Carpathians. In Bulgaria it is found in the Rila range and the northern Pirin; records from the Rodopi are erroneous. Elsewhere in the Balkan peninsula it has been recorded from eastern Albania, Bosnia and the Yugoslav–Greek border in Macedonia, but all these records require confirmation. In Siberia it is found in the eastern Altai and the mountains west of Lake Baikal. It is a curious distribution, especially in view of its absence from the Caucasus, and not easy to explain.

*HABITAT*: Mostly in sheltered situations where the snow lies fairly late, on thin grass-

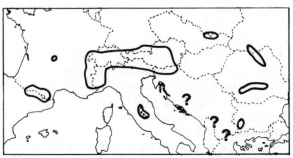

Map 68. Distribution of *S.androsacea* (unshaded and '?', also in Siberia) and *S.italica* (shaded)

land or fine gravel. The species is somewhat base-demanding, and is absent from certain regions of purely siliceous rock, but can hardly be called calcicole. It is commonest between 2000 and 2800m.

*ACCESS*: *S.androsacea* is sufficiently widespread in the Alps that it is almost certain to be seen in any extensive exploration at the right altitude. It may, however, be looked for with confidence on the Albula pass in eastern Switzerland (not far from the road), on the Gornergrat near Zermatt at about 2700m, and on the southern side of the Col d'Iseran (Savoie).

*CULTIVATION*: This is curiously difficult. Plants that look healthy through the late summer and autumn die in winter for no very obvious reason. It may be that they require conditions which simulate their winter snow-cover.

### 106. *Saxifraga depressa* Sternberg, *Revisio Saxifragarum* 42 (1810)

*HISTORY & NOMENCLATURE*: Described by Sternberg from plants brought to him by Bartolomeo Franco from 'Italiae superioris Monte Alto'. The only mountain on modern maps of north-eastern Italy to bear this name is near Belluno, and lies some 35km to the east of the present known range of the species. It may, perhaps, have grown there formerly, but it is possible that the name was also given at that time to another peak. The epithet *depressa* presumably refers to the rather flat leaf-rosettes.

*TYPE*: Not traced.

*DESCRIPTION*: Leafy shoots short, erect, compacted together to form a rather thick mat. Whole plant covered with short glandular hairs, densely on the basal leaves, moderately densely in the inflorescence, rather sparsely on the flowering stem and cauline leaves. Basal leaves 10–30 × 6–9mm, broadest near the tip and narrowed below to a not always clearly defined petiole, shortly 3-lobed, with obtuse lobes. Flowering stem up to 8cm, usually without a cauline leaf, rarely with 1, which may

be entire or 3-lobed. Flowers usually 3–7 in a compact cyme, with large, rather leaf-like bracts. Sepals 2mm, ovate, obtuse. Petals 3–5mm, oblong, not contiguous, pure white. Styles straight, erect. Seeds 0.6 × 0.45mm, brown, broadly oblong, truncate at one end, mucronate or subacute at the other, uniformly covered with very fine tubercles; raphe inconspicuous. Flowering season: June to August.

*ILLUSTRATIONS*: Plate 54
* Sternberg (1810, Plate 11)
  Engler & Irmscher (1916, Figure 70)
* Rasetti (1980, Plate 248)
* Finkenzeller & Grau (1985, p. 11)

*RECOGNITION*: The only species with which *S.depressa* is likely to be confused are *S.androsacea* and *S.italica*. *S.androsacea* has much longer hairs on the leaf-margin, has usually some entire leaves even if most are 3-lobed, and has seldom more than 2 flowers on a stem. For the differences from *S.italica* see under that species.

*VARIATION*: There is none that is not clearly due to the influence of the environment.

*HYBRIDS*: A hybrid with *S.androsacea* (*S. × vierhapperi* Handel-Mazzetti) has been described, and is probably correctly diagnosed.

*CHROMOSOME NUMBER*: Not known.

*DISTRIBUTION* (Map 69): Confined to a small area of the west-central Dolomites. Its

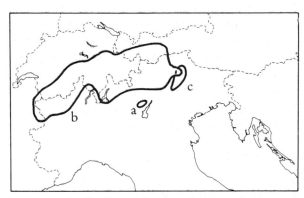

Map 69. Distribution of (a) *S.arachnoidea*, (b) *S.seguieri* and (c) *S.depressa*

southern limit is on the Cima d'Asta at 46°11′N, its northern limit at 48°29′N near Arabba. Its east-west range is even more restricted, from 11°38′ to 11°58′E. Within this range about a dozen stations are known, but nowhere is it really abundant.

*HABITAT*: Shady and often damp screes and rocks from 2100 to 2600m. It grows almost exclusively on the black, porphyritic intrusions which are common in this part of the Dolomites, but an occasional plant can be seen on the dolomite itself.

*ACCESS*: S.depressa grows in fair quantity at the Porta Vescovo, south and slightly west of Arabba, which lies on the main road from Cortina to Canazei. The locality may be reached from the north by cable-car from near Arabba, or from the south by a fairly short climb from the road which runs to the reservoir immediately north of the Marmolada.

*CULTIVATION*: Difficult, but perhaps not impossible. Plants have lived for two years in Dublin, but have not shown much growth. It is an attractive plant well worth growing.

## 107. *Saxifraga italica* D.A. Webb, *Feddes Repertorium* 68:209 (1963)

*SYNONYMS*: S.androsacea var. *tridens* Engler, *Monographie der Gattung Saxifraga L.* 198 (1872)
S.tridens of Engler & Irmscher, not of Haworth

*HISTORY & NOMENCLATURE*: Discovered by G. Jan, director of the museum at Milan, and sent by him to Engler under the name of S.tridens. Engler (1872) published it as a variety of S.androsacea, but in 1916 Engler & Irmscher raised it to the rank of species. The name S.tridens had, however, been used long before by Haworth, and Webb therefore gave it a new name in 1963.

*TYPE*: Plantae Neopolitanae 325. In pascuis elatioribus Femina morta (1800–2000 m.s.m.), Aprutii. 5 Aug. 1856. *E. & A. Huet de Pavillon*. (Lectotype: Kew (**K**), designated here.)

*DESCRIPTION*: A small plant with the general habit of the *androsacea*-group, consisting of a compact clump of short leafy shoots ending in leaf-rosettes. Leaves 6–15 × 2–4mm, tapered to a narrow base but not stalked, occasionally oblanceolate and undivided, but for the most part shortly 3-lobed, rather densely covered, as is the whole plant, with short glandular hairs. Flowering stems 2–4cm, bearing 1–2 entire or obscurely 3-toothed cauline leaves and 1–3 flowers. Sepals 2mm. Petals usually about 6 × 2–2.5mm, oblong to narrowly obovate, not contiguous, pure white. Styles relatively long, straight. Seeds not seen. Flowering season: July and August.

*ILLUSTRATION*:
Engler & Irmscher (1916, Figure 70)

*RECOGNITION*: The short leafy shoots, the 3-lobed, glandular-hairy leaves and the pure white petals distinguish it from most species except S.depressa. This is normally a much larger and coarser plant, with leaves mostly 6–9mm wide, with flowering stems mostly 4–7cm, often without a cauline leaf and often with more than 3 flowers. It must be admitted, however, that dwarfed specimens of S.depressa resemble S.italica rather closely.

S.exarata, which can have somewhat similar leaves and flowers, differs in its long leafy shoots, forming a compact cushion.

*VARIATION*: As might be expected from such a narrowly-restricted endemic, there is none of any taxonomic significance.

*HYBRIDS*: None has been reported.

*CHROMOSOME NUMBER*: $2n = 66$.

*DISTRIBUTION* (Map 68, p. 235): Confined to the higher peaks of the central Apennines, from the Monti Sibillini in the north to Monte Maiella in the south.

*HABITAT*: Limestone rocks and screes, from 2000 to 2500m.

*ACCESS*: We can give no advice from personal experience; herbarium specimens are mostly from the regions known as the 'Campo Pericoli' and the 'Femina morta' on the Gran Sasso d'Italia.

*CULTIVATION*: No information is available; probably difficult.

## 108. *Saxifraga seguieri* Sprengel,
*Mantissa prima Florae halensis* 40 (1807)

*SYNONYMS*: *S.sedoides* of Seringe and several authors, not of Linnaeus

*S.planifolia* var. *seguieri* Sternberg, *Revisio Saxifragarum* 28 (1810)

*HISTORY & NOMENCLATURE*: The species was first distinguished by Jean Francois Séguier, who saw it on Monte Baldo during his period of residence at Verona, and published it in his *Plantae Veronenses* (Séguier 1745) as *Saxifraga alpina minima, foliis ligulatis in orbem circumactis, flore ochroleuco*. Sprengel gave it a binomial in his honour.

*TYPE*: Not traced.

*DESCRIPTION*: A small plant, consisting of a number of short, more or less erect, crowded leafy shoots forming a dense mat, with most of the leaves in terminal rosettes. Leaves 10–25 × 1–3mm, oblanceolate, narrowed at the base to an indistinct petiole, entire, obtuse, covered densely or (more rarely) very sparsely with short glandular hairs, not more than 0.5mm long. Flowering stems 2–7cm, slender, simple or branched only at the top, usually with a single cauline leaf and 1–3 flowers; stem, cauline leaf, pedicels and hypanthia with glandular hairs usually rather longer and often more numerous than those of the basal leaves. Sepals 2mm, oblong-ovate, obtuse, hairless. Petals 2–3mm, oblong-elliptical, narrower than the sepals but usually slightly longer, usually dull, rather pale yellow, rarely dull greenish-white. Styles very short, outwardly curved. Seeds 0.75 × 0.35mm, black, truncate at one end and rounded to bluntly pointed at the other, uniformly covered with very low but broad papillae; raphe rather inconspicuous, finely tuberculate. Flowering season: late June to August.

*ILLUSTRATIONS*: Plate 55
    Coste (1902, p. 139)
    Engler & Irmscher (1916, Figure 68)
    Huber (1963, Figures 154, 155)
*  Finkenzeller & Grau (1985, p. 109)

*RECOGNITION*: Among species with soft, entire, obtuse leaves and dull yellow or off-white petals not more than 3mm long, *S. seguieri* can be distinguished from *S.fachinii* by its relatively long flowering stems which raise the flowers well above the leaves; from *S.presolanensis* and variants of *S.exarata* subsp. *moschata* by its very short leafy shoots and absence of a cushion-like habit; and from *S. presolanensis* also by the rounded, not notched, tips to the petals. In its general form it resembles *S.androsacea* but differs in the absence of long, non-glandular hairs and the smaller, dull-coloured petals.

*VARIATION*: There is considerable variation in the abundance of glandular hairs, especially on the basal leaves, and some variation in the colour of the petals, but it is fairly continuous and without any clear geographical basis, so that there are no varieties worth taxonomic recognition.

*HYBRIDS*: A hybrid with *S.androsacea* (*S. × padellae* Brügger) was described originally from the Bernina region, but since then has been reported from various other parts of the Swiss Alps. The existence of such a hybrid is quite probable, but the original description suggested merely a variant of *S.seguieri* with petals rather longer than usual. It is to be hoped that a fuller description and figures will soon be provided.

*CHROMOSOME NUMBER*: $2n = 66$.

*DISTRIBUTION* (Map 69, p. 236): *S.seguieri* is endemic to the Alps, and its centre is in Switzerland. Here, although commonest in the east, it is found almost throughout the higher ranges, except for the western part of the Bernese Oberland. In Austria it is confined to the Vorarlberg and western part of the Tirol. In Italy it is mainly in the western part of the Alps, but has some isolated stations as far east as the central Dolomites. In France it is extremely rare, but has been reported from near the Italian frontier in Savoy and the Hautes-Alpes.

*HABITAT*: Damp screes and north-facing slopes, usually in late snow-lies. Generally speaking it is calcifuge, but may be found occasionally on limestone or dolomite where leaching has allowed the accumulation of some humus. It is found mostly between 2200 and 2900m.

*ACCESS*: It is common in the Bernina region of Switzerland, and may also be seen on the northern side of the Schafberg, near Pontresina. Further west it can be seen above the Albula pass, and on the eastern side of the Furka pass, near the summit.

*CULTIVATION*: This seems to be difficult, as with many snow-lie species. It has little decorative value, and is not worth a great deal of trouble.

## 109. *Saxifraga muscoides* Allioni, *Auctuarium ad Synopsim Stirpium Horti Reg. Taurinensis* 35 (1773)

*SYNONYMS*: S.planifolia of Sternberg, not of Lapeyrouse
S.tenera Suter

*HISTORY & NOMENCLATURE*: This species seems to have been first described by Haller in 1768, but Allioni was the first to give it a binomial. There has been much confusion in the application of the name; it has been repeatedly equated with or substituted for *S. moschata* Wulfen, partly because of the similarity of the epithets, and partly because of an overall similarity of the plants. Many of the earlier records are accordingly to be referred to *S.moschata*. The epithet (moss-like) was chosen by Allioni; it is not particularly apt, but a small plant of the saxifrage when not in flower is to some extent suggestive of a moss such as *Grimmia*.

*TYPE*: Herbarium Allioni. Saxifraga [serpilifolia—deleted] muscoides. (Lectotype: Turin (**TO**), designated here.)

*DESCRIPTION*: Leafy shoots numerous, small, crowded to form a dense though soft cushion; in a large plant the leafy shoots may be as long as 10cm, but only the uppermost 1cm bears living leaves. Leaves mostly about 5 × 1.5mm, oblong to narrowly elliptical, entire, rounded at the apex, narrowed at the base but without a distinct petiole, crowded and overlapping, glandular-hairy at least on the margins, rather light green. Older dead leaves brown, but those only recently dead have a characteristic silvery-grey colour, at least towards the tip; this arises from the epidermis stripping off from the underlying tissues and allowing the interposition of a layer of air. Flowering stems 1–5cm, rarely to 8cm, slender, glandular-hairy, bearing 2–5 narrow leaves and 1–2 flowers. Sepals 2mm, ovate, obtuse. Petals 3.5–5mm, obovate, obtuse or slightly notched at the apex, contiguous, white, cream or pale yellow. Styles short, erect. Seeds 0.65 × 0.4mm, ellipsoid, bluntly pointed at one end, dark brown, smooth; raphe inconspicuous. Flowering season: June to August.

*ILLUSTRATIONS*: Plate 57
  Allioni (1785, Plate 61)
* Correvon (1894, Plate 58)
  Coste (1902, p. 139), as *S.planifolia* Lapeyrouse

*RECOGNITION*: The only other species which have obtuse, entire, glandular-hairy leaves and a compact, cushion-like habit are *S.facchinii*, *S.presolanensis* and some variants of *S.exarata* subsp. *moschata*. From all of these it differs in its contiguous, white or clear pale yellow petals, and from the last also in the silvery-grey colour of its recently dead leaves.

*VARIATION*: There is very little except in the colour of the petals.

*HYBRIDS*: A hybrid with *S.aphylla* (*S.* × *muretii* Rambert) has been described from eastern Switzerland, and is probably correctly diagnosed. The hybrid with *S.exarata* (*S.* × *wettsteinii* Brügger) from the Zermatt region must be considered rather more doubtful in view of the great variability of *S.exarata* here; also dubious is the alleged hybrid with *S. androsacea*.

CHROMOSOME NUMBER: 2n = 38.

DISTRIBUTION (Map 70): Endemic to the Alps, where it has a fairly wide, though somewhat discontinuous range from near Monte Viso (44°40'N) in the south, northwards and eastwards to the Bernina group in eastern Switzerland. There are a few outlying stations much further east in the Tauern range on the borders of Carinthia and Salzburg province in Austria. Records from the Pyrenees and the Apennines are erroneous.

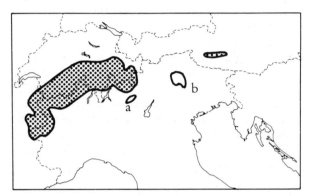

Map 70.  Distribution of *S.muscoides* (shaded), (a) *S.presolanensis* and (b) *S.facchinii*

HABITAT: Detritus and rock ledges in the high Alps. It is distinctly base-demanding, but seems to be commoner on base-rich schists than on limestone. Most of its stations lie between 2250 and 3000m, but it has been recorded as high as 4200m and as low as 1450m.

ACCESS: This is a plant of the high Alps, and few of its stations are of very easy access. It used to grow on a small cliff on the southern side of the Col du Galibier (Hautes-Alpes), but this station was destroyed in the construction of the tunnel; it is probably to be found on rocks higher up. It can also be seen on gravelly slopes near the summit of the Col d'Iseran; on the Gornergrat, near Zermatt, at 2500–2700m; and near the Sanetsch pass, north of Sion (Valais). It is nearly everywhere rather rare, and should not be collected except sparingly from a good-sized population.

CULTIVATION: As with many high alpines this is difficult; it is susceptible to rot in warm autumns and winters. A rigorous alpine-house regime might succeed, but we have not heard of any growers who have maintained it for more than a short time.

## 110. *Saxifraga facchinii* Koch, *Flora (Regensburg)* 25:624 (1842)

SYNONYMS: *S.planifolia* var. *atropurpurea* Koch, *Synopsis Florae germanicae et helveticae* 275 (1835)
*S.muscoides* var. *facchinii* (Koch) Engler, *Monographie der Gattung Saxifraga L.* 196 (1872)

HISTORY & NOMENCLATURE: Discovered first by Francesco Facchini, a doctor who lived at Vigo di Fassa, in the middle of the plant's very restricted area of distribution, and who brought it to the notice of Koch. As the synonymy shows, it has been treated as a variety of *S.muscoides* (to which it is certainly closely related), but its independent status as a species is now generally agreed.

TYPE: S.facchini. Seisseralp. [Stamped 'Ex herb. Koch']. (Lectotype: Erlangen (**ER**), designated here.)

DESCRIPTION: Leafy shoots mostly unbranched, forming small but fairly dense cushions, the lower parts of the shoots clothed in dead leaves, with rather few living leaves at the tip in an irregular rosette. Leaves 5–10 × 1–2mm, oblong-oblanceolate, obtuse, entire, gradually tapered to a narrow base but without a distinct petiole, rather densely glandular-hairy. The recently dead leaves, as in *S.muscoides*, are silvery-grey towards the tip, but this character, conspicuous in the living plant, tends to disappear on drying. Flowering stems 5–25mm, glandular-hairy, bearing one or more leaves and 1–4 very small flowers. Sepals 1.5mm, broadly ovate, obtuse. Petals 1.5–2mm, equalling or very slightly exceeding the sepals, narrowly obovate, with a narrow base and a truncate to slightly notched tip, dull yellow more or less tinged with purple, or sometimes entirely purple. Styles very short. Seeds 0.85 × 0.4mm, oblong with rounded ends, black, uniformly covered with fine tubercles, including the fairly conspicuous raphe. Flowering season: July.

*ILLUSTRATIONS*:
   Huber (1963, Figure 161)
\* Rasetti (1980, Plate 253)
\* Finkenzeller & Grau (1985, p. 109)

*RECOGNITION*: The soft, hairy, entire, obtuse leaves and the very small, dull-coloured petals distinguish this species from all others except *S.seguieri* and some variants of *S. exarata* subsp. *moschata*. Both these, however, have petals mostly at least 3mm long, with rounded or subacute tips, and lack the silvery-grey colour of the dead leaves.

*VARIATION*: Leaf-size and flower-colour vary considerably, but often on a single plant. A variant has been described from a single specimen in which the leaves have short lateral teeth (var. *leyboldii* Engler & Irmscher, *Pflanzenreich* 67 (IV.117):294 (1916) ), but it may well have been a hybrid.

*HYBRIDS*: None has been reported.

*CHROMOSOME NUMBER*: Not known.

*DISTRIBUTION* (Map 70, p. 240): Restricted to a small area of the western Dolomites, with its centre at 46°25′N, 11°40′E. It extends from the Latemar in the south-west through the Rosengarten and the Schlern to the Seiser Alm in the north, and eastwards to the Sassolungo group and the Marmolada. The whole area measures only 25 × 20km.

*HABITAT*: Screes and debris of dolomitic rock, less often in crevices in the solid rock. Mostly between 2250 and 2800m, but descending to 1800m, and ascending to 3360m on the Marmolada.

*ACCESS*: The most convenient way to see this species is to ascend in the chair-lift to the narrow col south of the Sassolungo (above the Sella pass) and to descend the scree on the western side of the col for about 75m; *S.facchinii* is fairly frequent on the shadier parts of the scree.

*CULTIVATION*: This is extremely difficult; we have traced no record of its having been kept in cultivation for more than a few months.

## 111. *Saxifraga presolanensis* Engler, in Engler & Irmscher, *Pflanzenreich* 67 (IV.117):302 (1916)

*HISTORY & NOMENCLATURE*: Discovered by Engler on 26 August 1894, on Pizzo di Presolana (Alps of Bergamo) in Italy, and named by him after the mountain.

*TYPE*: Südl. Bergamasker Alpen (Italien): Mte Arera, steile Felswände gegen Nordosten. 1800m. Kalk. 4.8.1956. *Merxmüller & Wiedmann 310/56*. (Neotype: Munich (**M**), designated by Merxmüller & Wiedmann (1957); there is an isotype at Kew, **K**.) Engler's original type, from Presolana, above Dezzo, was destroyed in Berlin.

*DESCRIPTION*: The habit varies considerably according to the degree of shelter or exposure. Plants exposed to the light and growing in vertical fissures form hemispherical cushions, compact but soft, and up to 12cm in diameter. Under overhanging ledges or at the mouths of small caverns it has a much more diffuse growth, with long, straggling leafy stems, and it was, unfortunately, one of these lax plants on which Engler based his original description. Leafy stems 4–8cm, slender, crowded, thickly furnished with leaves, the dead ones long-persistent. Leaves mostly c. 10 × 2–2.5mm, but on shaded shoots occasionally up to 22mm; narrowly oblong-elliptical to oblong-oblanceolate, obtuse, tapered at the base to a petiole which is usually short and ill-defined, but in the longest leaves is long and slender; fresh, rather pale green, densely covered with glandular hairs 0.5–0.75mm long. At least some of the recently dead leaves show the silvery-grey colour seen also in *S.muscoides* and *S.facchinii*; later they all turn brown. Flowering stems 6–10cm, very slender, somewhat flexuous, glandular-hairy but less densely than the leaves; cauline leaves 0–2. Flowers 2–8 in a very lax, flat-topped cyme. Sepals 1–1.5mm, obtuse. Petals 3–4 × 1–1.25mm, oblong-cuneate, tapered to a narrow base, usually rather deeply notched at the obtuse tip, translucent, impure white, variably tinged, especially along the 3 veins, with pale greenish-yellow. Styles 0.75mm. Capsule 3.5 × 3mm, almost spherical (unlike other species in the subsection). Seeds 0.65 × 0.35mm, ellipsoid with one end pointed and the other rounded, without papillae but covered all over with small tubercles, including the large and conspicuous raphe. Flowering season: July and August.

*ILLUSTRATIONS*: Plate 58
Engler & Irmscher (1916, Figure 69)
Merxmüller & Wiedmann (1957, p. 116)
* Finkenzeller & Grau (1985, p. 109)

*RECOGNITION*: The combination of entire, densely glandular-hairy leaves with narrow, notched, pale greenish-yellow petals is distinctive. It resembles *S.muscoides* closely in habit and leaves, but the flowers are very different. From *S.sedoides*, which has somewhat similar petals, it differs in its compact, cushion-like habit and in having all the leaves obtuse. obtuse.

*VARIATION*: As might be expected from such a narrow endemic there is none except that caused by environmental differences as described above.

*HYBRIDS*: None has been recorded.

*CHROMOSOME NUMBER*: $2n = 16$.

*DISTRIBUTION* (Map 70, p. 240): *S.presolanensis* is known only from a range of limestone mountains in the Italian Alps, which runs parallel to and somewhat to the south of the higher range known as the Alpe Orobie; it lies north of Lake Iseo, very close to the 46th parallel of latitude. Its highest peaks (Pizzo Arera and Pizzo di Presolana) just exceed 2500m. The known range of the saxifrage extends from Pizzo Arera in the west (9°54′E) to the Cimone di Bagozza in the east (10°15′E). A detailed map of the known localities is given by Arietti & Fenaroli (1960).

*HABITAT*: Vertical cliffs of limestone or dolomite, usually more or less north-facing, between 1800 and 2100m.

*ACCESS*: This is not an easy plant to find. The range on which it occurs, although not very high, is extremely steep, and for many of the plant's stations some mountaineering skill is needed. It is probably best looked for at the two ends of the chain, rather than on Pizzo di Presolana, but a large-scale map, together with a copy of the paper by Arietti & Fenaroli (1960), would greatly help in the search.

*CULTIVATION*: This is difficult, but not impossible. It lived for two years in Dublin, and for longer in the alpine garden at Munich, but like many hairy plants it is susceptible to rot in a mild autumn.

## 112. *Saxifraga sedoides* Linnaeus, *Species Plantarum* 405 (1753)

*SYNONYMS*: *S.hohenwartii* Vest ex Sternberg
*S.prenja* G. Beck von Managetta

*HISTORY & NOMENCLATURE*: First described, it would seem, by Séguier in his *Plantae Veronenses* (Séguier 1745). It is not clear why Linnaeus gave it the epithet *sedoides*, as there is no species of *Sedum* which it calls to mind, nor why he included Siberia in its geographical range.

*TYPE*: *S.sedoides*. Sheet 174.15 in the Linnean herbarium, Stockholm (**S**) has been designated as lectotype (Webb 1987a).
Subsp. *hohenwartii*. Not traced.
Subsp. *prenja*. G. Beck: Plantae Bosniae et Hercegovinae exsiccatae Nr.48. Saxifraga Prenja. Herceg. Ad nives montis Prenj Bjelašnica, c. 1800m. vii/1885. *G. Beck*. (Lectotype: Vienna (**W**), designated here.)

*DESCRIPTION*: Leafy stems straggling, more or less prostrate, forming a loose mat. Leaves mostly entire, but sometimes 3-toothed at the tip or with a small lateral tooth, 6–12 × 2–4mm, oblanceolate to narrowly oblong, tapered at the base to a scarcely distinct petiole, acute, mucronate or apiculate at the tip, furnished with long glandular hairs, mainly on the margins. Flowering stems 1–7cm, more or less erect, glandular-hairy, with 0–5 leaves and bearing 1–6 flowers in a lax cyme. Sepals 1.5–2 × 1mm, triangular-ovate, acute or mucronate. Petals 1.5–3mm, linear to ovate, dull yellow. Styles very short. Seeds 0.85 × 0.45mm, oblong with rounded ends, dark brown, minutely tuberculate; raphe inconspicuous. Flowering season: June to September.

ILLUSTRATIONS:
Fiori & Paoletti (1895, Figure 1656)
Huber (1963, Figure 155)
* Finkenzeller & Grau (1985, p. 109)

RECOGNITION: The very small, dull yellow petals, combined with the inferior ovary, acute to apiculate leaves and absence of bulbils or summer-dormant buds distinguishes this species from all others.

VARIATION: Apart from variation clearly induced by differences in habitat, this species varies in the number of flowers on a stem, the presence or absence of leaves on the flowering stems, the shape and size of the petals and, to some extent, in the frequency of lobed leaves. We follow Huber (1963) in recognising three subspecies.
(a) Subsp. **sedoides**. Leaves nearly all entire. Cauline leaves usually absent, rarely 1–2. Flowers 1–3. Petals lanceolate to narrowly ovate, acute, shorter than the sepals.
(b) Subsp. **hohenwartii** (Vest ex Sternberg) P. Schwarz, *Mitteilungen der thüringischen botanischen Gesellschaft* 1:104 (1949). Some leaves usually 3-lobed. Flowering stems usually with 3–5 leaves and 3–6 flowers. Petals linear, acute, at least as long as the sepals.
(c) Subsp. **prenja** (G. Beck) G. Beck, *Flora Bosne, Hercegovine i novipazarskog sandžaka* 474 (1923). Some leaves usually 3-lobed. Flowering stems without cauline leaves and with 1–3 flowers. Petals oblong, longer than the sepals, truncate or notched, sometimes with a slender point in the notch.

HYBRIDS: For a probable hybrid with *S.tenella* and a possible hybrid with *S.aphylla*, see under those species.

CHROMOSOME NUMBER: 2n = 64.

DISTRIBUTION (Map 71): Alps, central Apennines and the western part of the Balkan peninsula. In the Alps it is, like *S.aphylla*, confined to the northern and southern calcareous ranges, but, in contrast to *S.aphylla*, it is much commoner in the south than in the north. In the north it is found only in the Austrian Alps from 13° to 15°E, but in the south it ranges with only small interruptions from 9°30′ (east of Lake Como) to 14°45′E in the eastern Karawanken. Subsp. *hohenwartii* predominates in the south-eastern part of this range and subsp. *sedoides* in the north and west, but there is a fairly large zone of overlap, where intermediate plants can be found. In the Apennines only subsp. *sedoides* is known, and it is confined to the highest summits of the Abruzzi. In the Balkan peninsula the species is represented solely by subsp. *prenja*; this ranges from 44°20′N in the southern Velebit through Bosnia, Hercegovina and Montenegro to northern Albania.

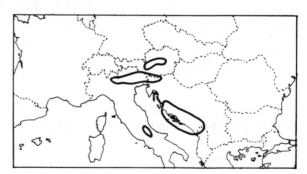

Map 71.  Distribution of *S.sedoides*

S.sedoides has been reported from the eastern Pyrenees, but the record is open to serious doubt. It is not accepted by Gaussen (1937); the only confirmatory specimen was in Berlin and is now destroyed; and the alleged station—sunny screes on the southern side of the Col de Nuria—looks most unsuitable.

HABITAT: Although it is occasionally seen on rock, by far the most characteristic habitat is limestone or dolomite scree, always shady and usually watered by melting snow-patches. It grows mostly between 1800 and 2800m, but can be found as low as 1250m and as high as

3230m. Pignatti (1982) writes feelingly that 'this little plant is one's constant companion in the wearisome ascent of the interminable dolomite screes, and its small, greenish flower symbolises the poverty and instability of the habitat'.

*ACCESS*: S.sedoides is most easily seen in the Dolomites; it grows on the slopes of the Sassolungo not far from the Sella pass, and at the Passo di Falzarego. It may also be seen near the summit of Monte Baldo (east of Lake Garda) and on the Iof Fuart in the Italian part of the Julian Alps.

*CULTIVATION*: This seems, as with many snow-lie species, to be almost impossible.

### 113. *Saxifraga aphylla* Sternberg, *Revisio Saxifragarum* 40 (1810)

*SYNONYM*: S.stenopetala Gaudin

*HISTORY & NOMENCLATURE*: Described by Sternberg from a specimen collected by Lindaker; it does not seem to have been known to the earlier botanists. The epithet refers to the lack of leaves on the flowering stem.

*TYPE*: 422. Saxifraga aphylla Sternb., in Styriae alpibus. (Lectotype: Kew (**K**), designated here.)

*DESCRIPTION*: Stems weak, more or less decumbent, forming an open mat or loose cushion; dead leaves long-persistent. Leafy shoots of the current year short, with a crowded tuft of leaves 7–12 × 2–6mm, of which some are oblanceolate and entire, but most are shortly 3-lobed at the apex, with obtuse lobes. There is no petiole; the lamina tapers gradually from near the tip to the base. They are rather sparsely glandular-hairy. Flowering stems 2–4cm, slender, usually leafless, terminal and axillary, erect, bearing a single flower, 7–8mm in diameter. Sepals 2mm, triangular, obtuse. Petals narrow-linear, slightly exceeding the sepals, greenish-yellow. Nectary-disc large. Styles 1.5mm, slender, divergent. Seeds 1.0 × 0.6mm, ellipsoid with

Figure 60. *S.aphylla*

rounded ends, dark brown, smooth. Flowering season: July to September.

*ILLUSTRATIONS*: Figure 60
  Huber (1963, Figure 157)
* Finkenzeller & Grau (1985, p. 109)

*RECOGNITION*: The combination of straggling habit, entire or shortly 3-lobed leaves without a distinct petiole, and narrow petals is distinctive. From *S.presolanensis* it differs in the dead leaves being brown, not silvery-grey, in the acute petals, the solitary flowers and the much shorter and sparser hairs on the leaves. From *S.sedoides* it is best distinguished by the obtuse leaves; in *S.sedoides* at least some are apiculate.

*VARIATION*: A variant with all the leaves entire has been described (f. *breyniana* G. Beck, *Flora von Nieder-Österreich* 2(1):674 (1892) ), but it is recorded only from exposed places at great heights, and it is very doubtful whether its distinctive characters are genetically fixed.

*HYBRIDS*: Hybrids with *S.muscoides* (*S.* × *muretii* Rambert) and with *S.sedoides* (*S.* × *angelisii* Strobl) have been reported. The former, once found in Glarus, Switzerland, sounds convincing; the latter, in view of the similarity of the parents and the variability of *S.sedoides*, needs confirmation.

*CHROMOSOME NUMBER*: Exact counts of $2n = 60$ and 64 have been recorded.

*DISTRIBUTION* (Map 72): An Alpine endemic, found mainly in the northern part of the chain. From its western limit at 8°E in the Bernese Oberland it extends fairly continuously through the calcareous Alps of eastern Switzerland, Bavaria and Austria as far as 15°30′E. In the southern Alps it is much more local, but it extends from the Bernina group to the western Dolomites.

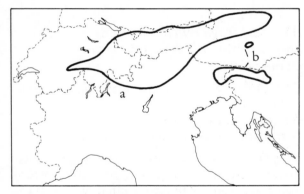

Map 72.   Distribution of (a) *S.aphylla* and (b) *S.tenella*

*HABITAT*: Screes and stony ground, especially where the snow lies late, nearly always on limestone. It is found mostly between 2100 and 2800m, but can range higher and lower.

*ACCESS*: Two places where the species may be seen in fair abundance are the Piz Padella, which stands over Samedan in the Engadin, and on north-facing screes near the summit of the Gösseck (47°24′N, 14°56′E) in Styria.

*CULTIVATION*: As with many snow-lie species this is very difficult. Plants reared from seed at Cambridge lived long enough to produce a single flower but died in their second winter.

**114.** *Saxifraga glabella* Bertoloni, *Giornale arcadico di Scienze, Lettere ed Arti* (Roma) 29:192 bis (1824)

*HISTORY & NOMENCLATURE*: Discovered ˙by Ursinio Asculano on Monte Maiella (central Apennines) in 1820 and sent by him to Bertoloni. The epithet *glabella* draws attention to the very nearly hairless condition of the lower parts of the plant. It is a distinct species and has never been confused with any other.

*TYPE*: Holotype probably destroyed and isotypes not traced.

*DESCRIPTION*: Leafy shoots ascending or straggling, short, numerous, forming a low cushion or loose mat. Leaves variable in size, but mostly 5–8 × 1–1.5mm, narrowly oblanceolate, obtuse, tapered at the base but scarcely stalked, somewhat fleshy, distant on the lower part of the shoot but aggregated into a loose rosette at the tip, hairless or with a very few marginal, glandular hairs. Hydathodes are difficult to observe on dried material and on most leaves none can be seen, but in a few there is an indication of one near the tip; in others again there seem to be a few irregularly disposed near the margins. In an Italian specimen we have seen small flakes of calcareous incrustation also irregularly disposed on the upper surface of the leaf. Flowering stems 4–10cm, slender, with about 5 cauline leaves similar to those of the leafy shoots but smaller; stems, cauline leaves, pedicels and hypanthia rather sparsely furnished with short hairs tipped with a black gland. Flowers 3–8 in a fairly compact cyme. Sepals 1.5 × 1mm, broadly ovate, obtuse, hairless. Petals 2–2.5mm, broadly obovate, contiguous, white. Styles short, straight, divergent. Seeds 0.55 × 0.3mm, ellipsoid, with bluntly pointed ends, light brown; surface granular but scarcely tuberculate; raphe rather inconspicuous. Flowering season: July and August.

Boissier (1872, p. 800) declared that on account of the submarginal lime-secreting hydathodes the species should be regarded as closely allied to *S.caesia*, and put it in his section *Aizoonia* (which included our section *Porphyrion*). No later writer appears to have followed him in this, but there has been no discussion of the problem, and it is to be hoped that a proper investigation of leaf-structure of living material will soon be attempted.

*ILLUSTRATIONS*:
\* Sternberg (1831, Plate 12)
Fiori & Paoletti (1895, p. 191)
\* Strid (1980, Plate 104)

*RECOGNITION*: The combination of small, pure white petals with soft, obtuse, almost hairless, entire leaves is characteristic.

*VARIATION*: There appears to be none of any consequence, except in the frequency of glandular hairs on the leaf-margins and in the inflorescence.

*HYBRIDS*: A hybrid with *S.spruneri* (*S. × degeniana* Handel-Mazzetti & Wagner) has been described from the Thessalian Olympus, but Aldén & Strid (1986) believe it to be merely a low-altitude variant of *S.spruneri*, and we are inclined to agree with them.

*CHROMOSOME NUMBER*: Not known.

*DISTRIBUTION* (Map 73): Although it was described from Italy, this is primarily a Balkan plant. From the Prenj Planina (north of Mostar) it extends southwards through the higher mountains of Hercegovina, Montenegro, northern Albania and Yugoslav Macedonia to the Jakupica (41°40′N). There are two isolated stations further south, in Greece: Timfi, in the northern Pindus, and the Thessalian Olympus.

In the central Apennines it is rare, and restricted to a narrow zone from Monte Terminillo and the Gran Sasso in the north to Monte Sirente and Monte Maiella in the south.

*HABITAT*: Shady screes, slopes and gullies where the snow lies late; always on limestone. It is commonest between 2000 and 2500m, but has been recorded as high as 2900m and as low as 1500m.

*ACCESS*: *S.glabella* is a high alpine, seldom abundant, and found mostly in wild country, so there is nowhere easy of access to see it in good quantity. In Italy, Monte Terminillo (where there is a road almost to the summit) looks the most promising spot; in the Balkans probably Durmitor in Montenegro.

*CULTIVATION*: No information is available.

## 115. *Saxifraga tenella* Wulfen, in Jacquin, *Collectanea Botanica* 3:144 (1790)

*SYNONYMS*: *Chondrosea tenella* (Wulfen) Haworth
*Saxifraga nitida* Schreber
*S.arenarioides* Brignoli & Brunhoff

*HISTORY & NOMENCLATURE*: Discovered by Karl von Zoys, probably in Slovenia, and sent by him to Wulfen, who was the first to describe it. The epithet signifies slender or delicate.

*TYPE*: Not traced.

*DESCRIPTION*: Leafy shoots numerous, short, prostrate to ascending, rather densely clothed with long, flexuous hairs, forming a fairly dense mat. Leaves 8–11 × 1mm, linear, keeled on the lower surface, with a very narrow translucent margin and a long, slender, translucent point, straw-coloured or silvery-grey, shiny, usually with a few marginal hairs, of which some, but not all, are glandular. On the upper surface near the tip is a single hydathode, sunk in a pit similar to those of lime-secreting species, but without any calcareous incrustation. Flowering stems up to 15cm, very slen-

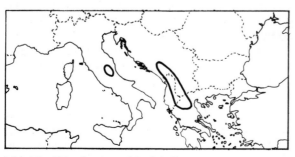

Map 73. Distribution of *S.glabella*

Plate 41.   *S.exarata* subsp. *exarata*

Plate 42.   *S.exarata* subsp. *moschata*

Plate 43.   *S.pedemontana* subsp. *pedemontana*

Plate 44.   *S. pedemontana* subsp. *cymosa* (Rila Mts, Bulgaria)

Plate 45.   *S.pedemontana* subsp. *cervicornis*

Plate 46.   *S. canaliculata*

Plate 47.   *S.intricata*

Plate 48.   *S. moncayensis*

Plate 49.  *S.fragilis* subsp. *fragilis*

Plate 50.  *S.cuneata*

Plate 51.  *S.aquatica*

der, hairless, bearing 4–7 widely spaced cauline leaves and a lax cyme of 3–9 flowers. Pedicels sparsely hairy above; hypanthium densely covered with short hairs. Sepals 1.5–2mm, hairless, triangular, apiculate. Petals 3mm, obovate, creamy-white, with 3 conspicuous veins. Styles 1mm, somewhat curved outwards. Seeds 0.6 × 0.3mm, dark brown, ellipsoid with one end truncate, the other bluntly pointed, covered evenly with rather widely spaced, low papillae; between them the surface is matt but without visible tubercles; raphe smooth, rather inconspicuous. Flowering season: June to August.

*ILLUSTRATIONS*: Plate 59
\* Seboth (1880, Plate 43)
  Huber (1963, Figure 161)
\* Rasetti (1980, Plate 258)

*RECOGNITION*: The combination of narrow, entire, bristle-pointed leaves with a not quite inferior ovary distingushes this species from all others except *S.vandelli*, *S.burseriana* and *S.conifera*. Of these the first two differ in their much larger petals and their compact, cushion-like habit; *S.conifera* differs in the possession at the flowering season of very conspicuous summer-dormant axillary buds, which are absent from *S.tenella*.

*VARIATION*: There is none of any consequence.

*HYBRIDS*: *S. × reyeri* Huter has been interpreted, probably correctly, as *S.sedoides × tenella*. It was found in the Julian Alps, just on the Italian side of the frontier with Yugoslavia.

A plant which arose as a chance seedling in the Vienna botanic garden in 1889 was interpreted as *S.moschata × tenella*, but was more probably a peculiar variant of *S.exarata* subsp. *moschata*.

*CHROMOSOME NUMBER*: $2n = 66$, but this is an old count requiring confirmation.

*DISTRIBUTION* (Map 72, p. 245): Endemic to a limited region of the eastern Alps, mainly on their southern side. Its headquarters is in the Julian Alps, both in Italy and Yugoslavia; from here it extends westwards to near Tol-

mezzo (13°10′E) and eastwards to 15°10′E in the hills bordering the valley of the Save below Ljubljana. There is one isolated station in Austria on the Grebenzen, 45km north of Klagenfurt.

*HABITAT*: Shady boulders and screes on calcareous rocks, often associated with mosses. It ranges from 700 to 2000m, being commonest about the middle of this range.

*ACCESS*: It is a rather elusive species, but is locally common in the western part of the Julian Alps, to the south-west of Tarvisio. It may also be seen in small quantity on limestone talus on the right bank of the Save near Zagorje, 40km downstream from Ljubljana.

*CULTIVATION*: This presents no special difficulty; the plant is hardy, and can be grown in a shady spot out of doors or in a pan under glass. Like many mat-forming species it needs occasional 'settling in' to the soil, as the prostrate shoots are rather slow to root. The flowers are too small to give an effective display, but the shining, straw-coloured or silvery foliage is distinctive and attractive.

## Subsection *Tridactylites* (Haworth) Gornall

Annuals or biennials. Leaves entire or shortly 3- to 5-lobed. Flowers small, on long pedicels, forming a lax, leafy panicle. Petals white (rarely red), usually slightly notched at the tip. Bulbils and summer-dormant buds absent. Ovary inferior or nearly so.

A small but widespread group of four species, extending to North Africa, south-western Asia and North America.

### The *tridactylites*-group

This taxonomically troublesome group of small-flowered annuals and biennials has been variously treated by different authors. Engler & Irmscher (1916) included the whole group in a single species (which, however, they designated a *typus polymorphus*). The treatment adopted here, which recognises four species

**Table 3. Summary of characters distinguishing species in the *Tridactylites*-group**

| Character | *S.tridactylites* | *S. adscendens* subspp. | | *S. blavii* | *S. osloensis* |
| --- | --- | --- | --- | --- | --- |
| | | *adscendens* | *parnassica* | | |
| Habit | annual, without a basal rosette at flowering | biennial, with well-developed basal rosette persistent till flowering | | biennial, but basal rosette with small leaves which begin to wither at flowering | biennial, but sometimes flowering in the first autumn as well as the following summer |
| Leaf-lobes | divergent | short, forwardly directed | long and somewhat divergent | short, forwardly directed | fairly short, slightly divergent |
| Pedicel length | usually 10–20mm in fruit | short in flower, elongating to 8mm in fruit | short in flower and fruit | usually 10–20mm in fruit | 6–8mm in fruit |
| Petal length | 2.5–3mm | 3.5–5mm | 3–4mm | 5mm, contrasting with the short hypanthium | c. 3.5mm |
| Capsule shape | subglobose, rounded at the base | obovoid, tapered at the base | subglobose, rounded at the base | subglobose to broadly ellipsoid, rounded at the base | obovoid, tapered at the base |
| Seed surface | coarsely papillose | finely tuberculate | finely tuberculate | coarsely papillose or finely tuberculate | coarsely papillose |

and two subspecies within one of them, is, however, in harmony with the views of Knaben (1954), who gave the most recent discussion of the group as a whole. As the distinctive characters of the taxa are rather subtle and confusing, we tabulate those that are most easily observed (Table 3).

## 116. *Saxifraga tridactylites* Linnaeus, *Species Plantarum* 404 (1753)

*HISTORY & NOMENCLATURE*: This species is too inconspicuous and without medicinal reputation to have attracted the notice of the mediaeval herbalists. The earliest reference to it which we can trace is by Gesner (1541), who called it *Nasturtiolum petraeum*. By Dodoens (1583) and many subsequent authors it was put in the genus *Paronychia*; it was Linnaeus who first put it under *Saxifraga*.

The epithet (three-fingered) refers to the commonest form of the leaves.

*TYPE*: Sheet 174.11 in the Linnean herbarium, Stockholm (**S**) has been designated as lectotype (Webb 1987a).

*DESCRIPTION*: A sparsely to rather densely glandular-hairy winter annual, varying greatly in habit and size according to situation. On rich, water-retaining soil it may reach a height of 20cm and bear more than 50 flowers on its numerous branches; on dry, poor soil it may produce a simple, very slender stem only 2.5cm tall, bearing 5–6 minute leaves and a single terminal flower. In dry, sunny situations the plant usually turns red with age. First-formed basal leaves spathulate, not lobed, much smaller than the succeeding leaves, withered at flowering time in well-grown plants, but still persistent and green in depauperate (and therefore prematurely flowering) plants; if persistent not forming a well-defined rosette. Subsequent basal and lower cauline leaves very variable, oblong, rhombic or almost semi-circular in outline, entire or more usually with 3 (rarely 5) oblong, oblanceolate, elliptical or triangular lobes, of which the central is the largest; sessile or with a petiole as long as the lamina. The largest leaves

may attain a size of 23 × 15mm (including petiole), but something like 10 × 4mm is more usual. Upper cauline leaves (which usually subtend flowers or branches of the inflorescence, and therefore may be termed bracts) successively smaller and less divided. Flowers in a diffuse cyme; pedicels ascending, usually 10–20mm but the uppermost often shorter. Hypanthium about 2.5 × 2.5mm in flower, rather larger in fruit, with a truncate or rounded base. Sepals 1.5 × 1mm, ovate, obtuse. Petals 2.5–3 × 1.5–2mm, narrowly obovate, entire or very slightly notched, erect to spreading, white. Ovary at least ¾ inferior; styles very short, diverging almost horizontally. Seeds 0.37–0.42 × 0.25–0.28mm, broadly oblong but somewhat tapered at one end, covered with fine tubercles and bearing a small number of much longer, blunt, cylindrical papillae. Flowering season: March to July, according to latitude. The flowers, in contrast to those of most species, are usually somewhat protogynous.

*ILLUSTRATIONS*:
\* Bonnier (1921, Plate 204)
  Ross-Craig (1957, Plate 6)
  Mądalski (1962, Plate 1320)
\* Huber (1963, Plate 143)

*RECOGNITION*: S.tridactylites cannot be confused with any species except the other members of this group. For the differential characters see Table 3.

*VARIATION*: As may be deduced from the description, this is a very variable plant, but although there may be some degree of ecotypic differentiation, most of the variation is purely environmental.

*HYBRIDS*: The hybrid with S.hypnoides is discussed under that species. S.tridactylites may also be one of the parents of S.osloensis (see under that species).

*CHROMOSOME NUMBER*: $2n = 22$.

*DISTRIBUTION* (Map 74): This is the most widespread species of saxifrage in Europe. It ranges over the whole continent except for the extreme north and much of the north-east. Its

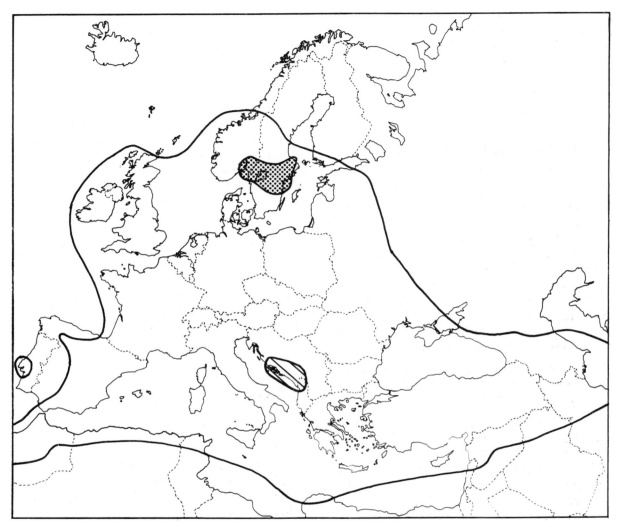

Map 74. Distribution of *S.tridactylites* (unshaded area, extends southwards to the High Atlas of Morocco and eastwards to north-eastern Iran); *S.osloensis* (shaded area in Scandinavia); and *S.blavii* (hatched area in the Balkans)

northern and eastern limit runs past the northern tip of Scotland, across central Norway and Sweden to south-western Finland, and from the gulf of Finland southwards to White Russia and thence through north-eastern Ukraine to the Sea of Azov. It reaches, therefore, only the western and southern fringes of the USSR.

Outside Europe it is known only from North-west Africa and south-western Asia, its eastward limit lying in the Kopetdag range on the borders of north-eastern Iran and the Turkmen SSR.

*HABITAT*: *S.tridactylites* is to be found in a wide range of open habitats, including walls, talus, railway-tracks, limestone pavement and open grassland on sand or gravel. It cannot be called strictly calcicole, but it is much commoner on limestone than on any other substratum. In northern Europe it grows mainly in sunny situations, but in southern Europe it is usually in the shade. It is mainly a lowland plant, but it ascends to at least 1500m in the Alps, the central Apennines and Greece, and to about 1800m in Spain.

ACCESS: Directions for finding such a common plant are scarcely needed; it is frequent in most parts of England and Ireland where there are sizeable exposures of the harder limestones. The best counties would seem to be Dorset, Derbyshire, western Yorkshire and the Burren district of Co. Clare.

CULTIVATION: Like most native annuals it is best not attempted in the open; it will either vanish or become a weed. If grown in a pan in a glass-house it is best given a good soil and watered freely in the early stages; then having raised sturdy plants, as soon as the first flowers appear, cut off the water supply and keep it in the sun. The leaves should turn red, and the small white flowers will show up well against them.

## 117. *Saxifraga adscendens* Linnaeus, *Species Plantarum* 405 (1753)

SYNONYMS: *S.petraea* of Oeder and many authors, but not of Linnaeus
*S.controversa* Sternberg
*S.bellardii* Allioni
*S.ramosissima* Schur
*S.oregonensis* (Rafinesque) Nelson
*Muscaria adscendens* (Linnaeus) Small

HISTORY & NOMENCLATURE: As the synonymy shows, a sad history of confusion surrounds this name. By 1753 Linnaeus seems to have had a fairly clear concept of it, but he had earlier put the name to a specimen of *S.aquatica* in the Burser herbarium, and this misuse of it continued for decades. Moreover his *S.tridactylites* var. *alpina* of 1753 was based partly on *S.adscendens* and partly on *S.petraea*.

The earliest description which clearly belongs to this species is that of Bauhin (1620) as *Sedum tridactylites alpinum majus tertium*.

The specific epithet is ill-suited to the plant, as its stem is stiffly erect; it probably was used originally to describe the stems of *S.aquatica*.

TYPE: *S.adscendens*. Sheet XVI(1).89 in the Burser herbarium, Uppsala (**UPS**), has been designated as lectotype (Webb 1987a).

Subsp. *parnassica*. Saxifraga controversa Sternberg. Parnassus, *Spruner*. (Lectotype:

Geneva (**G**), designated here; there are two other syntypes at Geneva, and others elsewhere, e.g. University of Göttingen (**GOET**).)

DESCRIPTION: Normally biennial, but possibly sometimes behaving in favourable situations as a winter annual; more or less glandular-hairy. Basal leaves forming a compact, well-defined rosette, of which at least the upper leaves remain green until flowering has begun; variable in form but usually oblanceolate-cuneate, shortly 3-lobed, with the lobes directed forward, more rarely entire or 5-toothed; petiole shorter than lamina. They may attain a length of 25mm, but 6–15mm is more usual. Cauline leaves usually about 8 (excluding bracts), nearly always 3-lobed, with the lobes directed more laterally than in the basal leaves. Flowering stem 4–25cm, rather stout, usually single, but in some luxuriant plants additional stems may arise from the axils of the rosette-leaves; very variable in the extent of its branching. Flowers usually 6–15, but up to 40 on the most luxuriant plants; pedicels very short in flower, but elongating in fruit up to 8mm. Hypanthium variable in form (see under the subspecies). Sepals c. 2mm, broadly triangular-oblong, obtuse. Petals 3–5mm, obovate, truncate or very slightly notched, contiguous, white, very rarely tinged with yellow or red. Ovary almost completely inferior; styles short, divergent, largely concealed by the sepals and petals. Seeds 0.35–0.45 × 0.2–0.27mm, broadly oblong, only slightly tapered at one end, covered all over (including the raphe) with very small tubercles, but without any coarse papillae. Flowering season: June to August.

ILLUSTRATIONS:
  Mądalski (1962, Plate 1321)
  Huber (1963, Figure 142)
  Harding (1970, p. 123)
* Strid (1980, Plate 97)

RECOGNITION: For the distinctions between this species and others of the *tridactylites*-group see p. 248. It has in the past been rather surprsingly confused with *S.petraea*, but only on the basis of inadequate descriptions without figures; the habit, leaf-shape and petal-size are very different. It has also been confused with *S.aquatica*, which is even harder to understand.

*VARIATION*: There is much variation in size and amount of branching; this, like the similar variation in *S.tridactylites*, is largely determined by nutrition and other variables of the habitat. It would seem, however, that plants of this species are seldom capable of flowering in quite as reduced a state as may be seen in *S.tridactylites*; this is, perhaps, correlated with its biennial habit. In Europe, variation in other characters is sufficiently well correlated to permit the recognition of two subspecies.

(a) Subsp. *adscendens*. Usually tall (up to 25cm) and with few, suberect branches. Hypanthium of most of the flowers considerably longer than wide and tapered at the base rather gradually into the pedicel. Sepals at least 1.5 times as long as broad. Petals 3.5–5mm.

Plants from the mountains of Bulgaria (Pirin and Rila) with petals turning reddish-pink before they fall, and with a very dense covering of gland-tipped hairs, have been distinguished as var. *discolor* (Velenovský) Stojanov & Stefanov, *Flora na Bălgarija* 551 (1924). It has recently been seen in Greece (Olympus).

(b) Subsp. *parnassica* (Boissier & Heldreich) Hayek, *Prodromus Florae Peninsulae balcanicae* 1:638 (1925). Usually less than 10cm high, freely branched, with spreading branches. Hypanthia all subglobose and truncate at the base. Sepals scarcely longer than broad. Petals 3–4mm.

*HYBRIDS*: None is known, but see under *S.osloensis*.

*CHROMOSOME NUMBER*: $2n = 22$ has been recorded for all subspecies.

*DISTRIBUTION* (Map 75): The European range of *S.adscendens* falls into two sectors, separated by quite a wide gap. The northern sector comprises Fennoscandia and some adjoining regions; the southern sector the mountains of southern and parts of central Europe.

The northern sector extends from 69°N in arctic Norway through much of Norway and Sweden southwards to 58°N, and thence across the Baltic to Estonia and south-western Finland, with some outlying stations in Russian Karelia near the northern shore of Lake Ladoga.

A gap of almost 1000km separates this area from its nearest station in central Europe, which is in the Polish Tatra. Hence it extends through most of the Carpathian range and is found on all the major ranges of the Balkan peninsula. In the Apennines it runs from Tuscany to the borders of Calabria and re-appears in the Madonie range in Sicily. It is scattered rather thinly over most of the Alps, and has been recorded from a few stations in the eastern and central Pyrenees. It is absent from the other mountains of Spain, and from the Auvergne, Jura, Vosges, Harz and Riesengebirge.

Outside Europe it extends eastwards only to Anatolia and the Caucasus, but it occurs also in a remarkably disjunct area in western North America (as subsp. *oregonensis*, see p. 285), where it grows here and there in the Rocky mountains from 56°N in British Columbia to south-western Colorado, and possibly also in Alaska. We know of no other seed-plant whose range is primarily European and which is found in western but not in eastern North America.

The range of subsp. *parnassica* is restricted to Greece (throughout the Pindus range and on the higher mountains on both sides of the Gulf of Corinth), south-eastern Albania, the central and southern Apennines and Sicily. (The record for Hercegovina by Murbeck (1891) is almost certainly an error for *S.blavii*.) Subsp. *adscendens* can be found occasionally within the territory of subsp. *parnassica*, but there is not much overlap.

*HABITAT*: *S.adscendens* normally favours a cool or damp, well-drained, more or less open habitat, and is usually, therefore, to be found on shaded rocks or screes, on the stony margins of mountain tracks, in thin, grassy turf in the mountains, or on gravelly stream-sides. It is mainly lowland in northern Europe, though it has been recorded at 1600m in Norway. In central and southern Europe it is found mainly

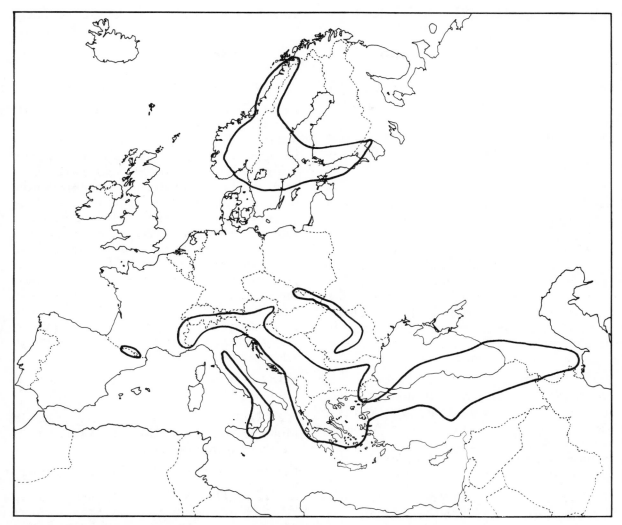

Map 75. Distribution of *S.adscendens* (also in North America)

between 1700 and 2800m, but can descend to 1250m and ascend as high as 3500m.

*ACCESS*: Although subsp. *adscendens* is widespread in the Alps it is nowhere plentiful. It seems to be commoner in Austria than in the other Alpine countries. It may, however, be seen in some quantity in the Polish Tatra, on talus at 1250m on the northern slopes of Giewont (only 6km from the centre of Zakopane). It is also fairly common on Pietra Arsa, in the Romanian Carpathians near Sinaia. Subsp. *parnassica* may be conveniently seen on Monte Mucchia (the southernmost peak of the Monte Morrone range), which lies immediately north-east of Sulmona, in the central Apennines, but is best ascended from the hamlet of Roccacaramanico on the other side. Here it is plentiful from 1800 to 2000m on thin, dry grassland, mixed with *S.tridactylites*.

*CULTIVATION*: This species is impossible to cultivate in Dublin for any length of time; the mild winters do not suit it. It has survived for a few years out of doors in eastern England, and Knaben (1954) cultivated it successfully in Oslo. It has little beauty, and is worth growing only for comparison with related species and for an analysis of its variation.

## 118. *Saxifraga blavii* (Engler) G. Beck von Managetta, *Annalen des k.k. naturhistorischen Hofmuseums (Wien)* 2:93 (1887)

*SYNONYMS: S.adscendens* var. *blavii* Engler, *Verhandlungen der k.k. zoologisch-botanischen Gesellschaft in Wien* 19:524 (1869)
*S.tridactylites* subsp. *blavii* (Engler) Engler & Irmscher, *Pflanzenreich* 67 (IV.117):228 (1916)

*HISTORY & NOMENCLATURE*: The epithet *blavii* derives from Dr Blau, German consul in Sarajevo, who brought the plant to the attention of Engler about 1868.

Most authors treat this as a variety or subspecies of *S.adscendens*, and it is only after some hesitation that we follow Beck and reinstate it as a species. *S.blavii* combines, as does *S.osloensis*, several features of *S.adscendens* with others of *S.tridactylites*, and it is tempting to suppose that, like *S.osloensis*, it may be of hybrid origin. No cytological information is, however, available.

*TYPE*: Saxifraga ascendens. Bosnien. Trebević bei Sarajevo. 11.VII.1928. *Karl Ronniger 28324*. (Neotype: Natural History Museum, Vienna (**W**), designated here; the holotype, from Romanija, east of Sarajevo, has been destroyed, and we can trace no isotypes.)

*DESCRIPTION*: A rather densely glandular-hairy biennial. Leaves of the basal rosette small (rarely more than 15mm), oblanceolate, entire or shortly 3-lobed with the lobes directed forward; cauline leaves similar but rather larger. Flowering stem 5–20cm, slender, branched from the base or only in the upper part, with ascending, somewhat flexuous branches. Flowers numbering 5–15 (–25). Pedicels 10–20mm, mostly very slender. Hypanthium very small in flower, enlarging to 3.5 × 3mm in fruit, truncate or slightly tapered at the base. Sepals 1.5 × 2mm, ovate. Petals 5 × 3.5mm, broadly obovate, contiguous or overlapping, truncate or slightly notched. Ovary inferior; styles short, divergent. Seeds 0.37–0.45 × 0.2mm, resembling those of *S. adscendens* in shape, usually coarsely papillose as in *S.tridactylites*, but sometimes finely tuberculate as in *S.adscendens*. Flowering season: June and July.

*ILLUSTRATIONS*: Plate 60
Engler & Irmscher (1916, Figure 50)

*RECOGNITION*: As may be inferred from p. 248, *S.blavii* differs from *S.adscendens* primarily in the early withering of its basal leaves, its long, slender pedicels and its usually coarsely papillose seeds. But it differs also in its general delicacy of habit and in the size of the petals in relation to the hypanthium. In absolute size and shape the petals can be matched by those of some specimens of *S.adscendens*, but the hypanthium on which they are set is so much smaller that a very different effect is produced. In a newly opened flower of *S.blavii* the calyx and hypanthium together are only 3mm long; in a flower of *S.adscendens* with petals of equal size they measure 4.5–5mm.

For differences from *S.tridactylites* and *S. osloensis*, see p. 248.

*VARIATION*: No significant variation is known.

*HYBRIDS*: None has been reported. In Montenegro it grows alongside *S.tridactylites* without any intermediates.

*CHROMOSOME NUMBER*: Not known.

*DISTRIBUTION* (Map 74, see p. 250): Endemic to western Yugoslavia and northern Albania. It extends from the Dinara Planina (north of Split) southwards through Hercegovina, southern Bosnia and western Serbia to Montenegro. We have seen no specimens from Albania, but there is a record in Engler & Irmscher (1916) from a station some 50km south of Shkodar.

*HABITAT*: Limestone rocks and debris, usually in the shade, mostly between 1000 and 2000m.

*ACCESS*: It grows in fair quantity among limestone rocks above the Čakor pass, and somewhat to the south of it; this pass is on the road between Peč (Serbia) and Andrijevica (Montenegro), and the locality is more easily accessible than it sounds. It also grows a few kilometres to the south, on the mountain which lies to the west of the lake at Plav.

*CULTIVATION*: We know of no attempts. As the most handsome of the *tridactylites*-group it would be well worth a trial.

## 119. *Saxifraga osloensis* Knaben, *Nytt Magasin for Botanikk* 3:118 (1954)

*HISTORY & NOMENCLATURE*: First recognised by Knaben, and named from the fact that it was originally found near Oslo. It is of interest in being the only saxifrage which can be confidently held to be an amphidiploid (this may be true also of *S.nathorstii* from Greenland (see p. 136), but there is some room for doubt). It seems to have arisen in post-glacial times by hybridisation between *S. adscendens* and *S.tridactylites* (both with $2n = 22$) and subsequent doubling of the chromosome number. In its morphology it is more or less intermediate between the parents in most characters, and although it is a somewhat critical taxon it can, with care, be distinguished from both of them.

*TYPE*: Oslo: Gaustadskogen på en noe fuktig klippe eksponert mot NV. Planteindividet hentet 20/10 1953. Det ble pottet og fotografert (Knaben 1954, fig. 1). Det ble oppbevart på sprit, og senere presset for å monteres i herb. Oslo. *Gunvor Knaben*. (Holotype: University of Oslo (O).)

*DESCRIPTION*: A winter annual, or sometimes a biennial which under certain conditions can flower in its first autumn as well as in the following summer; in habit and structure intermediate between *S.tridactylites* and *S. adscendens* subsp. *adscendens*, but in general appearance resembling the latter more closely. Basal leaves in a well-defined rosette, which in biennial plants persists to the final flowering; leaves 12–15mm, obovate-cuneate to spathulate, 3- to 5-lobed, with triangular lobes, larger and more divergent than those of *S.adscendens*; petioles broad and ill-defined, usually equal to or somewhat longer than lamina. Pedicel usually 6–8mm in fruit. Hypanthium considerably longer than broad, and somewhat tapered at the base. Sepals elliptic-ovate, c. 2.5mm. Petals c. $3.5 \times 2.5$mm, slightly notched at the tip, white. Seeds $0.5 \times 0.27$mm, oblong-cuneate (truncate at one end and tapered at the other), covered with fine tubercles and coarse papillae, as in *S.tridactylites*; raphe inconspicuous.

The irregularity of the flowering season is clearly caused by a not yet fully resolved tension between the annual habit of one parent and the biennial habit of the other.

*ILLUSTRATIONS*:
Knaben (1954, Figures 1, 3, 4; Plates I, II)

*RECOGNITION*: Distinguished from *S.tridactylites* by the longer hypanthium, usually lobed rosette-leaves, less deeply lobed cauline leaves and larger petals; from *S.adscendens* by the more divergent leaf-lobes, longer pedicels and coarsely papillose seeds; from *S.blavii* by the narrower, emarginate and somewhat shorter petals and the longer hypanthium.

*VARIATION*: None of any significance.

*HYBRIDS*: None is known.

*CHROMOSOME NUMBER*: $2n = 44$.

*DISTRIBUTION* (Map 74, p. 250): The range of *S.osloensis* as so far known is confined to a small area of southern Sweden and Norway. This runs from the Swedish coast north-east of Uppsala, past lake Hjälmaren to the northern and western shores of Lake Väneren, and thence to the Oslo region. This corresponds in part to the rather narrow zone of overlap between the two parent species in Scandinavia, *S.adscendens* being mainly northern in its distribution and *S.tridactylites* mainly southern.

It is quite possible, however, that it grows elsewhere in Europe, awaiting recognition, in regions where *S.adscendens* and *S.tridactylites* share the same territory. Knaben (1954) gave two good reasons for supposing this. First, because Drygalsky (1935) found that artificially produced $F_1$ hybrids between *S.adscendens* and *S.tridactylites* were, as might have been expected, partly but not entirely sterile, and the F$_2$ plants were almost entirely tetraploid and apparently identical with *S.osloensis*. Secondly, because Engler & Irmscher (1916, pp. 226–7) mentioned under the head of *S.adscendens* some aberrant forms which might perhaps be *S.osloensis*. These are mostly in the Tatra and adjoining ranges of the Polish–Czechoslovak border, but also in the southern Carpathians not far from Sinaia.

*HABITAT*: In the Oslo area, *S.osloensis* grows on rocks in various situations, but well-developed plants are found only on those that are moist or shady, often moss-covered. There are no published data relating to altitude, but it would seem that most of the localities lie below 300m.

*ACCESS*: It should probably not be difficult to find specimens in the two places near Oslo mentioned by Knaben (1954); the Gaustad woods and the islet of Torvøya. *S.adscendens* does not grow here, and it should be easy to distinguish *S.osloensis* from *S.tridactylites*.

*CULTIVATION*: Knaben (1954) cultivated it successfully in a frame in Oslo. The frames were darkened in winter and early spring and to some extent protected against frost. There seems to be no record of its cultivation elsewhere.

# 5

# Madeiran species

There are no saxifrages in the Azores, the Canary Islands or the Cape Verde Islands, but two species are known from the Madeiran archipelago. Both clearly belong to section *Saxifraga*, series *Ceratophyllae*, and resemble most closely those Spanish species of this series whose leaves are completely hairless and have instead numerous sessile glands, rendering them viscid. In particular they come close to *S.cuneata* and *S.trifurcata* in sharing with them the rather unusual position of the flowering stems; these are not terminal, but arise from the axils of some of the leaves of the previous season's growth.

*Saxifraga maderensis* D. Don is widespread and locally frequent on the high ground in the centre of the main island of Madeira. It forms fairly large, loose cushions on shady and often moist, vertical rocks. In the typical variety the leaves are semi-circular or kidney-shaped, fairly soft, cordate at the base, with a slender petiole longer than the lamina, which is divided, not very deeply, into a large number of obtuse to acute lobes. The inflorescence is a fairly open cyme of 6–13 flowers with white petals 5–10 × 3–6mm. Although the lamina is completely hairless, there are usually some glandular hairs on the pedicels and hypanthia and at the base of the petioles.

In three places near the centre of the island a variant has been found which was at first described as a separate species, but as intermediate plants are not uncommon it is best named *S.maderensis* var. *pickeringii* (Simon) D.A. Webb & R. Press, *Bocagiana* no.105:3 (1987). It is more robust than the typical plant, with rather more leathery leaves, which are rhombic or fan-shaped, and tapered gradually into a broad petiole. The leaf-lobes are acute to shortly apiculate. The flowers are fewer than in var. *maderensis* (not more than 6 in the cyme) but the petals are usually slightly larger.

*Saxifraga portosanctana* Boissier is the second of the two species, and is found, not on Madeira, but on the neighbouring island of Porto Santo, where it appears to be limited to the summit regions of the two principal peaks. It resembles *S.maderensis* in general habit, but the leaves are fleshier, with the lamina considerably longer than broad, divided into relatively few (never more than 9) obtuse lobes. The petals are long and narrow (10–11 × 3–4mm). There are no hairs at the base of the petiole, and the plant is completely hairless.

Both species are remarkably hardy, despite their southern origin, and can be grown out of doors in most parts of the British Isles. *S.portosanctana* and *S.maderensis* var. *pickeringii* are sufficiently strong growers to fill a pocket in the rock-garden fairly quickly; *S.maderensis* var. *maderensis* is rather less robust, and probably shows up best if grown under glass.

# 6

# African species

There are about 18 species of saxifrage native to Africa; 17 of them are found mostly in the Atlas Mountains of Morocco and Algeria, and these have been described in a recent account of the flora of North Africa by Maire (1980). The great majority belong to section *Saxifraga*, with subsection *Triplinervium* being particularly well represented. Ten species are essentially European in distribution, but have their most southerly stations in North Africa. They are: **S.cymbalaria, S.hederacea, S.longifolia, S.granulata, S.carpetana, S.dichotoma, S.tridactylites, S.rigoi, S.globulifera** and **S.pedemontana**, and we refer the reader to Chapter 4 for accounts of these. The last three are mainly represented by endemic subspecies.

In fact there are altogether 12 species and subspecies which are endemic to Africa, and for the most part they have been discovered only relatively recently. Only one was known in the eighteenth century (*S.globulifera* var. *spathulata*), three more were discovered in the nineteenth century, and the remaining eight were described between 1919 and 1931. They are dealt with below, beginning with the only one to occur outside North Africa.

*Saxifraga hederifolia* Hochstetter ex A. Richard grows above 3000m in the mountains of northern Ethiopia, and is among the most southerly and remote of all old-world saxifrages. It is a close relative of *S.cymbalaria* and allies but may be distinguished by its nearly inferior ovary, and the dilated bases of its petioles.

Of the seven species endemic to North Africa, five belong to series *Gemmiferae*, one to series *Ceratophyllae* and one to series *Cespitosae*. This suggests that the affinities of the North African saxifrage flora, not surprisingly, lie mainly in Spain, where these series are particularly well represented.

*Saxifraga globulifera* is represented by four variants in North Africa: the European var. *globulifera* and three others which may be distinguished as follows. Var. *oranensis* (Munby) Engler, *Monographie der Gattung Saxifraga L.* 194 (1872), ranging from Oran province in Algeria to the Rif mountains of northern Morocco, and var. *spathulata* (Desfontaines) Engler & Irmscher, *Pflanzenreich* 67 (IV.117):351 (1916), from Alger province, Algeria, and the Rif and Middle Atlas mountains of Morocco, have obtuse sepals, but are supposed to differ from their European relative in having oblong summer-dormant buds on long stalks. Var. *spathulata* may be further distinguished by its characteristically spathulate lower leaves; and var. *oranensis* by its hairless, shiny, broadly-lobed leaves, with petioles more than twice as long as the laminae. The third endemic variant is provisionally treated as subsp. *trabutiana* (Engler & Irmscher) Maire, *Flore de l'Afrique du Nord* 15:34 (1980); it comes from the mountains of the provinces of Alger and Constantine in north-eastern Algeria, and differs from all in its acute sepals.

**Saxifraga maweana** Baker is another distinctive African member of series *Gemmiferae*. It forms loose, rather elongated rosettes of basal leaves which are kidney-shaped and divided into 3–5 broad lobes, the lobes themselves further divided into segments. The petioles are more than twice the length of the laminae, and narrowly oblong summer-buds may be found in the axils. It is an attractive plant about 20cm tall, with large white flowers (petals 12–14mm long), which inhabits cool, shady rocks at middle elevations in the Rif mountains of northern Morocco.

**Saxifraga tricrenata** Pau & Font Quer, also from the Rif Mountains of Morocco, is much less distinctive. It looks very much like *S.rigoi* (see p. 176), differing allegedly, but unconvincingly, in its larger flowers with petals 10–14mm long, and ovoid rather than obovoid or oblong summer-buds. But in Europe the petals of *S.rigoi* are normally 12–15mm long and the shape of the summer-buds is somewhat variable; we think it best, therefore, to regard *S.tricrenata* as a variant of *S.rigoi*. It is true that North African material of *S.rigoi* has petals which are only 6–9mm long, and this single collection from the Rif Mountains has been named subsp. *maroccana* Luizet & Maire, *Bulletin de la Société d'Histoire naturelle de l'Afrique du Nord* 22:46,47 (1931), but until more material becomes available, it would be prudent to suspend judgement on the precise status of this plant or of *S.tricrenata*.

**Saxifraga embergeri** Maire is another plant rather like *S.rigoi*, but differs in its ovoid to sub-globose summer-buds and in its very small flowers (petals only 2.5–4mm long). It grows in wet flushes on basaltic or granitic rocks at low elevations in the Monts des Zaian (outliers of the Middle Atlas) in north-western Morocco.

The remaining two endemic members of series *Gemmiferae* are known only from their type-collections, and their status and affinities must therefore remain uncertain. Both were described in 1931.

**Saxifraga werneri** Font Quer & Pau forms loose mats and has a most striking inflorescence, 4–8cm tall, in which the branches arise at nearly every level, from the base of the flowering stem to the top. The leaves of the vegetative shoots have from 3 to 5 obtuse lobes and taper to short, broad petioles. In their axils are sub-globose summer-buds. The petals are 4–6.5mm long. It was collected from crevices of wet, calcareous rocks on Mount Kraa in the Rif Mountains of Morocco at an elevation of about 2000m.

**Saxifraga numidica** Maire was found on wet, calcareous rocks at an elevation of 1800 to 1900m in the Petite Kabylie of Constantine province, Algeria, where it forms stiff cushions in which some leafy shoots carry a single summer-bud near the apex. The leaves vary on a shoot from 3-lobed to entire, and the flowering stems are short, up to 3cm tall.

**Saxifraga maireana** Luizet is the lone representative of series *Cespitosae*. It is a most distinctive member, characterised by a high frequency of spathulate leaves on its leafy shoots. It forms neat but fragile cushions, which produce flowering stems 2–7cm tall, bearing from 1 to 4 flowers with pink (rarely white) petals. It can be found among shady rocks at elevations of 2400–2800m in the High Atlas of Morocco.

Finally there are two species assigned to series *Ceratophyllae*.

**Saxifraga luizetiana** Emberger & Maire, is another example of a species known only from its type-specimen, and again, for this reason, we must be cautious about interpreting its relationships. Although we have not seen the specimen, an illustration in Maire (1980) depicts a plant with a bizarre appearance. It has basal rosettes of glandular-hairy, lobed leaves with long petioles, in outline much like many members of series *Ceratophyllae*; its striking aspect, however, is due to its flexuous flowering stems, whose long branches intertwine to give a curiously tangled look. It was found in the Middle Atlas of Morocco at about 3000m on calcareous rocks.

*Saxifraga pedemontana* is divided into five, fairly well-marked subspecies (see p. 203). In North Africa, it is represented by the endemic subsp. ***demnatensis*** (Cosson ex Battandier) Maire, *Flore de l'Afrique du Nord* 15:25 (1980); this variant looks rather like subsp. *cervicornis*, but differs mainly in its larger, more leathery leaves with short, glandular hairs, and in its oblong sepals which are equal to, or only slightly longer than, the hypanthium. It grows among siliceous and calcareous rocks at elevations of 2800–3900m in the Middle and High Atlas of Morocco.

As far as cultivating North African species is concerned, the choicest subjects are *S.maireana* and *S.maweana*, although they need an alpine house to ensure good growth and survival through a northern winter. *S.pedemontana* subsp. *demnatensis* and the North African subspecies of *S.globulifera* are also occasionally met with in cultivation but, again, usually under glass.

# 7

# Near Eastern and Caucasian species

Of the saxifrages found in Europe, 15 species extend their range into south-western Asia, which, for the purpose of this note, is bounded on the east by the meridian of 55°E (in central Iran), and on the north by the northern foot-hills of the Caucasus. There are, however, in addition to these, at least eleven species which are endemic to this region. We say 'at least' because seven others have been described, but are insufficiently known for their taxonomic status to be assessed; they are not described below. It should be remembered in this connection that until quite recently all Soviet Floras were influenced by the very narrow species-concept associated with the name of Komarov.

These eleven species are all high-alpine, and are therefore confined to the relatively narrow compass of the Caucasus, central and eastern Turkey and northern Iran. Their affinities are, on the whole, with European species rather than with those of the Himalayan–Tibetan region, from which they are separated by a gap of 10 degrees of longitude. They all belong to subsection *Kabschia*, and most of them resemble *S.sancta* and *S.juniperifolia* in their floral structure, and in some cases their leaves.

There are, however, two species from other sections which are represented in south-western Asia by subspecies different from those which are found in Europe. One is *S.flagellaris*, which was originally described from the Caucasus; the Caucasus population therefore belongs to subsp. *flagellaris*. It differs from the high-arctic subsp. *platysepala*, which is the only subspecies found in Europe (Spitsbergen, see p. 41), in several features: its ovary is completely superior, its sepals are narrower and it has no glandular hairs on its runners. It is found throughout the main range of the Caucasus.

The other species is *S.paniculata*. Despite the wide variation in leaf-shape shown by the European populations, the leaf-tip is always obtuse to subacute, and the petals, though often heavily spotted with crimson-purple, have always a ground colour of white or pale yellow. In the Caucasus, and in the adjacent hill-country of Georgia, Armenia, Daghesten and Azerbaijan, extending into north-eastern Turkey and north-western Iran, the plants of this species have an acuminate leaf-tip, and in some variants, which have been named *S.kolenatiana* Regel, the petals are uniformly pink or crimson. It seems best to include all these plants under the subspecies *cartilaginea* (Willdenow) D.A. Webb, *Feddes Repertorium* 68:208 (1963). (Köhlein (1984, p. 81) attributed the combination *S.paniculata* subsp. *kolenatiana* to Webb, but this is an error.)

Turning now to the eleven endemic species of subsection *Kabschia*, we find that seven of them resemble *S.sancta* and *S.juniperifolia* in having yellow petals (white in one species) shorter than the stamens, or at most equalling them (series *Juniperifoliae*). All but one are found exclusively on rocks and scree-slopes in the Caucasus.

*Saxifraga caucasica* Sommier & Levier is intermediate between *S.juniperifolia* and *S.sancta*, having the marginal hairs confined to the base of the leaves, as in the former, but the hairless inflorescence of the latter.

*Saxifraga desoulavyi* Oettingen is close to *S.juniperifolia*, differing mainly in its flat-topped inflorescence (as in *S.sancta*), and its leaves, which are grooved above and keeled beneath.

*Saxifraga subverticillata* Boissier is of lax growth, with long leafy shoots, on which the leaves are arranged in irregular whorl-like groups, with bare stretches in between. The styles are remarkably long (up to 7mm).

*Saxifraga pseudolaevis* Oettingen, often erroneously grown under the name *S.laevis*, is fairly similar to *S.subverticillata* but more compact in habit, with relatively broad, oblong-obovate, mucronate leaves and a very compact inflorescence.

*Saxifraga scleropoda* Sommier & Levier has columnar leafy shoots densely clothed with small, overlapping, mucronate leaves, of which all but the uppermost are turned downwards. The inflorescence is long, with up to 19 flowers, all with very short pedicels.

*Saxifraga kotschyi* Boissier is not found in the Caucasus, except perhaps at its southern margin, but extends from central and eastern Turkey to north-western Iran. It is rather like *S.scleropoda*, but the leaves are larger, obtuse and not turned downwards, and the inflorescence is somewhat flat-topped, with fairly long pedicels to the lower flowers.

*Saxifraga artvinensis* Matthews is somewhat similar to *S.sancta*, but is unique in this group in having white petals. It also has longer pedicels and longer marginal hairs on the leaves. It is known only from north-eastern Turkey.

Finally, there are four species in which the petals are white or pink and longer than the stamens, and which show no close affinity to the *juniperifolia*-group but rather are more closely related to *S.marginata*, *S.lilacina* and their allies.

*Saxifraga iranica* Bornmüller is found on the Elburz range in northern Iran. It forms dense cushions of short, fat leafy shoots with closely overlapping leaves, which are broadly obovate, somewhat fleshy, 3–4mm long. The short flowering stem bears 3–6 flowers with petals up to 11mm long, which change from white to pink following pollination.

*Saxifraga wendelboi* Schönbeck-Temesy from northern and central Iran is very similar to *S.iranica*, but differs in its flowers, which have a more circular outline owing to the more broadly obovate petals.

*Saxifraga dinnikii* Schmalhausen occurs in the central Caucasus. It has fairly short leafy shoots with spreading, oblanceolate, acute or mucronate leaves up to 6mm long, usually curved downwards at the tip, and solitary flowers with purple petals.

*Saxifraga columnaris* Schmalhausen is known from only a few stations on the northern slopes of the eastern Caucasus. It is very distinct with its remarkably slender but fairly long leafy shoots, each clothed with minute, closely overlapping leaves rather like those of *S.diapensioides*, and terminating in a very short flowering stem bearing a single flower with white or pink petals.

The incompletely known species are: *S.koelzii* Schönbeck-Temesy (a species like *S.marginata*, but with pale yellow petals), and six others belonging to the *juniperifolia*-group: *S.carinata* Oettingen, *S.charadzeae* Otschiauri, *S.kusnezowiana* Oettingen, *S.mandenovae* Sojak, *S.ruprechtiana* Mandenova and *S. sosnowskyi* Mandenova.

Of the eleven endemic *Kabschia* species described above, *S.desoulavyi*, *S.subverticillata*, *S.pseudolaevis*, *S.kotschyi*, *S.iranica* and *S.wendelboi* are sometimes seen in cultivation, but from the decorative point of view, only *S.iranica* is in any way superior to their relatives in Europe.

Further details of most of the species mentioned in this chapter may be found in Horný *et al.* (1986).

# 8

# Asiatic species in cultivation

## (Himalayan region, China and Japan)

Almost all the Asiatic saxifrages that are in general cultivation belong to sections *Irregulares* or *Porphyrion*. Section *Irregulares* is one of the most distinctive groups of saxifrages and consists of about 15 species that are characterised by the extreme bilateral symmetry of the flowers. They are chiefly woodland plants with kidney-shaped to circular or ovate leaves, usually leafless flowering stems, and a superior or sub-superior ovary (rather like many species of section *Micranthes*). Several of them have been confused in the past and the whole group needs a taxonomic revision. There are two main centres of distribution, one in Japan and parts of neighbouring mainland Asia, and the other in south-western China at the eastern end of the Himalayan mountain chain. Only four species are in general cultivation; they flower in the summer or autumn, and need to be planted in a sheltered position because they are not reliably hardy.

*Saxifraga stolonifera* Meerburgh (*S.sarmentosa* Linnaeus fil.) is the most widespread species of its section, being the only one to extend from the Himalaya to Japan. It is probably the best-known species, with leaves that are dark green, hairy and marked with grey veins above, but reddish and hairless beneath. Its most prominent feature, however, is its slender, red runners, which root at intervals to generate new plants. The white flowers are borne in the autumn on a branched flowering stem up to 40cm tall, and consist of an upper set of 3 petals, which are about 3mm long and

ovate with red and yellow spots near the base, and a lower pair of unequal, narrowly elliptical petals 10–20mm long. Although usually seen as a house plant ('Mother of Thousands' or 'Strawberry Saxifrage'), there is at least one clone which is relatively hardy.

Very like *S.stolonifera*, but much smaller with flowering stems up to only about 10cm tall, is *S.cuscutiformis* C.Loddiges; it may be only a variant of *S.stolonifera* but is something of a puzzle because it is not known in the wild.

*Saxifraga veitchiana* I.B. Balfour from western China is similar to *S.stolonifera* in many respects, including the production of runners, but may be distinguished by its smaller size and green leaves which lack the grey veining. It produces flowering stems about 10cm tall in late summer and is rather hardier.

*Saxifraga cortusifolia* Siebold & Zuccarini is from Japan and differs from the preceding two species in a number of respects, perhaps the most obvious being that it usually lacks runners. Its leaves are fleshy and glossy green. The flowering stems are up to 40cm tall, and bear white flowers which have an upper set of 3 broadly ovate petals about 4mm long with yellow (rarely red) spots at the base, and a pair of very unequal, narrowly elliptical lower petals, the longer of which often hangs straight downwards.

*Saxifraga fortunei* J.D. Hooker (Figure 61) is another Japanese species and is often confused with *S.cortusifolia*. It differs in several characters, the most readily observable being the larger flowers, in which the upper petals are lanceolate or linear, gradually narrowed at the base, and not spotted. Furthermore, the seeds are smooth and not papillose as in *S.cortusifolia*. Other differences involve microscopic characters, including the inflorescence-hairs which are multiseriate instead of uniseriate as in *S.cortusifolia*. There are many variants present in gardens, mostly differing in leaf-shape and colour, and those with the foliage flushed red ('Rubrifolia' and 'Wada') are particularly attractive.

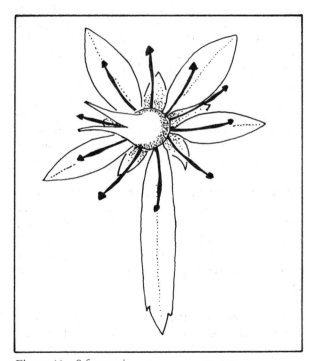

Figure 61. *S.fortunei*

The Asiatic species of section *Porphyrion* come mostly from the Sino–Himalayan region and a detailed account of nearly all of them is given by Horný *et al.* (1986). Only 12 of the 18 species claimed to be represented in collections have had their identities confirmed, but we expect these numbers to grow as more and more are introduced. They may be considered in three groups, in which the flower-colour ranges from red to white (never yellow).

The first group contains relatives of *S.marginata* and may be recognised by the leaves, which are alternate with recurved tips and usually with more than 5 lime-secreting hydathodes on the upper surface. The inflorescence may be branched (series *Marginatae*) or simple (series *Lilacinae*). The following species are in cultivation.

*Saxifraga stolitzkae* Duthie ex Engler & Irmscher grows on wet cliffs at elevations above 3000m in the mountains from Kumaun to Bhutan where it forms loose cushions, the leaves of which are 7–9mm long, with obtuse tips. The inflorescence is branched, with 4–7 flowers in which the sepals lack hydathodes, and the white or pink petals are 5–9mm long.

*Saxifraga cinerea* H. Smith is so similar to *S.stolitzkae* that Hara (1979) suggested that they could be united. However, the leaves are 9–12mm long, with acute tips, and the white petals are 8–10mm long. The only collection was made from a stony bank in Nepal at an elevation of 2700m.

*Saxifraga andersonii* Engler is a variable species in which the leaves are 5–10mm long, with subacute to obtuse, erect or recurved tips. The branched inflorescence bears up to 5 flowers, the sepals of which have 1–3 hydathodes, and the white or pale pink petals are 3–6mm long. It forms deep cushions or mats on rocky hillsides and river shingles in the mountains of Nepal, Bhutan and Tibet, usually at elevations above 3500m.

*Saxifraga alberti* Regel & Schmalhausen is somewhat like *S.andersonii* but the white petals are 6–7mm long. It is a native of the Pamir mountains at the western edge of the Himalayan ranges at elevations of 2200–2600m.

*Saxifraga lilacina* Duthie is widespread in the western Himalaya at elevations of 2800–4500m, where it forms cushions, the leaves of which are 3–5mm long. The flowers are borne singly on stalks, and have lilac petals 8–11mm long. Introduced to gardens early this century it is a parent of many important *Kabschia* cultivars.

*Saxifraga poluniniana* H. Smith is found in cultivation usually as var. **poluniniana**; it has leaves 5–6mm long, and stalked, solitary flowers with petals 10mm long, white, changing to pink. It is found on shady rock-faces at elevations of 3300–3500m in Nepal.

Also belonging to this group but whose presence in cultivation requires confirmation are *S.afghanica* Aitchinson & Hemsley and *S. clivorum* H. Smith.

The second group of species belongs to series *Subsessiliflorae* and is characterised by alternate leaves, each with a thickened, truncate tip bearing a hydathode sunk into it; sometimes there may also be two, much smaller, subsidiary hydathodes. The flowers are solitary and without (or occasionally with very short) stalks.

*Saxifraga pulvinaria* H. Smith makes a neat, dense cushion with columnar leafy shoots, the leaves of which are 2–4mm long. The flowers bear sepals, which are as long as broad or longer and lack a hydathode, and white petals 4–5 × 2–3mm. It grows on hillsides at elevations of 4000–6000m from Kashmir to Nepal.

*Saxifraga lolaensis* H. Smith is like *S.pulvinaria* but has sepals which are broader than long and have a hydathode near the tip. The creamy-white petals are 3.5 × 4.5mm and have a short, distinct claw. It has been collected from cliff-faces in Tibet at 3900m, and is doubtfully present in Nepal.

*Saxifraga hypostoma* H. Smith is another species similar to *S.pulvinaria*, but may be distinguished easily by the leaves whose tips have a membranous margin fringed with hairs. The sepals have a hydathode, and the white petals are 4 × 4mm. This is a Nepalese endemic, occurring high up in the mountains on rock ledges and screes at elevations of 4300–5250m.

*Saxifraga lowndesii* H. Smith is a much more sprawling plant and forms mats, the leaves of which are 5–7mm long. The sepals are slightly broader than long and the rose-lilac petals are 7 × 7mm. Also from Nepal, it occurs on wet rocks on steep hillsides at about 4000m.

*S.matta-florida* H. Smith belongs to this group and may be in cultivation but this needs to be confirmed.

The third group of species is closely related to the preceding series but is distinguished by its opposite leaves and consists of the Himalayan relatives of *S.oppositifolia*. Four or five species are in cultivation, but the identities of two or three of them are uncertain.

*Saxifraga vacillans* H. Smith is known only from the type gathering, which was made at about 4000m on a wet cliff-face in Bhutan, where it forms mats in which the leaves may be alternate on young, vigorous shoots; where they are opposite, the margins of each leaf-pair meet at an acute angle and are fringed with hairs or teeth at the base; the laminae are 3.5–5mm long with 3–7 hydathodes. The inflorescence has 1–2 flowers, the white petals of which are 5–6mm long. *S.duthiei* Gandoger, whose leaf arrangement is similar, is one of those species requiring confirmation.

*Saxifraga alpigena* H. Smith is found in Nepal at elevations of 3500–4200m where it forms deep cushions on rocky hillsides and river shingles. The margins of the opposite leaves are completely confluent and entire, with the laminae 1.5–2.5mm long, with 1 hydathode. The flowers are solitary on short stalks, with white petals 6mm long. Another species with a similar leaf configuration and which has been claimed to be in cultivation is *S.georgei* Anthony, but again, this needs to be confirmed.

*Saxifraga quadrifaria* Engler & Irmscher comes from Nepal and neighbouring Tibet at elevations of about 3000m. Plants with this name are sometimes met with in collections, but unfortunately the key characters noted by Smith (1958) do not match in detail with the description provided by Engler & Irmscher (1919). The problem is whether the margins of the leaf-pairs meet at an acute angle and have a fringe of hairs or teeth at the base, or whether the margins are confluent and entire. Smith claimed the former (although he did not see the type specimen and expressed reservations), whereas Engler & Irmscher said the leaves were glabrous and provided an illustration showing the leaves meeting at an *acute* angle! In most of the plants in cultivation, the margins of the leaf-pairs seem to be confluent and entire, but until the type specimen can be consulted, the problem of the application of the name must remain.

Another set of saxifrages with its headquarters in the Himalayan region is section *Ciliatae*. Although it contains about 150 species, only a tiny fraction is in cultivation. One of the reasons for this is that most of them are difficult to grow and they die out easily; thus only about six species are met with in collections outside botanic gardens. Three belong to the group of species closely allied to *S.hirculus* (series *Hirculoideae*), one produces summer-dormant buds in its leaf-axils and belongs to series *Gemmiparae*, and two produce runners and may therefore be assigned to the *S.flagellaris* group (series *Flagellares*).

**Saxifraga hookeri** Engler & Irmscher is very similar in appearance to *S.hirculus* but differs in its sepals, the veins of which converge to a point near the tip, rather than remaining separate as in *S.hirculus*. It grows at elevations of 3600–4700m in the eastern Himalaya and southern Tibet.

**Saxifraga diversifolia** Wallich ex Seringe is a distinctive but variable species from western China and Kashmir to Bhutan and southern Tibet, where it grows in woods and among shady rocks at elevations of 2600–5300m. It produces branched, leafy flowering stems up to 20cm tall, which bear golden to dull yellow flowers. The basal leaves are 1.5–3cm long and almost as wide, cordate and with long petioles; both laminae and petioles decrease in size up the stem, the petioles ultimately disappearing. Several varieties have been described which link the species to others in the series, and the complex needs a taxonomic revision.

**Saxifraga cardiophylla** Franchet is similar in height and in the shape of its leaves, but differs in that the cauline leaves are larger, not smaller, than the basal leaves. The inflorescence is sparingly branched and bears 4–8 orange-yellow flowers. It inhabits meadows at about 3500m in Sikkim, Sichuan and Yunnan.

**Saxifraga strigosa** Wallich, which belongs to series *Gemmiparae*, characterised by summer-dormant buds in the axils of the leaves, has an unbranched, leafy flowering stem whose leaves are toothed at the tip. It ranges from northern India and western China through the Himalaya to upper Burma, at elevations of 2800–4600m.

**Saxifraga brunonis** Wallich ex Seringe (*S. brunoniana* Wallich, *nomen nudum*) is a species with glabrous runners. It differs from *S.flagellaris* in its shorter sepals, 2–2.5mm long, $\frac{1}{3}$ to $\frac{1}{4}$ the length of the petals. It grows between 3300 and 4300m, from Kashmir to Bhutan and southern Tibet.

**Saxifraga mucronulata** Royle is similar and differs from *S.flagellaris* in its densely glandular-hairy runners, and petals which are only twice as long as the sepals. Most of the plants in cultivation belong to subsp. **sikkimensis** (Hultén) Hara, which occurs in the eastern Himalaya and southern Tibet.

Finally, there is one Asiatic representative of section *Micranthes* to be found in gardens.

**Saxifraga manschuriensis** (Engler) Komarov is a native of Manchuria and Korea, and is like *S.nelsoniana* in its general appearance, but is distinguished by its larger size, congested inflorescence and filaments which grow to about 6mm, exceeding the petals as the flowers mature.

# 9
# North American species

There are about 65 species of *Saxifraga* in North America: about 40 in the west, 8 in the east, and 16 which cross from Europe to the Arctic and often thence extend southwards in the mountains of the east or west. One species is endemic in Greenland. Ten sections are represented in all, by far the largest being section *Micranthes*, which has about 40 species. The other sections tally as follow: sections *Ciliatae* and *Mesogyne* (six species each), section *Trachyphyllum* (five species), sections *Porphyrion* and *Saxifraga* (two species each), and there is one species in each of sections *Merkianae*, *Heterisia*, *Ligulatae* and *Xanthizoon*. In the interests of brevity, the accounts that follow are comparative only in respect of a few basic characters; species are often described in relation to close relatives, with distinguishing features pointed out. Sufficient synonymy is given to enable the reader to follow recent Floras and the account by Engler & Irmscher (1916, 1919). The chromosome counts are published records based on North American populations, except for those marked with an asterisk, which are based on Asiatic material.

## Section *Ciliatae* Haworth
## (see p. 39 )

The six species of this section are found largely in the Arctic or subarctic, centred chiefly in Alaska.

*Saxifraga hirculus* Linnaeus (see p. 39 )
The European variant, subsp. *hirculus*, is circumpolar and is apparently consistently tetraploid ($2n = 32$). Diploid ($2n = 16$) populations that have smaller leaves and smaller flowers (about 15mm diameter) with rounded petals, are known from north-eastern Siberia, arctic North America (one outlier in Colorado) and Greenland, and these have been distinguished as subsp. *propinqua* (R. Brown) Löve & Löve.

*Saxifraga flagellaris* Willdenow (see pp. 41 & 263)
This is a highly polymorphic, circumpolar species in which Hultén (1964) has recognised ten subspecies, although Hara (1979) assigned two of these from the Himalayan flora to related species. Three subspecies occur in North America and intermediates are found where their ranges overlap.

The diploid subsp. *setigera* (Pursh) Tolmatchev ($2n = 16$) is very similar to the Caucasian subsp. *flagellaris* in its shallow hypanthium and superior ovary, but differs in its runners, which have glandular hairs (sometimes sparsely so); and in its cauline leaves, which are shorter than the internodes. It ranges from Siberia through Alaska and the Yukon to southern British Columbia; it also occurs in central Asia and China.

The other two subspecies are tetraploid ($2n = 32$). Subsp. *platysepala* (Trautvetter) Porsild differs from subsp. *setigera* in its broader sepals, which are ovate, obtuse and overlapping at the base; and in its hypanthium, which forms a characteristic lump beneath the sepals owing to the partially inferior ovary. Its cauline leaves are longer than the internodes. It has an arctic-circumpolar distribution, just extending into Europe (see p. 41).

Subsp. *crandallii* (Gandoger) Hultén is very similar to subsp. *platysepala*. It differs in its smaller, funnel-shaped hypanthium, which bears white, glandular hairs (as well as the more usual, black hairs); and in its narrower, upright petals. It is found in the Rocky Mountains from Montana southwards to New Mexico and Arizona.

*Saxifraga serpyllifolia* Pursh, *Flora Americae septentrionalis* 1:310 (1814). TYPE: Northwest coast of America, Cape Newnham, *D. Nelson*. (Holotype: British Museum (**BM**).)
A mat-forming plant, with leafy shoots arising from the axils of the lower basal leaves. Leaves 3–9mm long, spathulate, entire, fleshy, sessile. Flowering stems 2–8cm, sparingly leafy. Flowers usually solitary. Petals yellow, or rarely purple (var. *purpurea* Hultén), 4–7mm long, obovate with a short claw. Flowering season: July to August. $2n = 16^*$.

Wet sandy or gravelly places, or rocky ledges, from arctic Siberia and Japan through montane Alaska and the Yukon southwards to British Columbia.

*Saxifraga chrysantha* A. Gray, *Proceedings of the American Academy of Arts and Sciences* 12:83 (1877). TYPE: Colorado; three syntypes (*Parry 164*, *Parry 166* (both 1861) and *Hall & Harbour 199* (1862) are in the herbarium of Harvard University (**GH**) *S.serpyllifolia* subsp. *chrysantha* (A. Gray) W.A. Weber
Closely related to *S.serpyllifolia* and differing only in its slightly more oblong sepals which are reflexed (rather than ascending); its nearly hairless (rather than hairy) leaves; and its golden (rather than pale) yellow flowers. Flowering season: July to August.

Talus slopes, often near snow-banks or wet flushes, in the Rocky mountains of (Montana?), Utah, Wyoming, Colorado and New Mexico.

*Saxifraga aleutica* Hultén, *Svensk Botanisk Tidskrift* 30:522, Figure 4 (1936). TYPE: Aleutian Islands, Rat Island, 1.vii.1932, *Hultén 5977*. (Lectotype: Smithsonian Institute (**US**), designated here.)
A mat-forming plant arising from a tap-root. Leaves 2–5mm long, oblong to oblanceolate, entire, fleshy, without marginal hairs. Flowering stems 0.5–2.5cm, leafless. Flowers solitary, with greenish-yellow petals 2.5–3.5mm long, about equalling the sepals. Flowering season: July and August.

Gravelly soils on mountain tops in the Aleutian Islands.

*Saxifraga eschscholtzii* Sternberg, *Revisio Saxifragarum, Supplementum* I, 9 (1822). TYPE: Syntypes collected from St Lawrence Bay by Chamisso and Eschscholtz are at Leningrad (**LE**).
Forming rounded cushions. Leaves 1–3mm long, oblong to obovate, densely imbricate; the margins fringed with bristles. Flowering stems scarcely 1cm, leafless. Flowers solitary, with deciduous, yellow, white or pink petals. Dioecious. Flowering season: June. $2n = 12$.

Rock-ledges, cliffs and gravelly spits, from the Yukon and Alaska westwards to eastern Siberia.

# Section *Merkianae* (Engler & Irmscher) Gornall

This section has a superior ovary composed of carpels united to at least half-way. It has been segregated from section *Micranthes* because of its lack of crystals in the leaves, and its ovules with 2 integuments.

*Saxifraga tolmiei* Torrey & A. Gray, *A Flora of North America* 1:567 (1840). TYPE: Ex dupl. Hook. 1838; North West coast, *Tolmie*. (Lectotype: Harvard University (**GH**), designated here.)
A mat-forming plant, slightly woody at the base, with numerous leafy stems. Leaves entire, cylindrical or slightly revolute, 3–10mm long, spathulate or oblanceolate,

tapering to an indistinct petiole, with (var. *tolmiei*) or without (var. *ledifolia* (Greene) Engler & Irmscher) a few long hairs at the base. (The latter is the common variant of the species in California.) Flowering stems 3–12cm, leafy, bearing 1–4 flowers in a lax cyme. Petals 3–6mm long, up to twice as long as sepals, spathulate to broadly oblanceolate, white. Filaments club-shaped. Capsule streaked or spotted with purple. Flowering season: July to August. $2n = 30$.

Wet meadows or tundra, on scree-slopes or in rock-crevices, 1000–3000m. From Alaska southwards in the coastal mountains and Sierra Nevada to central California; also in the Bitterroot mountains of Montana and Idaho.

## Section *Micranthes* (Haworth) D.Don (see p. 47)

This is the largest and potentially most confusing group of saxifrages in North America. However, it is possible to recognise four subsections on the basis of a number of characters, the most important of which is the surface of the seeds, whose ribs may be ribbon-like or papillose, and whose cuticle may be knobbly, striate or diffusely wrinkled. Fortunately there are also larger features that are more easily apprehended, which are fairly well correlated with the nature of the seed surface and which can be used to place a species in its subsection with a reasonable degree of reliability. These are described at the appropriate points below.

## Subsection *Stellares* (Engler & Irmscher) Gornall

This subsection can be readily distinguished from the others by its prominently bracteate inflorescence, multiseriate glandular hairs, flowers with superior ovaries composed of carpels united to half-way and, often, irregular corollas, and seeds with papillose ribs and a knobbly cuticle. The filaments are always linear or awl-shaped. There are five North American species, including the European

*Saxigraga stellaris* Linnaeus (p. 55), which has three stations in eastern, subarctic Canada, and *Saxifraga foliolosa* R. Brown, an arctic and Rocky mountain plant which also occurs in Europe (p. 58).

*Saxifraga ferruginea* Graham, *Edinburgh new philosophical Journal* 7:349 (1829). TYPE: described from plants grown at Edinburgh from seed sent by *Richardson* in 1827 and flowered in September 1829. (Holotype: Edinburgh (**E**).)
*S.newcombei* (Small) Engler & Irmscher
A variable species. Leaves with lamina 1.5–5 (–10)cm long, spathulate to oblanceolate, tapering to a broad, indistinct petiole; margin sharply but irregularly toothed. Flowering stems 10–30cm. Inflorescence a diffuse panicle in which the flowers are sometimes replaced by bulbils (var. *macounii* Engler & Irmscher). Petals 3–5mm, the upper 3 clawed, with 2 yellow spots, the lower 2 elliptic-spathulate, not clawed, unspotted. Flowering season: usually July to August. $2n = 20, 38$.

Moist rocks and seepage slopes, 1500–2500m; from southern Alaska southwards through the Coast Ranges and Cascade Mountains to north-western California; also from the Rocky Mountains of eastern British Columbia to northern Idaho and western Montana.

*Saxifraga michauxii* Britton, *Memoirs of the Torrey botanical Club* 4:118 (1894). TYPE: Not traced.
*S.leucanthemifolia* of Michaux, not of Lapeyrouse
Much like *S.ferruginea* (and even more like *S.clusii*!), but distinguished by the larger coarser teeth (4–8 on each side) of its leaves. Flowering season: June to early September.

Moist rocks and seepage slopes in the Appalachians from Maryland to north-western Georgia.

*Saxifraga bryophora* A. Gray, *Proceedings of the American Academy of Arts and Sciences* 6:533 (1865). TYPE: California, Ebbett's pass, 1.viii.1863. *W.H. Brewer 1984*. (Lectotype: Harvard University (**GH**), designated here.)

Winter-dormant. Leaves with lamina 1–4cm long, oblong-oblanceolate to linear oblong, sessile; margin entire or minutely toothed. Flowering stems 5–20cm. Inflorescence laxly branched, the pedicels mostly deflexed, with bulbils. Petals 3–5mm, elliptical, clawed, with 2 yellow basal spots. Flowering season: July to August.

Wet, sandy or gravelly meadows and ledges, 1600–4500m, in the Sierra Nevada of California.

## Subsection *Cuneifoliatae* A.M. Johnson

This is a variable, poorly studied group, many species of which strongly resemble those in subsections *Micranthes* and *Rotundifoliatae*. It may be distinguished by its uniseriate, glandular hairs; its regular flowers, which have ovaries that are ¼ to ½ inferior, composed of carpels united up to half their length; and its filaments, which are linear or awl-shaped. Many of the species also have capsules which are dark purple or black at maturity. The principal distinctions, however, may be found on the seeds, which have ribbon-like ribs and a finely striate cuticle. Most of the species are Asiatic, centred in China, but about five occur in the Soviet Far East, three of them crossing into North America.

***Saxifraga nudicaulis*** D. Don, *Transactions of the Linnean Society of London* 13:366 (1822) TYPE: Northwest coast of America [Alaska], Sledge Island, *D. Nelson*. (Holotype: British Museum (**BM**).)
Like a diminutive *S.nelsoniana* but distinguished by markedly expanded petiole-bases, and flowering stems that are produced at the ends of slender runners. Leaves 1.5–4.5cm long. Flowering stems 5–16cm. Petals 4–5mm, white, cream or pink, elliptical. Flowering season: July. $2n = 40^*$.

Wet flushes in western Alaska and eastern Siberia.

***Saxifraga calycina*** Sternberg, *Revisio Saxifragarum, Supplementum* II, 10 (1831). TYPE: Not traced.
*S.davurica* of North American authors, but not of Willdenow
Leaves 1.5–4.5cm long (more than three times the width), obovate, coarsely toothed at the apex, tapering gradually to a broad petiole. Flowering stems 3–15cm. Inflorescence conical, only the lower flower-stalks branched (if at all). Petals 2–2.5mm long, elliptical with an indistinct claw. Carpels conical at maturity. Flowering season: June to August. $2n = 24^*$.

Wet flushes and by streams in the mountains of Alaska, the Yukon and eastern Siberia.

***Saxifraga unalaschensis*** Sternberg, *Revisio Saxifragarum, Supplementum* II, 9 (1831). TYPE: Unalaska, *Chamisso*. (Syntype: Leningrad (**LE**).)
*S.calycina* subsp. *unalaschensis* (Sternberg) Hultén
*S.davurica* var. *unalaschensis* (Sternberg) Engler
*S.davurica* of North American authors, but not of Willdenow
Like *S.calycina* but differing in its larger, broader, clawed petals; its ovoid carpels; and its shorter, broader petioles, with leaves less than three times as long as wide. Flowering season: July to August.

Wet flushes and by streams in tundra along the coast of western Alaska and the Aleutian Islands.

## Subsection *Micranthes* (Haworth) Gornall

This is the third, and largest, subsection of section *Micranthes*. Containing about 29 North American species (22 in the west and seven in the east), it can be distinguished by its ovary composed of carpels whose ovuliferous portions are wholly free (in other subsections they are at least partially united), its uniseriate, glandular hairs, regular flowers, and seeds with ribbon-like or papillose ribs and a diffusely wrinkled cuticle. On the basis of a correlation (admittedly imperfect) between the position of the ovary, the morphology of the nectary tissue, the presence of non-glandular, rufous hairs in the axils of the basal leaves (and often on the leaves themselves, especially when young) and the amount of toothing on the leaf-margin, we have grouped the species into three series, roughly along the lines adopted by Engler & Irmscher (1916). We suspect, however, that some of the species may be misplaced and that further observations may reveal their affinities more clearly. The work on some of the species by Elvander (1984) has been particularly useful in preparing this account.

## Series *Aulaxis* (Haworth) Gornall

Distinguished by a superior ovary, with carpels united only at the base, a thick, fleshy nectary-disc united to the outer walls of the carpels from the base to nearly half-way up, and rufous hairs often but not always present in the axils of the prominently toothed basal leaves.

*Saxifraga micranthidifolia* (Haworth) Steudel, *Nomenclator botanicus* 136 (1821). TYPE: Not traced.

Like *S.michauxii* in general appearance but usually larger. Leaves with lamina up to 35cm long, lanceolate to oblanceolate, coarsely to rather finely, but irregularly toothed, tapering to an indistinct petiole. Flowering stems 30–75cm. Petals 1.5–3.5mm, equal, elliptical to spathulate, narrowed to a short claw, with a yellow spot, shorter than stamens. Filaments club-shaped. Flowering season: May and June. $2n = 22$.

Moist rocks, seepage slopes and banks of streams in the mountains from New Jersey to Georgia.

## Series *Dermasea* (Haworth) Gornall

Distinguished by a superior to usually less than half inferior ovary (more so in one or two species) of carpels that are bottle-shaped at maturity and free nearly to the base, and which have a poorly developed, narrow, swollen band of nectary tissue at the base. The axils, and sometimes the undersides of the laminae, of the basal leaves often have at least a few rufous, non-glandular hairs, and their margins are usually conspicuously and sharply toothed. The series contains about 14 North American representatives, including a pair of arctic species, *Saxifraga nivalis* Linnaeus and *Saxifraga tenuis* (Wahlenberg) H. Smith, which also occur in Europe (p. 50). For convenience, the remaining species are here split into an eastern group and a western group, although we realise that this may not necessarily be a completely natural arrangement.

### *The Eastern Group*

This is a somewhat disparate set of five species which occupies two principal areas: the Appalachians and a zone west of the Mississippi river centred on the Ozark mountains. The taxonomy of the first three species has been discussed by Steyermark (1959), whom we follow.

*Saxifraga virginiensis* Michaux, *Flora Boreali-Americana* 1:269 (1803). TYPE: Plate 222, Figure 5 in *Phytographia*, part 3 (Plukenet 1692).

Closely allied to *S.occidentalis* and its relatives in the west. Leaves with lamina up to 9cm long, ovate to elliptical, tapering to a short, broad petiole; margin crenately to more sharply toothed. Flowering stems 6–50cm. Inflorescence conical, congested. Petals 3–6mm, elliptical to spathulate, unspotted, mostly 2- to 3-times as long as the sepals. Filaments linear to awl-shaped. Flowering season: March to May. $2n = 20, 28, 38$ (sometimes with supernumeraries).

Mossy rocks in woodland clearings from New Brunswick, Quebec and Minnesota southwards to Georgia, Alabama and Mississippi.

*Saxifraga palmeri* B.F. Bush, *American Midland Naturalist* 11:220 (1928). TYPE: Arkansas, Van Buren Co., four collections by *E.J. Palmer*

(*20731*, 10.iv.1922; *29710*, 19.iv.1926; *s.n.*, 29.iv.1922; *21020*, 30.iv.1922). (Syntypes: Arnold Arboretum (**A**).)

*S.virginiensis* var. *subintegra* Goodman

Like *S.virginiensis* but with entire to subentire leaves, more or less hairless pedicels, and mainly non-glandular hairs on the flowering stem. Flowering season: April and May.

Rocky, woodland glades in western Arkansas and eastern Oklahoma.

*Saxifraga texana* Buckley, *Proceedings of the Academy of Natural Sciences of Philadelphia* 1861:455 (1862). TYPE: 'Prairies, northeastern Texas', iii.1860 or 1861, *Buckley*. (Holotype: Academy of Natural Sciences of Philadelphia (**PH**).)

Leaves with lamina broadly ovate to ovate-oblong, tapering abruptly to a distinct petiole; margin more or less entire. Flowering stems up to 15cm. Inflorescence contracted into several compact cymules. Flowers with 3 or 4 carpels. Petals 2–3.5mm, broadly elliptical to obovate, tapering at the base to a broad claw, usually only slightly exceeding the sepals. Filaments linear to awl-shaped. Flowering season: late February to April.

Sandy bottom-lands and rocky, woodland glades, from south-western Missouri and adjacent Kansas southwards through Arkansas and Oklahoma to north-eastern Texas.

*Saxifraga caroliniana* A. Gray, *Memoirs of the American Academy of Arts and Sciences*, new series, 3:39 (1848). TYPE: Pl. e Mt. Carol. 1843. *A. Gray*. (Holotype: Harvard University (**GH**).)

Leaves with lamina to 14cm long, ovate to slightly obovate, tapering abruptly to a distinct petiole; margin coarsely to more finely toothed. Flowering stems 10–50cm. Inflorescence laxly branched. Petals 3–4mm, ovate, clawed, spotted. Filaments club-shaped. Flowering season: late April to June.

Wet flushes and stream-sides in the mountains from south-western Virginia, through North Carolina, to eastern Tennessee and Kentucky.

*Saxifraga careyana* A. Gray, *London Journal of Botany* 2:116 (1843). TYPE: In monte Grandfather dicto, Carolinae Septentrionalis. vii. 1841. *A. Gray & J. Carey.* (Lectotype: Harvard University (**GH**), designated here.)

*S.tennesseensis* Small

Like *S.caroliniana* but usually smaller. Laminae of basal leaves with at least some rufous hairs beneath. Petals more spathulate, unspotted. Filaments awl-shaped. Flowering season: May and June.

Wet flushes and stream-sides in the mountains of south-western Virginia, North Carolina and eastern Tennessee.

## The Western Group

The following taxa represent an exceedingly variable complex, which stretches from Alaska to Mexico. Although they sometimes intergrade in areas of contact, it appears that they largely replace one another as they extend southwards. Most are treated here as species, although the rank of subspecies may be more appropriate for some of them. They are described below in approximate geographical sequence, from north to south.

*Saxifraga reflexa* W.J. Hooker, *Flora Boreali-Americana* 1:249 (1832). TYPE: Arctic Sea, *Dr Richardson*. (Holotype: Kew (**K**); isotype: British Museum (**BM**).)

Leaves with lamina 1–2cm long, orbicular to ovate, oblanceolate or spathulate, tapering, sometimes abruptly, to a well-defined, broad petiole, with rufous hairs sometimes present in the axil; margin coarsely toothed; upper surface finely pubescent with short, greyish hairs, the lower surface often purplish. Flowering stems 9–60cm. Inflorescence lax, somewhat flat-topped. Petals 2–3mm long, shorter than or equalling the sepals, elliptic-oblong, without a claw, white with 2 yellow spots below the middle. Filaments club-shaped. Flowering season: June and July.

Tundra, heathland and open woods, from Alaska eastwards to the Yukon and southwards to northern British Columbia.

*Saxifraga occidentalis* S. Watson, *Proceedings of the American Academy of Arts and Sciences* 23:264 (1888). TYPE: British Columbia, Yale Mt., 17.v.1875, *J. Macoun* (Specimen A). (Lectotype: National Museum of Canada (**CAN**), designated by Krause & Beamish (1972).)

*S.reflexa* subsp. *occidentalis* (S. Watson) Hultén

*S.gormanii* Suksdorf

Leaves with lamina 1.5–3(–6)cm long, ovate, elliptical or rhombic, tapering abruptly to a distinct petiole, with rufous hairs in the axil and sometimes also on the upper or lower surface; margin usually coarsely and unevenly toothed. Flowering stems 8–20(–30)cm. Inflorescence lax to congested, pyramidal to rounded at the top, with flowers in clusters at the ends of strongly ascending branches. Plants with stiffly divaricate branching and more regular toothing of the leaf-margins have been distinguished as var. *dentata* (Engler & Irmscher) C.L. Hitchcock (*S.gormanii* Suksdorf). Petals 1.5–3.5mm long, exceeding sepals, ovate to oblong, sometimes narrowed to a claw, unspotted. Filaments linear or slightly club-shaped. Flowering season: late April to August. $2n = 20, 38, 40, 56, 58$.

Wet flushes and meadows, through British Columbia and the Rocky mountains of Alberta, south to Washington, north-eastern Oregon, Idaho, Montana and south-western Saskatchewan, then in the Rockies south to north-western Wyoming; var. *dentata* is disjunct in the Coast Range of northern and central Oregon, and in the lower Columbia River Gorge.

*Saxifraga rufidula* (Small) Macoun, *Ottawa Naturalist* 20:62 (1906). TYPE: Vancouver Island, Mt Finlayson, 17.v.1887, *J. Macoun*. (Holotype: National Museum of Canada (**CAN**).)

*S.occidentalis* subsp. *rufidula* (Small) Bacigalupi

*S.occidentalis* var. *rufidula* (Small) C.L. Hitchcock

Like *S.occidentalis* but basal leaves sharply and evenly toothed and often densely covered with rufous hairs beneath. Flowering stem usually less than 15cm. Inflorescence lax, flat-topped, tinged with purple; bracts and calyces often with rufous hairs. Filaments linear to awl-shaped. Flowering season: late April to early August. $2n = 20, 38, 56, 58$.

Wet, rocky ledges and seepage slopes in the Coast Range and western Cascades from southern British Columbia to north-western Oregon and the Columbia River Gorge; also from the Cascades of central Oregon to north-western California.

*Saxifraga marshallii* Greene, *Pittonia* 1:159 (1888). TYPE: California, Humboldt Co., Hoopa Valley, iv.1887, *C.C. Marshall*. (Holotype: University of Notre Dame (**NDG**).)

Like *S.occidentalis* but lamina ovate or oblong-ovate to elliptic-oblong, often with rufous hairs beneath; margin sharply and evenly toothed. Plants with leaves whose lamina is more ovate than oblong and whose petiole is only up to 1.5 times as long as the lamina (rather than up to 3 times as long) are distinguished as subsp. *idahoensis* (Piper) Krause & Beamish. Inflorescence lax, pyramidal, divaricate, with flowers not usually clustered at the ends of branches. Petals 2.5–4.5mm, about as long as sepals, narrowed to a claw, with 2 yellow spots at the base. Filaments strongly club-shaped. Flowering season: May and June. $2n = 20$.

Subsp. *marshallii* grows in deep shade by water-courses at elevations of 100–1500m in the Coast Ranges of western Oregon and north-western California; subsp. *idahoensis* is found on open or partly shaded, moist rock-ledges and slopes up to 2500m, from north-eastern Oregon, through central Idaho to western Montana, and also on the eastern slopes of the Cascades in central Washington.

*Saxifraga howellii* Greene, *Pittonia* 2:163 (1897). TYPE: Oregon, Coquelle River, 20.iv.1891, *Howell*. (Holotype: University of Notre Dame (**NDG**).)

Like *S.occidentalis* but usually smaller. Leaves with lamina 1–2cm long, oblong to ovate, tapering to a distinct petiole, with rufous hairs beneath; margin sharply and evenly toothed. Inflorescence lax, with few-flowered cymules. Petals 2.5–4.5mm, oblong, unspotted. Filaments linear to awl-shaped. Flowering season: March to May.

Damp rock-ledges and crevices, below 900m, from south-western Oregon to northern California.

**Saxifraga eriophora** S. Watson, *Proceedings of the American Academy of Arts and Sciences* 17:372 (1882). TYPE: Arizona, N. slope Santa Catalina Mts. 8000ft. alt. 2.v.1881. *Lemmon.* (Holotype: Harvard University (**GH**).)
Like *S.occidentalis* but leaves with lamina up to 1.5cm long, ovate to elliptical, tapering gradually to a distinct petiole, with dense, rufous hairs beneath. Inflorescence lax, flat-topped. Hypanthium campanulate rather than bowl-shaped, partially free from the ovary. Petals up to 4mm long, spathulate to oblong, without claws, pinkish. Filaments awl-shaped. Ovary more than half-inferior. Flowering season: April and May.

At about 2700m on the northern slopes of the Santa Catalina mountains in Arizona.

**Saxifraga mexicana** Engler & Irmscher, *Pflanzenreich* 67 (IV.117):42,43 (1916). TYPE: Mexico, Chihuahua, near Colonia Garcia, alt. 7500ft, 17.vii.1899, *Townsend & Barber 88.* (Lectotype: Kew (**K**), designated here.)
Like *S.occidentalis* but leaves often with a larger lamina, 3–6cm long, tapering, sometimes abruptly, to a broad petiole, rufous-hairy beneath; margin toothed or crenate. Inflorescence cylindrical, with flowers in tight clusters. Hypanthium campanulate. Petals up to 4mm long, oblong to spathulate. Flowering season: July to September.

At elevations of 2000–3000m in the northern ranges of the Sierra Madre Occidental, Mexico.

# Series *Micranthes* (Haworth) Gornall

Series *Micranthes* is characterised by an ovary which is usually more than half inferior and with a nectary-disc which is broad, fleshy, lobed or convoluted at the base, and mostly covers the ovuliferous portion of each carpel; by the lack of rufous, non-glandular hairs; and by the leaf-margins which are usually more or less entire. The filaments are linear to awl-shaped. All 12 species in this series occur in North America, with one of them, *Saxifraga hieracifolia* Willdenow, having a chiefly arctic distribution and thereby extending into Europe (see p.48).

**Saxifraga apetala** Piper, *Bulletin of the Torrey Botanical Club* 27:393 (1900). TYPE: Washington, Cascades of Kittitas, Chelan and King Counties, *Vasey 292.* (Isotype: Washington State University (**WS**).)
*S.integrifolia* var. *apetala* (Piper) M.E. Jones
*S.columbiana* var. *apetala* (Piper) Engler & Irmscher
Leaves with lamina 2–5cm long, narrowly to broadly ovate, tapering to a distinct petiole; margin entire. Flowering stems 6–15cm. Inflorescence 1–3cm long, congested, ovoid to cylindrical. Petals usually absent. Flowering season: March to August. $2n = 76$.

Spring-wet meadows and wet places at 600–2800m, on the eastern slopes of the Washington Cascades, and in western Montana.

**Saxifraga integrifolia** W.J. Hooker, *Flora Boreali-Americana* 1:249 (1833). TYPE: Near the mouth of the Columbia River, north-west coast of America, *Scouler.* (Lectotype: Kew (**K**), designated by Elvander (1984).)
Like *S.apetala* but rhizome with bulbils; leaves with lamina tapering abruptly, margin entire to minutely toothed; and flowering stems 15–30cm. Inflorescence 3–9cm, compact to rather lax, capitate to conical. Petals 2–4mm, obovate. Flowering season: March to May. $2n = 38$.

Spring-wet, mossy or grassy hillsides or bluffs, to 1000m, from Vancouver Island and

Plate 52.    *S.petraea*

Plate 53.   *S. arachnoidea* (Val di Lorina, Giudicarian Alps)

Plate 54.   *S.depressa*

Plate 55.   *S.seguieri*

Plate 56.   *S.latepetiolata*

Plate 57.   *S.muscoides*

Plate 58. *S.presolanensis*

Plate 59. *S.tenella*

Plate 60. *S.blavii*

coastal British Columbia southwards (mainly west of the Cascades) to northern California.

***Saxifraga nidifica*** Greene *Erythea* 1:222 (1893). TYPE: California, above Donner Lake, 20.vii.1893, *Greene*. (Lectotype: University of Notre Dame (**NDG**), designated by Elvander (1984).)
*S.columbiana* Piper
*S.integrifolia* var. *columbiana* (Piper) C.L. Hitchcock
*S.integrifolia* var. *leptopetala* (Suksdorf) Engler & Irmscher
*S.integrifolia* var. *claytoniifolia* (Canby ex Small) Rosendahl
*S.fragosa* Suksdorf ex Small
Two varieties are recognised. Var. ***nidifica*** is like *S.integrifolia* but with a cylindrical inflorescence bearing flowers in compact clusters, and with petals less than 2mm long, usually equalling or shorter than sepals. Var. ***claytoniifolia*** (Canby ex Small) Elvander is similar but lacks a bulbiliferous rhizome and has leaves with lamina 5–8cm long, broadly ovate to deltoid; a lax, conical inflorescence 7–15cm tall; and petals 2–3mm, longer than sepals, ovate, elliptical to orbicular. Flowering season: April to July. $2n = 38$ (var. *nidifica*), 20, 38 (var. *claytoniifolia*).

Var. *nidifica* grows in open meadows in pine woodland, whereas var. *claytoniifolia* is found on wet, mossy cliffs and hillsides. Both varieties grow east of the Cascades in Washington, Oregon and Idaho; var. *nidifica* extends also to western Montana, and southwards to northern Nevada and the Sierra Nevada of California.

***Saxifraga aprica*** Greene, *Bulletin of the Torrey Botanical Club* 23:25 (1896). TYPE: California, above Donner Lake, 20.vii.1893, *Greene*. (Holotype: University of Notre Dame (**NDG**).)
Like *S.apetala* but leaves with lamina elliptical to obovate, tapering to a moderately well-defined petiole; margin entire to minutely toothed above the middle. Inflorescence less than 2cm long, congested, capitate to somewhat flat-topped. Petals 1.8–3mm long, elliptical to linear. Flowering season: May to August. $2n = 20$.

Rocky, alpine meadows and snow-bed grassland, 1700–4500m; in south-western Oregon and northern California, also in the Sierra Nevada of California and Washoe Co., Nevada.

***Saxifraga rhomboidea*** Greene, *Pittonia* 3:343 (1898). TYPE: Arizona, Mt San Francisco, 19.vii.1889, *Greene*. (Lectotype: University of Notre Dame (**NDG**), designated by Elvander (1984).)
Leaves with lamina 1–3cm long, broadly ovate to rhombic, rarely elliptical, tapering abruptly to a distinct petiole; margin usually unevenly toothed. Flowering stems 7–20cm. Inflorescence 1–3cm long, congested, capitate, globose to cylindrical. Petals 2–4mm long, elliptical (rarely linear). Flowering season: April to August. $2n = 20, 38, 40, 56$.

Subalpine and alpine meadows, 1500–4550m, in the Rocky mountains from Montana to New Mexico, Utah and Arizona.

***Saxifraga tempestiva*** Elvander & Denton, *Madroño* 23:346 (1976). TYPE: Montana, Deer-lodge Co., Anaconda Range, Goat Flat, 1.1km W. of Storm Lake Pass, 21.vii.1974, *Elvander 492*. (Holotype: University of Washington (**WTU**).)
Leaves with lamina usually less than 1cm long, linear to obovate, tapering gradually to a broad, indistinct petiole; margin entire to minutely toothed. Flowering stems 3–8cm. Inflorescence less than 1cm long, congested. Petals less than 1.5mm long, linear, shorter than sepals. Flowering season: June and July. $2n = 10$.

Rocky ledges, steep slopes or snow-bed grassland, 2400–3150m, in western Montana.

***Saxifraga californica*** Greene, *Pittonia* 1:286 (1889). TYPE: California, Mt Tamalpais, 30.iii.1889, *Greene*. (Lectotype: University of Notre Dame (**NDG**), designated by Elvander (1984).)
*S.fallax* Greene
*S.parvifolia* Greene
Leaves with lamina 2–5cm long, ovate, tapering abruptly to a distinct petiole; margin toothed or crenate. Flowering stems 10–25cm.

Inflorescence 5–10cm long, lax, broadly obovoid. Petals 2.5–4.5mm long, oblong to suborbicular. Flowering season: December to April.

Damp, shady rocks, banks or fields, often in woodland, to 1200m, from south-western Oregon to the Coast Ranges and western slopes of the Sierra Nevada of California.

***Saxifraga hitchcockiana*** Elvander, *Systematic Botany Monographs* 3:34 (1984). TYPE: Oregon, Clatsop Co., Saddle Mountain, 20. vi.1915, *Gorman 3561*. (Holotype: University of Washington (**WTU**).)
*S.occidentalis* var. *latipetiolata* C.L. Hitchcock
Leaves with lamina 4–10cm long, elliptical to obovate, tapering gradually to a broad, indistinct petiole; margin usually with broad, coarse, rounded teeth. Flowering stems 10–15cm. Inflorescence 5–10cm long, lax, somewhat flat-topped. Petals 2–5mm long, elliptical. Flowering season: May to July. $2n = 76$.

Wet rocks and ledges on mountain-top balds in north-western Oregon.

It has been suggested that this species originated from hybridisation between *S.oregana* and *S.rufidula* (Elvander 1984).

***Saxifraga oregana*** Howell, *Erythea* 3:34 (1895). TYPE: Oregon, Lake Labish, near Salem, 28.vi.1893, *Howell 1498*. (Holotype: Berkeley (**UC**).)
*S.montanensis* Small
Leaves with lamina 10–25cm long, linear to oblanceolate, tapering gradually to a broad, indistinct petiole; margin sparsely toothed to almost entire. Flowering stems 25–60cm. Inflorescence 6–15cm long, usually lax, conical to cylindrical, with flowers in clusters at the ends of ascending branches. Petals 2.5–4mm long, linear to elliptical to narrowly obovate. Flowering season: March to July. $2n = 38, 76$.

Marshy meadows, 150–2500m; from the Cascades of Washington and Oregon to the Sierra Nevada of California, extending eastwards in Oregon to the Rocky mountains of Idaho and western Montana; disjunct in Colorado.

***Saxifraga pensylvanica*** Linnaeus, *Species Plantarum* 399 (1753). TYPE: Sheet 575.4 in the Linnean herbarium, London (**LINN**) has been designated as lectotype by Webb (1987a).
A variable species much like *S.oregana*, from which it apparently consistently differs only in chromosome number and distribution. Two subspecies and their putative hybrid are sometimes recognised (Burns 1942), although whether the complex variation pattern permits this is questionable. Plants with lanceolate leaves, narrowly lanceolate petals and carpels oblong at maturity, united only at the base are subsp. *pensylvanica*. A distinctive variant of this, with carpels strongly divergent at maturity is var. *forbesii* (Vasey) Engler & Irmscher. Plants with ovate-lanceolate leaves, ovate to elliptical petals and ovoid to ellipsoid carpels united to ⅕ their length, are subsp. *interior* G.W. Burns. Flowering season: April to June. $2n = 56$ (subsp. *pensylvanica*), 112 (subsp. *interior*). The putative inter-subspecific hybrid (subsp. × *tenuirostrata* G.W. Burns) is partially sterile and has $2n = 84$.

Marshy meadows from Maine and Ontario to Minnesota, southwards to Missouri and Virginia.

***Saxifraga subapetala*** E. Nelson, *Erythea* 7: 169 (1899). TYPE: Yellowstone National Park, Obsidian Creek, 24.vii.1899, *Nelson & Nelson 6089*. (Holotype: Laramie (**RM**).)
*S.oregana* var. *subapetala* (E. Nelson) C.L. Hitchcock
*S.rydbergii* Small ex Rydberg

Some populations of this species, especially those in which the flowers have a full complement of 5 petals, bear a strong resemblance to *S.hieracifolia* (see p. 48). It appears to differ in its longer leaf-laminae (3–15cm), glandular rather than non-glandular hairs at the base of the flowering stem, and petals often absent or, if present, usually fewer than 5, 1–2mm long, elliptical, pink to purple. Flowering season: May to July. $2n = 76$.

Subalpine and alpine meadows, wet banks or rock-ledges, 1250–3000m, from south-western Montana to northern Wyoming.

## Subsection *Rotundifoliatae* A.M. Johnson

This group shares with subsection *Stellares* a superior ovary with partially united carpels, but it differs most obviously in its orbicular to kidney-shaped leaves (versus obovate to oblong or ovate elsewhere), in possessing uniseriate glandular hairs, club-shaped filaments (at least in North American species) and seeds with ribbon-like ribs and a diffusely wrinkled cuticle. The four North American species of this subsection are natives of the Pacific Northwest, although one of them, *S.nelsoniana* D. Don, stretches westwards across Asia as far as north-eastern Europe. The following account owes much to the work of Calder & Savile (1960).

*Saxifraga nelsoniana* D. Don (see p. 52)
This species is very variable both morphologically and cytologically (chromosome numbers range from $2n = 28$ to $2n = $ c. 88, mostly counted from Asiatic populations) and is represented by six subspecies in North America. The following key, adapted from Calder & Savile (1960), works quite well:

1. Inflorescence-hairs mostly short, erect, prominently glandular ..................... 2
   Inflorescence-hairs long, wavy, mostly non-glandular (or with reduced glandular heads) ......................................... 3
2. Leaves with a few hairs or none; inflorescence-branches slender, lax; north-eastern Europe, Siberia. subsp. *aestivalis* (Fischer & Meyer) D.A. Webb
   Leaves pubescent; inflorescence-branches stout, usually congested; Yukon, Alaska, Bering Sea islands, eastern Siberia ......... ............................ subsp. *nelsoniana*
3. Largest leaves with 9–12 teeth; capsules 6–12mm long; Queen Charlotte Islands and adjacent British Columbia .... subsp. *carlottae* (Calder & Savile) Hultén
   Largest leaves with 12–18 teeth; capsules 3–8mm long ................................. 4
4. Inflorescence lax; hairs appressed; Coast Ranges and Cascades of British Columbia

and Washington ....... subsp. *cascadensis* (Calder & Savile) Hultén
Inflorescence congested; hairs ascending .. 5
5. Leaves thick, fleshy; carpels united 70–85 per cent of their length; Aleutian Islands .......... subsp. *insularis* (Hultén) Hultén
   Leaves thin; carpels united 25–75 per cent of their length ................................. 6
6. Largest leaves 2.3–7.7mm wide; carpels united 40–75 per cent of their length; Gulf of Alaska ............. subsp. *pacifica* (Hultén) Hultén
   Largest leaves 1–3.8mm wide; carpels united 25–60 per cent of their length; Yukon to Keewatin and northern Rocky mountains .... subsp. *porsildiana* (Calder & Savile) Hultén

*Saxifraga odontoloma* Piper, *Smithsonian miscellaneous Collections* 50:200 (1907). TYPE: Washington, Chelan Co., Mt Stuart, 24.vii. 1893, *Sandberg & Leiberg 570*. (Holotype: Smithsonian Institution (**US**).)
*S.arguta* of North American authors, not of D.Don
*S.punctata* subsp. *arguta* Hultén
*S.odontophylla* of Piper, not of Wallich
Like *S.nelsoniana* but with slightly irregular flowers, the larger petals of which are 2–4mm long, broadly elliptical to orbicular, truncate or cordate at the base with 2 yellow or green spots, and narrowed abruptly to a slender claw. Flowering stems 20–65cm, with an inflorescence 7–32cm long, laxly branched. Flowering season: July to September. $2n = 24, 48$.

Wet meadows and watersides, above 1500m; Coast Ranges and Cascades of southern British Columbia and Washington; Sierra Nevada of California; north-eastern Oregon, Idaho and Montana, southwards in the Rocky mountains to New Mexico and Arizona.

*Saxifraga lyallii* Engler, *Verhandlungen der kaiserlich-königlichen zoologisch-botanischen Gesellschaft in Wien* 19:542 (1869). TYPE: Rocky Mts, lat. 49°N, at 6500ft elevation, 1861, *D. Lyall*. (Isotype: Kew (**K**).)
Similar in some respects to *S.odontoloma* and hybridising with it where their ranges overlap.

It differs in its leaves which are 0.8–8cm long, spathulate to fan-shaped, and taper at the base. Flowering stems 7–30cm. Inflorescence 2–15cm long, lax, slender-cylindrical. Petals 2.5–5mm, broadly elliptical to suborbicular, with a short claw, white to cream, usually with 2 yellow or green spots. Smaller plants with flowering stems 4–15cm and spathulate leaves are subsp. *lyallii*; larger plants with flowering stems 9–30cm and fan-shaped leaves are subsp. *hultenii* Calder & Savile. Flowering season: July to September. $2n =$ c. 56, c. 58.

By watersides or wet, stony meadows at alpine elevations. South-eastern British Columbia, south-western Alberta and adjacent Montana; south-western British Columbia and adjacent Washington (subsp. *lyallii*). Central and southern Alaska, Yukon south to northern Washington and southern Alberta (subsp. *hultenii*).

***Saxifraga spicata*** D. Don, *Transactions of the Linnean Society of London* 13:354 (1822). TYPE: Northwest coast of America [Alaska], Sledge Island, *D. Nelson*. (Holotype: British Museum (**BM**).)
Leaves 7–26cm long, cordate, orbicular or kidney-shaped, with 21–45 coarse teeth. Flowering stems 15–70cm. Inflorescence showy, spike-like with slender, compact panicles. Petals 3–4.5mm long, oblong, clawed, yellowish. Filaments club-shaped at first but later elongated and attenuated, reaching a length of more than 6mm at maturity. Flowering season: July.

Moist rocks and stream-sides in tundra or heaths in Alaska and the Yukon.

# Section *Heterisia*
# (Rafinesque ex Small) A.M. Johnson

The only species in this section has a superior ovary composed of carpels united for at least half their length. It has been segregated from section *Micranthes* because of its often leafy flowering stem, its lack of foliar crystals, its granular pollen-wall, its 2 integuments and its smooth seeds (without ribs or papillae).

***Saxifraga mertensiana*** Bongard, *Memoires de l'Académie impériale des Sciences de St.-Péters-bourg, sixiéme serie. Sciences mathématiques, physiques et naturelles* 2:141 (1832). TYPE: Sitcha, *Mertens*. (Holotype: Leningrad (**LE**); isotype: Kew (**K**).)
Leaves with lamina 2–8cm long, kidney-shaped to orbicular, more or less hairy; margin shallowly crenately lobed, the lobes secondarily toothed or crenate; petiole up to five times as long as lamina, often with long hairs. Flowering stems 15–40cm. Inflorescence laxly branched, usually with at least some of the flowers replaced by bulbils. (Plants with a complete set of flowers are var. *eastwoodiae* (Small) Engler & Irmscher, but they have no geographical coherence and are doubtfully distinct.) Petals 4–5mm, oblong-elliptic to obovate, truncate or with a short claw, white. Filaments club-shaped. Flowering season: April to August. $2n = 36$, c. 48, c. 50.

Mossy rocks and cliffs, below 2500m. From southern Alaska southwards to north-western California; Sierra Nevada of California; eastwards through southern British Columbia to north-western Montana, Idaho and north-eastern Oregon.

# Lime-secreting species

Next are four species with lime-secreting hydathodes, primarily with arctic-circumpolar distributions and occurring also in Europe. One of them, *S.aizoides* Linnaeus (section **Xanthizoon** Grisebach), is described fully on p. 135 and requires no further comment here.

***Saxifraga oppositifolia*** Linnaeus (section **Porphyrion** Tausch, see p. 105)
Most populations of this species from Alaska, the Yukon, northern British Columbia and the Canadian Arctic archipelago have sepals bearing slender, glandular hairs on the margins. These populations may be divided into two subspecies: (a) subsp. *smalliana* (Engler & Irmscher) Hultén, in which the leaves are small and stiff in 4 very distinct, densely packed rows, whose flowering stems lack leaves in the

upper part, and whose sepals are hairless on the back; and (b) subsp. *glandulisepala* Hultén, in which the leaves are larger and less densely packed, whose flowering stems have leaves in the upper part, and the backs of whose sepals have both glandular and non-glandular hairs. The two subspecies, however, are not always easy to tell apart, although they do seem to differ consistently from the more southerly subsp. *oppositifolia*, whose sepals have stout, non-glandular hairs on the margins. The relative distributions of the northern subspecies are imperfectly known. Subsp. *smalliana* occurs at least in the area of Beringia, extending eastwards to the Yukon, whereas subsp. *glandulisepala* is more widespread, especially in coastal areas. Two chromosome races of the species are known in North America ($2n = 26$ and 52), although to what extent this variation is taxonomically correlated is not known.

*Saxifraga nathorstii* (Dusén) Hayek, *Denkschriften der kaiserlichen Akademie der Wissenschaften. Mathematisch-naturwissenschaftliche Klasse* 77:661 (1905). TYPE: Svenska Grönlandsexpeditionen 1899. Groenlandia orientalis, Sophia-Strasse, 15.viii.1899. *Nathorst.* (Lectotype: Copenhagen (**C**), designated here.)
*S.oppositifolia* var. *nathorstii* Dusén, *Botaniska Notiser* 1901:73, 76 (1901)

A variable species, but usually resembling *S.oppositifolia* more than *S.aizoides*. It forms a loose mat. Leaves alternate or opposite, ovate-lanceolate, with marginal hairs. Flowers 12–15mm, larger than in *S.oppositifolia*. Petals dirty red, orange-yellow or yellow. Flowering season: July and August. $2n = 52$.

On marshes, heathland and alluvium in eastern Greenland.

This species is probably a polyploid hybrid between *S.oppositifolia* and *S.aizoides* (Böcher 1983).

*Saxifraga paniculata* Miller (section *Ligulatae* Haworth, see p. 124).
This is an amphiatlantic species whose populations from Iceland, Greenland and north-eastern North America have been distin-guished as subsp. *neogaea* (Butters) Löve & Löve ($2n = 28$). Differences from European material are supposed to lie in the seed-coat, the papillae of which are claimed to be half as long and less uniformly arranged than in subsp. *paniculata*; also, the margins of the sutures of the dehiscent capsule are supposedly thicker in subsp. *neogaea*. However, in our opinion, the variation in central European populations is great enough to obscure these distinctions, and we see no taxonomically significant differences.

# Section *Trachyphyllum* (Gaudin) W.D.J. Koch (see p. 138)

The account of this section is based largely on the work of Calder & Savile (1959), who we believe constructed a workable classification of North American populations, although the recent treatment of Asiatic plants (Khokhrjakov 1979) disagrees in several respects, over and above that of the narrow species concept adopted. The whole complex needs to be re-examined over its entire range in order to improve our understanding of the patterns of variation.

*Saxifraga bronchialis* Linnaeus (see p. 142)
North American populations may be divided into two subspecies which differ, apparently, only in details of petal-shape and spotting from the European subsp. *spinulosa*.

Plants in which the petals are spotted entirely with yellow and are clawed are subsp. *funstonii* (Small) Hultén ($2n = 28, 48, 66, 92, 112$, all counts based on Asiatic populations); they range from Kamchatka, Alaska and the Yukon to north-western British Columbia.

Plants in which the petals are truncate, with deep red spots towards the apex and yellow spots at the base, are subsp. *austromontana* (Wiegand) Piper ($2n = 26$); they range from central British Columbia and south-western Alberta southwards through Washington to north-eastern Oregon, and through the Rocky mountains to New Mexico.

*Saxifraga cherlerioides* D. Don, *Transactions of the Linnean Society of London* 13:382 (1822). TYPE: Camtschatka, *Merk* (Isotype: Leningrad (**LE**).)
*S.bronchialis* subsp. *cherlerioides* (D. Don) Hultén
Leaves 2–5(–7) × 1–1.8mm, spathulate, with an obtuse apex, occasionally mucronate; marginal hairs without glands. Flowering stems 2–6.5cm, sparingly branched. Petals 3–5mm long, elliptical, not clawed, cream to yellow-brown (when dry), upper surface with some yellow spots, rarely also with a few red spots at or above the middle. Flowering season: July. $2n = c. 26^*$.
Rock-ledges, talus slopes and gravelly flats in the western Aleutian Islands, Kamchatka and eastern Siberia.

*Saxifraga vespertina* (Small) Fedde, *Just's botanischer Jahresbericht* 33:613 (1906). TYPE: Washington, Grays Harbor Co., Baldy Peak, *Conard 302*. (Holotype: New York (**NY**).)
*S.bronchialis* var. *vespertina* (Small) Rosendahl
Leaves 4–10.5 × 1.6–3.3mm, spathulate, with an obtuse or acute apex, sometimes mucronate, entire or with a small tooth on each side of the apex; marginal hairs stout, without glands. Flowering stems 2.5–7.5(–11.5)cm, sparingly branched. Petals 4–6mm, elliptical, not clawed, white, with spots yellow towards the base, orange or red above. Flowering season: July and August. $2n = 26$.
Rock-crevices, talus and scree slopes. Washington in the Olympic Peninsula and southern Cascades; Columbia River Gorge; Clatsop Co., Oregon.

*Saxifraga tricuspidata* Rottböll, *Skrifter, som udi et Kiobenhavnske selskab af laerdoms og videnskabers elskere ere fremlagte og oplaeste* 10:446 (1770). TYPE: [Greenland] 1739. *Egede*. (Holotype: Egede herbarium, Copenhagen (**C**).)
Leaves cuneate or oblanceolate, 6–15 × 1.5–4.5(–6.5)mm, many with 3 apical, mucronate teeth; margins with short, glandular hairs. Flowering stems 4–10(–24)cm, branched above. Petals 4–7mm, two to three times

as long as the sepals, elliptical, not clawed, white to cream with yellow, orange and red spots in sequence from the base up. Flowering season: June to August. $2n = 26$.
Five variants have been recognised and an account is given by Calder & Savile (1959); of importance from the point of view of possible confusion with *S.bronchialis* is f. **subintegrifolia** (Abromeit) Polunin, in which nearly all the leaves are entire or have only 1 small tooth.
Rock-ledges, talus slopes and gravelly flats. Alaska, Yukon and south in British Columbia and western Alberta to 52°N; eastwards through northern Canada to western and eastern Greenland; southwards sparingly to Lake Superior.

*Saxifraga taylorii* Calder & Savile, *Brittonia* 11:248 (1959). TYPE: British Columbia, Queen Charlotte Is., below Mt de la Touche, near head of Fairfax Inlet, Tasu Sound, west coast of Moresby Island, 16–17.viii.1957. *Calder & Taylor 23511*. (Holotype: Agriculture Canada, Ottawa (**DAO**); isotype: Kew (**K**).)
Leaves 4.5–10 × 2.5–5.5mm, spathulate, nearly always with 3 mucronate, apical lobes; margins conspicuously cartilaginous, with non-glandular hairs. Flowering stems 3.5–12.5cm, branched above. Petals (3.5–)4.5–7mm, elliptical, short-clawed, white, sometimes tinged with pink, without spots. Flowering season: June to August. $2n = 26, 52$.
Alpine rocky cliffs and talus slopes on the Queen Charlotte Islands.

# Section *Mesogyne* Sternberg
(see p. 144)

Six species from this section occur in North America, three of them also in Europe: *Saxifraga cernua* Linnaeus ($2n = 52, 70, 72$), *Saxifraga rivularis* Linnaeus ($2n = 52$) and *Saxifraga hyperborea* R. Brown ($2n = 26$) (see pp. 146–51).

*Saxifraga radiata* Small, *North American Flora* 22:128 (1905). TYPE: Sinus St Laurentii, *Chamisso* (Holotype: Leningrad (**LE**).)

*S.exilis* of Stephan ex Sternberg, not of Pollini Like *S.sibirica* but basal leaves with shorter petioles. Sepals shorter, 2–3.5(–4)mm, ovate to lanceolate. Ovary ¼ to ⅓ inferior. Styles divergent. Flowering season: July and August. $2n = 26, 48^*, 52$.

Wet meadows, snow-bed grassland and stream-sides in British Columbia, the Yukon, Alaska and north-eastern Siberia.

**Saxifraga bracteata** D. Don, *Transactions of the Linnean Society of London* 13:367 (1822). TYPE: Not traced.
Like *S.sibirica* but cauline leaves 3- to 6-lobed, kidney-shaped or truncate, with petioles of the lower ones longer than the laminae; the uppermost leaves crowding the congested, near-capitate inflorescence. Petals c. 5mm long, orbicular, clawed. Flowering season: June and July. $2n = 26^*$.

Rock-ledges and talus slopes in coastal Alaska and northern British Columbia, the Aleutian Islands, Kamchatka and northern Japan.

**Saxifraga flexuosa** Sternberg, *Revisio Saxifragarum, Supplementum* II, 38 (1831). TYPE: Not traced.
*S.rivularis* var. *flexuosa* (Sternberg) Engler & Irmscher
*S.debilis* Engelmann
*S.hyperborea* subsp. *debilis* (Engelmann) Löve, Löve & Kapoor
Like *S.rivularis* but inflorescence strict, pedicels erect. Glandular hairs on pedicels short and straight, not long and crinkly. Hypanthium narrowly, rather than broadly, campanulate. Sepals shorter than hypanthium. Petals clawed. Flowering season: July and August. $2n = 26$.

Tundra and subalpine and alpine hollows under boulders. From Kamchatka and north-eastern Siberia, through the Aleutian Islands, montane Alaska and the Yukon, southwards to southern British Columbia and Alberta, then sparingly in the Rocky mountains to Colorado.

# Section *Saxifraga* (see p. 151)

Finally there are just two species from section *Saxifraga* which extend into North America.

**Saxifraga adscendens** Linnaeus (see p. 251)
North American populations of this otherwise European–Caucasian species have been distinguished as subsp. **oregonensis** (Rafinesque) Bacigalupi ($2n = 22$) on account of their smaller stature (3–10cm), smaller petals (2–6mm) and broader cauline leaves (3–5mm); the last two characters, however, fall within the range of variation seen in Europe.

Southern Alaska and the Yukon southwards through the Rocky mountains to northern Washington, north-eastern Oregon and adjacent Idaho, and in Utah and Colorado.

**Saxifraga cespitosa** Linnaeus (see p. 186)
This is an extremely variable circumpolar species which needs a thorough biosystematic study. In North America, three races are currently distinguished in the Pacific Northwest, and a further two or three in the Arctic.

Populations whose petals are shorter than c. 6mm, less than 2.5 times as long as the triangular to ovate sepals, and with scanty pubescence, are distinguished as subsp. **exaratioides** (Simmons) Engler & Irmscher ($2n = 80$). Rocky mountains from British Columbia and Alberta southwards to Colorado, New Mexico and Arizona.

Similar plants from the Arctic, but with solitary flowers (rather than the usual 2–4) have been named subsp. **uniflora** (R. Brown) Porsild; the relationship of the arctic *S.sileneflora* Chamisso, with oblong rather than obovate-globose capsules, to this and subsp. *exaratioides* is unclear.

Populations whose petals are up to 10mm long, more than 2.5 times the length of the oblong-lanceolate sepals, include the typical subsp. **cespitosa**, which occurs in the Canadian arctic archipelago, eastwards through Quebec and Greenland to Europe.

Another large-flowered variant, with probably the strongest claim to recognition, is subsp. *subgemmifera* Engler & Irmscher, a sprawling, loose mat, whose leafy shoots and basal leaves bear long, often cobweb-like, hairs, and in whose axils summer-dormant buds are produced; the relationship of this subspecies to species in series *Gemmiferae* is unclear. Washington and Oregon (also British Columbia and Montana?).

A related, but more compact variant without summer-dormant buds, is var. *emarginata* (Small) Rosendahl; it has a similar distribution to var. *subgemmifera*, but occurs at higher elevations and extends further north, into central British Columbia, and also further south, disjunctly in northern California.

Members of series *Cespitosae* from South America are: *S.adenodes* Poeppig (Chile); *S.magellanica* Poiret, *sensu lato* (Ecuador to Chile); *S.boussingaultii* Brongniart (Ecuador); and *S.pavonii* D. Don (Chile, Argentina).

## ALIEN SPECIES
North American records of the following species (Shetler & Skog 1978; Kartesz & Kartesz 1980) are either erroneous or refer to introductions:

*S.davurica* Willdenow—sometimes reported from Alaska, but apparently restricted to eastern Siberia; American records are mainly of *S.calycina* Sternberg (Hultén 1973).

*S.* × *geum* Linnaeus—recorded from Newfoundland; alien. Almost certainly in error for *S.hirsuta*.

*S.hirsuta* Linnaeus—recorded from Newfoundland; alien.

*S.sibthorpii* Boissier—reported from the American Pacific Northwest, probably in error for the weedy *S.cymbalaria* var. *huetiana*.

*S.stolonifera* Meerburgh—naturalised in California.

*S.tridactylites* Linnaeus—naturalised in British Columbia (Taylor & MacBride 1977).

*S.umbrosa* Linnaeus—recorded from Newfoundland; alien. Probably confused with *S. hirsuta*.

## EXCLUDED SPECIES
We exclude the following two North American species from the genus *Saxifraga*:

*Saxifraga fragarioides* Greene, *Bulletin of the Torrey Botanical Club* 8:121 (1881)
This species seems better placed in its own genus, as *Saxifragopsis fragarioides* (Greene) Small. It is distinguished from *Saxifraga* by the unicellular hairs on the flower-stalks, the filaments winged at the base, the petiole jointed at its junction with the lamina and the smooth seeds.

Rock-crevices at elevations of 1500–3000m in south-western Oregon and northern California.

*Saxifraga nuttallii* Small, *Bulletin of the Torrey Botanical Club* 23:368 (1896)
This species needs further investigation to determine its affinities. It has trailing, leafy flowering stems, with laminae obovate to elliptical, entire or 3-lobed at the tip, a lax, 2- to 6-flowered inflorescence and an inferior ovary. It is distinguished from *Saxifraga* chiefly by the presence of a free hypanthium and, for the present, we shall follow Johnson (1927) in assigning it to its own genus, as *Cascadia nuttallii* (Small) A.M. Johnson

Damp, shaded cliffs and ledges, below 700m, in the Columbia River Gorge in Washington and Oregon, and in northern California.

## HORTICULTURAL NOTES
Many North American species are rather tricky to maintain in cultivation, possibly because they often require the fairly exacting drainage conditions associated with spring snow-melt and summer drought. Although many of them lack charm or are just plain ugly, some would make delightful subjects in woodland or for the rock- or bog-garden, and the more notable species are mentioned below.

There are several species which would lend themselves to cultivation in a woodland garden. These include *S.ferruginea* and *S.michauxii* and vigorous species like *S.virginiensis* and *S.pensylvanica*, although the latter is not exactly a choice plant.

Potential rock-garden subjects include all the North American species of section *Trachyphyllum*, which form neat mats or cushions. Of similar habit is *S.tolmiei*, a very pretty plant which should do well if the correct drainage could be established. Another attractive, neat plant is *S.rufidula* which would be at home growing among shady rocks. *S.eschscholtzii* would be worth growing for its attractive silvery-hairy foliage, although it would probably be susceptible to winter wet and do better in a pan in a cold house.

For the bog-garden, we recommend trials of species belonging to subsection *Rotundifoliatae*, especially *S.nelsoniana* and *S.odontoloma*, which make a delightful show *en masse*.

# Bibliography

Aldén, B. & Strid, A. (1986) 'Saxifraga L.', in A. Strid (ed.), Mountain flora of Greece, 1:359–80, Cambridge

Allioni, C. (1785) Flora Pedemontana, vol. 2, Turin

Andersen, Ø.M. & Øvstedal, D.O. (1989) 'Anthocyanin patterns of European Saxifraga species', Biochemical Systematics & Ecology, (in press)

Arietti, N. & Fenaroli, L. (1960) 'Cronologia dei reperti e posizione sistematica della Saxifraga presolanensis Engler, endemismo orobico', Quaderni dell'Istituto botanico dell'Università e Laboratorio crittogammico di Pavia, 15:5–28

———— (1972) 'Saxifraga arachnoidea Sternb., endemismo dell'Insubria orientale', Studi Trentini di Scienzi naturali B, 49:66–101

Ball, J. (1878) Spicilegium florae maroccanae, London

Barnley, T.P. (1967) European flowers in colour, London

Bauhin, C. (1620) Prodromus theatri botanici, Frankfurt

———— (1623) Pinax theatri botanici, Basel

Bell, K.L. & Bliss, L.C. (1980) 'Plant reproduction in a high arctic environment', Arctic and Alpine Research, 12:1–10

Bentham, G. (1826) Catalogue des plantes indigènes des Pyrénées et du Bas-Languedoc, Paris

Bertoloni, A. (1819) Amoenitates italicae, Bologna

———— (1840) Flora italica, vol. 4, Bologna

Biasoletto, B. (1841) Relazione del Viaggio nell'Istria, Dalmazia e Montenegro, 1838, Trieste

Böcher, T.W. (1983) 'The allotetraploid Saxifraga nathorstii and its probable progenitors S.aizoides and S.oppositifolia', Meddelelser om Grønland: Bioscience, 11:1–22

Böcher, T.W., Holmen, K. & Jacobsen, K. (1968) The flora of Greenland, Copenhagen

Bohm, B.A., Bhat, U.G. & Miller, J.M. (1984) 'Further studies of flavonoids in Saxifraga', Biochemical Systematics & Ecology, 12:367–8

Boissier, E. (1839–1845) Voyage botanique dans le Midi de l'Espagne pendant l'Année 1837, Paris

———— (1872) Flora orientalis, vol. 2, Geneva & Basel

Bonnier, G. (1921) Flore complète illustrée en couleurs de France, Suisse et Belgique, vol. 4, Paris

Borgen, L. & Reidar, E. (1983) 'Chromosome numbers of flowering plants from northern Norway and Svalbard', Nordic Journal of Botany, 3:301–6

Brath, E. (1948) 'Historisches und geographisches uber Saxifraga paradoxa Sternberg', Phyton (Austria), 1:63–70

Britton, N.L. & Brown, A. (1897) An illustrated Flora of the northern United States, Canada and the British Possessions, vol. 2, New York

Brown, S. (1907) Alpine flora of the Canadian Rocky mountains, New York

Brunfels, O. (1530) Herbarum vivae icones, Strasbourg

Burnat, E. (1901) Flore des Alpes maritimes, vol. 3, Geneva

Burns, G.W. (1942) 'The taxonomy and cytology of Saxifraga pensylvanica L. and related forms', American Midland Naturalist, 28:127–60

Buxbaum, J.C. (1728) *Plantarum minus cognitarum Centuria* I, St Petersburg

Cain, S.A. (1944) *Foundations of plant geography*, New York

Calder, J.A. & Savile, D.B.O. (1959) 'Studies in Saxifragaceae, II. *Saxifraga* sect. *Trachyphyllum* in North America', *Brittonia*, 11:228–49

―――― (1960) 'Studies in Saxifragaceae, III. *Saxifraga odontoloma* and *Lyallii*, and North American subspecies of *S.punctata*' *Canadian Journal of Botany*, 38:409–35

Casas, J.F. & Jimenez, A.C. (1982) *Plantas silvestres de la Peninsula iberica (rupicolas)*, Madrid

Cavanilles, A.J. (1795) *Icones et descriptiones plantarum*, Madrid

Chambers, K.L. (1964) '*Saxifraga eschscholtzii* Sternb.', *Madroño*, 17:203–4

Chiarugi, A. (1925) 'Nuova stazione italiana della "*Saxifraga cernua* L." e sua distribuzione nella catena alpina', *Bulletino della Società botanica italiana*, 1925:131–40

―――― (1934) 'Sull' ecologia della "*Saxifraga cernua* L." al limite meridionale dell' area geografica', *Nuovo giornale botanica italiana* (nov. ser.), 40:572–5

Clusius, C. (1576) *Rariorum aliquot Stirpium per Hispanias observatarum Historia*, Antwerp

―――― (1583) *Rariorum aliquot Stirpium per Pannoniam, Austriam et vicinas quasdam provincias observatarum Historia*, Antwerp

―――― (1611) *Curae posteriores*, Leiden

Colgan, N. (1900) 'Botanical notes on the Galway and Mayo highlands', *Irish Naturalist*, 9:111–8

Colmeiro, M. (1846) *Catálogo metódico de plantas observadas en Cataluña*, Madrid

Colonna, F. (1616) *Minus cognitarum rariorumque nostro coelo orientium stirpium Ecphrasis*, Rome

Conolly, A.P. (1976) 'Use of the scanning electron microscope for the identification of seeds, with special reference to *Saxifraga* and *Papaver*', *Folia Quaternaria*, 47:29–32

Cordus, V. (1561) *Annotationes in Pedacii Dioscoridis Anazarbei de Materia medica libros* V, Strasbourg

―――― (1563) *Stirpium descriptionis liber quintus*, Strasbourg

Correvon, H. (1894) *Flore colorée de poche à l'usage du touriste*, Paris

Coste, H. (1902) *Flore descriptive et illustrée de la France*, vol. 2, Paris

Coventry, B.O. (1927) *Wild flowers of Kashmir*, vol. 2, London

Curtis, W. (1821) *Flora Londinensis*, 2nd edn, vol. 4, London

Demiri, M. (1981) *Flora ekskursioniste e Shqiperise*, Tirana

Desfontaines, R.L. (1798) *Flora Atlantica*, vol. 1, Paris

Diaz, T.E. & Fernandez Prieto, J.A. (1983) 'Aportaciones al conocimiento del género *Saxifraga* L., Seccion *Dactyloides* Tausch, de la Cordillera Cantábrica', *Anales del Jardin botánico de Madrid*, 39:247–72

Dillenius, J.J. (1732) *Hortus Elthamensis*, London

Dodoens, R. (1583) *Stirpium historiae pemptades sex*, Antwerp

Don, D. (1822) 'A monograph of the genus *Saxifraga*', *Transactions of the Linnean Society of London*, 13:341–452

Drygalsky, U. (1935) Uber die Entstehung einer tetraploiden, genetisch ungleichmässigen F$_2$ aus der Kreuzung *Saxifraga adscendens* L. × *Saxifraga tridactylites* L.', *Zeitschrift fur induktive Abstammungs- und Vererbungslehre*, 69(2/3):278–300

Ehrhart, F. (1790) *Beiträge zur Naturkunde*, vol. 5, p. 47, Hanover

Elvander, P.E. (1982) 'Gynodioecy in *Saxifraga integrifolia* (Saxifragaceae)', *Madroño*, 29:269–70

―――― (1984) 'The taxonomy of *Saxifraga* (Saxifragaceae) section *Boraphila* subsection *Integrifoliae* in western North America', *Systematic Botany Monographs*, 3:1–44

Engler, H.G.A. (1867) 'Beiträge zur Naturgeschichte des Genus *Saxifraga* L.', *Linnaea*, 35:1–124

―――― (1869) 'Index criticus specierum atque synonymorum generis *Saxifraga*', *Verhandlungen der zoologisch-botanischen Gesellschaft in Wien*, *19*:513–56

────── (1872) *Monographie der Gattung Saxifraga L.*, Breslau

────── (1891) 'Saxifragaceae', in H.G.A. Engler & K.A.E. Prantl (eds), *Die natürlichen Pflanzenfamilien, III*, 2a:41–93, Leipzig

────── (1930) 'Saxifragaceae', in H.G.A. Engler & K.A.E. Prantl (eds), *Die natürlichen Pflanzenfamilien*, 2nd edn, 18a:74–226, Leipzig

Engler, H.G.A. & Irmscher, E. (1916, 1919) 'Saxifragaceae: *Saxifraga*', *Das Pflanzenreich*, *67, 69* (IV.117):1–448 (1916), 449–709 (1919), Leipzig

Eurola, S. (1972) 'Germination of seeds collected in Spitsbergen', *Annales Botanici Fennici*, 9:149–59

Farrer, R. (1911) *Among the high hills*, London

────── (1919) *The English rock-garden*, vol. 2, London

Favarger, C. (1957) 'Sur deux critères nouveaux utilisables dans la taxinomie des Saxifragacées', *Revue de Cytologie et de Biologie végétales*, 18:125–37

Federov, A. (ed.) (1969) *Chromosome numbers of flowering plants*, Leningrad

Felsko, E. (1959) *Portraits of wild flowers*, Oxford

Fenaroli, L. (1925) *Flora delle Alpi*, Milan

Ferguson, I.K. (1972) 'Notes on the pollen morphology of *Saxifraga nathorstii* and its putative parents, *S.aizoides* and *S.oppositifolia*', *Kew Bulletin*, 27:475–81

Ferguson, I.K. & Webb, D.A. (1970) 'Pollen morphology in the genus *Saxifraga* and its taxonomic significance', *Botanical Journal of the Linnean Society*' 63:295–311

Finkenzeller, X. & Grau, J. (1985) *Alpenblumen*, Munich

Fiori, A. & Paoletti, G. (1895) *Iconographia Florae italicae*, Padua

Fischer, F.E.L. & Meyer, C.A. (1835) *Index seminum hort. Petropolitani*, St Petersburg

Flahault, C. (1912) *Nouvelle Flore des Alpes et des Pyrénées*, vol. 3, Paris

Font Quer, P. (1927) 'La flora de las Pitiusas y sus afinidades con la de la Península Ibérica', *Memorias de la Real Academia de Ciencias y Artes de Barcelona*, 20:109–54

Fuchs, H.P. (1960) 'Kleine Beiträge zur Nomenklatur der Schweizer Flore', *Bericht der schweizerischen botanischen Gesellschaft*, 70:46–9

Galloe, O. (1910) 'Saxifragaceae, 2. The biological leaf anatomy of the Arctic species of *Saxifraga*', *Meddelelser om Grønland*, 36: 237–94

Gaussen, H. (1937) 'Catalogue-Flore des Pyrénées: Saxifragaceae', *Le Monde des Plantes*, Nos. 386–87

Gesner, K. (1541) *Historia plantarum et vires*, Basel

Gmelin, J.G. (1769) *Flora sibirica*, vol. 4, St Petersburg

Godfree, J.S. (1979) '*Saxifraga cernua* L. A report on seed formation', *B.S.B.I. News*, 2(23):27

Goldblatt, P. (ed.) (1981) 'Index to plant chromosome numbers 1975–1978', *Monographs in Systematic Botany from the Missouri Botanical Garden*, vol. 5, Missouri Botanical Garden

────── (ed.) (1984) 'Index to plant chromosome numbers 1979–1981', *Monographs in Systematic Botany from the Missouri Botanical Garden*, vol. 8, Missouri Botanical Garden

────── (ed.) (1985) 'Index to plant chromosome numbers 1982–1983', *Monographs in Systematic Botany from the Missouri Botanical Garden*, vol. *13*, Missouri Botanical Garden

Gornall, R.J. (1986) 'Trichome anatomy and taxonomy of *Saxifraga* (Saxifragaceae)', *Nordic Journal of Botany*, 6:257–75

────── (1987a) 'Foliar crystals in *Saxifraga* and segregate genera (Saxifragaceae)', *Nordic Journal of Botany*, 7:233–8

────── (1987b) 'An outline of a revised classification of *Saxifraga* L.', *Botanical Journal of the Linnean Society*, *95*: 259–72

Govoruhin, V.S. (1937) *Flora Urala* [in Russian], Sverdlovsk

Grey-Wilson, C. (1985) 'Plants in peril, 4. *Saxifraga florulenta*', *Kew Magazine*, 2:232–4

Griffiths, G.C.D. (1972) 'Studies on boreal Agromyzidae (Diptera), 1. *Phytomyza* miners on Saxifragaceae', *Quaestiones Entomologicae*, 8:67–80

Guinea, E. (1949) *Viscaya y su paisaje vegetal*, Bilbao

Gunnerus, J.E. (1772) *Flora norvegica*, vol. 2, Trondheim

Hablizl, C.L. (1785) '*Fizičeskoe opisanie Tavričeskoj oblasti*', St Petersburg

Halácsy, E. de (1901) *Conspectus Florae graecae*, vol. 1, Leipzig

Haller, A. (1742) *Enumeratio methodica stirpium Helveltiae indigenarum*, vol. 1, Göttingen

―――― (1768) *Historia stirpium indigenarum Helvetiae inchoata*, vol. 1, Bern

Hallier, E. (1886) *Flora von Deutschland*, 5th edn, vol. 26, Gera

Hamel, J.L. (1953) 'Contribution à l'étude cyto-taxinomique des Saxifragacées', *Revue de Cytologie et de Biologie végétales*, 14:113–313

―――― (1957) 'Les chromosomes somatiques d'une saxifrage supposée hybride, *Saxifraga Hausmannii* A. Kerner', *Publications du Muséum national d'histoire naturelle*, 17:169–73

Hara, H. (1979) 'Saxifragaceae', in H. Hara & L.H.J. Williams (eds), *An enumeration of the flowering plants of Nepal*, 2:149–56, London

Harding, W. (1970) *Saxifrages*, London

Haworth, A.H. (1803) *Miscellanea naturalia*, London

―――― (1812) *Synopsis plantarum succulentarum*, London

―――― (1821) *Saxifragëarum enumeratio*, London

Hayek, A. (1905) 'Monographische Studien über die Gattung *Saxifraga*, 1. Die Sektion *Porphyrion* Tausch', *Denkschriften der kaiserlichen Akademie der Wissenschaften*, Wien, 77:611–709

―――― (1925) *Prodromus Florae Peninsulae Balcanicae*, vol. 1, Berlin-Dahlem

Heathcote, E.D. (1891) *Plants of the Engadine*, Winchester

Hideux, M. & Abadie, M. (1986) in S. Blackmore & I.K. Ferguson (eds), *Pollen and spores: form and function*, London

Hitchcock, C.L. & Cronquist, A. (1961) *Vascular plants of the Pacific Northwest, part 3: Saxifragaceae to Ericaceae*, Seattle

Hooker, J.D. (1889) '*Saxifraga latepetiolata*', *Botanical Magazine*, 115: Plate 7056

Hooker, W.J. (1847) 'Catalogue of Mr Geyer's collection of plants', *London Journal of Botany*, 6:206–55

Hooker, W.J. & Arnott, G.A.W. (1832) *The botany of Captain Beechey's voyage*, part 3, London

Hornibrook, M. (1926) 'Hybrid saxifrages', *Journal of the Royal Horticultural Society*, 51:49–57

Horný, R. & Webr, K.M. (1985) *Nejkrásnější lomikameny*, Prague

Horný, R., Webr, K.M. & Byam-Grounds, J. (1986) *Porophyllum saxifrages*, Stamford [1986] 1987

Host, N.T. (1827) *Flora austriaca*, vol. 1, Vienna

Huber, H. (1963) 'Saxifragaceae', in G. Hegi, *Illustrierte Flora von Mitteleuropa*, 2nd edn, 4(2):130–218, Munich

Hultén, E. (1930) 'Flora of Kamchatka: *Saxifraga*', *Kongliga Svenska Vetenskapsakademiens Handlingar*, series 3, 8:11–20

―――― (1945) *Flora of Alaska and Yukon*, vol. 5, Stockholm

―――― (1958) *The amphi-atlantic plants*, Stockholm

―――― (1964) 'The *Saxifraga flagellaris* complex', *Svensk Botanisk Tidskrift*, 58:81–104

―――― (1968) *Flora of Alaska and neighbouring territories*, Stanford, California

―――― (1973) 'Supplement to *Flora of Alaska and neighbouring territories*', *Botaniska Notiser*, 126:459–512

Irving, W. & Malby, R.A. (1914) *Saxifrages or rockfoils*, London

Johnson, A.M. (1923) 'A revision of the North American species of the section *Boraphila* Engler of the genus *Saxifraga* (Tourn.)L.', *University of Minnesota Studies in Biological Sciences*, 4:1–109

——— (1927) 'The Status of *Saxifraga nuttallii*', *American Journal of Botany*, 14: 38–43

Johnson, T. (1641) *Mercurii botanici pars altera*, London

Kaplan, K. (1981) 'Embryologische, pollen- und samenmorphologische Untersuchungen zur Systematik von *Saxifraga* (Saxifragaceae)', *Bibliotheca Botanica*, 134:1–56

Kartesz, J.T. & Kartesz, R. (1980) 'A synonymized checklist of the vascular flora of the United States, Canada, and Greenland', in *The biota of North America*, volume 11, Chapel Hill, North Carolina

Kevan, P.G. (1972a) 'Floral colours in the high arctic with reference to insect-flower relations and pollination', *Canadian Journal of Botany*, 50:2289–316

——— (1972b) 'Insect pollination of high arctic flowers', *Journal of Ecology*, 60:831–47

Khokhrjakov, A. (1979) '*Saxifraga* L. sectionis *Trachyphyllum* Gaud. Asiae boreali-orientalis', *Novitates systematicae plantarum vascularium*, 15:157–64

Knaben, G. (1954) '*Saxifraga osloensis* n.sp., a tetraploid species of the *Tridactylites* section', *Nytt Magasin for Botanikk*, 3:117–38

Knuth, P. (1908) *Handbook of flower pollination*, based upon Herman Müller's work *The fertilizaton of flowers by insects*. Translated by J.R.A. Davis, vol. 2, Oxford

Köhlein, F. (1984) *Saxifrages and related genera* [translated from the German by D. Winstanley], London

Krause, D.L. & Beamish, K.I. (1972) 'Taxonomy of *Saxifraga occidentalis* and *S.marshallii*', *Canadian Journal of Botany*, 50:2131–41

Kurt, J. (1929) 'Über die Hydathoden der Saxifrageae', *Beihefte zum botanischen Centralblatt*, 46:203–46

Kuzmanov, B. (1970) 'Saxifragaceae', in D. Jordanov, *Flora Reipublicae popularis bulgaricae*, 4:652–704, Sofia

Lapeyrouse, P.P. de (1795–1801) *Figures de la Flore des Pyrénées*, Paris

Lausi, D. (1967) '*Saxifraga berica* (Béguinot) D.A. Webb e *Asplenium lepidum* Presl sui Colli Berici', *Giornale botanica italiana*, 101:223–30

Leresche, L. & Levier, E. (1880) *Deux excursions botaniques dans le nord de l'Espagne et le Portugal*, Lausanne [1881]

Levin, D.A. (1973) 'The role of trichomes in plant defense', *Quarterly Review of Biology*, 48:3–15

Lid, J. (1963) *Norsk og svensk Flora*, Oslo

Lindman, C.A.M. (1964) *Nordens Flora*, 2nd edn, vol. 2, Stockholm

Linnaeus, C. (1732) 'Florula Lapponica', *Acta Societatis regia Literaria et Scientiarum Sueciae*, 3:46–58

——— (1737) *Flora Lapponica*, Amsterdam

——— (1753) *Species Plantarum*, Stockholm

——— (1755) *Centuria Plantarum* I, Uppsala

——— (1759) *Systema Naturae*, 10th edn, vol. 2, Stockholm

——— (1762) *Species Plantarum*, 2nd edn, Stockholm

Linskens, H.F. (1964) 'Notiz zur Anatomie und Oekologie von *Saxifraga arachnoidea* Sternb.', *Archivio botanico*, 40:173–6

Losa, M. (1957) 'Catálogo de las plantas que se encuentran en los montes palentino-leoneses', *Anales del Instituto botánico A.J.Cavanilles*, 15:243–376

Losa, M. & Montserrat, P. (1950) *Aportacion al conocimiento de la flora de Andorra*, Zaragoza

Löve, Á. (1983) *The flora of Iceland*, Reykjavik

Löve, Á. & Löve, D. (1961) 'Some nomenclatural changes in the European flora, II. Subspecific categories', *Botaniska Notiser*, 114:48–56

Luizet, D. (1910) 'Contribution à l'étude des saxifrages du groupe des *Dactyloides* Tausch, 3e article', *Bulletin de la Société botanique de France*, 57:595–603

———— (1913) 'Contribution à l'étude des saxifrages du groupe des *Dactyloides* Tausch, 14e article', *Bulletin de la Société botanique de France*, 60:32–9

Mądalski, J. (1962) *Florae Poloniae Terrarumque adiacentium Iconographia*, vol. 11, part 5, Warsaw

Magnol, P. (1697) *Hortus regius monspeliensis*, Montpellier

Maire, R. (1980) 'Saxifragaceae', in *Flore de l'Afrique du Nord*, 15:5–69, Paris

Malagarriga Heras, R. de P. (1974) *Plantae Sennenianae. IV.* Saxifraga *(T.)L.*, Barcelona

Marschall von Bieberstein, F.A. (1843) *Centuria Plantarum rariorum Rossiae meridionalis*, part 2, St Petersburg

Marsden-Jones, E.M. & Turrill, W.B. (1930) 'The history of a tetraploid saxifrage', *Journal of Genetics*, 23:83–92

———— (1934) 'Further breeding experiments with *Saxifraga*', *Journal of Genetics*, 29:245–68

———— (1956) 'Additional breeding experiments with *Saxifraga*', *Journal of Genetics*, 54:186–93

Mateo, G. (1983) 'Aportacion al conocimiento de la Flora Valenciana: el genero *Saxifraga*', *Collectanea Botanica*, 14:337–45

Matthews, V.A. (1972) '*Saxifraga* L.', in P.H. Davis (ed.), *Flora of Turkey*, 4:249–59, Edinburgh

McKenna, M.C. (1983) 'Holarctic landmass rearrangement, cosmic events, and Cenozoic terrestrial organisms', *Annals of the Missouri Botanical Garden*, 70:459–89

Merxmüller, H. (1956) 'Ueber einige Reliktpflanzen der Sudwestalpen', *Jahrbuch des Vereins zum Schutze der Alpenpflanzen und -Tiere*, 1956:115–20

Merxmüller, H. & Wiedmann, W. (1957) 'Ein nahezu unbekannter Steinbrech der Bergamasker Alpen', *Jahrbuch des Vereins zum Schutze der Alpenpflanzen und -Tiere*, 1957:115–20

Micevski, K. & Mayer, E. (1970) 'Zur Kenntnis der *Saxifraga grisebachii* Degen et Dörfler', *Feddes Repertorium*, 80:599–605

Miller, J.M. & Bohm, B.A. (1980) 'Flavonoid variation in some North American *Saxifraga* species', *Biochemical Systematics & Ecology*, 8:279–84

Moggi, G. (1985) *The Macdonald Encyclopedia of alpine flowers*, London

Molyneux, T. (1697) 'A discourse concerning the large horns frequently found underground in Ireland', *Philosophical Transactions of the Royal Society of London*, 19:489–512

Moore, R.J. (ed.) (1973) 'Index to plant chromosome numbers 1967–1971', *Regnum Vegetabile*, vol. 90, Utrecht

———— (ed.) (1974) 'Index to plant chromosome numbers for 1972', *Regnum Vegetabile*, vol. 91, Utrecht

———— (ed.) (1977) 'Index to plant chromosome numbers for 1973/74', *Regnum Vegetabile*, vol. 96, Utrecht

Moreau, F. (1984) 'Contribution phytodermalogique à la systématique des Saxifragacées sensu stricto et des Crassulacées', *Revue de Cytologie et de Biologie Végétales — le Botaniste*, 7:31–92

Morison, R. (1680) *Plantarum Historia universalis oxoniensis, Pars secunda*, Oxford

Murbeck, S.S. (1891) *Beiträge zur Kenntniss der Flora von Südbosnien und der Hercegowina*, Lund

Nicholson, G. (1886) *The illustrated dictionary of gardening*, vol. 3, London

Nordhagen, R. (1930) 'En botanisk ekskursjon i Eikisdalen', *Bergens Museums Arbok, Naturvidenskapelig Rekke*, no. 8

Palla, E. (1897) *Atlas der Alpenflora*, 2nd edn, vol. 2, Graz

Pallas, P.S. (1776) *Reise durch verschiedene Provinzen des russisches Reich*, vol. 3, St Petersburg

Pan, J.T. (1978) 'The genus *Saxifraga* in Qing-Zang plateau', *Acta Phytotaxonomica Sinica*, *16*(2):11–35

Parkinson, J. (1640) *Theatrum botanicum*, London

Pawłowska, S. (1953) 'De nonnullis Saxifragis carpaticis et balcanicis', *Acta Societatis Botanicarum Poloniae*, 22:227–44

―――― (1966) 'De positione systematica speciei *Saxifraga wahlenbergii* Ball (=*S.perdurans* Kit.)', *Fragmenta Floristica et Geobotanica*, *12*:337–47

Perkins, W.E. (1978) 'Systematics of *Saxifraga rufidula* and related species from the Columbia River Gorge to south-western British Columbia', PhD thesis, University of British Columbia

Philp, J. (1934) 'Note on the cytology of *Saxifraga granulata* L., *S.rosacea* Moench, and their hybrids', *Journal of Genetics*, 29:197–201

Pignatti, S. (1969) '*Saxifraga etrusca* nova sp. aus dem nördlichen Apennin nebst einer Übersicht über die *Saxifraga aspera*—*Sax. bryoides* Verwandtschaft', *Giornale botanico italiano*, *103*:169–81

―――― (1982) '*Saxifraga*', in S. Pignatti (ed.), *Flora d'Italia*, *1*:505–32, Bologna

Pitschmann, H. & Reisigl, H. (1959) 'Endemische Blutenpflanzen der Sudalpen zwischen Luganersee und Etsch', *Veröffentlichungen des geobotanisches Institutes Rübel in Zürich*, *35*:44–68

Plukenet, L. (1692) *Phytographia*, London

Pona, J. (1601) *Plantae seu simplicia, ut vocant, quae in Baldo monte et in via ab Verona ad Baldum reperiuntur*, Antwerp

Pugsley, H.W. (1936) 'The British Robertsonian saxifrages', *Journal of the Linnean Society (Botany)*, *50*:267–89

Pursh, F. (1814) *Flora Americae septentrionalis*, London

Rasetti, F. (1980) *I fiori delle Alpi*, Rome

Ray, J. (1688) *Historia Plantarum*, vol. 2, London

Reichenbach, H.G.L. (1832) *Flora germanica excursoria*, Leipzig

―――― (1899) *Icones florae germanicae et helveticae*, vol. 23, Gera

Rivas Martinez, S. (1963) 'Estudio de la Vegetación y Flora de las Sierras de Guadarrama y Gredos', *Anales del Instituto Botánico Cavanilles*, *21*:13–325

Rohlena, J. (1942) *Conspectus florae montenegrinae*, Prague

Rønning, O.I. (1964) *Svalbards Flora*, Oslo

Ross-Craig, S. (1957) *Drawings of British plants*, part 10, London

Roth, A.W. (1789) *Tentamen Florae germanicae*, vol. 2, Leipzig

Rottboell, C.F. (1772) *Descriptiones plantarum rariorum*, Copenhagen

Rouy, G. (1901) *Illustrationes plantarum Europae rariorum*, part 16, Paris

Rouy, G. & Camus, E.-G. (1901) *Flore de France*, vol. 7, Asnières

Savage, S. (1945) *A catalogue of the Linnaean herbarium*, London

Savile, D.B.O. (1973) 'Revisions of the microcyclic *Puccinia* species on Saxifragaceae', *Canadian Journal of Botany*, *51*:2347–70

―――― (1975) 'Evolution and biogeography of Saxifragaceae with guidance from their rust parasites', *Annals of the Missouri Botanical Garden*, 62:354–61

Săvulescu, T. (1956) *Flora Republicii populare Romîne*, vol. 4, Bucharest

Schönbeck-Temesy, E. (1967) 'Saxifragaceae', in K.H. Rechinger (ed.), *Flora Iranica*, no. 42, Graz

Schmidt, H. 1930. 'Zur Funktion der Hydathoden von *Saxifraga*', *Planta*, *10*:314–44

Schrader, H.A. (1809) *Hortus Gottingensis*, Göttingen

Schrank, F. (1821) *Plantae rariores Horti Academici Monacensis*, vol. 2, Munich

Schwaighofer, K. (1908) 'Ist *Zahlbrucknera* als eigene Gattung beizubehalten oder wieder mit *Saxifraga* zu vereinigen?', *Sitzungsberichte der kaiserliche Akademie der Wissenschaften, mathematisch-naturwissenschaftliche Klasse*, Abt.1, *117*:25–52

Seboth, J. (1880) *Alpine plants painted from Nature*, vol. 2 [translated by A. Bennett], London

Séguier, J.F. (1745) *Plantae Veronenses*, Verona

Seringe, N.C. (1830) 'Saxifragaceae', in A.-P. De Candolle (ed.), *Prodromus systematis naturalis regni vegetabilis*, 4:17–47, Paris

[Sherard, W.] (1689) *Schola botanica*, Amsterdam

Shetler, S.G. & Skog, L.E. (1978) 'A provisional checklist of species for *Flora North America* (revised)', *Monographs in Systematic Botany from the Missouri Botanical Garden*, vol. 1, Missouri Botanical Garden

Sibthorp, J. & Smith, J.E. (1823) *Flora Graeca*, vol. 4, London

Sims, J. (1814) '*Saxifraga ceratophylla*', *Botanical Magazine*, *40*:Plate 1651

Siplivinsky, V.N. (1971) 'Generis *Saxifraga* L. species Asiaticae e sectione *Trachyphyllum* Gaud.', *Novitates systematicae plantarum vascularium*, *8*:147–58

Small, J.K. (1905) '*Saxifraga, Muscaria, Chondrosea, Saxifragopsis, Micranthes, Spatularia, Leptasea, Ocrearia, Heterisia, Antiphylla*', *North American Flora*, *22*:126–57

Smith, H. (1958) '*Saxifraga* of the Himalaya, 1. Section *Kabschia*', *Bulletin of the British Museum (Natural History) (Botany)*, 2:85–129

―――― (1960) '*Saxifraga* of the Himalaya, 2. Some new species', *Bulletin of the British Museum (Natural History) (Botany)*', 2:229–65

Smith, J.E. (1806) In J. Sibthorp & J.E. Smith, *Florae Graecae Prodromus*, vol. 1, London

Soltis, D.E. (1983) 'Supernumerary chromosomes in *Saxifraga virginiensis* (Saxifragaceae)', *American Journal of Botany*, *70*:1007–10

Sowerby, J. (1865) *English botany*, 3rd edn, by J.T. Boswell Syme, vol. 4, London

Stapf, O. (1928) '*Saxifraga × amabilis* Stapf', *Botanical Magazine*, *102*:Plate 9139

Stearn, W.T. (1957) 'An introduction to the *Species Plantarum* and cognate botanical works of Carl Linnaeus', in *Species Plantarum, a facsimile of the first edition, 1753*, Ray Society, London

Stebbins, G.L. (1984) 'Polyploidy and the distribution of the arctic-alpine flora: new evidence and a new approach', *Botanica Helvetica*, *94*:1–13

Stefánsson, S. (1948) *Flora Islands*, 3rd edn, Akureyri

Sternberg, K.M. (1810) *Revisio Saxifragarum*, Ratisbon

―――― (1822) *Revisio Saxifragarum, Supplementum I*, Ratisbon

―――― (1831) *Revisio Saxifragarum, Supplementum II*, Prague

Steudel, E.G. & Hochstetter, C.F. (1826) *Enumeratio plantarum Germaniae*, Stuttgart

Stevens, D.P. & Richards, A.J. (1985) 'Gynodioecy in *Saxifraga granulata* L. (Saxifragaceae)', *Plant Systematics & Evolution*, *151*:43–54

Steyermark, J.A. (1959) 'The taxonomic status of *Saxifraga palmeri*', *Brittonia*, *11*:71–7

Strid, A. (1980) *Wild flowers of Mount Olympus*, Kifissia

Symkiewicz, D. (1937) 'Contributions à la géographie des plantes, IV. Une nouvelle méthode pour la recherche des centres de distribution géographique des genres', *Kosmos*, *62*:1–15

Tausch, I.F. (1823) *Hortus Canalius*, Decas 1, Prague

Taylor, R.L. & MacBride B. (1977) *Vascular plants of British Columbia*, Vancouver

Threlkeld, C. (1727) *Synopsis Stirpium hibernicarum*, Dublin

Tiffney, B.H. (1985a) 'Perspectives on the origin of the floristic similarity between eastern Asia and eastern North America', *Journal of the Arnold Arboretum*, 66:73–94

―――― (1985b) 'The Eocene North Atlantic land bridge: its importance in Tertiary and modern phytogeography of the Northern Hemisphere', *Journal of the Arnold Arboretum*, 66:243–73

Tolmatchev, A.I. (1959) 'De *Saxifraga flagellare* Willd. et speciebus affinibus', *Notulae systematicae ex herbario Instituti botanici nomine V.L.Komarovii Academiae Scientiarum URSS*, *19*:156–87

Touring Club Italiano (1958) *Conosci L'Italia*, vol. 2: *La Flora*, Milan

Tournefort, J.P. (1694) *Élémens de Botanique*, vol. 1, Paris

———— (1703) *Corollarium*, Paris

Townson, R. (1797) *Travels in Hungary in the year 1793*, London

Wagner, J. (1935) 'Beiträge zur Flora von Griechenland', *Feddes Repertorium*, *38*:281–8

Wahlenberg, G. (1814) *Flora Carpatorum principalium*, Göttingen

Waldstein, F.A. & Kitaibel, O. (1799–1802) *Descriptiones et Icones Plantarum rariorum Hungaricae*, vol. 1, Vienna

Warming, E. (1909) 'The structure and biology of arctic flowering plants. 4.Saxifragaceae. 1.Morphology and biology', *Meddelelser om Grønland*, *36*:169–236

Webb, D.A. (1950a) 'Hybridization and variation in the Robertsonian saxifrages', *Proceedings of the Royal Irish Academy*, *53B*:85–97

———— (1950b) 'A revision of the Dactyloid saxifrages of north-western Europe', *Proceedings of the Royal Irish Academy*, *53B*:207–40

———— (1963) 'Saxifragaceae', in V.H. Heywood (ed.), *Notulae systematicae ad Floram Europaeam spectantes*, no. 2, *Feddes Repertorium*, *68*:198–210

———— (1964a) 'Saxifragaceae', in V.H. Heywood (ed.), *Notulae systematicae ad Floram Europaeam spectantes*, no. 4, *Feddes Repertorium*, *69*:153–4

———— (1964b) '*Saxifraga*', in T.G. Tutin *et al.* (eds), *Flora Europaea*, *1*:364–81, Cambridge

———— (1987a) 'Typification of the Linnean species of *Saxifraga*', *Botanical Journal of the Linnean Society*, *95*:227–51

———— (1987b) 'Taxonomic and nomenclatural notes on *Saxifraga* L.', *Botanical Journal of the Linnean Society*, *95*:259–72

———— (1988) 'A new subspecies of *Saxifraga cuneifolia* L.', *Botanical Journal of the Linnean Society*, *97*: 355

Widder, F.J. (1954) 'Die Nomenclatur von *Saxifraga aizoides* Linné', *Phyton (Austria)*, *5*:204–10

Willdenow, C.L. (1799) *Caroli a Linné Species Plantarum*, 4th edn, vol. 2, Berlin

Willkomm, M. (1874) 'Saxifragaceae', in M. Willkomm & J. Lange, *Prodromus Florae hispanicae*, *3*:104–26, Stuttgart

———— (1881–1885) *Illustrationes Florae hispanicae Insularumque Balearium*, vol. 1, Stuttgart

———— (1893) *Supplementum Prodromi Florae hispanicae*, Stuttgart

# Index

Synonyms, invalid names and names of hybrids of uncertain parentage are printed in *italics*. Names of species that are figured in the colour plates are printed in **bold**, together with the plate number. All other numbers refer to pages.

var. *subintegra* Goodman 276
wahlenbergii Ball 199
× wehrhahnii Horný, Sójak & Webr 85
wendelboi Schönbeck-Temesy 264
werneri Font Quer & Pau 260
× wettsteinii Brügger 194, 239
× wilczeckii Verguin & Neyraut ex Luizet 211
*willkommiana* Boissier ex Willkomm 212
'Wisley' 99
× yvesii Neyraut & Verguin ex Luizet 207, 211
× zimmeteri Kerner 66
'Zita' 97
Saxifragaceae 1
Saxifrageae 1, 15, 17
Saxifragopsis fragarioides (Greene) Small 286
scent 12
seeds 8–9
dispersal 13
self-incompatibility 12–13
*Sibiricae* Engler & Irmscher (grex) 144
*Spatularia foliolosa* (R. Brown) Small 58
stamen movements 12
Stellares (Engler & Irmscher) Gornall (subsection) 54, 273
stomata 6
Subsessiliflorae Gornall (series) 269
supernumerary chromosomes 12

Tetilla 1
*Tetrameridium* Engler (section) 76
*Trachyphylloides* Huber (section) 151
Trachyphyllum (Gaudin) Koch (section) 138, 283
Tridactylites (Haworth) Gornall (subsection) 247
*Tridactylites* (Haworth) Grisebach (section) 151
Triplinervium (Gaudin) Gornall (subsection) 170, 259
*Tristylea floribunda* (Dietrich) Jordan & Fourreau 133

vegetative reproduction 13
vine-weevil 26

Xanthizoon Grisebach (section) 135

*Zahlbrucknera paradoxa* (Sternberg) Reichenbach 232